Fundamentals of

PHYSICS

Books by Henry Semat

FUNDAMENTALS OF PHYSICS
Third Edition

INTRODUCTION TO ATOMIC AND NUCLEAR PHYSICS
Third Edition

PHYSICS IN THE MODERN WORLD

HENRY SEMAT, Ph.D.

Professor of Physics, The City College of New York

Fundamentals of

PHYSICS

THIRD EDITION

Holt, Rinehart and Winston
New York

27806-0417

Junе, 1961

To Edith Joan and Barbara Ann

To Edith, Joan and Barbara Ann

Preface

This book is written for a thorough one-year introductory course in physics. It uses algebra and trigonometry but no calculus. With that one limitation, it presents the subject in as rigorous and comprehensive a way as possible, although no previous knowledge of physics is assumed. The changes in this Third Edition have been made as a result of the experiences of the author with the earlier editions and the criticisms and comments of many teachers who have used the first and second editions in a variety of courses.

An attempt has been made to keep the size of this Third Edition about the same as that of the Revised Edition by omitting some material to provide space for new material. Most instructors prefer to make their own selection of material to take care of local situations in terms of the aims of the course, the preparation of the students, and the number of hours allotted to the course; they prefer to omit some topics from a large book rather than supplement a small book with additional topics.

Some of the specific changes made in the Third Edition are the subdivision of some of the longer chapters so that there are now five additional chapters; the addition of about 50 new diagrams and the revision of about 150 of the older drawings; the addition of new problems and the changing of numerical values in many of the older problems. The notation has been changed to conform more closely to the recommendations of the American Standards Association and the American Association of Physics Teachers, although some differences still exist. There is at present no agreement on the symbol to be used to represent *torque;* after searching through the letter symbols, I found that the letter G has very limited use in general physics and decided to adopt it as the symbol for torque. This necessitated changing the symbol for the constant of universal gravitation; I adopted the symbol G_o for this constant. This follows the trend of using the subscript zero with letters for physical constants.

As a result of many years of experience with courses at this level, I am convinced that there is no single system of units which is suitable for the entire subject. I have therefore used several different systems in the different parts of the text, with major emphasis on the cgs system and the British engineering system. The practical system of units is used in electricity as well as the cgs system, and units peculiar to atomic physics are used in Part Six on Atomics and Nucleonics.

As in the earlier editions, answers to odd-numbered problems are given in the Appendix. Answers to all the problems are available in a separate booklet to instructors desiring them.

Throughout the preparation of the three editions of this book, I have received invaluable assistance from my colleagues, from many teachers who have used the earlier editions, and from other physicists who have read the manuscripts in whole or in part. I wish to thank them for their contributions, although it is impossible to list the names of all of them here.

The following acknowledgment is taken from the Preface to the First Edition:

"Professor R. F. Paton of the University of Illinois, Professor A. B. Cardwell of Kansas State College, Professor Floyd C. Fairbanks of the University of Rochester, and Mr. Robert Shaw of the College of the City of New York have all read the entire manuscript and have given many helpful suggestions and criticisms for which I am genuinely grateful. These persons will find most of their suggestions incorporated in the book. My colleagues at the City College, Professors Hugh C. Wolfe (now at Cooper Union), Robert I. Wolff, and Mark W. Zemansky, have read various parts of the manuscript. I want to thank them, as well as Mr. Shaw, for many stimulating discussions and their assistance in developing methods of presenting difficult topics in an elementary way."

The following is from the Preface to the Revised Edition:

"In particular I wish to thank Professor Edward E. Miller, of the University of Wisconsin, and Professor W. W. Sleator, of the University of Michigan, for their criticisms of the first edition and their many helpful suggestions. Professor R. M. Whaley, of Purdue University, read the entire manuscript of this revised edition; I am greatly indebted to him for his criticisms and suggestions, most of which have been incorporated in this book. I owe a great deal to my colleague Professor Mark W. Zemansky for reading the entire manuscript and for many stimulating discussions during the revision. I also wish to thank my colleague Professor Charles A. Corcoran for many valuable discussions and for his continued interest in the development of this book."

The following persons have been particularly helpful in the preparation of this Third Edition and I wish to express my thanks and my appreciation to them:

Professor Joseph Dillinger of the University of Wisconsin, Professor Stephen S. Friedland of the University of Connecticut, Professor Paul H.

Kirkpatrick of Stanford University, Professor Paul E. Shearin of the University of North Carolina, Professor C. L. Church and Professor Fred W. Decker of Oregon State College.

I wish to thank Professor John W. DeWire, of Cornell University, for having read the entire manuscript of the Third Edition and for his valuable suggestions and criticisms.

Finally, I wish to thank my wife, Ray K. Semat, for typing all the manuscripts and for help with the proofs.

HENRY SEMAT

The City College of New York
January, 1957

Contents

Part One

MECHANICS

1
Fundamental Concepts

Physics is a fundamental science dealing with matter and energy. Although the history of physics dates back to antiquity, the modern science of physics may be said to begin with the work of Galileo (1564–1642), who developed the method of dealing with physical problems which is essentially that used today. A considerable body of knowledge had been accumulated before Galileo's time, particularly in mechanics and to a lesser extent in optics, although very little was known about the subjects of heat, sound, magnetism, and electricity. The method introduced into physics by Galileo consists principally of three steps. The first is to use previous knowledge and experience to delimit the new problem at hand, that is, to exclude from consideration all but the few relevant factors. The second is to perform controlled quantitative experiments on these few relevant factors. Thus in his classic researches on the laws of falling bodies, Galileo paid no attention at all to the size, or shape, or color, or weight of the bodies upon which he experimented. But he did perform many careful and quantitative tests on the relationships among the relevant factors, namely, the time of fall, the vertical height of fall, and the speed of fall. The third step is the most difficult of all and is also the most difficult one to describe. It may consist of an attempt to put the results of the experiments in such a form that they will fall within the compass of some known generalization or physical law, or, if this is not possible, the scientist may attempt to present some hypothesis or some generalization, preferably of a quantitative nature, as an outgrowth of these experiments. Such a hypothesis or generalization will usually suggest some new experiments to be tried. The results of these new experiments may be found to fit in with the new ideas, they may suggest slight modifications of these ideas, or they may even show that the hypothesis or generalization is incorrect for any one of a number of reasons such as insufficient data, lack of good quantitative data, or the neglect of factors which should not have been ignored.

3

The results of such experiments may be presented in different ways; for example, in the form of a *table* listing the results of the measurements, or in the form of a *graph* showing the relationship between two or more measured quantities, or in the form of an *equation* relating these quantities. Considerations of utility and elegance determine which method or methods are to be used in any particular case. All of these methods will be illustrated at appropriate places throughout this book.

For convenience in studying it, the science of physics is subdivided into several branches; the traditional subdivisions are mechanics, heat, sound, magnetism, electricity, and light. To these traditional subdivisions, we must now add one on atomic and nuclear physics. In each of these subdivisions, a different aspect of the behavior of matter is studied. For example, the behavior of bodies which are acted upon by external forces is studied in the subdivision of mechanics. We shall find that under some conditions a body subject to external forces remains at rest, while under different conditions the body may be set into motion, or if it is in motion, its motion may be changed by the action of external forces. We shall also find that bodies possess *energy* by virtue of their motion, or position, or state. In the subdivision of heat we shall be mainly concerned with the relationship between the physical properties of a substance and its temperature, and those changes which occur when energy in the form of heat is added to or removed from the substance. Each of the subdivisions of physics requires a special technique of experiment for measuring those quantities which are needed for expressing the behavior of matter in precise and exact forms.

Although this division of physics into several branches is useful in studying the subject, we shall find that these subdivisions are closely related to one another in the sense that principles or laws developed in one are generally carried over for use in the other branches. Furthermore, there is one unifying principle connecting all of the subdivisions of physics; this principle is known as the *principle of conservation of energy*, and it has stood the test of experience for over a century.

1-2   RELATIONSHIP OF PHYSICS TO OTHER SCIENCES

The methods and results of physics have had wide applications to the other sciences, particularly chemistry, biology, geology, psychology, and medicine. The engineering sciences are frequently considered as special fields of applied physics. The development of physics has played an important part in the progress of the other sciences, but it must not be assumed that this has been entirely a one-sided relationship. The advances in the other sciences have proved of great value and importance to physics in applying new ideas, in developing new tools for investigation, and in opening new fields of study. Some of these fields are so closely related to physics that they are given joint names such as physical chemistry, biophysics, and chemical physics.

Until recently the study of the science of physics has been confined to a small group of men and women. The increasing recognition of the fundamental position of physics in relation to the other sciences and to technology, as well as the satisfaction of one's intellectual curiosity concerning nature, has attracted an increasing number of persons to the study of physics. It is the aim of this book to enable such persons to obtain a good foundation in the fundamentals of physics.

1-3 FUNDAMENTAL CONCEPTS OF MECHANICS

Mechanics deals with the behavior of various types of bodies such as *particles, rigid bodies, liquids,* and *gases,* when subjected to the action of *external forces.* Under special conditions, the bodies may be in *equilibrium* under the action of these external forces; under other conditions, the motions of these bodies will be changed or *accelerated.* The italicized words represent some of the concepts used in the science of mechanics and form part of its technical language. For the student to understand these terms and be able to use them correctly, it is essential that they be defined accurately. Careful analyses of the quantitative concepts used in mechanics have shown that they can be classified into two groups, one known as the *fundamental concepts* consisting of three terms, *length, time,* and *mass,* and a second group known as the *derived concepts* consisting of all the other terms used in mechanics.

The difference between these two sets of terms lies in the fact that each one of the derived concepts can be defined accurately in terms of the fundamental concepts. But the fundamental concepts of length, time, and mass cannot be defined in any such manner; they require special consideration. The method of treating each of these concepts is to set forth a series of rules for its measurement or to outline a series of experiments for determining its magnitude. Two steps are usually involved in each case: one, that of setting up a *standard* and, two, that of setting up rules for obtaining multiples or subdivisions of the standard. These steps will be discussed for each of the fundamental concepts.

1-4 CONCEPT OF LENGTH. STANDARD AND UNITS

Most of us are familiar, in a general way, with the operations involved in measuring the length of an object, or in measuring the distance between two points. Such a measurement always involves the use of some measuring rod or tape whose length is known in terms of some *standard* of length.

The legal standard of length in the United States is the meter; the meter is the distance between the centers of two lines marked on a special platinum-iridium bar, known as the *standard meter,* when the bar is at 0°C. This standard meter is deposited at the International Bureau of Weights and Measures at Sèvres, France. Accurate copies of this standard meter have been distributed to various national physical laboratories such as the National Bureau of Standards in Washington, D.C. These copies are compared with the international standard in France at stated intervals of time.

The meter not only is the standard of length but is coming into increasing use as a *unit* of length in science and engineering. Another *unit of length* used in scientific work is the hundredth part of the meter and is called the *centimeter* (cm); that is,

$$1 \text{ centimeter} = \tfrac{1}{100} \text{ meter}$$

or   1 meter   = 100 centimeters.

The subdivision of the meter into 100 equal divisions can be made with a dividing engine, which is essentially an accurately made screw which advances through known equal distances for each rotation of the screw.

Table 1-1   Units of Length

English	Metric
3 feet = 1 yard 36 inches = 1 yard 5,280 feet = 1 mile	100 centimeters = 1 meter 10 millimeters = 1 centimeter 1,000 meters = 1 kilometer

Table 1-2   Conversion Factors

1 kilometer =	0.6214 mile
1 meter =	39.37 inches
1 foot =	30.48 centimeters
1 inch =	2.540 centimeters

In English-speaking countries other units of length are used in everyday life and in many engineering applications. In the United States, the *yard* is defined legally as 3,600/3,937 of the standard meter. In engineering work the *unit* of length is the *foot*, which is one third of a yard.

Other subdivisions and multiples of the meter and yard are in common use, and the English-speaking scientist or engineer frequently has to convert measurements and data from one set of units to another. Table 1–1 gives some of the more common units of length used, and Table 1–2 gives the conversion factors for these units. Figure 1–1 shows the relationship between the centimeter and the inch.

FIG. 1–1   Comparison of the inch and the centimeter.

In actual measurements, many different instruments are used, the type depending upon the magnitude of the length to be measured and the degree of accuracy required. Familiarity with such instruments is essential to a proper appreciation of the problems involved in the measurement of length. This can be gained only by work in the laboratory and in the field.

Illustrative Example. An important method for measuring distances is known as the *triangulation* method which makes use of the known properties of a plane triangle. For example, the corner C of a city lot is sighted from two points A and B, as in Figure 1–2, by means of a transit. This instrument is essentially a telescope with vertical and horizontal scales for determining its line of sight. A and B are 100 ft apart, the line of sight AC makes an angle of 90° with AB, while the line of sight BC makes an angle of 75° with AB. Determine the distance AC.

One method of solving this problem is to draw the figure to some convenient scale, say 100 ft = 1 in., using ruler and protractor, and then to measure the distance

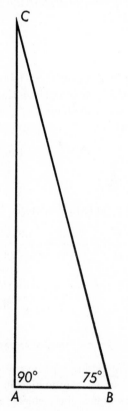

FIG. 1–2   Measuring distance by triangulation.

AC. When so measured, the line AC will be found to be about $3\frac{3}{4}$ in., so that the distance $AC = 375$ ft.

A second and more convenient method is to make use of some known trigonometric relationships. In any right triangle such as ABC, if A is the right angle, then the following relationships hold for the angle B: the *sine of B*, written sin B, is the ratio of the opposite side to the hypotenuse, or

$$\sin B = \frac{AC}{BC} ; \tag{1}$$

the *cosine of B*, written cos B, is the ratio of the adjacent side to the hypotenuse, or

$$\cos B = \frac{AB}{BC} ; \tag{2}$$

and the *tangent of B*, written tan B, is the ratio of the opposite side to the adjacent side, or

$$\tan B = \frac{AC}{AB} . \tag{3}$$

Tables of values for these trigonometric functions are given in Appendix A.

In this problem, since the distance AC is required, the distance AB is known, and the angle B is given, we can use Equation (3) for determining AC; that is,

$$\tan 75° = \frac{AC}{AB} ,$$

from which $\qquad\qquad AC = AB \tan 75°.$

From the table in Appendix A, we find that

$$\tan 75° = 3.732,$$

and, since $\qquad\qquad AB = 100 \text{ ft},$

we get $\qquad\qquad AC = 100 \text{ ft} \times 3.732,$

so that $\qquad\qquad AC = 373.2 \text{ ft}.$

1-5   CONCEPT OF TIME. STANDARD AND UNITS

All of us have some notions regarding the concept of time from our experiences with annual events, seasonal occurrences, and daily routine. The uses of watches, clocks, and radio time signals have become part of our everyday life. For the accurate measurement of time, we must choose a standard and decide upon methods for subdividing this standard. *The standard time interval used in scientific work is the mean solar day.* This standard makes use of the *apparent motion* of the sun with respect to an observer on the earth; this apparent motion is due to the rotation of the earth on its axis.   The instant at which the sun passes the meridian at the observer's place is called *local noon*.   The solar day is the time elapsed between two successive noons.   Careful measurements have shown that the solar days vary slightly at different times of the year.   The *mean solar day* is an average value taken over the year.

The *unit* of time used universally is the *second;* this is 1/86,400 of the mean solar day.   The instrument used for measuring time intervals is the *clock*.   The astronomical clock makes use of the periodic motion of a pendulum which is driven by means of a mechanism actuated by a descending weight.   Since the period of a pendulum at any given place depends upon the length of the pendulum, it is essential either that it be kept in a room at constant temperature, or that it be properly compensated so that its length will not vary with changes in temperature.   Portable clocks and watches use a balance wheel attached to a fine spring to provide the periodic motion necessary for accurate timing.   The balance wheel is usually driven by means of springs which have to be wound regularly.

1-6   CONCEPT OF MASS. STANDARD AND UNITS

Most of us have some idea of the meaning of the term *mass of a body*, but unfortunately this is generally confused with the term *weight*.   Since a real understanding of the concept of mass can come only after a study of the motion of bodies, for the present we shall confine our discussion to a statement of the standard of mass, the method of measuring mass, and the units commonly used.

The standard of mass is the kilogram, which is the mass of a certain piece of platinum kept at the International Bureau of Weights and Measures at Sèvres, France.   Two accurate copies of the standard kilogram are deposited at the National Bureau of Standards.   The instrument used in comparing masses is the delicate balance, which is an equal-arm balance (see Figure 1–3).   The two bodies whose masses are to be compared are placed in the pans of this instrument and, if a balance is obtained, are said to have equal masses.

The kilogram not only is the standard of mass but is coming into increasing use as a *unit* of mass in science and engineering.   The system of units based upon the meter as the unit of length, the kilogram as the unit of mass, and the second as the unit of time is called the mks system of units.

Another unit of mass used in scientific work is the *gram;* the gram is 1/1,000 of a kilogram.   The system of units based upon the centimeter as the unit of length, the gram as the unit of mass, and the second as the unit of time is called the cgs system of units.   Since the equality of masses can be determined by means of the delicate balance, it is a comparatively simple matter to construct multiples and subdivisions of the standard kilogram.

In English-speaking countries the unit of mass sometimes used by engineers is the *pound;* the pound is 1/2.2046 of a kilogram. The system

Fɪɢ. 1–3 A delicate balance. (Courtesy of Central Scientific Company.)

of units based upon the foot as the unit of length, the pound as the unit of mass, and the second as the unit of time, is called the fps system of units.

QUESTIONS

1. Consult an encyclopedia or other work of reference for the history of the origin of the standard meter.

2. The astronomers use the *sidereal* day for measuring time. The sidereal day is the interval between two successive passages of a star across the meridian. Take into account the rotation of the earth about its axis and show that the sidereal day is shorter than the solar day. How many sidereal days are there in a year?

3. Suggest the steps that must be taken to measure the distance between the moon and the earth by the triangulation method.

4. Suggest a method based upon the rules of plane geometry for subdividing a line of fixed length into 100 equal divisions.

5. How many millimeters are there in 1 m?

6. How many grams are there in 1 lb?

7. Observe the clocks in your home and at school. Can you determine (a) the mechanism used for obtaining periodic motion and (b) the mechanism used for running the clock?

PROBLEMS

1. Check the conversion factors given in Table 1–2 starting with the legal definition of the yard.

2. The Empire State Building is 1,245 ft tall and is observed by a man 5 miles away. What is the angle between the ground and the line of sight to the top of the building?

3. A ship at sea receives radio signals from two radio transmitters A and B 200 miles apart, one due south of the other. The direction finder shows that transmitter A is 30° south of east, while transmitter B is due east. How far is the ship from each transmitter?

4. A mountain peak is sighted from a point 12 km away. The line of sight makes an angle of 10° with the horizontal. Determine the height of the mountain peak in meters.

5. A radio antenna is sighted from a distance of 400 ft. The top of the antenna makes an angle of 20° with the ground. How high is the antenna?

6. The width of a river is measured by marking off a distance AB of 200 ft parallel to the river on one of its banks. A point C is sighted on the opposite shore directly across from A and along a line from B which makes an angle of 60° with AB. Determine the width of the river.

7. In a survey of a farm, observations are made with a transit, first from point A and then from point B 100 ft away. Point C is sighted at an angle of 67°20′ with respect to the base line AB when the transit is at A, while the line of sight from B to C makes an angle of 81°30′ with AB. How far is C from A and B?

2

Forces and Equilibrium

2-1 FORCE

Force is a concept which can be derived in terms of the fundamental concepts of length, time, and mass. The actual derivation will be considered later in our discussion of Newton's Laws of Motion (Chapter 4). For the present we shall limit ourselves to a discussion of those types of forces with which we are reasonably familiar. We know, for example, that we have to exert a force to support a body. The body may be placed on a table, or else it may be hung by means of a cord or a spring which is itself attached to the ceiling or the wall. If the body is not supported, it will fall. In this case, we say that there is a force pulling the body down, and it can be shown that this force is due to the attraction between the earth and the body. The *force* with which the *earth pulls the body down* is called the *weight* of the body.

In the above discussion, it was noted that the force supporting the body was exerted upward. The body supported in this way remains at rest, or, as we prefer to say, it is in *equilibrium* under the action of two forces, the weight pulling it down and the supporting force upward. It is reasonable to assume at this stage that these two forces acting on the body are equal in magnitude although they are opposite in direction. The next problem is to devise an instrument for measuring the magnitude of forces.

The results of many experiments have shown that a *spring balance* made of wire wound in the form of a helix, as in Figure 2–1, is suitable for measuring forces. Suppose this spring is suspended from some rigid support O and that OA represents the length L of the spring without any load on it. If we now hang a 1-lb mass on the spring, it will be stretched so that its lowest point A will go to a new position B, a distance x from A, and will come to rest at this point. At the point B, the body will be in equilibrium under the action of two forces, the pull of the earth on it, which we call the weight W of the 1-lb mass, and the pull F upward due to the stretched spring. These two forces are equal in magnitude and opposite in direction. If now an additional pound be added to the body suspended

12

from the spring, it is found from experiment that the lower end of the spring will go down an additional distance x, or the point A will have been displaced a total distance $2x$ from its original position. The pull of the

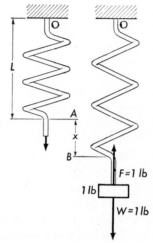

FIG. 2–1   Use of a spring for measuring force. The upward pull of the spring is equal to the weight of the body hanging at its lower end.

spring upward is now equal to the weight of the two pound masses. A scale may be attached to this spring to indicate the positions of its lower end when the spring exerts a force equal to the weight of 1 lb, 2 lb, 3 lb, and so forth.

The displacement of the lower end of a spring produced by the application of a force depends upon the nature of the material of which the wire is made, the diameter of the wire, and the size of the helical coil. Within the limits of usefulness of the particular spring, any force F applied to the spring produces a displacement x directly proportional to it, or

$$F \propto x.$$

This means that if a force F_1 applied to the spring produces a displacement x_1 and another force F_2 applied to the same spring produces a displacement x_2, then these forces are in the same ratio as the displacements they produce; that is,

$$\frac{F_1}{F_2} = \frac{x_1}{x_2}, \tag{1}$$

or

$$\frac{F_1}{x_1} = \frac{F_2}{x_2}. \tag{2}$$

Equation (2) states that the ratio of the force applied to the displacement it produces is a constant. Denoting this constant by the letter k, we can write Equation (2) as follows:

$$\frac{F_1}{x_1} = \frac{F_2}{x_2} = k, \tag{3}$$

from which

$$F_1 = kx_1,$$

$$F_2 = kx_2,$$

or, in general,

$$\boxed{F = kx} \tag{4}$$

where F is any force applied to the spring and x is the displacement produced by this force. [In general, a proportionality sign ($\propto$) can always be replaced by an equal ($=$) sign and a constant.] The constant k depends upon the nature and design of the spring and is called the *constant of the spring*. For example, if a 10-lb weight increases the length of a spring 2 in., the constant of the spring is 5 lb/in. or 60 lb/ft.

The *unit* of *force* used in the engineering system and in practical work is expressed in terms of the pull of the earth or the *weight* of a 1-lb mass at a specified place on the earth's surface. This place, unless otherwise specified, is taken as at latitude 45°, at sea level. The term *weight of a pound mass* is frequently contracted to *weight of a pound* or even more frequently to a *pound weight*. Thus in speaking of a 20-lb weight or a weight of 20 lb, we always mean a force equal to the pull of the earth on a body whose mass is 20 lb.

Many different units of force are used in physics. The concepts, laws, and equations which will be developed in this chapter will be valid for any of these units. For the sake of clarity the pound will be the only unit of force used in this chapter. A more general discussion of force and systems of units will be deferred to Chapter 4.

2-2   VECTORS AND SCALARS

In the discussion of the concept of force, it was noted that the earth pulled *downward* on the body while the spring exerted a force *upward* on it. The *direction* in which the force acts is an important fact needed for its complete specification. The physical quantities length, time, and mass are completely specified by a number together with the proper units; such quantities are called *scalar quantities*. The other type of physical quantity such as force, velocity, acceleration, for which it is necessary to specify a *direction* as well as a number and units, is called a *vector quantity*. Although the methods developed in algebra are sufficient for the discussion of scalar quantities, they are inadequate for the treatment of vector quantities and must be supplemented by geometrical methods to give proper consideration to the direction of the vector quantities.

The method of representing a vector quantity is by means of a properly *directed line* in which the length of the line, drawn to an arbitrary scale, represents the *magnitude* of the vector quantity, while the direction in which the line, with an arrow-head at its end, is drawn represents the *direction* of the vector quantity. A line so drawn is called a *vector*. For example, the vector, representing a weight of 10 lb, would be drawn as a vertical line W with an arrowhead at its lower end. If the scale of the drawing is 5 lb/in., the line should be 2 in. long, as shown in Figure 2–2.

2-3 ADDITION OF FORCES. PARALLELO-GRAM METHOD

    In order to understand how to add vectors, let us consider different

W

Fig. 2–2   Vector method of representing a weight.

methods for supporting a heavy object.   No matter what particular method of support is used, its effect must be that of a force equal in magnitude to the weight of the object but in the opposite direction.   The simplest method

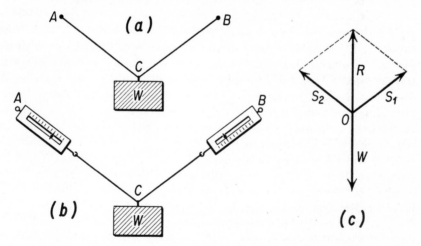

Fig. 2–3   Forces exerted by strings in supporting a weight.

is to exert a single force upward by means of a cord or a wire.   Another common method is to use two cords AC and BC attached to a common point C on the object and to two points A and B on the ceiling, as in Figure 2–3(a).   The forces exerted by the cords AC and BC must add up to a single force R equal in magnitude to the weight W of the object but opposite in direction.   If we can determine the forces exerted by these cords, we can find out how to add them to obtain the single force R.

The magnitude of the force exerted by the cord BC can be measured by untying the cord at B, tying it to one end of a spring balance, and attaching the other end of the spring balance to B, as in Figure 2–3(b).   In a similar way the force exerted by the cord AC can be determined.   Let S_1 represent the force exerted on the weight by the cord BC and let S_2 represent the force exerted by the cord AC on the weight.   The direction of S_1 is from C toward

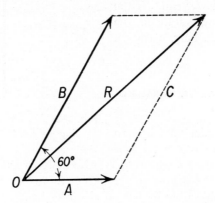

FIG. 2–4   Addition of two forces by the parallelogram method.

B since the cord exerts a pull on the body, while the direction of S_2 is from C toward A.   These two forces S_1 and S_2, when added, must yield a single force whose magnitude is equal to that of W and whose direction is opposite to that of W.   A single force which is equivalent in effect to two or more forces acting simultaneously on a body is called the *resultant force*.   There are several methods for determining the resultant of two forces.   One of these methods, in which the two forces S_1 and S_2 are used as the sides of a parallelogram, is illustrated in Figure 2–3(c).   Starting at some arbitrary point O and using some convenient scale, draw S_1 parallel to CB and S_2 parallel to CA.   Complete the parallelogram with S_1 and S_2 as sides.   The *resultant* of the vectors S_1 and S_2 is the diagonal R of the parallelogram and is in the direction shown, that is, between S_1 and S_2 and directed away from O.   This method of adding two vectors to determine their resultant is called the *parallelogram method*.   This resultant R is found by experiment to be equal in magnitude to the weight W supported by S_1 and S_2, and opposite in direction to W.

Illustrative Example.   Using the parallelogram method, determine the resultant of two forces, one of 20 lb acting horizontally and one of 40 lb acting upward at an angle of 60°, both forces acting simultaneously on a body.

Using a scale of 20 lb = 1 in., and starting at some arbitrary point O, draw the vector A 1 in. long and the vector B 2 in. long at an angle of 60° with A, as in Figure 2–4. Put arrowheads at the ends of the vectors A and B. Complete the parallelogram with A and B as sides and draw the diagonal R with an arrowhead at its end. The measured length of R is 2.7 in. Hence the resultant R is 54 lb at an angle of about 40° with the 20-lb force.

2-4 ADDITION OF FORCES. POLYGON METHOD

Another method for adding vectors is the *polygon method*. To add the vectors S_1 and S_2 of Figure 2–3 by the polygon method, start with either vector, say S_1, and draw it to scale parallel to CB, as in Figure 2–5. Start

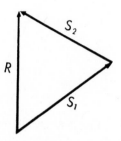

FIG. 2–5　Addition of two forces by the polygon method.

the vector S_2 at the end of S_1 and draw it to scale parallel to CA. The resultant is the vector R which begins at the origin of the first vector S_1 and terminates at the end of the second vector S_2. From a comparison of Figures 2–3 and 2–5, we notice that only one half of the parallelogram is used in the polygon method. Where more than two vectors have to be added, the polygon method is simpler than the parallelogram method. The vectors may be added in any order; each succeeding vector begins where the preceding vector ends. The resultant is a vector joining the origin of the vector drawn first to the end of the vector drawn last.

Illustrative Example. The four forces shown in Figure 2–6(a) act at one point on a body. Determine the resultant of these forces, using the polygon method.

Let us choose some convenient scale, say 20 lb = 1 in., for drawing the vectors representing these forces. Beginning at any arbitrary point O, draw one of these vectors to scale and parallel to the direction in which the force acts. In Figure 2–6(b) the first vector so drawn is the one representing the 20-lb force acting to the right. The remaining three vectors are then drawn in sequence. The resultant is the vector R drawn from the origin of the first vector to the end of the last vector. The measured length of R is $1\frac{11}{16}$ in., so that the magnitude of the resultant is 34 lb. The direction of the resultant is that shown in the figure; the measured value of the angle between the resultant and the vector representing the 20-lb weight is 79°.

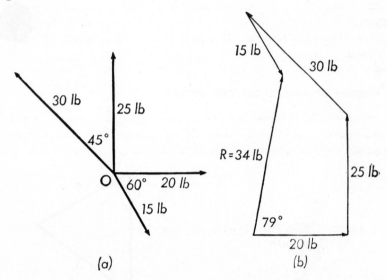

Fig. 2–6   Addition of four forces by the polygon method.

The result obtained is independent of the order in which the vectors are drawn. The student can easily verify this by adding these vectors in a different order.

2-5 EQUILIBRIUM UNDER THE ACTION OF THREE FORCES

There are various ways in which forces may act upon different types of bodies. In analyzing the behavior of these bodies, we shall first restrict our discussion to solid bodies which are acted upon by forces whose lines of action pass through a single point. Such a system of forces is said to be *concurrent*. In general, the effect produced by the action of a set of concurrent forces is to *change the state of motion* of the body upon which these forces act. The motion of the body is then said to be *accelerated*. However, in the special case when the set of concurrent forces which act on the body produces no change in its state of motion, the body is said to be in *equilibrium*. Experiment shows *that a body will be in equilibrium under the action of a set of concurrent forces whenever the resultant of these forces is zero, that is, when the sum of the forces, added vectorially, is zero.* The most commonly recognized case of equilibrium is the one in which the body remains at rest under the action of a system of forces. The other case of equilibrium is one in which the body moves with uniform motion in a straight line. The motion of a body will be discussed more fully in the next chapter.

We have already considered the case of a body in equilibrium under the action of two concurrent forces; in this case the two forces must be equal in magnitude and opposite in direction. The case of a body in equilibrium under the action of three concurrent forces may be treated by first adding two of the forces; the resultant of these two forces will be equal in magnitude and opposite in direction to the third force. However, the polygon method of adding forces is generally more useful in this case, because the three forces, when added vectorially, form a triangle, and the properties of a triangle are very well known. The polygon method will be used in several typical examples.

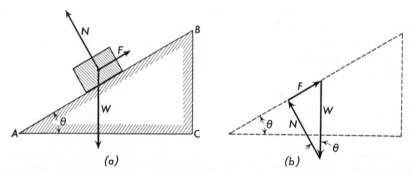

FIG. 2–7   (a) Forces acting on a body which is in equilibrium on a smooth inclined plane.   (b) Triangle of forces.

Consider the case of a body of weight W placed on a smooth plane inclined at an angle θ (theta) to the horizontal, as in Figure 2–7(a). Suppose we want to find the force F parallel to the incline needed to keep this body in equilibrium. The first requisite in solving any problem in mechanics is to determine which forces act *on* the body. In this case there are three forces acting on the body: the weight W acting down, the force F acting parallel to the incline AB, and the push N of the plane. Stating that the plane is smooth implies that the force N which it exerts on any body placed on it acts perpendicular to the surface of the plane AB. To construct the polygon of forces, draw a vector to represent W in magnitude and direction. Through the origin of the vector W draw a line parallel to AB, and through the end of W draw a line perpendicular to AB. This forms a triangle from which the lengths of N and F can be determined, as shown in Figure 2–7(b). The triangle of forces WFN is similar to the triangle ABC since the angle between N and W is equal to the angle θ.

Hence

$$\frac{F}{W} = \frac{BC}{AB} = \frac{h}{l},\tag{5}$$

and

$$\frac{N}{W} = \frac{AC}{AB} = \frac{b}{l},\tag{6}$$

in which l is the length of the plane, h is its height, and b is its base.

Solving Equation (5) for F, we get

$$F = W\frac{h}{l}\tag{7}$$

or

$$\boxed{F = W \sin \theta.}\tag{8}$$

Thus the force F needed to keep a body in equilibrium on a smooth inclined plane is only a fraction of its weight W; this fraction is determined by the ratio of the height to the length of the plane, or the sine of the angle θ.

Similarly, solving Equation (6) for N, we get

$$N = W\frac{b}{l}\tag{9}$$

or

$$\boxed{N = W \cos \theta.}\tag{10}$$

Thus the force N which an inclined plane exerts on a body placed on the plane is only a fraction of the weight of the body; this fraction is the ratio of the base of the plane to its length, or the cosine of the angle θ.

For example, suppose that a box weighing 150 lb is placed on a smooth inclined plane 20 ft long with the higher end 10 ft above the ground. The force F parallel to the incline necessary to keep this box in equilibrium is, from Equation (7),

$$F = 150 \text{ lb} \times \frac{10 \text{ ft}}{20 \text{ ft}} = 75 \text{ lb.}$$

Since the base b for this inclined plane is $10\sqrt{3}$ ft, the push N perpendicular to the plane is, from Equation (9),

$$N = 150 \text{ lb} \times \frac{10\sqrt{3}}{20} = 130 \text{ lb.}$$

Illustrative Example. A rope 10 ft long and of negligible weight has one end A attached to a beam, while a weight of 80 lb is attached to the other end B, as shown in Figure 2–8(a). A man pushes on this weight in a horizontal direction. Determine how big a force the man exerts if the cord stays at an angle of 30° with the vertical. Also determine the tension in the rope.

There are three forces acting on the body: its weight $W = 80$ lb, the horizontal force F, and the pull S exerted by the cord. Using a scale of 40 lb to the inch, draw the vector representing W 2 in. long [see Figure 2–8(b)]. Draw a horizontal line through the end of this vector and a line

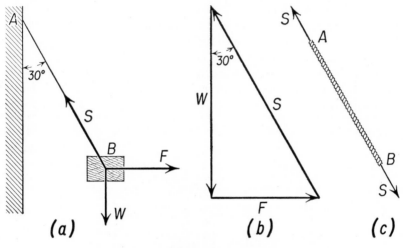

Fɪɢ. 2–8

at an angle of 30° to it through its origin. The intersection of these two lines determines the vectors representing F and S. The measured values of F and S determined from this construction are $F = 47$ lb and $S = 93$ lb. They can also be determined from the trigonometric relationships

$$F = W \tan 30° = 80 \text{ lb} \times \frac{\sqrt{3}}{3} = 46.2 \text{ lb},$$

$$S = \frac{W}{\cos 30°} = \frac{80 \text{ lb}}{0.866} = 92.5 \text{ lb}.$$

The cord AB is, of course, also in equilibrium. If we neglect the weight of the cord in comparison with the other forces acting on it, then the cord is in equilibrium under the action of two forces, the pull exerted by the weight on the cord at B and the pull exerted by the supporting beam on the cord at A. Hence these two forces must be equal and opposite in direction, as in Figure 2–8(c). Now, the force that the body exerts on the cord at B must be equal and opposite to the force S which the cord exerts on the body at B. Hence the force exerted by the beam on the cord at A must also equal S. Whenever a body is acted upon by two equal and opposite forces tending to stretch it, the body is said to be under *tension,* and the magnitude of the tension is the magnitude of either force.   Thus the tension in this rope is equal to *S.*

2-6   RESOLUTION OF VECTORS

In many problems in which vector quantities are involved, much valuable information can be obtained by a somewhat different method of analysis from that previously described.   This method involves the *resolution* of the vector quantities into their *components.*   Any number of vectors which, when added, form a single vector *R* may be considered as the components of this vector *R.*   Thus a vector may be resolved into any desired number of components.   However, in most cases of interest it is usually sufficient to resolve a vector into two components along two previously

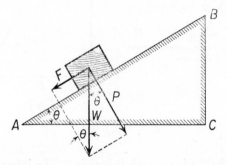

Fɪɢ. 2–9   Resolution of the weight *W* into two components *F* and *P.*

determined directions.   These two directions are usually chosen at right angles to each other.   The method of resolving a vector into two mutually perpendicular components will be illustrated by a reconsideration of the problem of a weight *W* placed on an inclined plane, as in Figure 2–9. Suppose it is desired to know how much of *W* acts parallel to the plane or, in other words, the component of *W* parallel to the plane.   Draw a line through one end of the vector *W* parallel to the plane; drop a perpendicular to this line from the other end of the vector *W.*   The point of intersection of these two lines determines the end of the vector which represents the component *F* parallel to the inclined plane.   An arrowhead placed at the end of this line shows the direction of *F.*   The component of the weight *W* which acts perpendicular to the plane can be determined in a similar manner by first drawing a line perpendicular to the plane through the beginning of the vector *W.*   The length of this component *P* is then determined by dropping a perpendicular onto this line from the end of *W.*   An arrowhead at the end of this line shows the direction of *P.*

The values of the components F and P can be expressed in terms of the weight W and the angle of inclination θ of the plane. From Figure 2–9, we see that

$$F = W \sin \theta \qquad (11)$$

and $$P = W \cos \theta. \qquad (12)$$

If the plane were frictionless, the component F would cause the weight to move down the plane with increasing speed. To keep the body in equilibrium on the plane, that is, either stationary or moving with uniform speed, a force equal and opposite to F must be exerted on the body [see Equation (8)]. The component P pushes the body against the plane; the plane must be strong enough to exert an equal and opposite force to prevent the body from crashing through the plane. This is the force N of Equation (10).

2-7   RECTANGULAR COMPONENTS

In dealing with several forces or any set of vectors, it will often be found convenient to resolve them along two mutually perpendicular directions; these two directions may be taken as those of a set of a rectangular

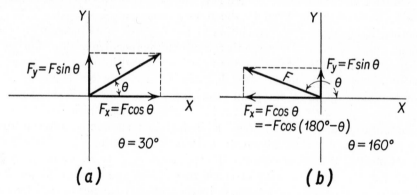

FIG. 2–10   Rectangular components of a force.

coordinate system XY, with the x-axis taken in any arbitrary direction, not necessarily horizontal. Figure 2–10(a) shows the method of determining the x and y components of a force F which makes an angle θ with the x-axis. Calling the x-component F_x, we see that

$$F_x = F \cos \theta;$$

similarly, the y-component is

$$F_y = F \sin \theta.$$

For example, if $F = 80$ lb and $\theta = 30°$, then the x and y components of F are

$$F_x = 80 \text{ lb } \cos 30° = 69.3 \text{ lb},$$

and $\qquad\qquad\quad F_y = 80 \text{ lb } \sin 30° = 40.0 \text{ lb}.$

If the angle that F makes with the x-axis is greater than 90°, it will generally be more convenient to use an acute angle such as the supplementary angle in actual calculations. For example, in Figure 2–10(b) the force $F = 230$ lb makes an angle $\theta = 160°$ with the positive x-axis. The rectangular components of F are

$$F_x = 230 \text{ lb } \cos 160° = -230 \text{ lb } \cos 20°$$

or $\qquad\qquad\quad F_x = -216 \text{ lb};$

also $\qquad\qquad\quad F_y = 230 \text{ lb } \sin 160° = 230 \text{ lb } \sin 20°$

or $\qquad\qquad\quad F_y = 78.7 \text{ lb}.$

2-8 ADDITION OF FORCES. ANALYTIC METHOD

The two methods previously described for the addition of forces are essentially geometric ones. There is a third method, the *analytic method* which reduces the problem to the more familiar algebraic type. This method is based upon the resolution of the forces into mutually perpendicular components. There are three mutually perpendicular directions in space, so that, in general, a vector may be resolved into three mutually perpendicular components. We shall limit our discussion, however, to forces which are all in one plane; such a system of forces is said to be *coplanar*. We shall at present further limit the consideration to forces whose lines of action pass through a single point; such forces are said to be *concurrent*. We shall later remove the latter restriction.

Consider the three concurrent coplanar forces A, B, C, shown in Figure 2–11. Let the point of concurrency O be the origin of a set of rectangular axes XY. Let θ_1, θ_2, θ_3 be the respective angles made by the vectors A, B, C with the x-axis.

From Figure 2–11(a), it is seen that the x-components of these forces are

$$A_x = A \cos \theta_1,$$

$$B_x = B \cos \theta_2,$$

$$C_x = C \cos \theta_3.$$

The sum of these x-components, designated by the symbol $\sum F_x$ ($\sum$ is the capital Greek letter sigma), is

$$\sum F_x = A_x + B_x + C_x$$

or
$$\sum F_x = A \cos \theta_1 + B \cos \theta_2 + C \cos \theta_3. \tag{13}$$

Similarly, the y-components of these forces are

$$A_y = A \sin \theta_1,$$

$$B_y = B \sin \theta_2,$$

$$C_y = C \sin \theta_3.$$

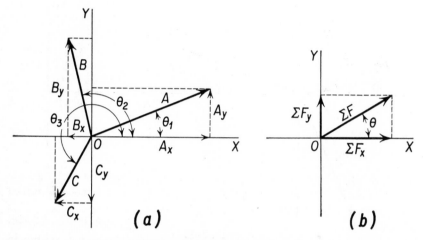

FIG. 2–11　Addition of three concurrent coplanar forces.

The sum of the y-components of these forces, designated by $\sum F_y$, is

$$\sum F_y = A_y + B_y + C_y$$

or
$$\sum F_y = A \sin \theta_1 + B \sin \theta_2 + C \sin \theta_3. \tag{14}$$

$\sum F_x$, the sum of the x-components of all the forces, acts in the x-direction and is the x-component of the resultant force [see Figure 2–11(b)]. $\sum F_y$, the sum of the y-components of all the forces, acts in the y-direction and is the y-component of the resultant force. The resultant force F is the vector sum of $\sum F_x$ and $\sum F_y$, and its magnitude is given by

$$\sum F = \sqrt{(\sum F_x)^2 + (\sum F_y)^2}. \tag{15}$$

The direction of the resultant force is designated by the angle θ that it makes with the x-axis; its value can readily be determined, since, as can be seen from the figure,

$$\tan \theta = \frac{\sum F_y}{\sum F_x}. \tag{16}$$

The resultant of all the forces is thus completely determined. The analytic method can be extended to any number of forces or to any other vector quantities.

Illustrative Example.   Determine the resultant of the following four forces: 150 lb at 20°, 100 lb at 120°, 80 lb at 170°, and 120 lb at 245°, all angles measured with respect to the positive x-axis.

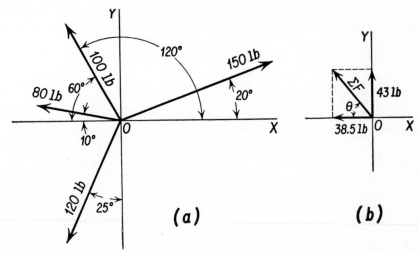

FIG. 2–12

The forces are shown in Figure 2–12(a) with their respective angles converted to acute angles with respect to the x-axis.

Now

$$\Sigma F_x = 150 \text{ lb} \cos 20° - 100 \text{ lb} \cos 60° - 80 \text{ lb} \cos 10° - 120 \text{ lb} \cos 65°,$$

so that $\Sigma F_x = 141 - 50.0 - 78.8 - 50.7 = -38.5 \text{ lb};$

and $\Sigma F_y = 150 \text{ lb} \sin 20° + 100 \text{ lb} \sin 60° + 80 \text{ lb} \sin 10° - 120 \text{ lb} \sin 65°,$

so that $\Sigma F_y = 51.3 + 86.6 + 13.9 - 108.8 = 43.0 \text{ lb},$

from which $\Sigma F = \sqrt{(38.5)^2 + (43.0)^2} = 57.6 \text{ lb}$

and $\tan \theta = -\dfrac{43.0}{38.5} = -1.117,$

so that $\theta = -48°10'$ with the negative x-axis,

or $180 - 48°10' = 131°50'$ with the positive x-axis,

as shown in Figure 2–12(b).

2-9 CONDITIONS FOR THE EQUILIBRIUM OF A PARTICLE

In mechanics, a body may be considered as a particle whenever it is acted upon by a set of concurrent forces. We have already considered the condition for the equilibrium of a particle acted upon by three concurrent forces. This condition is perfectly general and applicable to a particle which is acted upon by any number of concurrent forces. This condition is that the vector sum of all the concurrent forces acting on the body must equal zero.

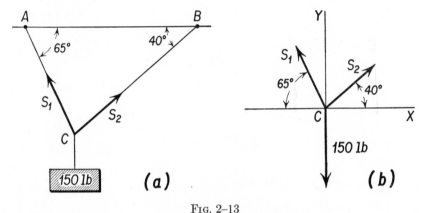

Fɪɢ. 2–13

If the body is acted upon by a set of coplanar concurrent forces, this *condition for equilibrium* may also be stated in terms of the components of these forces as follows: *the sum of the components of the forces along each of two mutually perpendicular axes must be zero*; or in the form of two equations:

$$\sum F_x = 0, \tag{17a}$$

$$\sum F_y = 0. \tag{17b}$$

Illustrative Example. The two ends of a rope are attached to two points A and B at the same horizontal level. A weight of 150 lb is suspended from a point C on the rope so that AC makes an angle of 65° with the horizontal and BC makes an angle of 40° with the horizontal, as shown in Figure 2–13(a). Determine the tension in each part of the rope.

Choose a set of XY axes with the origin coinciding with C, as shown in Figure 2–13(b). Call S_1 the tension in AC, and S_2 the tension in BC. Point C is in equilibrium under the action of the three forces S_1, S_2, and 150 lb, with S_1 and S_2 acting on C in the directions shown in the figure.

The conditions for equilibrium can now be written analytically as

$$\sum F_x = 0 = S_2 \cos 40° - S_1 \cos 65° \tag{18a}$$

and

$$\sum F_y = 0 = S_2 \sin 40° + S_1 \sin 65° - 150 \text{ lb.} \tag{18b}$$

From Equation (18a), we get

$$S_1 \cos 65° = S_2 \cos 40°.$$

This equation shows that the horizontal components of the tensions in the two cords are equal.

Putting in the values for $\cos 65°$ and $\cos 40°$, we get

$$0.4226S_1 = 0.7660S_2$$

or

$$S_1 = 1.81S_2.$$

Similarly Equation (18b) yields

$$0.648S_2 + 0.9063S_1 = 150 \text{ lb.}$$

Substituting the value of S_1 obtained above into this equation and solving for S_2, we get

$$S_2 = 65.6 \text{ lb}$$

and, therefore,

$$S_1 = 119 \text{ lb.}$$

2-10 MOMENT OF A FORCE; TORQUE

In our previous discussions, we considered systems of concurrent forces only. When the forces which act on a body do not pass through a single point, rotational motions may be produced. The effect of a force in producing rotation is determined by two factors: (1) the force itself and (2) its distance from some point considered as an axis of rotation. Suppose that a force F acts on a rigid body, as shown in Figure 2–14. Imagine an axis through point O perpendicular to the plane of the paper, such that the distance from O to the line of action of the force F is r. The effect of the force in producing rotation about the axis through O, called the *moment of the force* or the *torque*, is defined as *the product of the force and the perpendicular distance from the axis to the line of action of the force*. If G represents the torque, then

$$G = Fr. \tag{19}$$

As we view Figure 2–14, the torque will produce a rotation of the body in a counterclockwise direction about O as an axis; the torque G is then said to be in a counterclockwise direction. Figure 2–15 shows a rigid body acted upon by two forces F_1 and F_2 at distances r_1 and r_2 respectively, from an axis through O perpendicular to the plane of the paper. The torque produced by F_1 about O is $F_1 r_1$ in a counterclockwise direction;

the torque produced by F_2 about O is $F_2 r_2$ in a clockwise direction.   By convention a torque in a counterclockwise direction is usually called

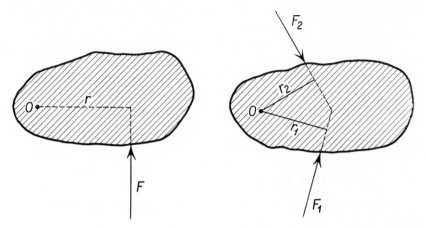

FIG. 2–14   Moment of a force F about   FIG. 2–15   Torques produced by two
      an axis through O.   forces F_1 and F_2 about an axis
                                        through O.

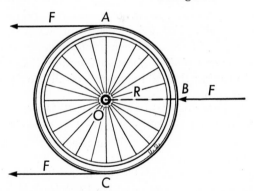

FIG. 2–16   The torque about the axis through O produced by the force F at A is
    in a counterclockwise direction; that produced by the force F at B is zero;
    that produced by the force F at C is in a clockwise direction.

positive, and one in a clockwise direction is usually called negative.   Thus the total torque produced by these forces about O as an axis is

$$G = F_1 r_1 - F_2 r_2. \tag{20}$$

The units of torque or moment of force are those appropriate to the product of a force and a distance, such as ft lb (pronounced *foot pounds*) and cm dyne.

Figure 2–16 shows a bicycle wheel of radius R mounted on an axle passing through the center O; the axle is supported in a rigid framework.

The wheel is acted upon by three equal and parallel forces at points A, B, and C. The moment of the force at A about O is $+FR$; that of the force at B is zero, since the line of action of F passes through O; and that of the force at C is $-FR$. The sum of the moments of these forces is zero; there will thus be no change in the rotational motion of the wheel.

Among the familiar examples of the application of a torque or moment of a force are the opening of a door by a force applied at a distance from the axis of rotation of the door which is along a line through the hinges, the use of a wrench in turning a nut on the bolt, and the torque produced in turning the steering wheel of a car by applying the force on the rim of the wheel. In each case the torque is the product of the force applied by the perpendicular distance from the axis to the line of action of the force.

2-11 EQUILIBRIUM OF A RIGID BODY

When a rigid body remains at rest under the action of a system of forces, the body is said to be in equilibrium. However, under certain special conditions, a body may be in equilibrium even when it is in motion. For example, a rigid body is in equilibrium if it moves in such a way that every particle in the body moves with uniform speed in a straight line. Another type of equilibrium is that of a wheel rotating about its axis with uniform angular speed. For a rigid body to remain in equilibrium when acted upon by a set of forces, two conditions must be satisfied:

(a) *The vector sum of all the forces acting on the body must be zero.* This is equivalent to saying that the resultant of all the forces acting on the body must equal zero.

(b) *The algebraic sum of the moments of all these forces, or of the torques, about any axis must be zero.* This is equivalent to saying that the sum of the clockwise torques about any axis must equal the sum of the counterclockwise torques about the same axis.

We have already considered cases of equilibrium in which all the forces acted through one point, and we have learned how to add forces vectorially. The same methods of addition still apply even though the forces do not act through a single point. In the case of equilibrium under concurrent forces, the second condition is automatically fulfilled. An interesting example, in which the forces do not act through a single point, is a *lever* used to lift a heavy weight by the application of a small force. Essentially a lever consists of a rigid bar AB, shown in Figure 2–17, capable of rotating about some point of support O known as the *fulcrum* or the axis. Suppose that a weight W is placed at the end A and that some vertical force F is applied downward at the end B to keep the lever in equilibrium in a horizontal position. Since both W and F act vertically downward, there must be a force P acting vertically upward at the fulcrum,

Applying the first condition of equilibrium, we get, for the magnitude of P.

$$P = W + F. \tag{21}$$

To apply the second condition of equilibrium, let us take moments of the forces about the point O. The moment of W about O is $+ W \times \overline{AO}$

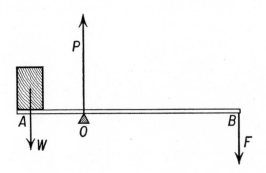

F<small>IG</small>. 2–17   Lever in equilibrium.

since it is counterclockwise; the moment of F about O is $- F \times \overline{OB}$ since this is clockwise; the moment of P about O is zero. Adding all the moments, we get

$$W \times \overline{AO} - F \times \overline{OB} + 0 = 0$$

or

$$W \times \overline{AO} = F \times \overline{OB},$$

from which $F \cdot \overline{OB} = W \overline{AO}$

$$\frac{W}{F} = \frac{\overline{OB}}{\overline{AO}}. \tag{22}$$

The distances $\overline{AO}$ and $\overline{OB}$ are called the lever arms of the respective forces W and F. Thus in the case of a lever, W and F are in the inverse ratio of their lever arms. By placing the fulcrum closer to W, we shall now need a smaller force F to lift W. The fulcrum may be placed at any point along the rod, and the positions of W and F may be moved around to get almost any desired result. Many of the more common tools, when analyzed, can be shown to be applications of the principle of the lever. Among these common tools are the shovel, crowbar, hammer, tongs, wrench, pliers, and scissors.

Illustrative Example. A bar 4 ft long supports five weights spaced 1 ft apart along the bar. Beginning at end A, these weights are 2 lb, 4 lb, 6 lb, 8 lb, and 10 lb, as in Figure 2–18. Determine where a single force must be applied to support this load.

Let the single force F which supports the bar be applied at point C at a distance d from A. From the first condition of equilibrium, we find easily that

$$F = 30 \text{ lb}.$$

To apply the second condition of equilibrium, take moments about an axis through A, obtaining

$$2 \text{ lb} \times 0 - 4 \text{ lb} \times 1 \text{ ft} - 6 \text{ lb} \times 2 \text{ ft} - 8 \text{ lb} \times 3 \text{ ft} - 10 \text{ lb} \times 4 \text{ ft} + F \times d = 0$$

or $$Fd = 80 \text{ ft lb},$$

so that $$d = \tfrac{8}{3} \text{ ft}.$$

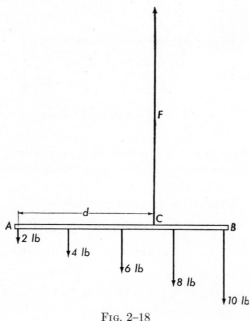

Fɪɢ. 2–18

2-12 CENTER OF GRAVITY

In all of our previous discussions in which it was necessary to consider the weight of a body, we represented it by a single force W downward. Actually the earth exerts a force of attraction on each particle of the body (see Chapter 6); the weight of the body is the resultant of all the forces which act on all the particles of the body. The weight W not only has magnitude and direction, but its line of action passes through a special point in the body known as the *center of gravity*. This can be shown with the aid of a simple experiment and the application of the two conditions of equilibrium.

We have already shown that a single force F acting vertically upward can be used to support a body of weight W. From the first condition of equilibrium, we know that $F = W$. However, this condition is not sufficient to ensure equilibrium, because if the force F is applied at any arbitrary point A in the body (see Figure 2–19), it will, in general, rotate about this point as an axis and then ultimately come to rest. It will now be in equilibrium under the action of the two forces F and W. From the second condi-

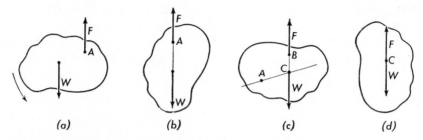

(a)   (b)   (c)   (d)

Fig. 2–19   Method of determining the position of the center of gravity C of a body.

tion of equilibrium, we know that the moments of these two forces are equal in magnitude and opposite in direction. When only two forces act on a body, this second condition of equilibrium can be fulfilled only if F and W act along the same straight line. If the body is now supported at some other point B, it will, in general, rotate about this point and then come to rest. Again, the force F at B and the weight W will act along the same straight line, this time the line passing through B. The lines which pass

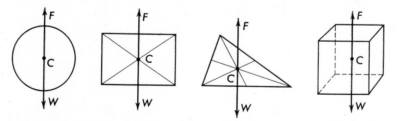

Fig. 2–20   Centers of gravity of some geometrically simple figures.

through A and B intersect at a point C which is the center of gravity of the body. If the structure of the body is such that it is possible to apply a single force $F = W$ at the center of gravity C, the body will be in equilibrium no matter how it is oriented.

The position of the center of gravity of a body can be found by means of an experiment similar to the one described above, that is, by suspending the body alternately from two convenient points in the body and using a plumb line to determine the vertical through each point. The point of intersection of these two vertical lines is the center of gravity of the body.

In many cases of practical interest, the position of the center of gravity of a body can be calculated with the aid of a simple theorem that the moment about any axis produced by the weight of the body acting through the center of gravity must equal the sum of the moments about the same axis produced by the weights of the individual particles of the body. If the body is homogeneous, that is, made of the same material throughout, and if it has some simple geometrical shape such as a circular plate, a square plate, a triangular plate or a cube, the results of the calculations show that the center of gravity is at the geometrical center, as shown in Figure 2–20.

2-13 CENTER OF GRAVITY AND STABILITY

The position of the center of gravity of a body is of very great importance to the stability of a body when it is acted upon by external forces.

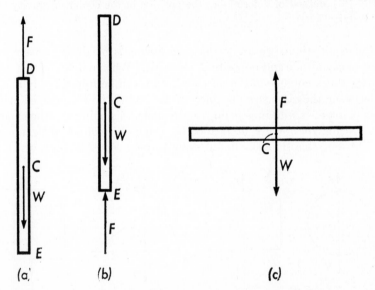

Fig. 2–21 Positions of equilibrium of a uniform homogeneous bar: (a) stable equilibrium, (b) unstable equilibrium, (c) neutral equilibrium.

At present we shall confine our discussion of stability to cases of equilibrium. Let us consider the equilibrium of a homogeneous bar of length L, width a, thickness b, and weight W. An additional force $F = W$, acting upward through the center of gravity, in this case the geometrical center of the bar, will keep it in equilibrium. Two possible ways of doing this are illustrated in Figure 2–21 (a) and (b); the stick may be supported at the top D or at the bottom E. In each case the bar will be in equilibrium; the first is a case of *stable* equilibrium, while the second is one of *unstable* equilibrium. A simple test of the stability of a body in any position of equilibrium is to displace it slightly from its equilibrium position; if, when released, it returns to its original position, that position is one of

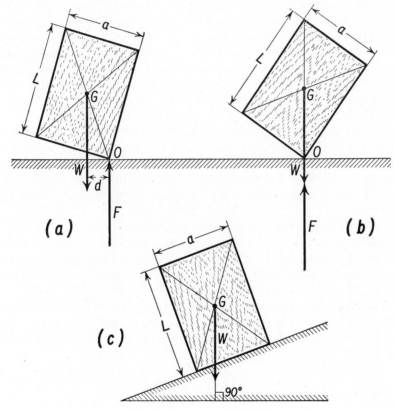

Fig. 2–22   Stability of a rectangular block.

stable equilibrium; if it does not return but continues moving in the direction in which it was displaced, the original position is one of unstable equilibrium. When a body in stable equilibrium is displaced slightly, its center of gravity is raised, and when released it falls back to its original position. When a body in unstable equilibrium is displaced slightly, its center of gravity is lowered, and when released it continues to go down until its center of gravity has reached the lowest possible position.

There is a third type of equilibrium known as *neutral* equilibrium. It is produced by supporting the body in such a way that a slight displacement of it does not change the height of its center of gravity as measured from any arbitrary position. In the case of the bar discussed above, this can be accomplished by putting a small pin through the center of gravity and hanging it from some support, as shown in Figure 2–21(c). A uniform circular cylinder lying on its side is in neutral equilibrium; a spherical ball on a level table is also in neutral equilibrium.

Illustrative Example. A rectangular wood block of length L, width a, thickness b, and weight W rests on a horizontal table. How far can the block be tilted without overturning?

Consider the position of the block after it has been tilted through some small angle, as in Figure 2–22. The weight of the block acts through its center of gravity, and the table exerts a force upward along the edge at O. When the block is released, these will be the only two forces acting on it. Taking moments about point O, we find that the force F acting through O has zero moment, and the weight W has a moment of Wd where d is the distance from O to the line of action of W. Since this torque is counterclockwise, the body will rotate back to its original upright position. The body may be tilted until d becomes zero, that is, until W passes through point O, and still return to its original position when released. When W passes through O, the body is in unstable equilibrium. If the block is tilted through a large angle so that the torque about O is clockwise, then, when released, the block will continue rotating in the same direction until a new position of equilibrium is reached. If this block were put on an inclined plane, as in Figure 2–22(c), it would not overturn as long as the line of action of the weight did not fall outside the base. It follows from this discussion that the lower the center of gravity, the greater is the stability of a body. In loading a car or truck, for example, it is important to put the heavier materials at the bottom to keep the center of gravity as low as possible.

2-14 ANALYTICAL METHOD IN STATICS

In the solution of the more difficult problems in mechanics, some methods will yield results more easily than others. In particular, when a rigid body is in equilibrium under the action of a set of coplanar forces, it is usually best to resolve each of the forces acting on the body into two components along directions at right angles to each other. These two directions, for example, may be the vertical and the horizontal directions. The first condition of equilibrium can then be written as two separate conditions:

(a) The algebraic sum of all the horizontal components of all the forces must equal zero.

(b) The algebraic sum of all the vertical components of all the forces must equal zero.

Stated in the form of two equations, the first condition for equilibrium becomes

$$\sum F_x = 0, \tag{17a}$$

$$\sum F_y = 0. \tag{17b}$$

The second condition for equilibrium of a rigid body, that the algebraic sum of the moments of all the external forces about any point O as an axis equals zero, written as an equation, becomes

$$\sum G_o = 0. \tag{23}$$

These three equations are the analytical expressions of the two conditions for the equilibrium of a rigid body acted upon by a set of coplanar forces. A wise choice of the point O will often simplify the solution of the problem.

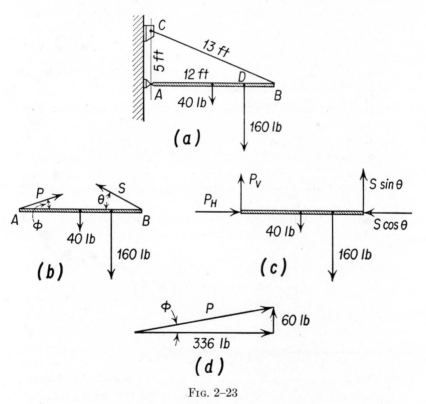

Fig. 2–23

To illustrate this method, let us consider a heavy uniform bar AB 12 ft long, as shown in Figure 2–23, which is fastened to the wall at A and is supported in a horizontal position by means of a wire rope extending from the end B to a point C on the wall 5 ft above A. The bar weighs 40 lb and supports a weight of 160 lb placed at a point D 9 ft from the wall. Determine the tension in the wire BC and the force exerted by the wall at A.

The forces acting on the bar AB, as shown in Figure 2–23(b), are its weight, 40 lb; the load of 160 lb; the tension S in the wire pulling in the direction BC at an angle θ to AB; the force P exerted by the wall on the bar at A. The direction of P is unknown at present; it is drawn at an arbitrary angle ϕ (phi) with the horizontal. P_V is the vertical component of P and P_H is its horizontal component; the vertical and horizontal components of S are $S \sin \theta$ and $S \cos \theta$, respectively. These are shown in Figure 2–23(c).

Using the equations for the equilibrium of a rigid body, we get

$$\sum F_x = 0 = P_H - S \cos \theta,$$

$$\sum F_y = 0 = P_V + S \sin \theta - 160 \text{ lb} - 40 \text{ lb}.$$

It will be convenient to determine the moments of the forces about an axis through point A, because the lines of action of three components P_V, P_H, and $S \cos \theta$ pass through it. The equation for the sum of the moments of the forces about point A becomes

$$\sum G_A = 0 = S \sin \theta \times 12 \text{ ft} - 40 \text{ lb} \times 6 \text{ ft} - 160 \text{ lb} \times 9 \text{ ft}.$$

From the last equation, we get

$$S \sin \theta = 140 \text{ lb}$$

for the vertical component of the tension in the wire.

From the dimensions given in Figure 2–23(a), we find that

$$\sin \theta = \tfrac{5}{13} \quad \text{and} \quad \cos \theta = \tfrac{12}{13}.$$

Hence $S = 140 \text{ lb} \times \tfrac{13}{5} = 364 \text{ lb}.$

Substituting the value of $S \sin \theta$ in the second equation yields

$$P_V = 200 \text{ lb} - 140 \text{ lb} = 60 \text{ lb};$$

from the first equation, we obtain

$$P_H = S \cos \theta,$$

so that $P_H = 364 \text{ lb} \times \tfrac{12}{13} = 336 \text{ lb}.$

Since its components are known, the magnitude and direction of P can readily be obtained. Referring to Figure 2–23(d), we note that

$$P = \sqrt{(336)^2 + (60)^2} \text{ lb},$$

so that $P = 341 \text{ lb}.$

The angle ϕ between P and the horizontal is such that

$$\sin \phi = \tfrac{60}{341} = 0.176,$$

from which $\phi = 10°10'.$

It will be noted that there were three unknown quantities S, P, and ϕ in this problem, and that we could write three independent equations and thus were able to determine these quantities.

QUESTIONS

1. Show that if a weight is hung from the middle of a cord, it will never be possible to get the cord to be horizontal.
2. Show that when a weight is hung from the middle of a cord whose two ends are tied to points on the same horizontal level, the vertical component of the tension in each part of the cord is always equal to half of the weight.
3. Using the second condition for equilibrium of a body, show that when a body is in equilibrium under the action of three nonparallel forces, these forces must pass through a single point; that is, the forces are concurrent.
4. Describe an experiment for determining the force exerted by the fulcrum of a lever.
5. Show that if the resultant of a set of concurrent forces is zero, the sum of the moments of these forces about any point is also zero.
6. Analyze each of the following tools as examples of levers: shovel, claw hammer, wrench, pliers, and scissors. Determine the position of the fulcrum in each case; point out the lever arm in each case.
7. Discuss the positions of stable, unstable, and neutral equilibrium of a body in the shape of a right circular cone.
8. What is the position of unstable equilibrium of a right circular cylinder?

PROBLEMS

1. A spring 16 in. long is hung from the ceiling. When a body weighing 12 lb is attached to the spring, its length is increased to 20 in. What is the constant of the spring?
2. A body weighing 7 lb is put on a spring whose constant is 2 lb/in. What is the increase in length of the spring?
3. When a body, whose mass is 15 gm, is hung from a spring, it is stretched 6 cm. Determine the constant of the spring.
4. The constant of a spring used in a spring balance is 4 lb/in. Determine the weight of a body which stretches the spring 1.8 in.
5. The spring of a Joly balance is made of very fine wire. When 1-gm masses are added successively to the spring, the recorded extensions of the spring in centimeters are as follows: 3.03, 6.00, 9.15, 12.25, 15.25. Plot a graph with the load on the spring, expressed in dynes, as ordinates and the extensions produced in the spring as abscissas. Determine the constant of the spring from this graph.

6. Determine the resultant of the following two forces which act simultaneously on the same body: 60 lb horizontally and 80 lb vertically.

7. Using a convenient scale, show graphically all possible values for the resultant of a 6-lb force and a 9-lb force which act simultaneously on a body.

8. Determine the resultant of two concurrent forces: one of 80 lb acting horizontally and the other of 140 lb making an angle of 145° with the horizontal force.

9. Determine the resultant of three concurrent forces: one of 50 lb acting horizontally to the right, another of 90 lb acting upward at an angle of 60° with respect to the horizontal force, and the third of 140 lb vertically upward.

10. A force of 320 lb is directed at an angle of 15° to the x-axis. Determine its components (a) in the x-direction and (b) in the y-direction.

11. The following forces act on a particle: 72 lb at an angle of 20°, 90 lb at an angle of 80°, 45 lb at 90°, and 130 lb at 110°, all angles measured with respect to the x-axis. Determine (a) the sum of their x-components and (b) the sum of their y-components. (c) Determine the resultant of these forces in magnitude and direction.

12. A body weighing 120 lb hangs from a cord which is attached to the ceiling. A horizontal force pushes the body out so that the cord makes an angle of 30° with the vertical. Determine the magnitudes of the horizontal force and the tension in the string.

13. A rope 20 ft long has its ends fastened to the tops of two tall poles 16 ft apart. A weight of 240 lb hangs at the center of the rope. Determine the tension in the rope.

14. A car weighing 3,500 lb is on a hill which rises 5 ft for every 100 ft of length. Determine the component of the weight which acts parallel to the hill.

15. A crate weighing 150 lb is held on a smooth inclined plane by means of a rope tied to this crate and to the top of the plane. If the inclination of the plane to the horizontal is 30°, (a) determine the tension in the rope and the push of the plane against the crate. (b) What will be the tension in the rope if it is used to pull the crate up the plane at a uniform rate? (c) Determine the tension in the rope if the crate is allowed to slide down with uniform motion.

16. A barrel weighing 125 lb is held on a smooth inclined plane by means of a force applied horizontally; the inclination of the plane is 30°. Determine the magnitudes of the horizontal force and the push of the plane.

17. In order to pull a car out of a rut, a man ties a rope around a tree and attaches the other end to the front bumper of the car. The man then pulls on the middle of the rope in a direction at right angles to the line from the tree to the car. (a) Determine the tension in the rope if the man exerts a force of 80 lb when the angle between the two parts of the rope is 160°. (b) What force does the rope exert in pulling the car forward?

18. A force of 560 lb acts at an angle of 140° with respect to the positive x-direction. Determine the components of this force (a) in the x-direction and (b) in the y-direction.

19. One end A of a rigid horizontal bar is attached to a wall, while the other end B is supported by a rope which is attached to a point C on the wall directly above A (Figure 2–23). The length of the bar AB is 12 ft, and the length of the rope BC is 13 ft. Determine the tension in the rope and the thrust exerted

by the bar when a weight of 4,000 lb is hung from *B*. Neglect the weights of the bar and rope.

20. A body weighing 175 lb is placed on a plane inclined at an angle of 20° to the horizontal. Determine the components of the weight (a) parallel and (b) perpendicular to the inclined plane.

21. A kite weighing 3 lb is flying with its plane surface at an angle of 30° to the vertical, while the cord attached to the kite makes an angle of 75° to the vertical. Determine the tension in this cord.

22. A box weighing 70 lb is held up by two ropes, one rope S_1 making an angle of 30° with the vertical, the other rope S_2 making an angle of 60°. Find the tension in each rope.

23. A uniform horizontal bar *AB*, 8 ft long and weighing 120 lb, is fastened to the wall at *A* while a steel cable 10 ft long extends out from a point *C* on the wall and is fastened to the bar at the point *B*. This bar supports a weight of 900 lb at a point *D* 6 ft from the wall. Determine the tension in the cable and the vertical and horizontal components of the force at *A*.

24. A torque of 5 ft lb is required to swing open a door which is 30 in. wide. What is the least force that must be exerted to open the door if it is applied (a) at a distance of 30 in. from the line of hinges; (b) at a distance of 24 in. from this line?

25. A man carries a bar 6 ft long which has two loads, one of 40 lb and the other of 60 lb, hung from its ends. At which point should the man hold the bar to keep it horizontal? Neglect the weight of the bar.

26. If the bar in the above example is uniform and weighs 20 lb, determine the point at which the man should hold the bar to keep it horizontal.

27. A load of 180 lb is hung from a bar 10 ft long at a point 6 ft from one end. Two men carry this bar in a horizontal position. How big a force does each man exert, assuming that the bar is supported at its ends?

28. An iron trap door 4 ft wide and 6 ft long weighs 90 lb. Its center of gravity is at its geometrical center. What force applied at right angles to it is required to lift this trap door (a) when it is horizontal; (b) when it has been opened so that it makes an angle of 30° with the horizontal?

29. A car weighing 3,200 lb has a wheel base of 120 in.; its center of gravity is 75 in. from the front wheels. Determine the force (a) that the two front wheels exert on the ground; (b) that the two rear wheels exert on the ground.

30. A car weighing 3,600 has a wheel base of 125 in.; its center of gravity is 80 in. from the front wheels. Two passengers sit in the front seat. If their combined weight is 400 lb and if their center of gravity is at a point 60 in. from the front wheels, determine the shift in the center of gravity produced by the passengers.

31. A boom in the form of a uniform pole weighing 400 lb is hinged at the lower end; the boom is held at an angle of 60° with the ground by means of a horizontal cable attached to its upper end. (a) Determine the tension in the cable when there is no load on the boom. (b) Determine the tension in the cable when a load of 1,000 lb is attached to the upper end.

32. A door 8 ft high and 3 ft wide weighs 80 lb, and its center of gravity is at its geometrical center. The door is supported by hinges 1 ft from top and bottom, each hinge carrying half the weight. Determine the horizontal component of the force exerted by each hinge on the door.

3

Motion of
a Particle

3-1 MOTION IS RELATIVE

In this modern age in which our daily lives are so vitally affected by high-speed modes of transportation and fast-moving machinery for the production of the necessities and the luxuries of modern living, most of us have acquired a fair knowledge of the behavior of moving objects. For anyone desiring to have a better knowledge of any aspect of this field, a more careful study of the motion of bodies and the laws governing these motions is essential. The motion of bodies had been observed and studied for centuries, but it was not until the time of Galileo (1564–1642) and Newton (1642–1727) that the laws underlying their motion were put on a firm scientific basis. In this chapter, we shall limit our discussion to the motion of particles without reference to any forces which may be involved. The motions of other types of bodies, as well as the effect of forces which may be acting on these bodies, will be discussed in subsequent chapters.

In all discussions of motion there are at least two objects involved: the body whose motion is being studied, and the object with reference to which the body is moving. When we say that a car is moving at 40 mi/hr, we imply that the motion is taking place relative to the road, or with respect to some point on the surface of the earth. A boat sailing in the river moves with respect to the river's banks, but it also moves with respect to the water in the river. The motion of an airplane may be considered relative to the surface of the earth, but it is also important to know its motion with respect to the air. As a matter of fact, it is easier to determine the latter motion. When we normally speak of the motion of a car, train, or airplane, without mentioning the reference system, we usually imply that the motion is taking place with reference to the earth, or to some object fixed on the surface of the earth. We sometimes call this object on the surface of the earth the *frame of reference* for the motion. When the frame of reference is not fixed to the surface of the earth, its nature and its motion relative to the surface of the earth must always be specified to avoid confusion.

42

3-2 UNIFORM MOTION IN A STRAIGHT LINE

The simplest type of motion is that in which a body traverses equal distances along a straight line in equal time intervals; this type of motion is called *uniform motion in a straight line.* The *speed* of this body is defined as the *distance traversed divided by the time elapsed;*

that is,
$$\text{Speed} = \frac{\text{distance}}{\text{time}},$$

or, in symbols,
$$v = \frac{s}{t}, \qquad\qquad (1)$$

in which v is the speed of the body and s is the distance it traversed in time t. Figure 3–1 (a) shows the distances traversed in equal intervals of time by a

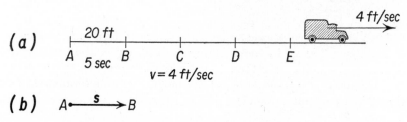

(a)

(b)

FIG. 3–1   (a) Equal distances are traversed in equal intervals of time when a body moves with uniform speed in a straight line.   (b) The vector **s** is the displacement from A to B.

body moving with uniform motion in a straight line. If the scale of the drawing is such that $AB = 20$ ft and the time interval is 5 sec, then the speed of the body is 4 ft/sec.

Whenever a number is used to specify the speed of a body, it must always be accompanied by the appropriate units such as feet per second, usually written ft/sec, or miles per hour, (mi/hr), or meters per second, (m/sec), or centimeters per second, (cm/sec), or any other appropriate units of distance and time.

One other aspect of motion is the direction in which it takes place. When we wish to specify that a body has moved from point A *to point B* [see Figure 3–1(b)], we can use a vector directed from A to B; this vector is called the *displacement* of the body from A to B. If s is the distance from A to B, the displacement is **s**, (printed in boldface type), a vector drawn from A to B.

To specify both the speed of a body and the direction of its motion, we use the term *velocity.* The velocity **v** of a body in uniform motion in a straight line is defined as the *displacement divided by the time during which the displacement occurred*, or, in symbols,

$$v = \frac{s}{t}.$$

(2)

The direction of the velocity is the same as that of the displacement. Velocity is thus a vector quantity. For example, if a train is moving due west with a uniform speed of 60 mi/hr, its velocity is 60 mi/hr west and would be represented by a vector drawn to a convenient scale. In Figure

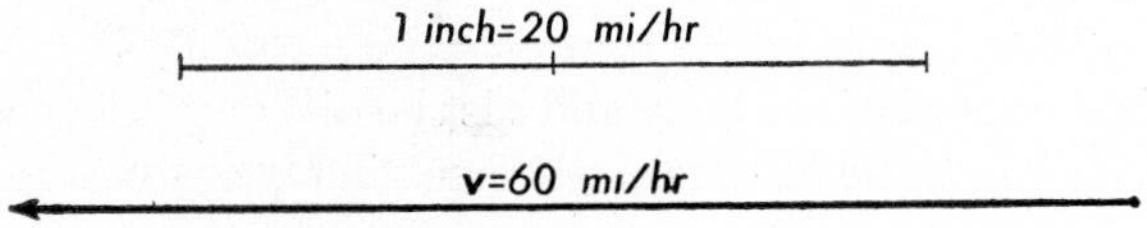

1 inch=20 mi/hr

v=60 mi/hr

Fig. 3–2

3–2, we have chosen a scale such that a length of 1 in. represents a speed of 20 mi/hr; the vector representing the velocity of the train is drawn 3 in. long and pointing in the conventional west direction.

The distance s traveled by a body moving with uniform speed v for a time t, is, from Equation (1),

$$s = vt.$$

(3)

For example, if an airplane maintains a constant speed of 320 mi/hr for 2 hr and 15 min, then the distance it travels in this time is, from Equation (3),

$$s = 320 \frac{mi}{hr} \times 2.25 \ hr,$$

from which $\qquad s = 720$ miles.

Some aspects of the motion of a body can be represented in an informative way with the aid of graphs. In the case of uniform motion in a straight line, if we plot the speed of the body as ordinate (along the vertical axis) and the time of the motion as abscissa (along the horizontal axis), the graph is a horizontal line, as shown in Figure 3–3. Since the height of this line above the abscissa is v and the length of this line is t, the product vt is the area of the rectangle formed by dropping perpendiculars from the ends of the line to the time axis. From Equation (3), we know that $s = vt$, hence this area yields the distance traversed by the body. In Figure 3–3, the speed $v = 60$ mi/hr and the elapsed time is 2.5 hr. The shaded area of the rectangle is, therefore, 60 mi/hr $\times$ 2.5 hr = 150 miles.

If the distance is plotted as ordinate and the time as abscissa, the graph of the motion is the straight line shown in Figure 3–4. This line

FIG. 3–3

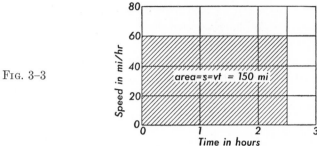

passes through the origin, and its *slope* is the speed of the motion. The slope can be found by taking any two points on the line and then dividing

FIG. 3–4

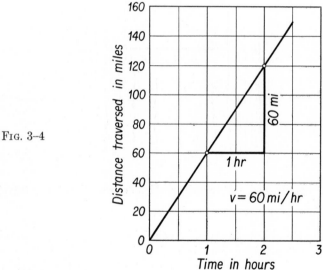

the vertical distance between them by the horizontal distance between these two points. The appropriate units must always be associated with the numbers read from a graph.

3-3 RELATIVE VELOCITIES

It is frequently important to be able to determine the velocity of a body with respect to one frame of reference when its velocity has been determined with respect to a second frame of reference which is in motion relative to the first one. For example, the velocity of a ship relative to the water can easily be measured by means of a device called a log, but what is usually desired is its velocity with respect to the shore, since the water is usually in motion relative to the shore. Again, the velocity of an airplane can easily be measured relative to the air, but the information usually desired is its velocity relative to the ground, since the air usually is in motion with respect to the ground.

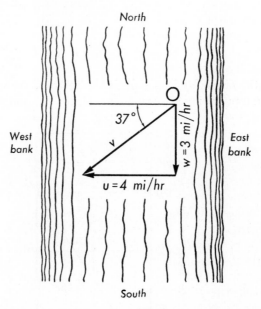

FIG. 3–5 A boat headed west in a river which flows south actually travels south of west.

To understand how these three velocities are related to each other, let us consider the case of a boat in a river in which the water is moving downstream with a velocity **w** relative to its banks. Let us assume that the boat, if left free, would float downstream with the current; that is, its velocity relative to the water would be zero, but its velocity relative to the banks would be the same as that of the water. Suppose, now, that the engines of the boat are started and that the boat moves with a velocity **u** relative to the water. Its velocity **v** relative to the banks will therefore be the resultant of the two velocities: the velocity **w**, which it acquires because it is moving with the water; and the velocity **u**, which it acquires relative to the water. Or in the form of an equation,

$$\mathbf{v} = \mathbf{w} + \mathbf{u}.$$

(4)

The three quantities involved are vector quantities, and the addition must be performed by vector methods. As a simple illustration, suppose that the velocity of the current in a river is 3 mi/hr south and that a boat heads toward the west with a velocity of 4 mi/hr with respect to the water, as shown in Figure 3–5. It is desired to find the velocity of the boat relative to the shore. In Figure 3–5, the velocity **u** of the boat relative to the water is added vectorially to the velocity **w** of the water relative to the shore to get the resultant velocity **v** of the boat relative to the shore. Its value is 5 mi/hr directed at an angle of 37° south of west.

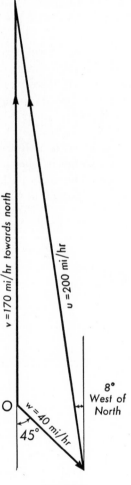

Fig. 3–6

Illustrative Example. An airplane has to fly from New York to Montreal due north. Suppose that its engines develop sufficient power so that in still air its speed would be 200 mi/hr. During the time of flight, there is a steady northwest wind of 40 mi/hr. Determine the direction in which the airplane should be headed in order to go due north, and calculate the speed with which it will travel.

There are thus two parts to the problem: one is to determine the direction of the velocity **u** relative to the air, its magnitude being known, and the second is to determine the magnitude of the velocity **v** relative to the ground, its direction being known. To solve this problem, start with the vector **w** representing the magnitude and direction of the wind, shown in Figure 3–6. Through the origin *O*, draw a vertical line in the direction of the vector **v** of arbitrary length. With the end of **w** as a center, draw an arc of the proper radius to represent 200 mi/hr to intersect this vertical line. This point of intersection is at the termini of both **v** and **u**. (If **w** is drawn 1 in. long, the radius of the arc should be 5 in. long. The measured length of **v** is $4\frac{1}{4}$ in.) The arrows are directed so that **v** is the resultant of **w** and **u**. From this construction, **v** is found to be 170 mi/hr due north, while the airplane must be headed so that its motion relative to the air is about 8° west of north.

3-4   INSTANTANEOUS SPEED AND VELOCITY

We have thus far confined our discussion to the simplest type of motion, that with constant velocity. Of very great interest is the motion of a body in which its velocity changes. Since velocity is a vector quantity, a change in velocity will occur whenever (a) the speed of the body changes while its direction of motion remains the same; (b) the direction of motion changes while its speed remains the same; or (c) its speed and the direction of its motion change simultaneously. Whenever the *velocity* of the body *changes* in any manner whatever, the motion of the body is said to be *accelerated.*

In order to be able to discuss accelerated motion, it is important to know how to specify the speed and the velocity of the body at any instant or at any point in its path. Suppose that the motion takes place along the straight line AB of Figure 3–7(a). We can define the *average speed* of

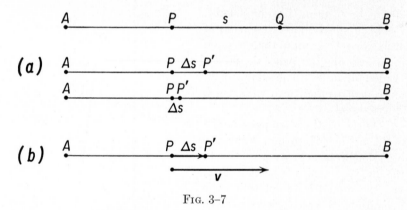

Fig. 3–7

the motion over any portion of the path such as PQ as the distance $s = PQ$, divided by the time t required to traverse this distance. Denoting the average speed by $\bar{v}$ (read v-bar), we can write this definition in the form of an equation as follows:

$$\bar{v} = \frac{s}{t}.$$

(5)

In the special case in which the speed is constant over the path, the average speed is the same as the constant speed v of Equation (1).

The instantaneous speed at any point, such as P, can be found by considering the motion which takes place in a very small time interval during which the body moves from P to some neighboring point P'. It is a common and convenient practice to represent a small change in a quantity, or a small increment in a quantity, by using the Greek letter Δ (delta) as a prefix to the symbol representing the quantity. Thus a small time interval is represented by the symbol Δt, and the small distance traversed in this time interval by Δs. The ratio of the small distance PP' or Δs to the time interval Δt yields the average speed during this motion. As the time interval Δt is chosen smaller and smaller, the point P' gets closer and closer to P, and the average speed over the path PP' approaches the value of the instantaneous speed at the point P. The *instantaneous speed* v at the point P is thus

$$v = \frac{\Delta s}{\Delta t} \qquad (6)$$

as the time interval Δt is made exceedingly small.

The distance from P to P' is the displacement $\Delta\mathbf{s}$ [see Figure 3–7(b)]. The *instantaneous velocity* $\mathbf{v}$ at P is defined as the very small displacement $\Delta\mathbf{s}$ divided by the small time interval Δt; that is,

$$\mathbf{v} = \frac{\Delta\mathbf{s}}{\Delta t} \qquad (7)$$

as Δt is made exceedingly small. The direction of the instantaneous velocity at P is the same as that of the displacement $\Delta\mathbf{s}$, and its magnitude is the instantaneous speed v at P.

The above considerations can readily be extended to motion along a curved path, sometimes called *curvilinear motion*. If the motion is along a curved path such as APB of Figure 3–8(a), the average speed of the body is again the distance traversed along the path divided by the elapsed time and is given by Equation (5). The instantaneous speed v at any point P is again obtained by considering the motion from P to a neighboring point P' during an exceedingly small time interval Δt; the value of the instantaneous speed is given by Equation (6).

In considering the instantaneous velocity $\mathbf{v}$ at P, however, the displacement $\Delta\mathbf{s}$ from P to P', in general, will not coincide with the actual path from P to P' [see Figure 3–8(b)]. But as the point P' is taken closer and closer to P, the displacement $\Delta\mathbf{s}$ practically coincides with the actual path along the curve, and in the limit, as the time interval becomes exceedingly small, does actually coincide with the path. The direction of the displacement is then *tangent to the path at P*. The instantaneous velocity at P is thus given by Equation (7) as before. The magnitude of the instantaneous velocity $\mathbf{v}$ at P is the instantaneous speed v at P, and the direction of the instantaneous velocity is tangent to the path at P, as shown in Figure 3–8(c).

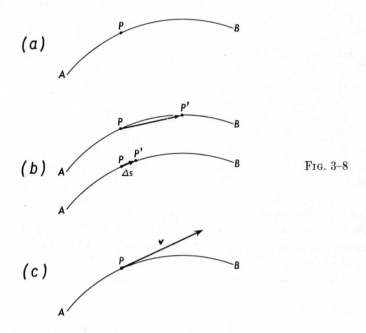

Fig. 3–8

3-5   ACCELERATION

The discussion of motion with varying velocity can be done best in a quantitative manner by the introduction of a new derived concept called *acceleration*. The *acceleration* of a body is defined as *the change in its velocity divided by the time during which the change takes place.*

$$\text{Acceleration} = \frac{\text{change in velocity}}{\text{time}}.$$

As illustrations of accelerated motion, we can discuss the motion of an airplane under a variety of conditions. As it prepares to take off, the airplane moves along the runway with increasing speed; if this speed is changing at a constant rate, its acceleration is constant and is in the direction of its motion. This is the simplest type of accelerated motion. At the instant of take-off, the direction of the acceleration changes so that it will have a vertical component upward; this is necessary to provide an upward component to the velocity in order to lift the plane off the ground. After the plane has reached the desired altitude and speed and has leveled off in flight, it continues with constant velocity, that is, with zero acceleration. If, during the flight, the plane makes a turn at constant speed, its motion is again accelerated because the direction of motion is changing. When an airplane is preparing to land, it reduces its speed for safe landing. While the speed is being reduced, its motion is also accelerated; this time the direction of the acceleration is opposite to the direction of motion.

If the velocity of the body initially is **u** and it changes so that after a time interval t its velocity is **v**, then the acceleration **a** is, from the definition,

$$\mathbf{a} = \frac{\mathbf{v} - \mathbf{u}}{t} \cdot \tag{8}$$

The acceleration **a** is a vector quantity and has the direction of the vector which represents the *change in velocity* (**v** − **u**).

If the motion takes place with constant acceleration, the magnitude and direction of the acceleration remain the same throughout the motion. If the acceleration changes in either magnitude or direction, or both, then Equation (8) yields the *average acceleration* over the time interval t. To obtain the *instantaneous acceleration*, we proceed as we did in the discussion of instantaneous velocity: we consider the change in velocity ($\Delta \mathbf{v}$) which takes place in an exceedingly small time interval Δt, so that

$$\mathbf{a} = \frac{\Delta \mathbf{v}}{\Delta t}, \tag{9}$$

and, as this time interval is made smaller and smaller, the average acceleration approaches as its limiting value that of the instantaneous acceleration.

In this chapter, we shall limit our discussion to motion with constant acceleration, leaving to later chapters the discussion of several cases of varying acceleration.

3-6 STRAIGHT-LINE MOTION UNDER CONSTANT ACCELERATION

The simplest type of motion with constant acceleration is that in which a body moves in a straight line with a speed which is either increasing at a constant rate or decreasing at a constant rate. Since the direction of the motion is always along the same straight line, we may rewrite Equation (8) for the acceleration as an equation among scalar quantities thus:

$$a = \frac{v - u}{t}, \tag{10}$$

in which u is the initial speed of the body, v its final speed after a time t has elapsed, and a the constant acceleration during this time interval.

For example, if an automobile, moving along a straight road, changes its speed from 15 mi/hr to 45 mi/hr in 5 sec at a constant rate, then its acceleration is

$$a = \frac{45 \text{ mi/hr} - 15 \text{ mi/hr}}{5 \text{ sec}} = 6 \frac{\text{mi}}{\text{hr sec}}.$$

We can convert the miles into feet and the hours into seconds thus:

$$6 \frac{\text{mi}}{\text{hr sec}} \times 5{,}280 \frac{\text{ft}}{\text{mi}} \times \frac{1}{3{,}600 \text{ sec/hr}}$$

and obtain for the acceleration

$$a = 8.8 \frac{\text{ft}}{\text{sec sec}} = 8.8 \frac{\text{ft}}{\text{sec}^2}.$$

Another way of saying this is that the speed of the automobile is being changed at the rate of 6 mi/hr each second during these 5 sec of its motion. It is very important to express the acceleration, as well as every other physical quantity, with the proper units. In the above example, 6 mi/hr is the same as 8.8 ft/sec; hence the acceleration can be expressed either as $6 \frac{\text{mile}}{\text{hr sec}}$ or as $8.8 \frac{\text{ft}}{\text{sec}^2}$. The symbols representing the units may be treated as algebraic quantities; thus $\frac{\text{ft}}{\text{sec sec}}$ may be written as $\frac{\text{ft}}{\text{sec}^2}$. The student will find it advantageous to write the units with the numbers; it is somewhat more cumbersome, but the results are more likely to be correct if this procedure is followed.

When the speed of a body is decreasing, the motion is spoken of as accelerated motion with the acceleration assigned a negative value. For example, an airplane which is approaching a landing field decreases its velocity from 250 mi/hr to 100 mi/hr in 20 sec. Since its initial velocity u is 250 mi/hr and its final velocity v is 100 mi/hr, its acceleration a is

$$a = \frac{100 \text{ mi/hr} - 250 \text{ mi/hr}}{20 \text{ sec}} = -7.5 \frac{\text{mi}}{\text{hr sec}}.$$

The question of positive or negative signs for the acceleration of a body is a matter of preference or convenience. In straight-line motion, if the direction of the motion is taken as the direction of the positive acceleration, then whenever the speed is increased the acceleration is positive, and whenever the speed is decreased the acceleration is negative. In other cases, particularly where the acceleration is continually changing direction or magnitude, or both, methods of assigning the sign to it are chosen so as to be both more convenient and more informative. Whenever the occasion arises, the reason for the choice of the sign of the acceleration will be indicated.

3-7 EQUATIONS OF MOTION FOR CONSTANT ACCELERATION

The equations of motion of a body moving with constant acceleration can be readily derived with the aid of a graph of the motion. Suppose that a body moving initially with a velocity u is given an acceleration a for a time t, during which its velocity increases to its final value v. If we plot the speed of the motion as ordinate and the time as abscissa, we get the straight line shown in Figure 3–9. The slope of this line is $(v - u)/t$,

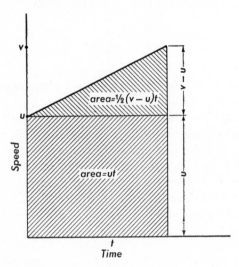

Fig. 3–9   Distance traversed is equal to the area under the straight line which starts at speed u and ends at speed v.

which is the acceleration of the body. The area under this line to the abscissa is the distance traversed by this body in time t. This area can be evaluated readily by noting that it consists of a rectangle whose base is equal to t and whose altitude is u, and a triangle whose base is also equal to t and whose altitude is $(v - u)$. Hence

$$\text{Area of rectangle} = ut,$$

$$\text{Area of triangle} = \tfrac{1}{2}(v - u)t,$$

$$\text{Total area} = ut + \tfrac{1}{2}vt - \tfrac{1}{2}ut$$

$$= \tfrac{1}{2}ut + \tfrac{1}{2}vt.$$

Therefore the distance traversed is

$$s = \tfrac{1}{2}(u + v)t.$$

(11)

From the definition of average speed given by Equation (5)

$$\bar{v} = \frac{s}{t},$$

(5)

we get, for the distance traversed,

$$s = \bar{v}t.$$

(5a)

By comparing Equations (11) and (5a), we find that

$$\bar{v} = \frac{u + v}{2} \; ;$$

(12)

that is, the average speed in straight-line motion under constant acceleration is half the sum of the initial and final speeds.

Equations (10), (11), and (12) are sufficient to describe completely the straight-line motion under constant acceleration. It is convenient, however, to have two additional equations, one expressing the distance in terms of the elapsed time and the acceleration, and the other expressing the final velocity in terms of the distance covered and the acceleration. These can be obtained from Equations (10), (11), and (12). Let us rewrite Equations (10) and (11) for convenience

$$a = \frac{v - u}{t},$$

(10)

$$s = \frac{u + v}{2} t.$$

(11)

Solving Equation (10) for v, we have

$$v = u + at,$$

(13)

and, substituting this value of v in Equation (11), we get

$$s = ut + \tfrac{1}{2}at^2,$$

(14)

which is one of the desired equations.

The other equation can be obtained by solving Equation (10) for t,

$$t = \frac{v - u}{a},$$

and, substituting this value in Equation (11), we have

$$s = \frac{v^2 - u^2}{2a},$$

or

$$\boxed{v^2 = u^2 + 2as,} \tag{15}$$

which is the other desired equation.

In many problems on motion, the body starts from rest; this means that the initial velocity u is zero. In such problems, Equations (10) through (15) assume simple forms. For example, Equations (11), (13), (14), and (15) become

$$s = \frac{v}{2}t, \tag{11$'$}$$

$$v = at, \tag{13$'$}$$

$$s = \tfrac{1}{2}at^2, \tag{14$'$}$$

and

$$v^2 = 2as. \tag{15$'$}$$

Illustrative Example. The runway on an airfield is 800 ft long. If an airplane has to acquire a speed of 120 mi/hr in order to leave the ground, determine the minimum constant acceleration of the airplane and the time it will take to acquire this speed.

The acceleration will be a minimum if the airplane travels the entire length of the runway before acquiring its final speed. Thus $s = 800$ ft, $u = 0$, $v = 120 \dfrac{\text{mi}}{\text{hr}} = 176 \dfrac{\text{ft}}{\text{sec}}$. Using Equation (11$'$), we get for t,

$$t = \frac{2s}{v} = \frac{2 \times 800 \text{ ft}}{176 \text{ ft/sec}} = \frac{100}{11} \text{ sec} = 9.1 \text{ sec.}$$

Knowing t, we can use any one of the equations containing a and t to solve for a, or we can use Equation (15$'$), which does not contain t. From Equation (15$'$), we get

$$a = \frac{v^2}{2s} = \frac{(176 \text{ ft/sec})^2}{2 \times 800 \text{ ft}} = 19.36 \frac{\text{ft}}{\text{sec}^2}.$$

3-8   FREELY FALLING BODIES

One of the most common examples of motion with constant acceleration is that of a body which is dropped from any height and allowed to fall
freely. This is the motion that was first carefully studied by Galileo. The
acceleration of a freely falling body can be determined by different types
of experiment. One type of experiment is to time the fall of an object

Fig. 3-10   Galileo Galilei (1564–1642). Founder of modern scientific method.
Discovered the laws of motion of freely falling bodies and of bodies moving
along inclined planes. Constructed a telescope with which he observed the
surface features of the moon and discovered four of the moons of Jupiter;
his observations helped establish the validity of the heliocentric theory of
the universe. (Courtesy of *Scripta Mathematica*.)

through a given height and then calculate the acceleration from Equation
(14′). The results of many different experiments performed under many
different conditions show that the acceleration of a freely falling body at
any point near the earth's surface is a constant for that particular place.
It varies slightly with latitude and altitude. For purposes of most calculations, the value of the acceleration of a freely falling body may be taken as
32 ft/sec^2 or 980 cm/sec^2. It will always be denoted by the letter g;

thus
$$g = 32 \frac{\text{ft}}{\text{sec}^2} \text{ vertically downward}$$

or
$$g = 980 \frac{\text{cm}}{\text{sec}^2} \text{ vertically downward.}$$

The acceleration of a freely falling body is sometimes called the acceleration due to gravity, since it is caused by the pull of the earth on the body. For very accurate calculations the value of g appropriate to the particular place should be used. These values can be found in tables of physical constants. For reference, a few values of g at different latitudes and at sea level are given in Table 3–1.

Table 3-1 Values of g

Latitude	g in cm/sec^2	g in ft/sec^2
0°	977.989	32.0862
30°	979.295	32.1290
45°	980.600	32.1719
60°	981.905	32.2147
90°	983.210	32.2575

A clearer understanding of the significance of acceleration can be obtained from the detailed consideration of the motion of a baseball that is dropped from the top of a very tall building or from a cliff. When we say that a ball is dropped, we mean that its initial velocity is zero. Since it is accelerated downward at the rate of 32 ft/sec^2, at the end of the first second it will have acquired a velocity of 32 ft/sec downward. Its average velocity during this first second is 16 ft/sec, and the distance traveled during this time is 16 ft. At the end of the second second, it will have acquired an additional velocity of 32 ft/sec so that its velocity will then be 64 ft/sec; at the end of the third second, it will again have acquired an additional velocity of 32 ft/sec so that its velocity at the end of 3 sec will be 96 ft/sec. Its average velocity during these 3 sec is 48 ft/sec, and the distance traversed is 144 ft. Figure 3–11 shows the positions of the ball at 1-sec intervals and the corresponding velocities.

In our discussion of freely falling bodies, the effect of the air on the motion of a body through it was neglected. This discussion thus presents only a first approximation to the actual motion. In many cases, this description is sufficiently accurate. However, when the velocity of the body is very great, such as the velocity of a bullet, or if the body is very small, such as a raindrop, or if the body presents a very large surface, such as a parachute, the resistance of the air plays a very important part in determining the motion of the body. These problems will be considered later in Chapter 4.

The equations developed for the motion of a body under constant acceleration are directly applicable to the discussion of the motion of freely falling bodies. Wherever the acceleration appears in one of these equations, it is simply necessary to replace it by its value $a = g$, and to remember that g is always directed downward.

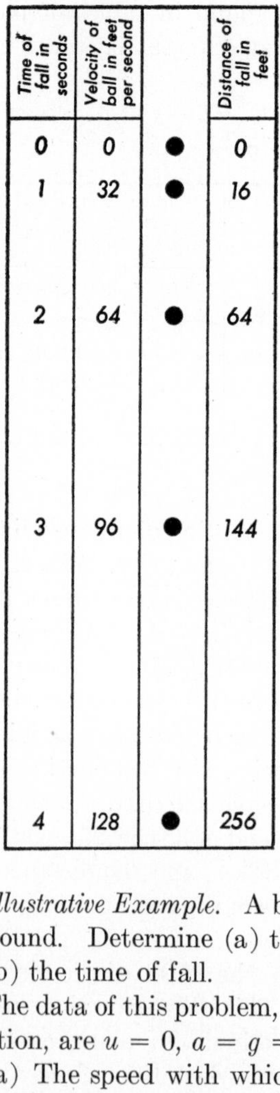

Time of fall in seconds	Velocity of ball in feet per second		Distance of fall in feet
0	0	●	0
1	32	●	16
2	64	●	64
3	96	●	144
4	128	●	256

FIG. 3–11   The free fall of a baseball, showing the positions of the ball at intervals of 1 sec and the corresponding velocities.

Illustrative Example. A ball is dropped from a height of 350 cm above the ground. Determine (a) the speed with which it will reach the ground and (b) the time of fall.

The data of this problem, in terms of the symbols used in the equations of motion, are $u = 0$, $a = g = 980$ cm/sec², $s = 350$ cm.

(a) The speed with which the ball reaches the ground can be determined with the aid of Equation (15′),

$$v^2 = 2gs,$$

or
$$v^2 = 2 \times 980 \frac{\text{cm}}{\text{sec}^2} \times 350 \text{ cm,}$$

so that $\qquad\qquad\qquad v^2 = 980 \times 700 \text{ cm}^2/\text{sec}^2,$

from which $\qquad\qquad\quad v = 830 \text{ cm/sec}.$

(b) The time of fall can be determined with the aid of Equation (13'), using the above value of v thus:

$$v = gt,$$

from which $\qquad\qquad\qquad t = \dfrac{v}{g}.$

Putting in numerical values, we get

$$t = \frac{830 \text{ cm/sec}}{980 \text{ cm/sec}^2},$$

from which $\qquad\qquad\quad t = 0.85 \text{ sec}.$

Illustrative Example. A rock is thrown downward from a tall cliff with an initial velocity of 20 ft/sec. Determine (a) its velocity at the end of 2 sec and (b) the distance it has traveled in this time.

The data of this problem are

$$u = 20 \text{ ft/sec}, \qquad a = g = 32 \text{ ft/sec}^2, \qquad t = 2 \text{ sec}.$$

The velocity of the stone can be found with the aid of Equation (13) thus:

$$v = 20 \frac{\text{ft}}{\text{sec}} + 32 \frac{\text{ft}}{\text{sec}^2} \times 2 \text{ sec},$$

from which $\qquad\qquad\quad v = 84 \text{ ft/sec}.$

The distance s which the rock traveled in these 2 sec can be found by substituting numerical values in Equation (14),

yielding $\qquad s = 20 \dfrac{\text{ft}}{\text{sec}} \times 2 \text{ sec} + \tfrac{1}{2} \times 32 \dfrac{\text{ft}}{\text{sec}^2} \times 4 \text{ sec}^2,$

so that $\qquad s = 104 \text{ ft}.$

A more general method of treating all problems of motion in the earth's gravitational field, where the acceleration of each body is g, is to choose a set of axes with the origin at the point from which the body is projected and treat the equations of motion as equations among vector quantities. We shall consider several different cases in this and the following sections to illustrate this method.

Illustrative Example. Suppose that a ball is thrown vertically upward with an initial velocity of 80 ft/sec. Determine (a) how high it will go, (b) what velocity it will have as it moves down past its original point of projection, (c) its position 6 sec after it was thrown upward, and (d) the velocity with which it will be moving at this time.

Let us choose a set of coordinates with the origin O at the point of projection, and let us take the y-axis as the line of motion (see Figure 3–12). The displacement from the origin will be measured by the y-coordinate of the ball; it will be considered positive above the origin and negative below the origin. The acceleration is downward and will be designated as $-g$.

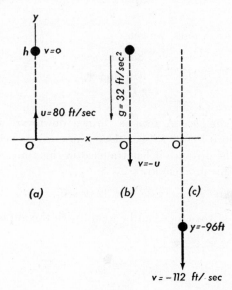

(a)   (b)   (c)

FIG. 3–12   (a) A ball thrown upward reaches a height h at which $v = 0$.   (b) On its return journey it passes the origin with a speed equal to its initial speed but in the opposite direction.   (c) Position and velocity of the ball 6 sec after it started its motion.

The equation for the displacement of the ball can be obtained from Equation (14) by setting $s = y$ and $a = -g$, thus getting

$$y = ut - \tfrac{1}{2}gt^2,$$

and the equation for the velocity at any instant is, from Equation (13),

$$v = u - gt.$$

A positive sign for the velocity means that the motion is upward; a negative sign means that the motion is downward.

The third equation of importance in this discussion is obtained from Equation (15) and is

$$v^2 = u^2 - 2gy.$$

(a) At the highest point of the path the ball will stop momentarily; this means that $v = 0$. Let us call the coordinate of the body at the highest point $y = h$. Putting these values in the last of the above equations yields

$$0 = u^2 - 2gh,$$

from which

$$u^2 = 2gh$$

and

$$h = \frac{u^2}{2g},$$

so that

$$h = \frac{(80 \text{ ft/sec})^2}{2 \times 32 \text{ ft/sec}^2}$$

or

$$h = 100 \text{ ft.}$$

(b) When the ball falls down and passes its original point, its displacement $y = 0$. To determine its velocity at this point, we can use the last equation again, obtaining

$$v^2 = u^2 \quad \text{when} \quad y = 0,$$

so that

$$v = \pm u.$$

In other words, its speed as it passes its original point of projection is the same as its initial speed. Since it is moving down, we choose the negative sign as the appropriate one; that is,

$$v = -u.$$

(c) To find the position of the falling body after 6 sec of motion, we can substitute numerical values in the first of the above equations, obtaining

$$y = 80 \frac{\text{ft}}{\text{sec}} \times 6 \text{ sec} - \tfrac{1}{2} \times 32 \frac{\text{ft}}{\text{sec}^2} \times 36 \text{ sec}^2,$$

so that

$$y = -96 \text{ ft.}$$

The negative sign shows that the ball has reached a point 96 ft below the origin or 196 ft below the highest point of its path.

(d) The velocity at the end of 6 sec can be found by substituting numerical values in the second of the above equations, obtaining

$$v = 80 \frac{\text{ft}}{\text{sec}} - 32 \frac{\text{ft}}{\text{sec}^2} \times 6 \text{ sec},$$

so that

$$v = -112 \text{ ft/sec};$$

that is, it is moving downward with a speed of 112 ft/sec. This is the same speed that a body would acquire if it fell from a height of 196 ft with zero initial speed.

3-9 MOTION OF A PROJECTILE

The motion of a projectile after it leaves the muzzle of the gun is a special case of a freely falling body in which the initial velocity of the projectile is directed at any arbitrary angle to the vertical. We shall again limit our discussion to the ideal case in which air resistance is neglected. Suppose that a bullet is fired horizontally with an initial velocity **u**, as illustrated in Figure 3–13. Once the bullet leaves the muzzle of the gun,

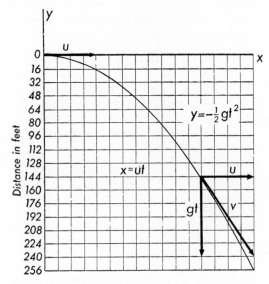

Fig. 3–13 Path of a bullet fired horizontally is a parabola.

its acceleration is vertically downward and equal to **g**. This means that in addition to its horizontal motion with velocity **u**, the bullet will acquire an additional velocity vertically downward equal to gt; that is, the downward velocity will increase with the time just the same as if it were dropped. The actual velocity **v** at any instant will be the vector sum of these two velocities; that is,

$$\mathbf{v} = \mathbf{u} + \mathbf{g}t \qquad (16)$$

Its direction can be determined by means of the parallelogram rule, shown in Figure 3–13. It will be noted that Equation (16) is identical with Equation (13), but it must be remembered that the velocities **u** and $\mathbf{g}t$ are at right angles to one another and that **v** must be obtained by adding these two velocities vectorially.

To determine the path of the bullet, let us choose a set of rectangular coordinates with the origin O situated at the muzzle of the gun and the initial velocity u along the x-axis. The velocity u in the x direction does not change; therefore the distance traversed in this direction in time t is simply

$$x = ut. \tag{17}$$

Since the initial velocity has no component in the y direction, we can treat this as though the bullet were dropped from point O with zero initial velocity in the y direction, and hence the distance traversed in the y direction is

$$y = -\tfrac{1}{2}gt^2. \tag{18}$$

These values of x and y are plotted in Figure 3–13, and the curve obtained shows the path of the bullet. To obtain the equation of the path, solve Equation (17) for t and substitute its value in Equation (18), getting

$$y = -\frac{g}{2u^2}x^2. \tag{19}$$

This is the equation for the path, which is a parabola. The velocity **v** of the particle at any point along this path is given by Equation (16); its direction is always *tangent to the path*.

Illustrative Example. A bomber flying eastward with a velocity of 240 mi/hr drops a bomb from an elevation of 1,600 ft. Assuming that we can neglect air resistance, determine where the bomb will land and how long it will take to get there.

Since the bomb was in the airplane until the instant it was released, its initial velocity is the same as that of the airplane; that is, $u = 240$ mi/hr $= 352$ ft/sec. We can obtain the time of fall for the bomb from Equation (18). Substituting $y = -1,600$ ft, we get

$$1{,}600 \text{ ft} = \tfrac{1}{2} \times 32\frac{\text{ft}}{\text{sec}^2} \times t^2,$$

from which $\qquad\qquad t = 10$ sec.

Using Equation (17), we can find where it will strike the ground 10 sec after it was released:

$$x = 352\frac{\text{ft}}{\text{sec}} \times 10 \text{ sec} = 3{,}520 \text{ ft.}$$

The bomb will strike at a distance of 3,520 ft east of the point at which it was released. The velocity with which the bomb will strike the ground will be the vector sum of the horizontal velocity

$$u = 352 \text{ ft/sec}$$

and the vertical velocity $\qquad gt = 320$ ft/sec.

Hence $$v = \sqrt{(352)^2 + (320)^2}\ \frac{\text{ft}}{\text{sec}} = 476\ \frac{\text{ft}}{\text{sec}}$$

directed at an angle of about 42° with the horizontal.

3-10   MOTION OF A PARTICLE WITH CONSTANT ACCELERATION

We have thus far considered two special cases of motion of a particle in a region of space where its acceleration is constant in magnitude and direction: (a) one in which the direction of the acceleration is parallel to the initial velocity, in which case the path is a straight line; (b) the other in which the acceleration is at right angles to the initial velocity, in which case the path is a parabola. The most general case of motion of a particle in a region of space where its acceleration is constant is that in which the initial velocity of the particle makes any arbitrary angle with the acceleration; the path in this case is also a parabola. Typical examples of such motions are a ball thrown at some angle to the horizontal and a bullet fired from a gun at an angle to the horizontal. Later we shall consider similar motions of electrically charged particles such as electrons, protons, and alpha particles, moving through uniform electric fields, regions in which these particles move with constant acceleration.

As typical of this general case, consider the motion of a bullet which is fired from a gun so that its initial velocity **u** makes an angle θ with the horizontal, as shown in Figure 3–14. By resolving the initial velocity

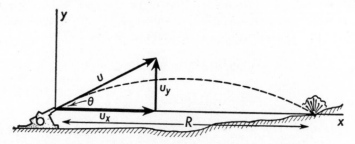

FIG. 3–14   Path of a projectile fired at an angle θ.

into two components, u_x in the horizontal direction and u_y in the vertical direction, the motion of the bullet can be considered as consisting of two distinct types. The motion in the horizontal direction is one of constant velocity u_x, and the distance x traversed in time t is

$$x = u_x t. \tag{20}$$

The motion in the vertical direction is the same as that of a ball thrown upward with an initial velocity u_y. Its acceleration is $-g$. The position

y of the particle in the vertical direction at any time t is, from Equation (14),

$$y = u_y t - \tfrac{1}{2}gt^2.\tag{21}$$

To determine the equation of the path, solve Equation (20) for t and substitute this value in Equation (21), obtaining

$$y = \frac{u_y}{u_x}x - \frac{1}{2}\frac{g}{u_x^2}x^2.\tag{22}$$

This path is a parabola; the projectile will rise to a certain maximum height H and then start down again and reach the ground at a distance R from the origin. This distance R is called the *range* of the projectile. Its value can be determined from Equation (22) by setting $y = 0$, since the bullet reaches the ground again, and setting $x = R$.

$$0 = \frac{u_y}{u_x}R - \tfrac{1}{2}\frac{g}{u_x^2}R^2,$$

from which

$$R = \frac{2u_x u_y}{g}.\tag{23}$$

Equation (23) gives the range of the projectile in terms of the components of the initial velocity u. These components can be written in terms of u and the angle θ as follows:

$$u_x = u\cos\theta,$$

$$u_y = u\sin\theta,$$

so that

$$R = \frac{2u^2 \sin\theta\cos\theta}{g},$$

from which

$$R = \frac{u^2}{g}\sin 2\theta.\tag{24}$$

Equation (24) shows that the range of a gun depends upon the square of the initial velocity of the projectile and upon the sine of twice the angle of elevation of the gun. Now the maximum value of the sine function is 1, so that the maximum range of the gun is

$$R_{\max} = \frac{u^2}{g}\tag{25}$$

when

$$\sin 2\theta = 1,$$

which occurs when $$2\theta = 90°$$

or $$\theta = 45°.$$

Hence the maximum range is obtained when the angle of elevation of the gun is 45°.

At the highest point in its path, at $y = H$, the vertical component of the velocity v_y will be zero. The value of the vertical component at any point is given by Equation (15); in terms of the symbols used in this discussion, this equation becomes

$$v_y^2 = u_y^2 - 2gy.$$

At the highest point, $y = H$ and $v_y = 0$, so that

$$H = \frac{u_y^2}{2g}$$

or $$H = \frac{u^2 \sin^2 \theta}{2g}.$$

The maximum height that can be attained by a projectile having an initial velocity u is simply

$$H_{\text{max}} = \frac{u^2}{2g}$$

and occurs when the projectile is fired vertically upward.

Illustrative Example. A gun fires a shell with a muzzle velocity of 1,200 ft/sec at an angle of elevation of 30°. Determine the range and the time of flight of the projectile. What is the maximum range of this gun?

In this problem $u = 1,200$ ft/sec and $\theta = 30°$. Substituting these values in Equation (24), we get

$$R = \frac{(1,200 \text{ ft/sec})^2}{32 \text{ ft/sec}^2} \sin 60°,$$

from which $$R = 39,000 \text{ ft} = 7.4 \text{ miles.}$$

The time of flight t can be obtained from Equation (21) by setting $y = 0$

and $$u_y = u \sin 30° = \frac{u}{2} = 600 \frac{\text{ft}}{\text{sec}},$$

$$0 = 600 \frac{\text{ft}}{\text{sec}} \times t - \tfrac{1}{2} \times 32 \frac{\text{ft}}{\text{sec}^2} \times t^2,$$

from which $$t = \frac{600}{16} \text{ sec} = 37.5 \text{ sec.}$$

The maximum range of this gun is, from Equation (25),

$$R_{\max} = \frac{(1,200 \text{ ft/sec})^2}{32 \text{ ft/sec}^2} = 45,000 \text{ ft} = 8.5 \text{ miles.}$$

QUESTIONS

1. Describe some examples of uniform straight-line motion which you have recently observed.

2. A ball is thrown vertically upward with an initial speed u. With what speed will it return to its starting point?

3. An airplane travels due east at a constant elevation with constant speed. Is it moving with uniform velocity?

4. One ball is dropped from the top of a building, while another one is thrown forward at the same instant. Which ball will strike the ground first?

5. Show that the speeds of a projectile are the same at any two points in its path which are at the same elevation. Are the velocities at these two points the same?

6. A man standing at a height H above the ground throws one ball upward with an initial speed u and another ball downward with the same initial speed u. Compare the final velocities of these two balls when they reach the ground.

7. A train is moving with uniform speed along a level road. A man on the observation platform drops a ball. What is the path of the ball as observed (a) by the man on the train and (b) by another person standing at a short distance from the tracks?

8. A boy seated on one side of a train throws a ball to another boy seated directly opposite him. If the train is moving with uniform velocity, what is the path of the ball (a) with reference to the train and (b) with reference to the ground? What is the difference in each of these paths if the train moves with uniformly accelerated motion?

9. In a laboratory experiment, an air rifle is clamped in position and aimed by sighting along the barrel. The target is released just as the bullet leaves the muzzle of the gun. Show that the bullet will always hit the target.

10. If there is no wind, raindrops fall vertically with uniform speed. A man driving a car on a rainy day observes that the tracks left by the raindrops on the side windows are all inclined at the same angle. What conclusions can you draw about the motion of the car? Show how the speed of the raindrops can be determined from the inclination of these tracks and the readings of the speedometer.

PROBLEMS

1. A car is driven over a measured mile in 1.2 min. Determine the average speed of the car (a) in miles per hour and (b) in feet per second.

2. A jet airplane travels with a constant speed of 960 mi/hr. Determine the distance it traverses in 20 sec.

3. A river steamer can travel at the rate of 15 mi/hr in still water. How

long will the trip between two cities 60 miles apart take (a) downstream and (b) upstream, if the river current is 3 mi/hr?

4. A ferryboat which can sail at the rate of 10 mi/hr in still water travels straight across a river $\frac{1}{2}$ mile wide in which there is a current of 2 mi/hr. (a) What is the velocity of the ferryboat? (b) How long does a trip take?

5. The first three runners in a 100-yd race were clocked in 9.5 sec, 10.0 sec, and 10.5 sec, respectively. What was the average speed of each runner?

6. An airplane has a normal speed of 300 mi/hr in still air. How long will it take for a 600-mile trip (a) when there is a head wind of 50 mi/hr; (b) when there is a tail wind of 50 mi/hr?

7. An airplane heads due north with a velocity of 300 mi/hr. A west wind is blowing with a velocity of 60 mi/hr. What is the velocity of the airplane relative to the ground?

8. An airplane whose normal speed in still air is 260 mi/hr must travel due east. (a) What course must the aviator set for the plane when there is a steady northeast wind of 80 mi/hr? (b) How long will it take to travel 1,200 miles?

9. A car is traveling at a constant velocity of 50 mi/hr on a level road on a rainy day. The tracks of the raindrops on the side windows make an angle of 30° with the vertical. Assuming negligible wind velocity, determine the velocity of the raindrops.

10. An automobile starting from rest acquires a speed of 40 mi/hr in 12 sec. (a) What is its average acceleration? (b) What distance will it cover in this time?

11. How long will it take for a car starting from rest to acquire a speed of 60 mi/hr if its acceleration is 14 ft/sec^2?

12. The brakes are applied to the wheels of a locomotive when it is traveling at 70 mi/hr. It comes to rest 32 sec after the brakes are applied. What is its average acceleration?

13. An automobile which is traveling at a speed of 65 mi/hr must be brought to a stop within 150 ft. What is the minimum acceleration that must be given to the car to accomplish this?

14. An airplane taking off on a runway 1,200 ft long must acquire a speed of 90 mi/hr to get safely into the air. (a) What is the minimum safe acceleration for this airplane? (b) How long will it take for the airplane to acquire this speed when so accelerated?

15. A car approaching a turn in the road has its speed decreased from 50 mi/hr to 20 mi/hr while traversing a distance of 120 ft. (a) What was its acceleration and (b) how long did it take to traverse this distance?

16. A boy drops a stone from a bridge 75 ft above the water. (a) With what speed did the stone strike the water? (b) With what speed would the stone have struck the water if it had been thrown down with a speed of 24 ft/sec?

17. A boy throws a ball vertically upward and catches it 1 sec later. (a) How high up did the ball go? (b) With what speed was it thrown upward?

18. A boy throws a stone horizontally with a speed of 40 ft/sec from a cliff 256 ft high. (a) How long will it take the stone to strike the ground? (b) Where will the stone land? (c) With what velocity will the stone strike the ground?

19. A small block starting from rest takes 5 sec to slide down an inclined

plane 120 cm long. (a) What was its acceleration and (b) with what speed did it reach the bottom of the incline?

20. Two horizontal wires are placed parallel to each other 100 cm apart, one directly above the other. A falling ball is clocked as it passes each of these wires. If the time elapsed is 0.20 sec, determine the speed the ball had when it passed each wire.

21. Fighter planes fly at 35,000 ft elevation. What must be the muzzle velocity of an antiaircraft shell to reach this height? Neglect friction.

22. A rifle fires a bullet with a speed of 50,000 cm/sec. If the elevation of the rifle is 30° with the horizontal, determine (a) the range of the bullet on horizontal ground and (b) the velocity of the bullet when it reaches the ground.

23. A gun fires a shell with a speed of 1,500 ft/sec. What is the maximum range of this gun? Neglect air resistance.

24. A projectile is fired vertically upward with an initial velocity of 1,800 ft/sec. (a) How high does it rise? (b) What velocity will it have 6 sec after leaving the gun? (c) What is its altitude 6 sec after leaving the gun? Neglect air resistance.

25. A car moving with a speed of 30 mi/hr reaches the top of a hill. As it goes down the hill its speed increases to 60 mi/hr in 45 sec. (a) What is the acceleration of the car and (b) what distance does it travel in this time?

26. A stone thrown horizontally from a hill takes 6 sec to reach the ground. Determine the height of the hill.

27. A stone is seen to pass a window 200 cm high in 0.3 sec. (a) Determine the average speed of the stone. (b) Determine the speed with which it reaches the level of the top of the window. (c) Determine the height above this point from which it fell.

28. The distance between two stop lights on a cross-town street is 800 ft. If the acceleration of a certain car, both positive and negative, is kept at 6 ft/sec², and if the speed limit on this street is 20 mi/hr, determine the minimum time to traverse this distance.

29. Rockets have been fired which have reached heights of 100 miles. What is the maximum speed such a rocket can have when it falls to the ground? What factors tend to reduce this speed?

30. A ball is thrown a distance of 65 ft in 1.2 sec. Assuming that it was caught at the same level as it was thrown, determine how high the ball rose in its path of motion.

Book error!
should be
uniform acceleration

4

Force and Motion

All of us have many times had the experience of setting a body in motion. If we analyze any of these experiences, we readily recall that in each case some *force* was required to start the object moving. In throwing a ball, moving a piece of furniture, or pulling a sled, the force needed to start the object moving is supplied by one's muscular effort as a push or a pull. In more complex cases, such as setting a car or an airplane in motion, the analysis, although more complicated, will also show that a force is required to start the body moving.

There are many cases in which the force that acts on the body to produce the motion is not directly discernible. One such case is exemplified by a freely falling body. It was Newton who first showed that the acceleration of a freely falling body is produced by a force which acts between the earth and the body. This force is called the *force of gravity;* it will be considered in greater detail in Chapter 6. We shall come across other such "action at a distance" forces in electricity and magnetism and in molecular and atomic physics.

Once a body has been set in motion by the action of a force, it will not necessarily stop moving when the force is removed. A car in motion will not stop moving when the engine is disengaged; the car continues to move in its original direction if the road is straight and level. It will take a long time for the car to come to rest. To make it stop sooner, the brakes have to be applied to exert a force to oppose the motion. A sled in motion along a level road will continue to move in a straight line along the road, although with diminishing speed. The reduction in speed is due to the action of a force, known as the *force of friction,* between the runners of the sled and the ground. If there is clean snow on the ground, the force of friction will be very small; if ashes or sand have been dumped on the snow, the force of friction will be greater, and the sled will come to rest much sooner.

The above examples illustrate the fact that a *force is required to change the state of motion of a body.* It was Sir Isaac Newton (1642–1727) who

70

first recognized the relationship between force and the state of motion of the body on which it is acting. He epitomized the entire science of mechanics in the form of three statements which have become known as Newton's laws of motion. These laws will be stated in the next section; a detailed discussion of each of these laws will then follow in the succeeding sections and in some of the other chapters.

FIG. 4-1   Sir Isaac Newton (1642–1727). One of the greatest physicists of all time, he developed the law of universal gravitation; epitomized the subject of mechanics in the three laws of motion which bear his name; made important contributions to optics. The publication of his *Principia*, the Mathematical Principles of Natural Philosophy, in 1687, was an epoch-making event for science. (Courtesy of *Scripta Mathematica*.)

In discussing the relationship between force and the motion of a body, we consider only those forces which act *on* the body; that is, only the *external forces* affect the motion of the body. When the resultant or vector sum of all the external forces which act on the body is not zero, it is often referred to as an *unbalanced force*. The latter term will frequently be used in the following discussions.

4-2 NEWTON'S LAWS OF MOTION

Newton's three laws of motion can be stated as follows:
(a) *A body at rest will remain at rest and a body in motion will continue in*

motion with constant speed in a straight line, as long as no unbalanced force acts on it.

(b) *If an unbalanced force acts on a body, the body will be accelerated; the magnitude of the acceleration is proportional to the magnitude of the un- balanced force, and the direction of the acceleration is in the direction of the unbalanced force.*

(c) *Whenever one body exerts a force on another, the second body exerts a force equal in magnitude and opposite in direction on the first body.*

4-3 NEWTON'S FIRST LAW

Newton's first law states that a body at rest will remain at rest and a body in motion will continue in motion with constant speed in a straight line, as long as no unbalanced force acts on it.

An examination of this first law shows that a body at rest and a body moving with constant velocity have one characteristic in common: there is no unbalanced external force acting upon either one. This is the case when the resultant of all the external forces acting on the body is zero. As we have already seen, this is the condition for the equilibrium of a particle; or if it is a body of appreciable size, this is the condition for equilibrium providing the forces act through a single point, in which case the body can be treated as a particle.

According to Newton's first law, a train moving at a constant velocity along a level track is in equilibrium. It is acted upon by several external forces whose resultant is zero. Consider the forces acting on a train of cars being pulled by a locomotive (see Figure 4–2). The weights W_1, W_2, W_3,

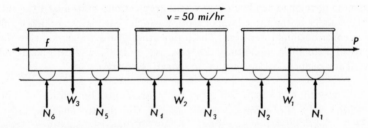

Fig. 4–2   A train moving with constant velocity has no unbalanced force acting on it.

of the cars act vertically downward through the respective centers of gravity. They are opposed by the forces N_1, N_2, N_3, and so forth, which the tracks exert upward on the wheels of the train to support the weight. The sum of these upward forces must equal the total weight of the train. There are also frictional forces which oppose the motion of the train. Some of these frictional forces occur between the wheels and the tracks and in the wheel bearings; there is also another type of frictional force owing to the resistance of the air to motion through it. All of these frictional forces are represented in the figure by the single force f. The effect of these frictional forces would be to reduce the speed of the train; to prevent this reduction in speed, the locomotive supplies a force P equal to f in magnitude but in the forward direction. There is no unbalanced force acting on the train when it is moving with constant velocity.

Implicit in the statement of Newton's first law is a property common to all objects: the property known as *inertia*. The inertia of a body is that property of a body which is exemplified by the fact that a body at rest will remain at rest unless acted upon by an unbalanced force, and a body in motion will continue to move with uniform velocity unless acted upon by an unbalanced force.

Galileo had previously arrived at the concept of inertia from the analysis of the results of an experiment in which a ball was allowed to roll down an inclined plane AB and then roll up another inclined plane BC attached to the first one at B (see Figure 4–3). He found that when the

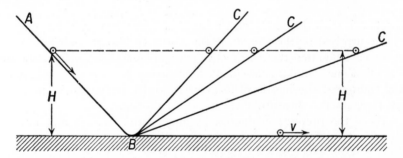

FIG. 4–3 Height to which a ball can ascend after rolling down the first inclined plane should always be the same no matter what the angle of inclination of the second plane may be.

ball started from a height H above the lowest point of the first plane, it reached a height almost equal to H on the second plane. As the angle of inclination of the second plane was made smaller, the height it reached was still almost equal to H, but it traveled a longer distance along the length of the plane. When the inclination of the second plane was reduced to zero, that is, when it was horizontal, the ball traveled along the plane for its entire length. Presumably, if the length of the horizontal plane were to be increased indefinitely, the ball would continue to move with the same speed in the same straight line except for the effect of such external forces as friction and air resistance.

There are several simple experiments which can be used to demonstrate the property of inertia. Suppose we take two similar opaque bottles and fill one with lead shot, leaving the other empty, and then cork each one. There should be no way of distinguishing these bottles through their appearance. If a person first pushes the one filled with lead shot along the table, he will exert a certain muscular effort (see Figure 4–4). If he then

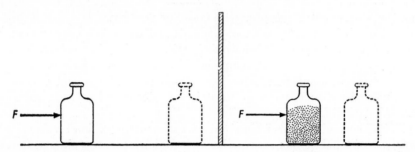

FIG. 4–4   Bottle on right contains lead shot, bottle on left is empty; bottles otherwise identical. If the same muscular effort is applied for same length of time in moving each one, empty bottle will acquire much greater speed.

repeats this with the empty one, using about the same muscular effort, he will be surprised by the rapidity of the motion he imparts to it. He would readily conclude that the inertia of the second bottle is much less than that of the first one. In our subsequent discussion of Newton's second law, we shall show that the inertia of a body is directly related to its mass and that the mass is a measure of the inertia of the body.

Since the property of inertia is implied in Newton's first law, the latter is often referred to as the *law of inertia*.

4-4 NEWTON'S SECOND LAW

Newton's second law states that if an unbalanced force acts upon a body, the body will be accelerated; the magnitude of the acceleration is proportional to the magnitude of the unbalanced force, and the direction of the acceleration is in the direction of the unbalanced force.

The significance of Newton's second law can be brought out by an analysis of a few laboratory experiments in which forces are applied to bodies under a variety of conditions. Suppose we first perform an experiment using a small car mounted on a track; friction effects can be made negligibly small by having the car equipped with wheels mounted on ball bearings. The mass of the car can be measured on an equal-arm balance. Let us now apply a horizontal force F_1 to the car by means of a spring balance attached to it, as shown in Figure 4–5. If this force F_1 acts for a time t, say **2** sec, the car will move some distance s_1 under the action of this force. Since the car was initially at rest ($u = 0$), this distance will be given by the equation $s_1 = \frac{1}{2}a_1t^2$, so that the acceleration a_1 can be readily determined. The acceleration a_1 is in the direction of the force F_1. Let

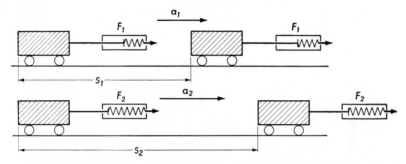

FIG. 4–5   Force F_1 produces an acceleration a_1 and force F_2 applied to the **same** car produces an acceleration a_2, such that $F_1/F_2 = a_1/a_2$.

us now repeat this experiment but this time apply a larger force F_2 for the same length of time $t = 2$ sec. The distance s_2 traveled in this time will be given by $s_2 = \frac{1}{2}a_2t^2$; the new acceleration a_2 can readily be calculated. If we compare the forces F_1 and F_2 and the accelerations a_1 and a_2 produced by them, we shall find that the ratio of the forces is the same as the ratio of the accelerations, or, in symbols,

$$\frac{F_1}{F_2} = \frac{a_1}{a_2}.$$

Rewriting this equation, we get

$$\frac{F_1}{a_1} = \frac{F_2}{a_2}.$$

The interpretation of the above equation is that the ratio of the unbalanced force which acts on a body to the acceleration it produces is a constant. Or

$$\frac{F_1}{a_1} = \frac{F_2}{a_2} = M,$$

from which

$$\frac{F_1}{a_1} = M$$

and

$$\frac{F_2}{a_2} = M,$$

where M is a constant; M is called the *mass* of the body.

In general, if F is an unbalanced force which acts on this body and a is the acceleration produced by it, then

$$\frac{F}{a} = M,$$

or

$$\boxed{F = Ma.}$$ (1)

Equation (1) is a mathematical statement of Newton's second law of motion. The mass M, which is the ratio of the force F acting on the body to the acceleration a produced by this force, is a measure of the *inertia* of the body. We have already considered the concept of inertia in a qualitative way (§4–3). We can now examine it in a quantitative manner, and thus further illustrate the concept of mass, by considering a variation of the above experiment in which forces are applied to bodies of different masses to produce the same acceleration in each case. Suppose that the mass of the car in this experiment is 600 gm. Let us apply a force F to it by means of a spring balance and thus produce an acceleration a; this acceleration is determined by measuring the distance s traversed by the body during the time t that the force was acting on it. Let us now load the car with an additional 600 gm, so that the total mass of the system is 1,200 gm. After a few trial runs, we can produce the same acceleration a with the loaded car as that produced with the empty car (see Figure 4–6). If fric-

FIG. 4–6   The same acceleration is produced on each car. When the mass of the system is doubled, the force must be doubled to produce the same acceleration.

tion is still negligible, the reading of the spring balance will now be practically twice as big as in the former case; that is, if the mass of the system is doubled, the force required to produce a given acceleration will have to be doubled. This experiment can be repeated with a different load in the car each time. If the acceleration is kept the same for each experiment, then the force required to produce this acceleration will be proportional to the total mass of the system which is accelerated.

An instructive variation of the above experiments is one in which the same force acts on bodies of different masses, and the accelerations produced are then measured. For example, if a given force, as measured by the reading of the spring balance which pulls the car, acts on the empty car and produces some acceleration a, then the same force acting on the car

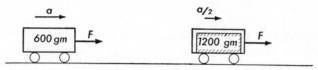

Fig. 4–7   When a force F acts on a mass of 600 gm, it produces an acceleration a; when it acts on a mass of 1,200 gm, it produces an acceleration of $a/2$.

loaded so that its mass is twice as big will produce an acceleration of $a/2$ (see Figure 4–7). If this experiment is repeated with a variety of loads in the car, it will be found that the acceleration is inversely proportional to the total mass of the car and its load.

4-5 SYSTEMS OF UNITS

When numerical values are used with an equation involving physical quantities, such as Equation (1), these numerical values must be accompanied by appropriate units. There are many different sets of units in actual use today, each set consistent within itself, each chosen for some special merit which it is supposed to have for the particular group of experiments or investigations under consideration. Quantities expressed in one set of units can be converted into any other set of units. Most physicists prefer to base the systems of units upon length, mass, and time as the fundamental concepts. Of these systems, the one most widely used is the cgs system in which the centimeter, gram, and second are the units for the respective fundamental quantities.

In the cgs system of units, the mass of a body is expressed in grams, and the acceleration is expressed in centimeters per second per second. A unit of force must be introduced that will be consistent with Equation (1). This unit of force is called a *dyne* and is defined as that *force which, acting on a one-gram mass, produces an acceleration of one centimeter per second per second.*

Suppose that a force F acts on a body whose mass is 1 gm and that it produces an acceleration of 1 cm/sec^2, then Equation (1) would read

$$F = 1 \text{ gm} \times 1 \, \frac{\text{cm}}{\text{sec}^2} = 1 \text{ gm} \, \frac{\text{cm}}{\text{sec}^2} = 1 \text{ dyne.}$$

For example, the force required to give a 5-gm mass an acceleration of 30 cm/sec^2 is, from Equation (1),

$$F = 5 \text{ gm} \times 30 \frac{\text{cm}}{\text{sec}^2}$$

$$= 150 \text{ dynes.}$$

Another system which is being used now is the mks system of units based upon the meter, kilogram, and second as the respective units of length, mass, and time.   The unit of force in the mks system is the *newton*, which is defined as that *force which, acting on a one-kilogram mass, produces an acceleration of one meter per second per second.*

If a force F acts on a body whose mass is 1 kg and produces an acceleration of 1 m/sec^2, then, from Equation (1), we have

$$F = 1 \text{ kg} \times 1 \frac{\text{m}}{\text{sec}^2} = 1 \text{ kg} \frac{\text{m}}{\text{sec}^2} = 1 \text{ newton.}$$

We can obtain the relationship between a newton and a dyne from the above equation; thus

$$1 \text{ newton} = 1 \text{ kg} \times 1 \frac{\text{m}}{\text{sec}^2}$$

$$= 1,000 \text{ gm} \times 100 \frac{\text{cm}}{\text{sec}^2},$$

so that   1 newton = 100,000 dynes.

Illustrative Example.   Determine the unbalanced force required to give a car whose mass is 1,200 kg an acceleration of 3 m/sec^2.

Using Equation (1),

$$F = Ma$$

and, substituting values for M and a, we get

$$F = 1,200 \text{ kg} \times 3 \frac{\text{m}}{\text{sec}^2},$$

from which $F = 3,600$ newtons.

The above two systems of units are based on the metric system.   The system based on the English system of units, the so-called "fps system," is not widely used and will be mentioned here merely for the sake of completeness.   The fps system is based on the foot, pound, and second as the respective units of length, mass, and time.   The unit of force in this system is the *poundal*, which is defined as that *force which, acting on a one-pound mass, produces an acceleration of one foot per second per second.*

Illustrative Example. The force F required to give a 5-lb mass an acceleration of 14 ft/sec² is

$$F = 5 \text{ lb} \times 14 \frac{\text{ft}}{\text{sec}^2},$$

so that $F = 70$ poundals.

In everyday language the word "pound" is commonly used as a unit of mass and as a unit of force. Usually one can infer from the context of the statement whether the pound is used as a unit of force or as a unit of mass. For example, in Chapter 2, the pound was used consistently as a unit of force. To avoid ambiguity, the terms pound force (lb force) and pound mass (lb mass) should be used.

Modern engineering practice tends to avoid the use of the pound mass by introducing a new unit of mass called a *slug*. The *slug* is defined as *that unit of mass which, when acted upon by a force of one pound, will acquire an acceleration of one foot per second per second.* Since a pound mass would acquire an acceleration of 32.17 ft/sec² when acted upon by a 1-lb force, 1 slug is equal to 32.17 lb mass.

With the slug as the unit of mass, Newton's second law, in the form given by Equation (1) $F = Ma$, is directly applicable. For example, the force required to give a body whose mass is 14 slugs an acceleration of 8 ft/sec² is, from Equation (1),

$$F = 14 \text{ slugs} \times 8 \frac{\text{ft}}{\text{sec}^2},$$

from which $F = 112$ lb.

If the weight W of a body is the only force which acts on it, it is a freely falling body and, as we have seen, has an acceleration equal to g. We can apply Newton's second law to a freely falling body by setting $F = W$ and $a = g$ in the equation

$$F = Ma, \tag{1}$$

obtaining

$$W = Mg. \tag{2}$$

Whenever the weight of a body is given in pounds, its mass in slugs can be found with the aid of Equation (2); solving this for M, we obtain

$$M = \frac{W}{g}. \tag{3}$$

For example, the mass of a body whose weight is 161 lb is

$$M = \frac{161 \text{ lb}}{32.17 \text{ ft/sec}^2} = 5 \text{ slugs.}$$

Table 4-1   Systems of Units

System	Mass	Length	Time	Force
Metric absolute—cgs	Gram	Centimeter	Second	Dyne
Metric absolute—mks	Kilogram	Meter	Second	Newton
British gravitational	Slug	Foot	Second	Pound

If the mass of the body does not enter explicity into the problem, it is often convenient to eliminate it from Equation (1) by substituting its value from Equation (3), obtaining

$$F = \frac{W}{g} a. \tag{4}$$

In Equation (4), F and W are expressed in the same units, say pound force, and a and g are expressed in the same units, such as feet per second per second. In European countries, where the metric system is in common use, F and W could be expressed in terms of kilograms of force, or grams of force, and a and g in meters per second per second or centimeters per second per second.

For most of the illustrative examples and problems, we shall use the approximate value of g of 32 ft/sec^2. When more accurate results are needed or desired, the more accurate values of g will be used.

Illustrative Example. If a body weighing 12 lb is given an acceleration of 8 ft/sec^2, the force acting on the body is, from Equation (4),

$$F = \frac{12 \text{ lb}}{32 \text{ ft/sec}^2} \times 8 \frac{\text{ft}}{\text{sec}^2} = 3 \text{ lb.}$$

4-6 APPLICATIONS OF NEWTON'S SECOND LAW

The following are typical examples of the application of Newton's second law of motion, first, to a single particle, and second, to a system of particles; the term particle is used in its technical sense.

Illustrative Example. A loaded car has a mass of 2,800 gm. (a) What horizontal force is required to give this car an acceleration of 80 cm/sec^2? (b) What velocity will this car acquire if it starts from rest and the force acts on it for 8 sec?

(a) Using Equation (1),

$$F = Ma$$

and, substituting values for M and a, we get

$$F = 2{,}800 \text{ gm} \times 80 \frac{\text{cm}}{\text{sec}^2},$$

so that $\qquad\qquad\quad F = 224{,}000 \text{ dynes.}$

(b) The velocity of the car can be determined with the aid of the equation

$$v = u + at,$$

with $u = 0$, $a = 80 \text{ cm/sec}^2$, and $t = 8 \text{ sec}$, yielding

$$v = 80 \frac{\text{cm}}{\text{sec}^2} \times 8 \text{ sec},$$

so that $\qquad\qquad\qquad v = 640 \frac{\text{cm}}{\text{sec}}.$

Illustrative Example. A box weighing 120 lb is placed on a smooth table. A cord tied to this box passes over a smooth pulley fixed to the edge of the table. Another box weighing 40 lb is fastened to the other end of the cord, as shown in Figure 4–8 (a). Determine the acceleration of the two boxes and the tension in the cord.

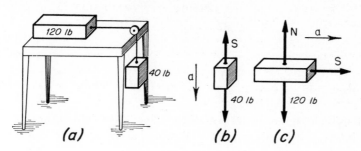

Fig. 4–8

Let us consider each body separately. Figure 4–8 (b) shows the two forces which act on the box hanging from the string; these are the weight of the box, 40 lb downward, and the tension S in the string which pulls upward on the box. We know from experience that this box will be accelerated downward, hence the weight of the box, 40 lb, must be greater than the tension S. The resultant force F on this box is

$$F = W - S = 40 \text{ lb} - S,$$

and, using the form of Newton's second law as given by Equation (4), we can write

$$40 \text{ lb} - S = \frac{40 \text{ lb}}{32 \text{ ft/sec}^2} \times a,$$

in which a is the acceleration of the box.

Now, considering the forces which act on the box on the table [Figure 4–8 (c)], we have, first, its weight of 120 lb which acts downward, second, the push N of the table upward, and third, the tension S in the string which pulls the box toward the right. Since there is no acceleration in the vertical direction, we can write immediately

$$N = 120 \text{ lb}.$$

The only force acting in the horizontal direction is the tension S in the cord; hence, from Newton's second law, we can write

$$S = \frac{120 \text{ lb}}{32 \text{ ft/sec}^2} a,$$

where a is the acceleration of this box and has the same magnitude as the acceleration of the 40-lb box since the two are tied together by a cord of fixed length.

We now have two equations and two unknowns, S and a, and we can therefore determine their values. Eliminating S between these two equations, we get

$$40 \text{ lb} - \frac{120 \text{ lb}}{32 \text{ ft/sec}^2} a = \frac{40 \text{ lb}}{32 \text{ ft/sec}^2} a,$$

from which $a = 8 \text{ ft/sec}^2,$

so that $S = \dfrac{120 \text{ lb}}{32 \text{ ft/sec}^2} \times 8 \text{ ft/sec}^2 = 30 \text{ lb}.$

The tension in the cord is 30 lb and is less than the weight of the box hanging from it. Also it is this force of 30 lb which accelerates the 120-lb body.

4-7   WEIGHT AND MASS

The relationship between weight and mass can best be shown by considering two freely falling bodies at the same place on the earth's surface. If one has a weight W and a mass M and the other has a weight w and a mass m, then, applying Equation (1) to each of these bodies, we get

$$W = Mg,$$

$$w = mg,$$

from which
$$\frac{W}{w} = \frac{M}{m}.$$

(5)

Equation (5) shows that the magnitudes of the weights of two bodies at the same place are in the same ratio as their masses, or, generally speaking, that weight is proportional to mass.

As we go from one place to another, the value of g changes. It varies with latitude, as shown in Table 3–1, and also decreases with increasing altitude (see Chapter 6). The mass of a body, however, remains constant, unless the body is moving with speeds comparable with the speed of light, in which case the mass of the body increases over its mass at rest. We shall consider such cases in Chapter 36.

In the discussions in this book, unless otherwise stated, we shall adopt the value $g = 980$ cm/sec$^2 = 9.80$ m/sec^2. The weight of a body will then be given by Equation (2).

Illustrative Example. A 50 gm mass attached to the end of a string is pulled upward with an acceleration of 49 cm/sec^2. Determine the tension in the string.

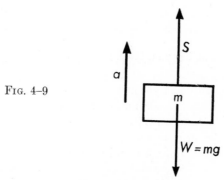

Fig. 4–9

There are two forces acting on the 50-gm mass: its weight $W = mg$ downward, and the tension in the string S upward, illustrated in Figure 4–9 Since the acceleration is upward, the tension S is greater than the weight W The unbalanced force is directed upward and is

$$F = S - W = S - mg,$$

so that
$$S - mg = ma$$

or
$$S = mg + ma,$$

from which
$$S = 50 \text{ gm} \times 980 \, \frac{\text{cm}}{\text{sec}^2} + 50 \text{ gm} \times 49 \, \frac{\text{cm}}{\text{sec}^2},$$

$$S = 51{,}450 \text{ dynes.}$$

4-8 MOTION ON A SMOOTH INCLINED PLANE

When a block whose mass is M is placed on a smooth inclined plane, as shown in Figure 4–10 (a), the block will be accelerated down along the plane. The forces which act on this block are its weight $W = Mg$ and the push N of the inclined plane against the block. When there is no friction, the only direction in which a plane surface can exert a force on a body placed on it is normal or perpendicular to the surface. The resultant of the two

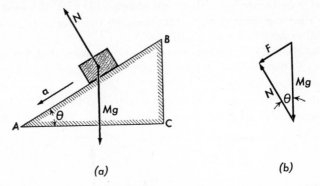

(a)   (b)

FIG. 4–10   Forces acting on a block placed on a frictionless inclined plane.

forces Mg and N must be a force parallel to the plane. This resultant F can be found by the usual vector method: draw Mg vertically downward; through the end of Mg, draw a line perpendicular to the plane AB; it will make an angle θ with Mg [see Figure 4–10 (b)]. Through the beginning of the vector Mg, draw a line perpendicular to N and hence parallel to the plane. Draw arrowheads at the ends of N and F as shown. These vectors determine the relative magnitudes of F, N, and Mg, respectively.

From Figure 4–10 (b), we can see that

$$\sin \theta = \frac{F}{Mg},$$

so that

$$F = Mg \sin \theta. \qquad (6)$$

Putting this value of F in Newton's second law

$$F = Ma,$$

we get

$$Mg \sin \theta = Ma,$$

from which

$$a = g \sin \theta. \qquad (7)$$

Thus the acceleration of a body on a frictionless inclined plane depends upon the sine of the angle of inclination but is independent of the mass of the body. This is one of the reasons why Galileo was able to study the laws of motion using bodies moving down comparatively smooth inclined planes.

Illustrative Example. A body whose mass is 500 gm is projected up a frictionless inclined plane with an initial velocity of 150 cm/sec. The plane is 200 cm long and is inclined at an angle of 30° to the horizontal. (a) Determine the resultant force which acts on this body; (b) determine its acceleration. (c) How far up the plane will it travel before coming to rest? (d) With what speed will it return to its starting point?

(a) The forces acting on this body are the same as those shown in Figure 4–10 (b) with the angle θ equal to 30°. The resultant force acting down the plane is thus

$$F = Mg \sin 30° = 500 \text{ gm} \times 980 \frac{\text{cm}}{\text{sec}^2} \times \frac{1}{2},$$

from which $F = 245{,}000$ dynes.

(b) The acceleration produced by this force is

$$a = g \sin 30° = \tfrac{1}{2}g$$

or $a = 490 \text{ cm/sec}^2.$

(c) The distance s that the body will travel up the plane can be found with the aid of the equation

$$v^2 = u^2 + 2as$$

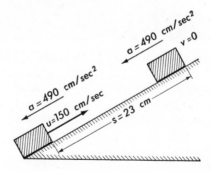

Fig. 4–11

with $u = 150$ cm/sec, $v = 0$, and $a = -490$ cm/sec^2 since its direction is opposite to u (see Figure 4–11). Substituting these values in the above equation yields

$$0 = \left(150 \frac{\text{cm}}{\text{sec}}\right)^2 - 2 \times 490 \frac{\text{cm}}{\text{sec}^2} \times s,$$

from which $s = \dfrac{22{,}500}{2 \times 490} \text{ cm} = 23 \text{ cm}.$

(d) Even though it has come to rest at this point momentarily, it still has the acceleration a down the plane. Starting at this point with $u = 0$, the body will acquire a velocity v given by

$$v^2 = 2as.$$

Since a and s have the same values as in the motion up the plane, the numerical value of v when the body returns to its starting point will be the same as its speed u with which it was projected up the plane. Note the similarity between this motion and the motion of a ball thrown vertically upward.

4-9 FRICTIONAL FORCES

Frictional forces always act to oppose the motion of one body over another when parts of their surfaces are in contact. Some of the frictional forces are desirable and necessary, such as friction between the tires of a car and the roadway, and friction between the brake lining and the brake drum

FIG. 4–12 Photograph showing the result of sliding a piece of copper on an unlubricated steel surface. Horizontal magnification 200, vertical magnification 2,000. *C* represents pieces of copper adhering to the steel; *H* represents holes from which pieces of steel have been plucked by the copper. (Courtesy of *Journal of Applied Physics*. Photograph by F. P. Bowen, A. J. W. Moore, and D. Tabor.)

in the braking mechanism of a car. The former type is essential in the starting of a car and the control of its motion on the road. The latter type is essential in slowing down or stopping the motion within given distances. Frequently, however, frictional forces are undesirable since they cause wear and tear of the parts and materials involved, as in the case of a wheel rotating on its axle or in the motion of a piston in a cylinder.

Friction between solid bodies can be classified into two types, *sliding friction* and *rolling friction*. Sliding friction occurs whenever the surface of one body slides over another; this is the kind of friction that exists between the brake lining and the brake drum of the braking mechanism on a wheel of a car or an airplane. Rolling friction exists between the wheels of a car and the road when no slipping occurs.

The exact nature of the force of friction is not known, but some of the effects produced by these forces have been studied very extensively. When a piece of copper is made to slide over a piece of steel, for example, microscopic examination of the surfaces shows that small pieces of copper are embedded in the steel and small pieces of steel are embedded in the copper (see Figure 4–12). Large forces must be brought into play to produce such effects, although these forces act only through very small distances.

Frictional forces and their effects may be reduced to some extent by the use of lubricants. There are many different varieties of lubricants in use: solids such as soap, grease, graphite; liquids such as oils; and gases such as air and hydrogen. The general effect of the introduction of a lubricant is to replace the original frictional forces by the sliding of one layer of the lubricant over another layer of the same lubricant. A small film of the lubricant adheres to the lubricated surfaces, and then sliding takes place between the remaining layers of the lubricant.

Fig. 4–13 Photograph of a roller bearing, with part of the outer cup cut away to show the tapered rollers, the cage which maintains the proper spacing between them, and the inner race or cone. (Courtesy of Timken Roller Bearing Company.)

Another common method of reducing friction is to change the type of the frictional force from one of sliding friction to one of rolling friction. This is done by placing either ball bearings or roller bearings between the surfaces which are moving relative to one another (see Figure 4–13).

4-10 COEFFICIENT OF SLIDING FRICTION

It is important to be able to determine the magnitude of the force of friction between two bodies whose surfaces slide over one another. This may be obtained with the aid of a simple experiment. Suppose, for exam-

ple, that we want to know the force of friction when one steel surface slides
on another such surface.   Let us take a small rectangular block of this steel
S and place it on another flat, horizontal steel sheet R, as shown in Figure
4–14.   By pulling horizontally on S with a spring balance, the force F

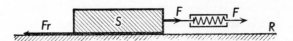

FIG. 4–14   Measuring the force of friction.

required to move it with uniform speed against the force of friction F_r
between the two surfaces can be read directly on the spring balance.   It will
be found that the reading of the spring balance just before motion starts is
greater than after the body is set in motion with uniform speed.   The force
of friction which opposes the starting of the motion is called the force of
starting friction, while the force of friction which opposes the sliding of one
body over the other is called the force of *sliding friction* or *kinetic friction.*
The force of starting friction is always greater than the force of kinetic
friction.

That the force F is actually equal to the frictional force F_r which
opposes the motion of S on R can easily be demonstrated by mounting R on
rollers and attaching one end of R to another spring balance by means of a
string passing over a pulley, as shown in Figure 4–15.   When there is sliding

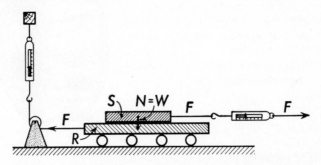

FIG. 4–15   Determination of the force due to sliding friction.

of S on R, the two spring balances will give practically identical readings.
The force of friction F_r acts on S so as to oppose its motion and is equal and
opposite to F.

The results of many experiments show that the magnitude of the
frictional force F_r is proportional to the force N pressing the two surfaces
together.   That is,

$$F_r \propto N,$$

or
$$F_r = fN. \tag{8}$$

The dimensionless factor of proportionality f is called the *coefficient of friction* between the two surfaces. The force N pressing the two surfaces together is *normal*, that is, perpendicular to these surfaces (see Figure 4–16).

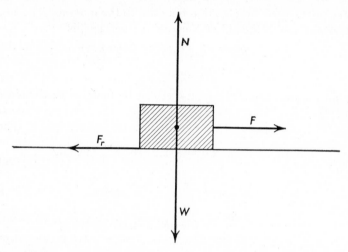

Fig. 4–16 Forces acting on a body which is moving with uniform motion on a rough surface.

When the surfaces are horizontal, the normal force acts in a vertical direction; in many such cases N is equal to the weight of the body. The coefficient of friction f is found to depend almost exclusively on the nature of the two sliding surfaces. Within reasonable limits, the coefficient of friction for any two substances is independent of the area of contact and of the speed of the relative motion of the two bodies. Coefficients of friction have been determined for many different kinds of surfaces; a few of these values for sliding friction are given in Table 4–2.

Table 4-2   Coefficients of Sliding Friction

Materials		Materials	
Wood on wood, dry	0.25–0.50	Metal on metal, dry	0.15–0.20
Metals on oak, dry	0.50	Steel on agate, dry	0.20
Leather on metals, dry	0.56	Masonry on dry clay	0.51

Illustrative Example. A sled and its passenger weigh 96 lb. The sled is given a speed of 15 ft/sec on a level road. If the coefficient of friction between the steel runners and the snow is 0.07, determine how far the sled will travel before coming to rest.

The normal force acting on the sled is equal to the total weight; hence $N = 96$ lb. The force of friction is, from Equation (8),

$$F_r = 0.07 \times 96 \text{ lb} = 6.72 \text{ lb}.$$

This force produces an acceleration opposite to the motion. The acceleration, determined with the aid of Newton's second law, is

$$a = \frac{F_r}{M} = \frac{6.72 \text{ lb}}{\frac{96}{32} \text{ slugs}} = 2.24 \text{ ft/sec}^2.$$

The distance s that the sled will travel can be found with the aid of the equation

$$v^2 = u^2 + 2as,$$

with $v = 0$, $u = 15$ ft/sec, and $a = -2.24$ ft/sec^2, yielding

$$0 = \left(15 \frac{\text{ft}}{\text{sec}}\right)^2 - 2 \times 2.24 \frac{\text{ft}}{\text{sec}^2} \times s,$$

from which $\qquad s = \dfrac{225}{2 \times 2.24} \text{ ft} = 50.2 \text{ ft.}$

4-11 MOTION ON A ROUGH INCLINED PLANE

We have already seen (Section 4–8) that a body of mass M, when placed on a smooth inclined plane, is acted upon by two forces: its weight $W = Mg$, and the normal force due to the push of the plane on it. The resultant F of these two forces is parallel to the plane and accelerates the body down the plane. We showed that

$$F = Mg \sin \theta = W \sin \theta, \qquad (6)$$

where θ is the angle of inclination of the plane with the horizontal. If we resolve the weight of the body into two components, one parallel to the plane and the other normal to it, as shown in Figure 4–17, it will be seen that the parallel component is $W \sin \theta$ and the normal component is $W \cos \theta$. Thus the component of the weight parallel to the plane is equal to the force F which accelerates the body down the plane.

If the body is placed on a rough inclined plane and allowed to slide down it, a third force, produced by the friction between the body and the plane, now acts on it. This frictional force F_r acts to oppose the motion of the body along the plane (see Figure 4–18). If the inclination of the plane is sufficiently large so that F is greater than F_r, the body will be accelerated down the plane by a force equal to the resultant of these two forces,

$F - F_r$. Since these are the only forces which act in a direction parallel to the inclined plane, we can write, applying Newton's second law to this motion,

$$F - F_r = Ma, \qquad (9)$$

where a is the acceleration down the plane.

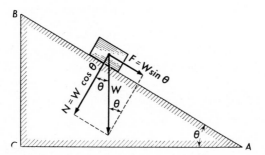

Fig. 4–17   Resolution of the weight W into two components: F parallel to the inclined plane and N normal to it.

Since the body moves parallel to the inclined plane, there is no acceleration normal to it. The forces that act normal to the plane are N and the normal component of the weight, which is equal to $W \cos \theta$, and their vector sum must be zero, thus

$$N - W \cos \theta = 0,$$

so that $\qquad\qquad N = W \cos \theta = Mg \cos \theta. \qquad (10)$

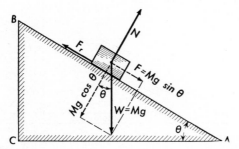

Fig. 4–18   Analysis of the forces acting on a body which is sliding down a rough inclined plane.

The relationship between the frictional force and the normal force is that given by Equation (8)

$$F_r = fN,$$

so that $\qquad\qquad F_r = fMg \cos \theta, \qquad (11)$

where f is the coefficient of sliding friction between the body on the plane and the surface of the plane. Substituting the value of F from Equation (6) and the value of F_r from Equation (11) into Equation (9), we get

$$Mg \sin \theta - fMg \cos \theta = Ma,$$

from which $a = g \sin \theta - fg \cos \theta.$ (12)

Thus the acceleration of a body down a rough inclined plane is less than on a smooth plane by a term which contains the coefficient of friction f as well as a function of the angle θ. Equation (12) reduces to Equation (7) when f is zero, that is, when there is no friction.

If the angle of the above plane is reduced to a value $\theta = \theta_c$ at which the acceleration of the body becomes zero, then Equation (12) becomes

$$0 = g \sin \theta_c - fg \cos \theta_c,$$

from which $\sin \theta_c = f \cos \theta_c$

or

$$\boxed{\tan \theta_c = f.}$$ (13)

Equation (13) shows that this critical value of the angle of inclination does not depend upon the weight of the body on the plane but depends only upon the coefficient of sliding friction between the two surfaces. This equation also suggests a simple method of determining the coefficient of sliding friction for a great many substances .

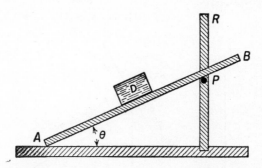

FIG. 4–19   The angle θ can be varied by raising or lowering the peg P attached to the vertical rod R. When $\theta = \theta_c$, a small push will cause the block D to slide down with uniform speed.

A simple laboratory experiment for determining the coefficient of sliding friction is sketched in Figure 4–19. AB is a board whose surface is made of the material to be tested. D is a block which is also made of the material to be tested. If the angle of inclination θ is very small, the block will not slide down the plane. The experiment consists in increasing the angle of inclination slowly; at each new value of θ, the block is given a slight push down the plane. If it stops moving, the angle θ is again increased until, when $\theta = \theta_c$, the block, when started, continues to move down the plane with uniform speed. The angle of the plane is then measured. The experiment should be repeated several times, and the average value of the angle should be determined from these measurements. The tangent of this angle can then be found in the table of trigonometric functions, and the numerical value of the coefficient of sliding friction can be determined.

Illustrative Example. A heavy wooden crate weighing 200 lb is pulled up a wooden plane, inclined at an angle of 20°, by a force of 150 lb. The coefficient of friction between the surfaces is 0.30. (a) Determine the acceleration of the crate. (b) If the rope hauling it breaks, discuss the subsequent motion of the crate.

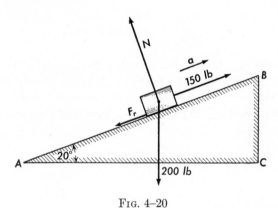

FIG. 4–20

(a) Figure 4–20 shows the forces which act on the crate as it moves up the plane. The force N which the plane exerts on the crate is perpendicular to its surface and is equal to the normal component of the weight, since there is no acceleration normal to the plane. Hence

$$N = W \cos \theta$$

$$= 200 \text{ lb} \times \cos 20°$$

$$= 200 \text{ lb} \times 0.9397,$$

or $$N = 187.9 \text{ lb.}$$

The force of friction is

$$F_r = fN$$

$$= 0.3 \times 187.9 \text{ lb.}$$

or $F_r = 56.4$ lb

and acts down the plane, opposing the upward motion.

The component of the weight parallel to the plane is

$$F = W \sin \theta$$

$$= 200 \text{ lb} \times 0.3420,$$

or $F = 68.4$ lb

and also acts down along the plane.

The resultant force up the plane is therefore

$$(150 - 56.4 - 68.4) \text{ lb} = 25.2 \text{ lb}.$$

The acceleration up the plane can be found with the aid of Newton's second law, yielding

$$a = \frac{25.2 \text{ lb}}{\frac{200}{32} \text{ slugs}} = 4.03 \text{ ft/sec}^2.$$

(b) When the rope breaks, the crate is pulled down by the component of the weight $F = 68.4$ lb. The frictional force $F_r = 56.4$ lb is now reversed since it always acts in a direction to oppose the motion. The resultant force now is, therefore, 12 lb down the plane, and the new acceleration a_1 is

$$a_1 = \frac{12 \text{ lb}}{\frac{200}{32} \text{ slugs}} = 1.92 \text{ ft/sec}^2.$$

4-12 MOTION THROUGH THE AIR

Objects falling through the air are acted upon not only by the force of gravity but also by the resistance of the air. Some of this resistance may be due to the viscosity of the air and the rest to turbulence. Because of this resistance, the velocity acquired by a body falling through the air is less than that acquired by a freely falling body falling through the same height. Experience shows that the resistance of the air to motion through it increases as the velocity of the body increases. In many cases, if the time of fall is sufficiently large, the body will reach a *limiting velocity*, at which time the force due to the resistance of the air is equal to the weight of the body. The body then continues moving downward uniformly with this limiting velocity.

Consider the case of a raindrop of weight W which has just started falling toward the earth's surface, as illustrated in Figure 4–21. Initially its acceleration is g, but, as its velocity increases, the air exerts a force R upward. For simplicity, let us assume that the resistance varies directly with the velocity of the raindrop, or, in the form of an equation,

$$R = Kv, \qquad \text{(14)}$$

where K is a constant of proportionality determined by the surface area of the raindrop and the viscosity of the air. Its numerical value will depend upon the units used in expressing v and R. As the velocity of fall increases, the force R increases until it becomes equal to the weight of the raindrop. If v_L is the velocity of the raindrop when $R = W$, then

$$R = Kv_L = W,$$

or $\qquad v_L = \dfrac{W}{K}.$ (15)

Thus the limiting velocity of fall v_L of the raindrop depends upon its weight. The larger and heavier raindrops acquire greater limiting velocities. When the raindrops reach the surface of the earth, the heavier drops are moving faster than the lighter ones.

Fig. 4–21 Forces acting on a body falling through a resisting medium such as air.

Another important case where use is made of the limiting velocity of fall occurs when someone bails out of an airplane. Again the initial motion is one with acceleration g, but the resistance of the air opposes this motion. In army tests, men bailed out of airplanes at very great heights and did not open their parachutes until within about 2,000 ft of the ground. Because of air resistance, the velocity acquired by these men reached a limiting value of about 120 mi/hr with parachutes still closed. Of course, with parachutes open, the limiting velocity is much smaller than 120 mi/hr, permitting safer landing. Because of the very large area of the parachute, the force exerted by the air at any given velocity is very great, and a lower limiting velocity is reached very quickly. A modern parachute is designed so that the motion of the air past it can to some extent be controlled by the one using the parachute to secure greater safety and comfort in its use.

4-13 PAIRS OF FORCES. NEWTON'S THIRD LAW

In our discussion of Newton's first and second laws, our attention was focused on one body on which a set of external forces acted. If we now analyze the origin of each of these forces, we find that each force is produced by the action of some other body on the one under discussion. If we push a trunk along the floor, the trunk exerts a force against our hands. If a ball is hit with a bat, there is not only a force exerted by the bat on the ball, but also a force exerted by the ball on the bat. An automobile which is standing still pushes down on the ground at each of the surfaces of contact between its tires and the ground. At each region of contact, the ground exerts a force upward equal to that exerted by the car. *Newton's third law states that whenever one body exerts a force on another, the second body exerts a force equal in magnitude and opposite in direction on the first body.* This law is sometimes called the law of *action* and *reaction*.

As an illustration of Newton's third law, consider the manner in which a car is set into motion. To start the car moving forward, there must be an unbalanced horizontal force acting on the car. To produce this horizontal force, the engine is started and then connected by means of gears and shafts to the rear wheels, causing them to turn in a clockwise direction, as shown in Figure 4–22. Because of the friction between the tires and the

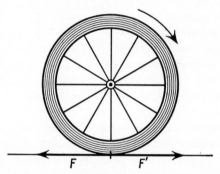

Fɪɢ. 4–22 Force F' exerted by the ground on the wheel is equal in magnitude, but opposite in direction to, the force F exerted by the wheel on the ground.

ground, the wheels exert a force F to the left (backward) on the ground; the ground exerts an equal and opposite force F' forward on the rear wheels. It is this horizontal force F' which makes the car go forward. To understand that it is the push of the ground on the driving wheels which makes the car go forward, just think of driving experiences on a winter day with ice on the ground, when the friction between the tires and the ground is very small. What usually happens is that the wheels spin in a clockwise direction, but, since there is little frictional force available, the wheels merely spin around and the car does not move.

4-14 IMPULSE AND MOMENTUM

One convenient method of considering the effect of a force is to determine the change in velocity produced by it during the time that it acts. If the initial velocity of the body is u and its final velocity is v, then, if the acceleration a is constant, we have

$$a = \frac{v - u}{t},$$

in which t is the time required to produce this change in velocity. Now, from Newton's second law, we have

$$F = ma,$$

where F is the force producing the acceleration and m is the mass of the body. Substituting the value of a into this equation, we get

$$F = m \frac{v - u}{t},$$

from which

$$\boxed{Ft = mv - mu.}$$
(16)

The product of the force by the time during which it acts is called the *impulse* produced by the force. The product of the mass of a body by its velocity is called the *momentum* of the body. It should be noted that momentum is a vector quantity; the direction is that of the velocity of the body. Equation (16) states that *the impulse produced by a force is equal to the change in momentum of the body on which the force acts.* This equation may be considered another way of stating Newton's second law. It is extremely useful in cases in which the force acts for very short intervals of time. In batting a ball, for example, the force that the bat exerts on the ball acts only during the time that they are in contact. Since the time of contact is extremely small, the impulsive force acting during this time is very great. When two airplanes collide, the duration of the collision is very short; hence the force acting on each airplane is very great.

In the collision between two bodies, each one experiences a change in momentum, and each one exerts a force on the other. If there are no forces acting on these bodies other than those brought into play during collision, we may treat these two bodies as a single system and show that the total momentum of the system after collision is equal to the total momentum possessed by the system before collision. Suppose we imagine two spheres which are moving in the same direction, as in Figure 4–23(a), one sphere of mass m moving with velocity u and the other sphere of mass M moving with a greater velocity U. Suppose that the line joining the centers of these spheres is parallel to these velocities. When they collide, the larger sphere will exert a force F on the smaller sphere, as in Figure 4–23(b), and the smaller sphere will exert a force F' on the larger one. From Newton's third law, we can say that these two forces are equal in magnitude but opposite in direction; that is,

$$F = -F'. \tag{17}$$

The collision will last for some time t, and after this the spheres will move with new velocities v and V, respectively. Applying Newton's second law to the smaller sphere, we get

$$F = m\frac{v - u}{t},$$

and, for the larger sphere, Newton's second law yields

$$F' = M\frac{V - U}{t}.$$

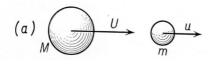

Fig. 4–23 Central collision of two spheres: (a) velocities before collision, (b) forces acting during collision, (c) velocities after collision.

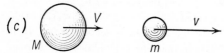

Substituting these values for F and F' in Equation (17), we get

$$m\frac{v - u}{t} = -M\frac{V - U}{t},$$

from which

$$mv - mu = -MV + MU,$$

so that

$$\boxed{mv + MV = mu + MU.} \tag{18}$$

Equation (18) states that the total momentum of the system after collision is equal to the total momentum of the system before collision. This is one statement of a very general principle known as the *principle of the conservation of momentum.* This principle states that *if no external force acts on a system, the total momentum of the system remains unchanged.* In applying this principle, one must remember that momentum is a vector quantity; if the direction of the velocity is reversed, then the momentum of the body changes sign. An interesting illustration of this principle is the firing of a gun. The system consists of a gun of mass M and a shell of mass m and some powder of negligible mass. Before the shell is fired from the gun, the system is at rest and therefore has zero momentum. The shell is fired by the explosion of the powder in the barrel of the gun. The only forces acting on the gun and the shell are those due to the pressure developed by the exploding powder. These forces act as long as the shell remains in the barrel of the gun. There are no external forces acting on the system. If the shell leaves the gun barrel with a velocity v, it will have a momentum mv. From the principle of conservation of momentum, the gun must move backward with a velocity $-V$ and momentum $-MV$ such that

$$mv - MV = 0$$

or $$mv = MV. \tag{19}$$

This is well known to anyone who has ever fired a gun. This backward motion of the gun is usually called the *recoil* of the gun.

Illustrative Example. A block of balsa wood whose mass is 600 gm is hung from a cord of negligible weight. A bullet whose mass is 2 gm and which has a muzzle velocity of 28,000 cm/sec is fired into this block at close range and becomes embedded in it. Determine the velocity with which the balsa block is set into motion.

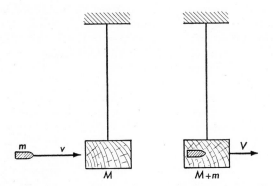

Fig. 4–24   (a) Initial momentum of system as bullet approaches balsa-wood target is mv. (b) Final momentum of system after bullet has penetrated target $(M + m)V$.

If we consider the bullet and the balsa-wood block as a single system, there is no external force acting on it; hence the momentum of the system will remain constant. The initial momentum of the system before the bullet penetrates the wood is simply the momentum mv of the bullet, since the block of wood is not in motion (see Figure 4–24). When the bullet penetrates the block of wood, both move together with a common velocity V, and the final momentum of the system is $(M + m)V$, where M is the mass of the block of wood. From the principle of the conservation of momentum, we can write

$$mv = (M + m)V,$$

from which

$$V = \frac{m}{M + m}\,v,$$

and, substituting numerical values, we get

$$V = \frac{2 \text{ gm}}{602 \text{ gm}} \times 28,000 \, \frac{\text{cm}}{\text{sec}}$$

$$= 93.3 \text{ cm/sec.}$$

QUESTIONS

1. A car is moving with a uniform velocity of 60 mi/hr. What is the resultant force acting on the car?

2. A driver starts a car moving. Analyze the forces which act on the car and state explicity which of these moves the car forward.

3. A man stands in a streetcar and faces to the front. (a) What will happen to the man when the car suddenly starts moving forward? (b) After the car has been moving forward for some time, the brakes are suddenly applied; discuss the motion of this man at this time.

4. Try the following simple experiment: place a sheet of paper on the table and then put a glass of water on it. Pull the paper slowly; describe what happens. Now pull the paper very rapidly; again describe what happens. Explain the different results obtained in these two cases.

5. A man rows a boat to a dock. The man attempts to step from the boat to the dock without first securing the boat to it. Discuss the probable motion of the man and the boat.

6. A small, flat car stands in the middle of a room. A boy starts running and lands on the car. Discuss the motion of the boy and the car.

7. A small, flat car stands in the middle of a room. A boy, in running across the room, steps on the car and off again. Describe what happens to the car in this process.

8. A toy balloon is blown up and attached to a toy car with the open end of the balloon toward the rear. Discuss the motion of the car as the air leaves the balloon.

9. Two boys on ice skates hold a rope between them. One boy is much heavier than the other. Discuss their motions when one of the boys pulls on the rope.

10. Apply the principle of conservation of momentum to a ball bouncing off a wall (a) when the ball moves perpendicular to the wall and (b) when the ball strikes the wall at an angle less than 90°.

11. An inexperienced person firing a rifle sometimes keeps the butt of the rifle a short distance from his shoulder. What will happen when the rifle is fired?

12. A car is traveling over a muddy road. Discuss the path taken by the pieces of mud which fly off the tires.

13. Analyze the forces acting when a horse pulls a wagon. Explain why (a) the wagon goes forward and (b) the horse goes forward

PROBLEMS

1. How big a force is required to give a 60-gm mass an acceleration of 150 cm/sec^2?

2. What constant force is required to give a body weighing 160 lb an acceleration of 4 ft/sec^2?

3. An automobile weighing 3,000 lb and starting from rest acquires a speed of 40 mi/hr in 12 sec. Assuming that the acceleration is uniform, determine the unbalanced force which is acting on the automobile during this time.

4. A box whose mass is 350 gm rests on a table. A steady horizontal force is applied to this box. After 5 sec the box has acquired a speed of 60 cm/sec. Determine the force acting on the box. Neglect friction.

5. A box of 800-gm mass is projected across a horizontal table with an initial speed of 150 cm/sec. It comes to rest on the table after having traversed a distance of 240 cm. Determine the frictional force opposing the motion.

6. A box whose mass is 1,500 gm is given an acceleration of 250 cm/sec^2 on a horizontal surface. (a) Determine the resultant force acting on the box. (b) If the box starts from rest, determine the speed it will acquire in 8 sec.

7. A train weighing 450 tons has its speed increased from 20 mi/hr to 60 mi/hr in 15 sec. What force is supplied by the locomotive to produce this acceleration?

8. A steel cable supports an elevator weighing 2,800 lb. What is the tension in the cable when the elevator is moving (a) upward with a uniform velocity of 600 ft/min and (b) downward with a uniform velocity of 500 ft/min?

9. A steel cable supports an elevator weighing 2,400 lb. Starting from rest, the elevator acquires a velocity upward of 600 ft/min in 2 sec. (a) What is the unbalanced force acting on the elevator? (b) What is the tension in the cable?

10. The elevator of Problem 9, when going down, acquires a velocity of 500 ft/min in 2 sec. (a) What is the unbalanced force acting on the elevator? (b) What is the tension in the cable?

11. A steel ball whose mass is 250 gm is attached to the end of a cord. The ball is pulled upward with an acceleration of 180 cm/sec^2. Determine (a) the unbalanced force acting on the ball and (b) the tension in the cord.

12. A cube whose mass is 1,800 gm rests on a smooth table. A cord which is attached to the center of one face of the cube passes over a frictionless pulley at the edge of the table. A steel ball whose mass is 900 gm is fastened to the free end of the cord. Determine (a) the acceleration of each body and (b) the tension in the cord.

13. A box weighing 72 lb is placed on a smooth horizontal table. A cord which is connected to the center of one face of the box passes over a smooth pulley at the edge of the table. A steel ball weighing 48 lb is then fastened to the

other end of the cord.   Determine (a) the acceleration of each body and (b) the tension in the cord.

14. Two boxes, one weighing 24 lb and the other weighing 6 lb, are attached to the ends of a cord.   The cord is placed over a frictionless pulley which is free to rotate about a horizontal axis.   Determine the acceleration of each weight.

15. A cord passes over a fixed frictionless pulley in an Atwood machine. A cylinder whose mass is 3,000 gm is suspended from one end of the cord and another cylinder whose mass is 2,500 gm is suspended from the other end. Determine (a) the acceleration of the system and (b) the tension in the cord.

16. A series of frictionless inclined planes all have the same heights but have different lengths.   Show that the time required for an object to slide down any of these planes is directly proportional to the length of the plane.

17. A car weighing 3,600 lb and moving with a speed of 20 mi/hr reaches a hill having a 5 per cent grade and starts coasting downhill.   Determine (a) the component of the weight acting downhill; (b) the speed the car will acquire if it coasts for 400 ft, assuming friction is negligible.

(Note: A hill having a 5 per cent grade is one which rises 5 ft for every 100 ft of length.)

18. A body whose mass is 2,500 gm is projected up an inclined plane with an initial velocity of 400 cm/sec.   The plane is inclined at an angle of 30° to the horizontal, and the coefficient of friction between the plane and the body is 0.2. Determine (a) how far up the plane it will go before coming to rest, (b) its acceleration down the plane, and (c) the speed it will have when it reaches its starting point.

19. Determine the force required to pull a trunk weighing 140 lb across a room if the coefficent of sliding friction between the floor and the trunk is 0.6.

20. A heavy box weighing 1,600 lb is being pulled up an inclined plane which rises 4 ft for every 20 ft of length.   If the coefficient of friction is 0.6, determine the force necessary to move it up the incline at constant speed.

21. A box slides down a 30° inclined plane with an acceleration of 5 ft/sec^2. Determine the coefficient of friction between the box and the plane.

22. In the determination of the coefficient of sliding friction, it is found that a steel block will slide down a steel inclined plane with uniform motion when the angle of the plane is 10°.   Determine the coefficient of friction between these two steel surfaces.

23. A box whose mass is 2,400 gm rests on a table.   A cord tied to this box passes over a frictionless pulley at the edge of the table.   A cylinder whose mass is 1,000 gm is hung from the free end of the cord.   The coefficient of friction between the box and the table is 0.25.   Determine (a) the acceleration of the box, (b) the tension in the cord, and (c) the distance the cylinder will move in 3 sec.

24. A boy takes a running start with a sled and acquires a speed of 12 ft/sec. If the coefficient of friction between sled and snow is 0.10, how far will the sled move on a level road before coming to rest?

25. A boy coasts down a hill on a sled, reaching level ground with a speed of 30 ft/sec.   If the coefficient of friction between the steel runners and the snow is 0.05 and the boy and sled weigh 120 lb, how far will the sled travel before coming to rest?

26. Show that, if the force due to the resistance of the air varies with the square of the velocity of a falling body, the limiting velocity of fall is proportional to the square root of the weight of the body.

27. A bullet whose mass is 2 gm is fired from a rifle with a muzzle velocity of 30,000 cm/sec into a piece of balsa wood mounted on a car with frictionless wheels. The total mass of the balsa wood and car is 1,200 gm. Determine (a) the initial momentum of the system and (b) the velocity of the balsa wood and car after the bullet was embedded in the wood.

28. A rubber ball whose mass is 400 gm is bounced against a floor. The velocity with which it strikes the floor is 800 cm/sec. Assuming perfect elasticity, determine (a) the velocity with which it will rebound, (b) the change in momentum of the ball, and (c) the impulse produced.

29. Two men, one weighing 175 lb and the other weighing 125 lb, are on ice skates. Each holds one end of a taut rope. The heavier man exerts a force of 25 lb on the rope. (a) How big a force does the lighter man exert? (b) What is the acceleration of each man? Neglect friction.

30. A 5-gm bullet is fired from a gun whose barrel is 60 cm long. The bullet leaves the gun with a muzzle velocity of 25,000 cm/sec. (a) What was the average force acting on the bullet? (b) What is the momentum of the bullet when it leaves the gun?

31. A man driving a golf ball gives it a speed of 3,000 cm/sec. (a) If the mass of the golf ball is 50 gm, what impulse was imparted to it by the driver? (b) If the time of impact between the golf ball and driver was 0.004 sec, determine the average force acting on the golf ball.

5

Work and Energy

5-1 WORK DONE BY FORCES

An extremely important concept that has been developed in physics is that of the *work done* on a body by the action of some external agent which exerts a force on this body and produces motion. For example, whenever someone lifts a body, he does work by exerting a force upward on it and moving it upward. Whenever a steam locomotive pulls a train, a series of processes takes place in the steam engine of the locomotive which enables it to exert a force on the train and move it in the direction of the force. The term *work*, as used in physics, is a technical term. Whenever work is done by an external agent on a body, *the work done is the product of the force which acts on the body and the distance through which the body moves while the force is acting on it, provided that the force and the distance through which the body moves are parallel to each other.* Or, in symbols,

$$\mathcal{W} = Fs,$$ (1)

where $\mathcal{W}$ is the work done, F is the force acting, and s is the distance through which the body moves while the force acts on it. Work is a scalar quantity.

For example, if a heavy trunk is pulled along the floor through a distance of 12 ft by a force of 50 lb acting horizontally, the work done is

$$\mathcal{W} = 50 \text{ lb} \times 12 \text{ ft} = 600 \text{ ft lb}.$$

If the force F and the distance s are not parallel, then only that component of the force which is in the direction of the motion does the work. For example, if we have a very low trunk, it may be more convenient to pull with a force F at some angle θ with respect to the ground, as shown in Figure 5–1. The component of F in the direction of the motion is $F \cos \theta$; if the trunk is moved through a distance s while this force is acting on it, the work done $\mathcal{W}$ is

$$\mathcal{W} = Fs \cos \theta.$$ (2)

Suppose that in this case the trunk is pulled by means of a rope tied to it, and that the force acting on the trunk is 40 lb at an angle of 30°. If the trunk is moved through a distance of 15 ft, the work done by this force is

$$\mathcal{W} = 40 \text{ lb} \times 15 \text{ ft} \times \cos 30°$$

$$= 40 \times 15 \times \frac{\sqrt{3}}{2} \text{ ft lb} = 520 \text{ ft lb}.$$

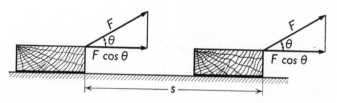

FIG. 5–1   Work done by a force F acting at an angle θ to the direction of its motion is $Fs \cos \theta$.

In lifting a body vertically with uniform speed through a height h, the force exerted upward is equal to the weight W of the body and the work done is

$$\boxed{\mathcal{W} = Wh.}$$ (3)

5-2   UNITS FOR EXPRESSING WORK

There are several different units that are used for expressing the work done. In every case the unit used must be equivalent to the product of a force by a distance. In the examples above, the unit of work contains both factors; the *ft lb* is a unit commonly used in engineering for expressing work. In the cgs system the analogous unit would be the *dyne cm*. However, this unit is usually replaced by a single term, the *erg: one erg is the work done by a force of one dyne acting through a distance of one centimeter*, or

$$1 \text{ erg} = 1 \text{ dyne cm}.$$

For example, the work done in lifting a body of mass 2,000 gm through a height of 30 cm is

$$\mathcal{W} = Wh = mgh,$$

so that

$$\mathcal{W} = 2{,}000 \text{ gm} \times 980 \frac{\text{cm}}{\text{sec}^2} \times 30 \text{ cm}$$

or

$$\mathcal{W} = 58{,}800{,}000 \text{ ergs}.$$

In the mks system, the unit of work is the *joule*. A joule is defined as the work done by a force of one newton acting through a distance of one meter; that is,

$$1 \text{ joule} = 1 \text{ newton} \times 1 \text{ m}.$$

For example, if a force of 25 newtons, acting on a body, moves a distance of 12 m in the direction of the force, the work done is

$$\mathcal{W} = 25 \text{ newtons} \times 12 \text{ m}$$

$$= 300 \text{ joules}.$$

The relationship between the joule and the erg can be found readily from the facts that 1 newton = 100,000 dynes, and 1 m = 100 cm, so that

$$1 \text{ joule} = 10,000,000 \text{ ergs}.$$

5-3 NOTATION IN POWERS OF TEN

The significance of very large numbers, and also that of very small numbers, may become obscured because of the large number of figures or of zeros that are needed to express them in the ordinary notation. A more convenient method of notation for both large and small numbers is the use of powers of 10 to indicate the position of the decimal point. The notation will become evident by an inspection of the following tables. For large numbers, we can write

$$1 = 10^0$$
$$10 = 10^1$$
$$100 = 10^2$$
$$1,000 = 10^3$$
$$10,000 = 10^4$$
$$100,000 = 10^5$$
$$1,000,000 = 10^6$$
$$10,000,000 = 10^7 \quad \text{and so forth.}$$

For small numbers, we can write

$$0.1 = 10^{-1}$$
$$0.01 = 10^{-2}$$
$$0.001 = 10^{-3}$$
$$0.0001 = 10^{-4}$$
$$0.00001 = 10^{-5}$$
$$0.000001 = 10^{-6}$$
$$0.0000001 = 10^{-7}$$

Thus we can write

$$1 \text{ joule} = 10^7 \text{ ergs}$$

and 10^{-7} joule $= 1$ erg

and $58,800,000$ ergs $= 5.88 \times 10^7$ ergs $= 5.88$ joules.

5-4 WORK AND ENERGY

An important question which arises from this discussion concerns the results of the work done by the various forces which act on different bodies. In some cases, the results are immediately obvious. For example, the work done by a force which accelerates a body produces a change in its speed; the work done in lifting a body produces an increase in the height of the body with respect to its former position; the work done against frictional forces produces an increase in the temperature of one or more of the bodies involved. In other cases, the results may not be so obvious. Some bodies may become charged electrically; others may become magnetized. These changes will be discussed at the appropriate places in the text. One general conclusion can be drawn here; that is, that whenever work is done, some change is produced in the body or system of bodies on which the forces acted. To describe these changes, another technical term is used. We say that the work done produces *a change in the energy of the body or system of bodies*. In the first case above, the energy of motion or the *kinetic energy* of the body is changed; in the second case, the positional energy or *potential energy* of the body is increased. In each case, *the change in energy is defined as equal to the work done on the body or system of bodies*. From this, it follows that the units used in expressing the energy of a system are the same as the units of work.

5-5 POTENTIAL ENERGY OF POSITION

When a weight W is lifted through a height h, the work done is Wh (see Figure 5–2). This represents the increase in the energy of the body due to a change in its position in the earth's gravitational field. For example, if a body has been raised a height h above the floor, it has the possibility or potentiality of doing work when falling to the floor. Some appropriate mechanism can be constructed so that when this body falls it can do work on the mechanism and give up the energy that it had because of its position. If the initial position of the body is taken as the position of zero potential energy, the potential energy of the body at a height h above this position is equal to the work done in lifting the body through this height. Therefore the potential energy $\mathcal{E}_p$ of this body is now

$$\mathcal{E}_p = Wh. \qquad\qquad (4)$$

For example, an airplane which is flying at an altitude of 15,000 ft has a greater amount of potential energy than it had at sea level. If sea level is taken as the zero level of potential energy, then its potential energy at any

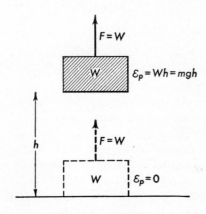

$F = W$

W $\mathcal{E}_p = Wh = mgh$

Fig. 5-2   The work done in lifting a body increases its potential energy.

h

$F = W$

W $\mathcal{E}_p = 0$

other altitude h is given by Equation (4). If the weight of this airplane is 10 tons, its potential energy $\mathcal{E}_p$ at the altitude of 15,000 ft is

$$\mathcal{E}_p = 10 \text{ tons} \times 15,000 \text{ ft}$$

$$= 10 \times 2,000 \text{ lb} \times 15,000 \text{ ft}$$

$$= 3 \times 10^8 \text{ ft lb.}$$

The potential energy of a body can also be expressed in terms of its mass by substituting for W in Equation (4) its value $W = mg$, yielding

$$\mathcal{E}_p = mgh. \tag{5}$$

For example, if a body whose mass is 75 gm is raised to a point 150 cm above the table, its potential energy relative to the table height as the zero level of potential energy is, from Equation (5),

$$\mathcal{E}_p = 75 \text{ gm} \times 980 \frac{\text{cm}}{\text{sec}^2} \times 150 \text{ cm}$$

$$= 1.10 \times 10^7 \text{ ergs}$$

$$= 1.10 \text{ joules.}$$

The potential energy of a body in the earth's gravitational field is sometimes called *gravitational potential energy* to distinguish it from other forms of potential energy. Since, in all practical cases, we are concerned only with *changes in the gravitational energy of a body or system of bodies,* the actual choice of the zero level of potential energy is arbitrary. **The** potential energy of a body may be either positive or negative, depending upon the choice of the zero level.

5-6 KINETIC ENERGY

The kinetic energy $\mathcal{E}_K$ of a body moving with speed v can be determined by calculating the work done in accelerating it from rest to the speed v (see Figure 5–3). Suppose that a constant force F acts on the body of mass m for a distance s in the direction of F; then the work done is

$$\mathcal{W} = Fs.$$

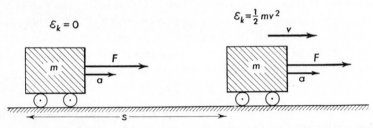

FIG. 5–3   The work done by a force in accelerating a body increases its kinetic energy.

Now, from Newton's second law,

$$F = ma,$$

so that

$$\mathcal{W} = mas.$$

But we know that

$$v^2 = 2as \quad \text{[Equation (15$'$) in Chapter 3]};$$

therefore

$$\mathcal{W} = m\frac{v^2}{2}.$$

The work done in accelerating the body is equal to the change in its kinetic energy. When it was at rest, the body had no kinetic energy; now that work has been done on it, its kinetic energy has been increased by an amount equal to the work done. Hence the kinetic energy of the body is

$$\mathcal{E}_K = \tfrac{1}{2}mv^2. \tag{6}$$

For example, a rifle bullet whose mass is 6 gm, fired from a rifle with a muzzle velocity of 45,000 cm/sec, has an amount of kinetic energy $\mathcal{E}_K$ equal to

$$\mathcal{E}_K = \tfrac{1}{2} \times 6\ \text{gm} \times \left(45,000\ \frac{\text{cm}}{\text{sec}}\right)^2$$

$$\doteq 6.08 \times 10^9\ \text{ergs} = 608\ \text{joules}.$$

Illustrative Example.   Determine the kinetic energy of an automobil
weighing 4,000 lb moving at 60 mi/hr.

The mass of the automobile is $m = \dfrac{4,000}{32}$ slugs, and its speed $v =$
60 mi/hr = 88 ft/sec.   Putting these values into Equation (6), we get

$$\mathcal{E}_K = \tfrac{1}{2} \frac{4,000}{32} \text{ slugs} \times \left(88 \frac{\text{ft}}{\text{sec}}\right)^2$$

$$= 484,000 \text{ ft lb}.$$

If this car is brought to rest by an application of the brakes, the work
done by the frictional forces would have to be equal to the loss in kinetic
energy of the automobile, which would be 484,000 ft lb.   If we assume that
the average value of all the frictional forces acting on the car while it is
being brought to rest is F, then the distance s that the car will move
before coming to rest is given by the equation

$$Fs = \tfrac{1}{2}mv^2.$$

If we compare the stopping distances of the same car for different initial
speeds, assuming that the frictional forces are the same, we note that the
distance s varies with the square of the speed at the time that the brakes
are first applied.   Thus if the brakes are applied when the car is moving at
60 mi/hr, it will travel four times as far before coming to rest as it will when
the car is moving at 30 mi/hr.

5-7   POWER

In many cases, the time during which a given amount of work is done
is of great importance.   The term *power* is defined as the work done divided
by the time during which this work is done, or

$$P = \frac{\mathcal{W}}{t},$$ (7)

in which P represents the power and t the time during which the work
$\mathcal{W}$ is done.   For example, if a hoisting engine lifts a 200-lb weight through
50 ft in 4 sec, the power supplied by the engine is

$$P = \frac{200 \text{ lb} \times 50 \text{ ft}}{4 \text{ sec}} = 2,500 \frac{\text{ft lb}}{\text{sec}}.$$

There are several other practical units used to express power.   The
horsepower (hp) is defined as

$$1 \text{ hp} = 550 \frac{\text{ft lb}}{\text{sec}}.$$ (8)

In the above problem, the power delivered by the engine may be expressed as

$$P = \frac{2,500}{550} \text{ hp} = 4.55 \text{ hp}.$$

Another unit of power is the *watt* which is defined as

$$1 \text{ watt} = 1 \frac{\text{joule}}{\text{sec}}. \tag{9}$$

The relationship between the power expressed in watts and that expressed in horsepower is

$$746 \text{ watts} = 1 \text{ hp}.$$

If, in Equation (7), we substitute for the work $\mathcal{W}$ its value in terms of the force F and the distance s through which it moves, we get

$$P = F \frac{s}{t}.$$

But if the body on which the force is acting moves with velocity v, then

$$v = \frac{s}{t}.$$

Therefore
$$\boxed{P = Fv.} \tag{10}$$

The power delivered to a body is the product of the force acting on it and the velocity of the body.

Illustrative Example. An engine is delivering 1,200 hp to an airplane in level flight at a uniform air speed of 300 mi/hr. Determine the total of all the resisting forces acting on the airplane.

An airplane flying with uniform velocity is in equilibrium. Hence the force supplied by the engine must be equal and opposite to all the resisting forces acting on the airplane. This force can be found by means of Equation (10).

Now
$$1,200 \text{ hp} = 1,200 \times 550 \frac{\text{ft lb}}{\text{sec}},$$

and
$$300 \frac{\text{mi}}{\text{hr}} = 440 \frac{\text{ft}}{\text{sec}}.$$

From Equation (10),
$$F = \frac{P}{v};$$

therefore
$$F = \frac{1,200 \times 550}{440} \text{ lb} = 1,500 \text{ lb}.$$

5-8 CONSERVATION AND TRANSFORMATION OF ENERGY

The concept of the energy of a body or system of bodies is much broader than may be inferred from the few cases mentioned above. Other forms of energy besides mechanical energy are electrical energy, heat energy, chemical energy, and radiant energy. More than a century of experience has led to the formulation and to the establishment on a firm foundation of the *principle of the transformation and conservation of energy.* This is the most general principle in physics and serves as the unifying principle for the entire subject. The principle states that *energy may be transformed from one type to another without loss, and that in a closed or isolated system the total amount of energy remains constant.*

One of the chief contributions of the science of physics to the service of society is the part it has played in the location and harnessing of vast new sources of energy and the direction and conversion of this energy into forms easily available for special purposes. For example, the energy released by the combustion of coal can be converted into mechanical energy by means of a steam engine. The steam engine can then be used to drive a locomotive or a ship, or it can be used in an electric power plant to drive an electric generator and supply electrical energy. Another important source of energy is that released in the combustion of oil and gasoline. Automobiles, airplanes, tanks, tractors, and ships utilize some of this energy in appropriate internal-combustion engines. A discussion of the operation of these engines and the energy changes taking place will be given in Part Two.

In addition to the fuels mentioned above, another source of energy is the potential energy of water in lakes at high altitudes; these lakes may be either natural lakes or artificial lakes formed behind dams. The kinetic energy of the water in the many rivers of the world can also be harnessed for our use. The energy of the water can be used to drive water wheels and water turbines and either used at the source or converted into electrical energy and transmitted where and when desired. The energy from both fuels and water can ultimately be traced back to the energy supplied by the sun. The sun is sending radiant energy to us all the time; at present the rate at which this energy is reaching us is about $\frac{1}{6}$ hp/sq ft. About 2 million horsepower are absorbed for every square mile of the earth's surface. Some of this energy is utilized by plants and may become fuel for man, animal, and engine. A small fraction of solar energy is utilized by solar engines and converted into mechanical energy.

Within the next few years, a new and practically limitless source of energy will become available from the conversion of mass into more convenient and desirable forms of energy. It was Albert Einstein who first showed, from his work on the theory of relativity (1905), that mass and energy are equivalent. On the basis of the equivalence of mass and energy, ordinary matter, because it has mass, can be looked upon as a highly concentrated form of energy. It will be shown later that one gram of mass is equivalent to 9×10^{13} joules or to 25 million kilowatt hours of energy (see Section 36–3). The task of the scientist and engineer is to find safe and practicable methods for transforming mass into other forms of energy. One method now in use depends upon the *nuclear fission* of the very heavy elements such as uranium, thorium, and plutonium (see Chapter 40). Other methods of converting mass into different forms of energy will undoubtedly be discovered in the future. In this chapter we shall consider only those changes that take place between the different forms of mechanical energy.

5-9 KINETIC AND POTENTIAL ENERGY TRANSFORMATIONS

One of the simplest forms of energy transformation takes place when a body is thrown upward. Suppose that a ball of mass m is thrown up with an initial velocity u. At the instant it leaves the hand, it has an amount of kinetic energy given by

$$\mathcal{E}_K = \tfrac{1}{2}mu^2.$$

As it goes up, its speed, and hence its kinetic energy, decreases while its potential energy increases (see Figure 5–4). Assuming that it loses no energy because of the resistance of the air, it will finally stop at a height h above its starting point. At this height h it will have no kinetic energy; all of its energy will have been converted into potential energy mgh. Applying the principle of the transformation of energy, we can write

$$mgh = \tfrac{1}{2}mu^2, \tag{11}$$

from which

$$u^2 = 2gh$$

and

$$h = \frac{u^2}{2g}.$$

As is well known, the ball will fall from this highest point, losing potential energy and gaining kinetic energy until it reaches the starting point again. At this point it will have acquired a final speed v_f such that

$$\tfrac{1}{2}mv_f^2 = mgh$$

or

$$v_f^2 = 2gh. \tag{12}$$

Thus the speed with which it reaches the starting point is the same as the speed with which it was thrown upward. It will be noted that this is exactly the same result as that obtained in our discussion of the motion of freely falling bodies.

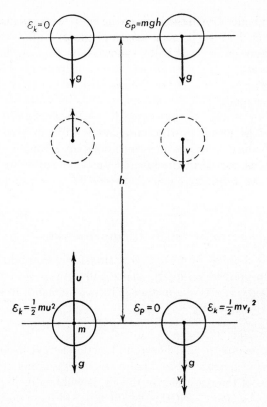

$\mathcal{E}_k = 0$ $\mathcal{E}_p = mgh$

g g

v v

h

u

$\mathcal{E}_k = \frac{1}{2} mu^2$ $\mathcal{E}_p = 0$ $\mathcal{E}_k = \frac{1}{2} mv_f^2$

m

g g

v_f

Fig. 5–4   Energy changes which take place when a ball is thrown upward and then returns to its starting position.

5-10   ENERGY TRANSFORMATIONS IN THE MOTION OF A SIMPLE PENDULUM

The motion of a simple pendulum provides another interesting example of the transformation of energy.   A simple pendulum consists of a small ball of weight mg attached to one end of a thin string of negligible weight and of length L.   The other end of the string is attached to some fixed point O, as shown in Figure 5–5.   When at rest, the string hangs vertically with the ball at its lowest position C.   Let us call the energy of the pendulum zero when it is in this position.   When the ball is pulled aside from its lowest position, with the string kept taut, it moves in the arc of a circle of radius L.   Suppose that it is moved to position A, at which point it is at a height h above its lowest position.   Because of the work done in lifting the ball through this height, its potential energy is now mgh.   When the ball is released, it moves back to its lowest position and its energy, while remaining constant in amount, changes from potential to kinetic energy.   At any point in its path, its total energy is the sum of the potential and kinetic energy and is equal to the original potential energy mgh.

At the lowest point C, all of its energy is kinetic, and if v is its speed at this point, then

$$\tfrac{1}{2}mv^2 = mgh,$$

or

$$v^2 = 2gh.$$

This is exactly the speed it would have acquired had it fallen through a vertical height h instead of moving in the arc of a circle. However, the direction of its motion is different. It is moving tangent to the circle so that at the lowest point its velocity is horizontal. According to Newton's

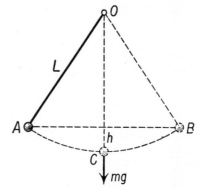

FIG. 5–5 Motion of a simple pendulum.

first law, it tends to keep moving in this direction, but, since it is attached to a string, the ball is forced to deviate from this path and move in a circular arc. This causes it to be raised above its lowest position, thereby gaining potential energy at the expense of the kinetic energy. If no energy is lost to the outside, it will reach point B at a height h equal to that from which it started. It will then proceed back again to the lowest point C and on to the original starting position A. Then, of course, the motion will be repeated.

5-11 ELASTIC VIBRATIONS

Bodies which are acted upon by external forces generally undergo changes in size or shape. The helical spring described in Chapter 2 is an important example of a body which changes its size and shape under the action of external forces. We showed there that if the spring is fixed at one end and a force F is applied to the other end, an extension x is produced which is proportional to F and is given by the equation

$$F = kx, \tag{13}$$

where k is the constant of the spring.   This equation shows that the force varies at a constant rate, beginning with the value zero when the spring is unstretched to the value F when the spring has been stretched an amount x.

To calculate the work done in stretching the spring an amount x, we may take the average value of the force acting through this distance. Since the force varies at a constant rate, its average value is one half the sum of the initial and final values; in this case it is $F/2$.   Therefore the work done in stretching the spring is

$$\mathcal{W} = \frac{Fx}{2}, \tag{14}$$

or, since $F = kx$, the work done in stretching the spring may be written as

$$\mathcal{W} = \tfrac{1}{2}kx^2. \tag{15}$$

Since work was done in stretching the spring, it has more energy now than in the unstretched state.   The energy of a stretched spring may be thought of as *energy of elasticity*. This type of energy is generally included as one of the forms of potential energy.

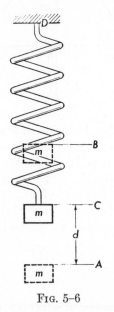

FIG. 5-6

Suppose we take a helical spring of length L and fasten one end of it to a fixed support at D, as shown in Figure 5–6. If we attach a body of mass m and weight W to the other end, the spring will be stretched by an amount b, and the body will come to equilibrium at point C. At this point, there are two forces acting on the body: its weight W downward, and the force $F_1 = kb$ exerted by the spring acting upward. Since the body is in equilibrium, we may write

$$F_1 = W = kb.$$

If this body is now pulled down an additional distance d to a point A and then released, it will move upward to a point B a distance d above C, and then move down again through C back to A, and then back to B, and continue this vibratory motion indefinitely, assuming that there are no losses of energy owing to friction, air resistance, and so forth.

During this vibratory motion, the energy of the system is continually changing from potential to kinetic energy and back to potential energy.

If we start with this system at its equilibrium position C and pull the body down to A, the amount of work done in stretching the spring and lowering the weight a distance d is, from Equation (15),

$$\mathcal{W} = \tfrac{1}{2}kd^2. \tag{16}$$

If we call the energy of this system zero when the body is at rest at C, then Equation (16) gives the total amount of energy the system possesses when the spring is stretched. At point A the body is not in motion, and hence all of this energy is in the form of potential energy. As the body moves up from A, some of this potential energy is changed to kinetic energy, and at C all of this energy is kinetic energy; hence at this point the body is moving with maximum speed. Because of the inertia of the body, it keeps moving beyond C and some of its kinetic energy is transferred back into potential energy until it reaches point B, at which point all of its energy is in the form of potential energy again. As it moves back toward A, similar transformations of energy from potential to kinetic and back to potential energy occur.

Illustrative Example. A 6-lb weight, when placed on a vertical spring, stretches it 2 in., at which point it is in equilibrium. The weight is then pulled down an additional 4 in. and released. Determine the energy of the vibrating system.

Using Equation (13), letting $F = 6$ lb and $x = 2$ in. or $\tfrac{1}{6}$ ft, we can find k, which is

$$k = \frac{6 \text{ lb}}{2 \text{ in.}} = 3\,\frac{\text{lb}}{\text{in.}} = 36\,\frac{\text{lb}}{\text{ft}}.$$

Taking the zero level of energy as the equilibrium position of the weight on the spring, we find that the work done in stretching the spring an additional 4 in. is, from Equation (16),

$$\mathcal{W} = \tfrac{1}{2}kd^2 = \tfrac{1}{2} \cdot 3\,\frac{\text{lb}}{\text{in.}} \times (4 \text{ in.})^2 = 24 \text{ in. lb} = 2 \text{ ft lb}.$$

Hence the energy of the vibrating system, which is equal to the work done on it, is 24 in. lb or 2 ft lb.

5-12 DETERMINING WORK BY GRAPHICAL METHODS

We have so far considered only very simple cases in which work was done, that is, either by a constant force or by a force which varied in a simple manner with the distance through which the body moved under its action. In both these, and in more complex cases, the work $\mathcal{W}$ can be evaluated graphically by plotting a curve showing the variation of the force with the distance. The force is generally the ordinate and the distance is the abscissa.

Figure 5–7 shows the case of work done by a constant force F acting for the distance s. Since $\mathcal{W} = Fs$, the work done is given by the area under the curve, that is, by the shaded rectangle. We have used the numerical values $F = 80$ lb and $s = 6$ ft, so that $\mathcal{W} = 480$ ft lb.

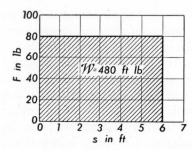

FIG. 5–7 Graph showing work done by a constant force.

Figure 5–8 shows the work done in stretching a spring. In this case, $F = kx$, which is the equation of a straight line passing through the origin. When $x = d$, the force is $F = kd$; the work done is the area

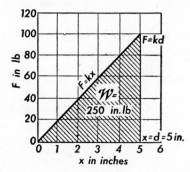

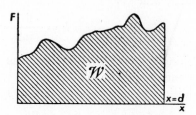

FIG. 5–8 Graph showing work done by a force which varies with the displacement x.

FIG. 5–9 Graphical method of determining work done by a variable force.

under the curve; that is, the area of the triangle formed by the curve $F = kx$, the x-axis from 0 to d, and the vertical line at $x = d$. The area of this triangle is

$$\tfrac{1}{2} \times d \times kd = \tfrac{1}{2}kd^2,$$

in agreement with Equation (16), for the work done in stretching a spring. In plotting the graph, we used the numerical values $k = 20$ lb/in., $d = 5$ in., so that $\mathcal{W} = 250$ in. lb.

Figure 5–9 is a graph showing the work done in a case in which the force varies in a complex manner with the distance. The work done in a distance from $x = 0$ to $x = d$ is the area under the curve. The area may be measured in any one of a variety of ways, for example, with a planimeter, or by ruling a series of parallel, equally spaced vertical lines and determining the areas so formed, assuming each one to be a rectangle, and so forth.

5-13   MECHANICAL EFFICIENCY OF SIMPLE MACHINES

Many different types of machines are used for doing mechanical work. These machines can be considered as made of one or more *simple machines* such as the inclined plane, the lever, the pulley system, and the screw and nut. Usually a simple machine does work in lifting a weight W through a height h. To enable the machine to do this work, a force F is applied to

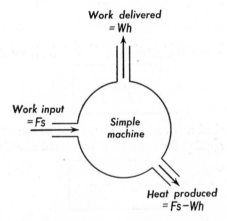

FIG. 5–10   Work and energy relations of a simple machine.

it, and it acts for a distance s. In actual performance, less work is delivered by the machine than is put into it. The difference between the work put in and the work delivered by the machine usually appears in the form of heat because of the work done against frictional forces (see Figure 5–10). The *mechanical efficiency* e of a machine is defined as

$$e = \frac{\text{work delivered by machine}}{\text{work put into machine}}$$

or, in symbols,

$$e = \frac{Wh}{Fs}.$$ (17)

In the ideal case, that is, in a frictionless machine, the efficiency $e = 1$, or 100 per cent; for this case, Equation (17) becomes

$$1 = \frac{Wh}{Fs},$$

from which

$$\frac{W}{F} = \frac{s}{h}. \tag{18}$$

There are usually two reasons for using a simple machine: one is that the magnitude of the force applied is generally less than the weight of the object lifted; the other is that the required force may be applied in a more convenient direction. The ratio R_1 of the weight lifted to the force applied in the ideal case of a frictionless machine is called the *ideal mechanical advantage;* that is,

$$R_I = \frac{W}{F}. \tag{19}$$

Eliminating W/F between Equations (18) and (19), we get

$$R_I = \frac{s}{h}. \tag{20}$$

The actual mechanical advantage R_A is defined as the ratio of the weight lifted to the force applied for the case of an actual machine; that is,

$$R_A = \frac{W}{F}. \tag{21}$$

The efficiency of an actual machine, as given by Equation (17), can be rewritten as follows:

$$e = \frac{W/F}{s/h},$$

and, substituting the values of W/F from Equation (21) and s/h from Equation (20) into the above equation, we get

$$e = \frac{R_A}{R_I}. \tag{22}$$

The efficiency of a machine is thus the ratio of the actual mechanical advantage to the ideal mechanical advantage.

The usefulness of Equation (22) lies in the fact that it presents us with a simple method for evaluating the efficiency of a machine in terms of easily measurable quantities. The weight lifted and the force applied in

the actual machine are readily measurable with spring balances, and the
ratio of s/h can usually be determined from the geometry of the machine.
We shall illustrate this with a few typical examples.

Illustrative Example.   A heavy crate weighing 260 lb is pulled up an inclined plane which is 13 ft long with one end 5 ft above the ground.   The

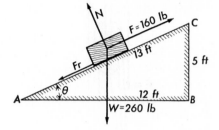

Fɪɢ. 5–11   Forces acting on a body
   being pulled up an inclined plane.

force required to pull the crate up the plane is 160 lb.   (a) Determine the
mechanical efficiency of this inclined plane.   (b) Determine the coefficient
of friction between the crate and the plane.

(a) The forces acting on the crate are shown in Figure 5–11.   From
Equation (22), the efficiency is

$$e = \frac{R_A}{R_I}.$$

Now

$$R_A = \frac{W}{F} = \frac{260 \text{ lb}}{160 \text{ lb}} = \frac{13}{8}$$

$$R_I = \frac{s}{h} = \frac{13 \text{ ft}}{5 \text{ ft}} = \frac{13}{5}.$$

Hence

$$e = \frac{13/8}{13/5} = \frac{5}{8} = 0.625 = 62.5 \text{ per cent.}$$

(b) The coefficient of friction f is given by

$$f = \frac{F_r}{N},$$

where F_r is the force of friction which opposes the motion.   Let us assume
that the motion of the crate up the plane takes place with uniform velocity,
that is, that the body is in equilibrium.   For the components of the forces
parallel to the plane, we have

$$160 \text{ lb} - F_r - 260 \text{ lb} \times \sin \theta = 0,$$

and, for the components perpendicular to the plane, we have

$$N - 260 \text{ lb} \times \cos \theta = 0,$$

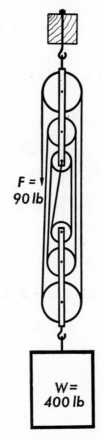

F = 90 lb

W = 400 lb

Fɪɢ. 5–12   Pulley system.

where θ is the angle of the plane with the horizontal. From the geometry of the triangle we can evaluate $\sin \theta$ and $\cos \theta$; thus

$$\sin \theta = \tfrac{5}{13},$$

$$\cos \theta = \tfrac{12}{13}.$$

The equation containing F_r yields

$$F_r = 160 \text{ lb} - 260 \text{ lb} \times \tfrac{5}{13},$$

from which $F_r = 60$ lb.

The equation containing N yields

$$N = 260 \text{ lb} \times \tfrac{12}{13},$$

from which $N = 240$ lb.

Substituting these values of F_r and N into the equation for determining the coefficient of friction, we get

$$f = \frac{60 \text{ lb}}{240 \text{ lb}}$$

from which $f = 0.25$.

Illustrative Example. The pulley system sketched in Figure 5–12 is used to hoist a safe weighing 400 lb. The force exerted on the free end of the rope is 90 lb. Determine the efficiency of this pulley system. The expression for the mechanical efficiency is

$$e = \frac{R_A}{R_I}. \tag{22}$$

Now
$$R_A = \frac{400 \text{ lb}}{90 \text{ lb}} = \frac{40}{9}.$$

To determine R_I, we note from the geometry of the pulley system that, when the weight goes up a distance h, each strand of the rope pulling on the movable pulley also goes up a distance h. Since there are six strands pulling up on it, the free end of the rope must travel a distance $s = 6h$ when the movable pulley moves up a distance h.

Hence
$$R_I = \frac{s}{h} = 6.$$

The efficiency of this pulley system is therefore
$$e = \frac{40/9}{6} = \frac{40}{54} = 0.74.$$

Illustrative Example. The jackscrew sketched in Figure 5–13 is used to lift a weight of 800 lb. The pitch of the screw is 0.5 in., and the lever to which the force is applied is 18 in. long. If the efficiency of this machine is 0.25, determine the force which must be applied at the end of the lever to lift the weight.

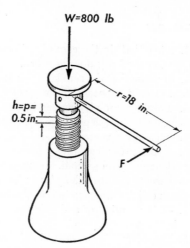

FIG. 5–13   Jackscrew.

In lifting the weight through a height h equal to the pitch of the screw, a force F must be applied at right angles to the lever and must turn it through one complete revolution, that is, through a distance $s = 2\pi r$, where r is the length of the lever measured from the axis of the screw to the point where the force is applied.

Hence
$$R_I = \frac{s}{h} = \frac{2\pi \times 18 \text{ in.}}{0.5 \text{ in.}} = 72\pi.$$

The efficiency is
$$e = \frac{R_A}{R_I},$$

from which
$$R_A = eR_I.$$

Substituting $e = 0.25$ and $R_I = 72\pi$, we get
$$R_A = 0.25 \times 72\pi = 18\pi.$$

Now, from Equation (21),

$$R_A = \frac{W}{F} \; ;$$

therefore

$$\frac{W}{F} = 18\pi,$$

and

$$F = \frac{W}{18\pi} = \frac{800 \text{ lb}}{18\pi},$$

from which

$$F = 14.1 \text{ lb.}$$

QUESTIONS

1. Show that, in the case of uniform circular motion, the centripetal force which acts on the body does no work.

2. Suppose that the zero level for measuring the potential energy of a body is shifted. Does the potential energy of the body change? Explain your answer.

3. Two boys are playing ball in a moving train. Does the kinetic energy of the ball at any instant depend upon the speed of the train? Explain your answer.

4. Is energy a vector or a scalar quantity?

5. A soldier carries a heavy pack on a hike. How much work does he do in hiking (a) across level ground, (b) up a hill, (c) down a hill?

6. Discuss the work done by a pitcher when he pitches a baseball. Through what distance is a force exerted on the baseball?

7. In the motion of a simple pendulum, show that the work done by the tension in the string is zero.

8. Consider a lever as a simple machine and show that its mechanical advantage is the ratio of the lengths of the two lever arms, if friction is neglected.

9. Derive the relationship between watts and horsepower.

PROBLEMS

1. A trunk weighing 150 lb is pulled across a floor for a distance of 18 ft by a horizontal force of 50 lb. How much work is done?

2. A man pulls a sled by means of a cord attached to it, exerting a force of 24 lb at an angle of 60° with the horizontal. How much work is done in pulling this sled for a distance of 250 ft?

3. (a) Calculate the work done in lifting a body whose weight is 140 lb through a height of 9 ft. (b) How much is the increase in its potential energy?

4. A body whose mass is 15 kg is lifted through a height of 3 m. Calculate the increase in its potential energy.

5. Determine the kinetic energy of an airplane whose weight is 40 tons if it is moving with a speed of 250 mi/hr.

6. A body weighing 100 lb is pushed up a rough inclined plane by a force of 75 lb acting parallel to the plane. The plane is inclined at an angle of 30° with the horizontal and is 28 ft long. (a) How much work is done in moving the body to the top of the inclined plane? (b) What is its potential energy when at the top of the plane? (c) How much work was done against friction?

7. A force F acting on a body for a distance s produces a change in its speed from u to v. Show that $Fs = \frac{1}{2}mv^2 - \frac{1}{2}mu^2$, where m is the mass of the body.

8. By "stepping on the gas," a driver speeds up a car from 15 mi/hr to 45 mi/hr in 11 sec. The weight of the car is 3,600 lb. Determine (a) the change in kinetic energy of this car and (b) the resultant force acting on the car during this time.

9. A body weighing 90 lb slides down an inclined plane 16 ft high and 80 ft long. It reaches the bottom of the incline with a speed of 24 ft/sec. (a) What is its potential energy at the top of the inclined plane? (b) How much kinetic energy does it possess when it reaches the bottom of the plane? (c) Determine the force of friction between the body and the plane.

10. A box weighing 150 lb slides down an incline 20 ft long from the second floor of a building to the first floor 12 ft below. The frictional force exerted on the box by the incline is 48 lb. (a) How much potential energy does the box lose in sliding down? (b) How much energy is used up in moving the box against the frictional force? (c) How much kinetic energy does the box have when it gets to the bottom? (d) What velocity does the box have when it gets to the bottom? (e) What is the coefficient of sliding friction between the box and the plane?

11. A simple pendulum consists of a thin string of negligible mass with a steel ball of 400 gm mass attached to one end. The distance from the point of support to the center of the ball is 100 cm. The ball is pulled aside until the string makes an angle of 30° with the vertical. (a) How much potential energy does the pendulum have in this position? (b) With what velocity will the ball reach the lowest position after it is released?

12. A body whose weight is 30 lb is attached to a helical spring and lowered gently. The spring is stretched 1.5 in. The spring is pulled down 4 in. from this equilibrium position and released. Determine (a) the energy of this vibrating system and (b) the period of the motion.

13. A force of 12 lb acting horizontally is sufficient to pull a loaded sled with constant velocity on horizontal snowy ground. The weight of the sled and its load is 150 lb. (a) Determine the coefficient of friction between the sled and the snow. (b) What force must be exerted to pull the sled by means of a cord making an angle of 30° with the horizontal? (c) How much work is done in pulling the sled 50 ft by means of this cord?

14. What power must be delivered to a car which is moving with a speed of 45 mi/hr if the sum of all the resisting forces acting on the car is 400 lb?

15. How much power must a man weighing 160 lb develop if he runs up a flight of stairs 9 ft high in 5 sec?

16. The engines of a fighter plane deliver 2,500 hp to keep the plane in level flight with a constant velocity of 400 mi/hr. Determine the sum of all the forces opposing the motion of the plane.

17. The pulley system sketched in Figure 5–14 consists of an upper fixed block containing two pulley wheels and a lower movable block also containing two pulley wheels. (a) A body of weight W is attached to the movable block.

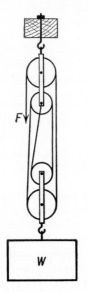

How big a force F would have to be applied to lift the weight uniformly if there were no friction? (b) In one such pulley system, a force of 90 lb was needed to lift a 240-lb weight. What was the efficiency of this simple machine? (c) What was its mechanical advantage?

18. In the pulley system sketched in Figure 5–12, both the fixed block and the movable block contain three pulley wheels. (a) What would be the mechanical advantage of this simple machine if there were no friction? (b) Determine the efficiency of this machine when a force of 50 lb applied to the free end of the rope is required to lift a body weighing 220 lb attached to the movable block. (c) What is the actual mechanical advantage in this case?

19. A body weighing 96 lb drops from a height of 4 ft above the top of a spring and compresses it. If the constant of the spring is 12 lb/in., determine the decrease in length of the spring.

Fig. 5–14 Pulley system.

20. A spring 2 ft long is suspended vertically. The constant of the spring is 5 lb/in. A body weighing 20 lb is attached to the free end of the unstretched spring and then is allowed to drop. Determine the increase in length of the spring.

21. Show that, when the angle of inclination of an inclined plane is equal to the critical angle θ_c for sliding friction, its efficiency as a machine is 0.50.

22. A body of weight W is pulled up a 30° incline. If the coefficient of friction between the body and the inclined plane is 0.2, determine the efficiency of this plane as a machine.

23. An ivory ball having a mass of 100 gm and moving with a velocity of 80 cm/sec strikes a stationary ivory ball of equal mass. The velocity is parallel to the line joining the centers of the balls. Assuming a perfectly elastic collision, determine the velocity of each ball after collision.

(Hint: Use the principles of conservation of momentum and conservation of energy.)

24. An ivory ball having a mass of 400 gm and moving with a velocity of 90 cm/sec strikes a stationary ivory ball having a mass of 100 gm. Assuming a central collision and perfect elasticity, determine the velocity of each ball after collision.

25. The hammer of a pile driver weighs 1,500 lb and falls through a height of 6 ft to drive a pile into the ground. (a) How much energy does the hammer have when it strikes the pile? (b) If the pile is driven in a distance of 6 in., determine the average resisting force acting on the pile.

26. The screwthread of an automobile jack has a pitch of 0.25 in. and is operated by a lever 2 ft long, as shown in Figure 5–13. If the efficiency of this jack is 0.25, determine the force that must be applied to the end of the lever to lift a load of 1,200 lb.

27. Using the principle of conservation of energy, show that the mechanical advantage of a lever is equal to the ratio of the lever arms.

28. The output of an electric motor used to operate a hoist is 5 hp. Determine the velocity with which the hoist can be lifted if the total weight of the hoist and its load is 300 lb.

29. A bullet whose mass is 3 gm is moving with a velocity of 500 m/sec. It strikes and penetrates a wooden target suspended from a cord 100 cm long. The mass of the target is 3,000 gm. (a) Determine the velocity imparted to the target. (b) Determine the initial kinetic energy of the bullet. (c) Determine the kinetic energy of the target after the bullet has penetrated it. (d) Account for the difference in the initial and final kinetic energies of this system.

6

Circular
Motion

6-1 UNIFORM CIRCULAR MOTION

In our previous study of accelerated motion, we restricted ourselves to those types of motion produced by the action of a force which remains constant in magnitude and direction throughout the motion. The particular path followed by the body depends upon the direction of the initial velocity relative to the direction of the force. When the initial velocity is parallel to the direction of the force, that is, either in the same direction or opposite to it, or when the initial velocity is zero, the path of the body is

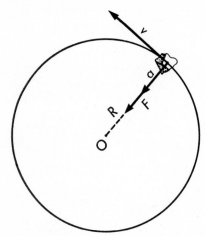

Fig. 6–1 Force F acting on a stone which is moving with uniform motion in a circular path is directed toward the center of the circle.

a straight line. When the initial velocity is at any other angle to the direction of the force, the path of the body is a parabola. We shall now consider another important type of motion, that known as *uniform motion in a circle*, that is, motion in a circular path in which the speed of the body remains constant, but its direction of motion changes continually. We shall show that this type of motion is produced by a force which is constant in magnitude but continually changing its direction in such a way that it is always at right angles to the velocity of the body.

128

Consider a particle moving with velocity v in a horizontal circular path of radius R, as in Figure 6–1. The direction of the velocity is always tangent to the path. If the force F acts at right angles to the velocity, it can have no component in the direction of the velocity; that is, it cannot change the speed of the body. The only effect of the force is to change the direction of the motion. Since the radius of a circle is always at right angles to the tangent, the force F must act along a radius. Furthermore, the force must be directed *toward the center of the circle*. To prove this, we need merely to consider what would happen if no unbalanced force acted on the particle. We know, from Newton's first law, that the particle would continue to move with uniform velocity v, and such a motion would take it along a tangent, and hence away from the center of the circle. To bring it back toward the center requires that there be an acceleration toward the center, hence there must be an unbalanced force acting toward the center of the circle. One way of supplying such a force is to tie one end of a flexible string to the particle and tie the other end to a pin at the center of the circle. Suppose that this particle is a small stone moving on a smooth horizontal table. Since the string is flexible, it can only support a tension; hence it must exert a pull on the stone toward the center.

6-2 CENTRIPETAL AND CENTRIFUGAL FORCES

Since the force which acts on a particle moving with uniform circular motion is directed toward the center, then, according to Newton's second law, the acceleration produced by this force must also be directed toward the center. We can derive the expression for this acceleration in terms of the speed of the particle and the radius of the circle by considering two

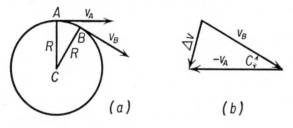

(a)   (b)

Fig. 6–2

neighboring positions A and B of a particle moving with uniform speed in a circle of radius R as shown in Figure 6–2(a). The velocity of the particle at A is v_A, and its velocity at B is v_B. The *change in velocity* Δv of the particle is the vector difference $(v_B - v_A)$. To find the difference between these two vectors, choose any scale and draw vector v_B parallel to itself and in the same direction. At the end of v_B draw a vector parallel to v_A but opposite in direction; make its length the same as that of v_B, since both of them have the same magnitude. The vector so drawn is $-v_A$. Now draw a vector directed from the beginning of v_B to the end of $-v_A$. This vector is Δv. If Δt is the time taken to go from A to B, the acceleration a of the particle is

$$a = \frac{\Delta v}{\Delta t}. \tag{1}$$

The change in velocity Δv is obtained by subtracting the vector v_A from the vector v_B and is shown in Figure 6–2(b). The triangle formed by these vectors and the triangle ABC are similar, since they are both isosceles triangles and have equal angles at C. We may therefore write

$$\frac{\Delta v}{v_A} = \frac{AB}{AC} = \frac{AB}{R}. \tag{2}$$

If the two positions A and B of the particle are very close together, we may consider the length of the chord AB as practically equal to the length of the arc AB, that is, equal to the distance traversed by the particle in time Δt. If v is the speed of the particle, we may write

$$\text{arc} \quad AB = v\,\Delta t$$

and
$$v_A = v.$$

Substituting these values in Equation (2), we get

$$\frac{\Delta v}{v} = \frac{v\,\Delta t}{R}$$

or
$$\frac{\Delta v}{\Delta t} = \frac{v^2}{R}, \tag{3}$$

which, with the aid of Equation (1), becomes

$$a = \frac{v^2}{R}. \tag{4}$$

A glance at Figure 6–2 shows that when the angle C is very small, the vector Δv is at right angles to the velocity v_A and is directed toward the center of the circle.

We can apply Newton's second law

$$F = ma$$

to a particle of mass m moving with uniform circular motion to determine the force which acts on it. Substituting the value for the acceleration from

Equation (4), we get

$$F = m \frac{v^2}{R}$$ (5)

for the magnitude of the force acting toward the center when the body is moving with uniform circular motion. This force acting toward the center is called the *centripetal force*. It must be remembered that the centripetal force acts *on* the body moving in a circular path.

Referring again to the stone that is being whirled around at the end of a string, we note that the centripetal force is the pull of the string *on the stone*. According to Newton's third law, the stone exerts an equal and opposite force *on the string*. This reaction is sometimes referred to as the *centrifugal force*. This centrifugal force exists only as long as the stone is whirled in a circle by the string. If the string is cut during the circular motion, there will no longer be a centripetal force acting on the stone; hence there will be no centrifugal force that the stone can exert. The instant the string is cut, the stone will continue to move in the direction it was moving at that time; that is, the stone will go off at a tangent to the circle.

Illustrative Example. A stone weighing 0.5 lb tied to a string 2 ft long is placed on a smooth horizontal table. The other end of the string is tied to a pin at the center of the table. The stone is given a push and acquires a speed of 6 ft/sec. (a) Determine the tension in the string. (b) If the breaking strength of the string is 15 lb, determine the maximum speed with which the stone can be whirled.

(a) The mass of this stone is

$$m = \frac{0.5 \text{ lb}}{32 \text{ ft/sec}^2} = \frac{1}{64} \text{ slug.}$$

The centripetal force F required to keep it moving in a horizontal circle of radius $R = 2$ ft with a speed $v = 6$ ft/sec is, from Equation (5),

$$F = \frac{1}{64} \text{ slug} \times \frac{36 \text{ ft}^2/\text{sec}^2}{2 \text{ ft}},$$

so that $F = 0.28$ lb.

(b) If the breaking strength of the string is 15 lb, then this represents the maximum centripetal force that it can apply to the stone. Using this value for F in Equation (5) and letting v be the maximum velocity, we get

$$15 \text{ lb} = \frac{1}{64} \text{ slug} \times \frac{v^2}{2 \text{ ft}},$$

from which $$v^2 = 1{,}920 \; \frac{\text{ft}^2}{\text{sec}^2},$$

so that $$v = 43.9 \; \frac{\text{ft}}{\text{sec}} \cdot$$

6-3 BANKING OF A CURVED ROAD

A car or train rounding a curve can be considered as moving in an arc of a circle or in some cases in a series of such arcs of slightly different radii. In order to move the car in a circular path of radius R, an outside force must act on the car, and this force must be directed toward the center of the circle. In the case of an automobile rounding a curve, this force is

Fɪɢ. 6–3   Photograph of cars traveling at high speeds around a banked curve. (Courtesy of General Motors Corp.)

supplied by the friction between the road and the tires. If the speed of the car is very great, the frictional force may not be sufficiently large to supply the necessary centripetal force to make the car move in this circular path. The car may move toward the outer part of the road and thus travel in a curve of larger radius, or it may even go off the road. This happens more often when the road is wet or icy, since the friction between the tires and the road is then much reduced.

When high speeds are normally used on curved roads, the roads are frequently banked for safer travel; that is, the outer part of the road is built at a higher level than the inner part, as shown in Figure 6–3. The proper angle θ for banking the road is one for which the normal force N that the

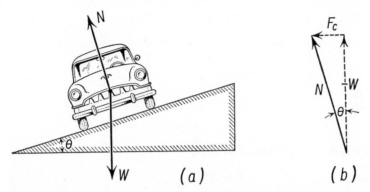

FIG. 6–4   (a) Car moving on a curve in a road banked at angle θ to the horizontal. (b) The components of the normal force N are $-W$ and F_c.

road exerts on the car will have a vertical component equal and opposite to W and a horizontal component sufficient to produce the required centripetal force F_c for a given speed v [see Figure 6–4(a)]. From Figure 6–4(b), it will be noted that

$$\tan \theta = \frac{F_c}{W},$$

and, since $F_c = mv^2/R$ and $W = mg,$

we get $\tan \theta = \dfrac{v^2}{Rg}.$ **(6)**

If the speed of the car exceeds the proper speed given by Equation (6), then there must be enough friction between the tires and the ground to supply the necessary additional centripetal force for the car to go around the curve safely.

Illustrative Example. A car weighing 4,000 lb goes around a curved road at 60 mi/hr. The curve is a circular arc of 2,400 ft radius. Determine (a) the centripetal force that the road must exert on the car and (b) the angle at which the road must be banked for this to be the proper speed.

(a) The magnitude of the centripetal force is given by Equation (5)

$$F = m\frac{v^2}{R}.$$

Now $$v = 60 \text{ mi/hr} = 88 \text{ ft/sec}$$

and $$m = \frac{W}{g} = \frac{4{,}000 \text{ lb}}{32 \text{ ft/sec}^2} \text{ ;}$$

hence $$F = \frac{4{,}000 \text{ lb}}{32 \text{ ft/sec}^2} \times \frac{(88 \text{ ft/sec})^2}{2{,}400 \text{ ft}} \text{ ,}$$

from which $$F = 403 \text{ lb.}$$

(b) The angle of banking θ, is given by

$$\tan \theta = \frac{v^2}{rg} \text{ ;}$$

hence $$\tan \theta = \frac{(88 \text{ ft/sec})^2}{2{,}400 \text{ ft} \times 32 \text{ ft/sec}^2} \text{ ,}$$

from which $$\tan \theta = 0.10,$$

so that $$\theta = 5°50'.$$

6-4 NATURE OF CENTRIFUGAL FORCE

In our previous discussion of circular motion, we referred the motion to a fixed frame of reference such as a stationary table or the railroad tracks on the earth. We, the observers, imagined ourselves to be on or in this fixed frame of reference. We could then easily see or imagine the *centripetal force* which acted on the body in circular motion, such as the string pulling on the stone, or the tracks pushing on the wheels of the train, or the friction between the road and the tires pushing on the tires of the automobile. In each case, the *centrifugal force*, or the reaction of the body in circular motion to the object exerting the centripetal force, was also readily discernible. But if we now imagine ourselves transferred to the moving object, that is, imagine ourselves inside the moving frame of reference, the phenomena will then take on a different appearance and our description of them will be somewhat altered.

Suppose, for example, that we are inside a train which is moving at uniform speed, and that the train is leaving the straight portion of the track and entering the curved or circular portion. The passengers in the train may be seen to move, or appear to be thrown, toward that side of the car which is on the outside of the curve. If the passengers were unaware of the fact that the train was going in a circular path, they might explain their new motion or acceleration toward the outside of the circle as being due to the action of some horizontal force. Or suppose that a ball had been placed on the floor of the car while the train was moving with uniform speed along the straight portion of the track. The ball would have remained there undisturbed until the train started going around the curve. It would then roll toward the side of the car further removed from the center of the circular path. An observer inside the car might ascribe this motion to the action of a "centrifugal force" on the ball; to an observer outside the train, that is, in the stationary frame of reference, the ball would simply be moving in the same straight line along which it had been moving during the time that the train was on the straight portion of the track. This follows directly from Newton's first law of motion, since there is no unbalanced force acting on the ball.

The description of many of the phenomena which occur in circular motion may be much simpler when referred to the moving frame of reference. To avoid serious error, it is at all times necessary to know the particular frame of reference used in the discussion. The behavior of particles in a system which is moving in a circular path is sometimes compared to the behavior of particles in the earth's gravitational field. For example, we know that the effect of the earth's gravitational field is to give every particle at a particular place on the earth the same acceleration g downward. In one of the above examples, we saw that a ball in a train moving in a circular path is apparently accelerated with respect to the train in a direction away from the center by the centrifugal force. This acceleration, measured inside the train, is $a = v^2/R$, independent of the mass of the ball. The same would be true for any other particle which is free to move inside the train. We may thus say that, to an observer inside the moving frame of reference, there exists a field very similar to a gravitational field in its effect but directed away from the center. In many practical examples, such as the effect on a person in an airplane moving in a circular path, or in the description of the action of a centrifuge (see Section 9–10), this central acceleration is compared numerically to g. For example, an aviator, coming out of a power dive, moves in a curved path which we shall take as circular. It has been found from experiment that, in order for the pilot to avoid blacking out in coming out of this power dive, the acceleration of the airplane in the circular motion should not exceed $6.9g$.

6-5 MOTION IN A VERTICAL CIRCLE

An interesting and important type of circular motion is that which takes place in a vertical plane, for example, when an airplane loops the loop. Occasionally a motorcycle stunt rider will ride on the inside of a vertical circular track, or a ball can be made to roll completely around the inside of a vertical circular track. The motion is not uniform, and the speed varies from point to point on the circle. Suppose we confine our attention to a particle which acquires its speed by sliding down a frictionless inclined plane (see Figure 6–5) and then starts going up on the inside of the circular track. It is obvious that the danger point is the highest point A on the track. The particle must negotiate this point with the proper speed if it is to travel safely around the track.

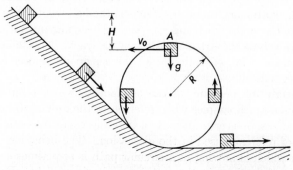

Fɪɢ. 6–5

Suppose for a moment the particle is at point A under the track and has zero speed. Since the force of gravity is the only force which acts on it, the particle will be simply a freely falling body with an acceleration of g downward directed through the center of the vertical circle. To negotiate the highest point safely, the particle must have a minimum speed v_0, such that its acceleration, which is v_0^2/R in a circle of radius R, is at least equal to g; that is,

$$g = \frac{v_0^2}{R},$$

from which $\qquad\qquad\qquad v_0^2 = Rg$

and $\qquad\qquad\qquad\qquad v_0 = \sqrt{Rg}.$ \hfill (7)

If the speed of the particle is greater than this minimum speed, its acceleration toward the center will be greater than g; this means that the track will have to supply a force toward the center to keep it moving in the circular path. If its speed is less than this minimum safe value of v_0, the particle will leave the track and follow the parabolic path of a projectile (see Figure 6–6).

One method by which a particle can acquire the necessary speed in order to travel around the vertical circle is first to slide down an inclined plane attached to this circular path; it will have to start at a sufficient height H above the highest point A of the circle to acquire the minimum safe speed v_0. If we neglect losses due to friction, the speed v which the particle will acquire in moving down a plane of height H is

$$v^2 = 2gH.$$

But we know that at the top of the circle

$$v_0^2 = Rg.$$

Equating these two values of the velocity, we obtain

$$R = 2H,$$

$$H = \frac{R}{2};$$

that is, the particle must start at a height at least equal to $R/2$ above the point A in order to pass the top safely. Actually it will have to start at some point above this to make up for the loss in speed due to friction.

FIG. 6–6   Multiflash photograph of a ball which starts on an inclined plane but does not acquire sufficient speed to loop the loop in a vertical circle. (Reproduced by permission from *College Physics*, 2nd ed., by Sears and Zemansky, 1952; Addison-Wesley, Cambridge, Mass.)

Illustrative Example. A small toy car with ball-bearing wheels goes around a vertical circle whose radius is 2 ft. (a) Determine the minimum speed it must have at the top of the circle. (b) Determine its speed halfway down the circle. (c) Determine its speed at the bottom of the circle. If the car weighs 0.5 lb, determine the force that the track exerts on it (d) at the top and (e) at the bottom. Neglect friction effects.

(a) The minimum speed that the car must have at the top of the track to pass it safely is given by

$$v_0 = \sqrt{Rg};$$

substituting numerical values, we get

$$v_0 = \sqrt{2 \text{ ft} \times 32 \text{ ft/sec}^2}$$

or

$$v_0 = 8 \text{ ft/sec.}$$

(b) There are two forces acting on the car—its weight mg and the push of the track. The force provided by the track is always at right angles to the velocity, and hence it cannot produce a change in the speed; it can only produce a change in the direction of motion. The change in speed can come only from the other force, its weight mg. It has already been shown that the speed acquired by a body moving down a smooth inclined plane does not depend upon its length but only upon its height H. This theorem can be generalized to state that the speed acquired by a body moving down any frictionless path is the same as that it would have acquired if it had fallen through the same height H. Hence, if the initial speed of a body is v_0, its final speed v is given by

$$v^2 = v_0^2 + 2gH.$$

In this case, $$v_0^2 = Rg \quad \text{and} \quad H = R,$$

and, calling the speed halfway down $v = v_1$, we get

$$v_1^2 = Rg + 2Rg = 3Rg.$$

Hence $$v_1 = \sqrt{3Rg} = \sqrt{3 \times 2 \text{ ft} \times 32 \text{ ft/sec}^2},$$

so that $$v_1 = 13.9 \text{ ft/sec}.$$

(c) At the bottom of the plane, $H = 2R$; hence the speed v_2 will be

$$v_2^2 = Rg + 2g \times 2R = 5Rg,$$

so that $$v^2 = \sqrt{5Rg} = \sqrt{5 \times 2 \text{ ft} \times 32 \text{ ft/sec}^2}$$

or $$v_2 = 17.9 \text{ ft/sec}.$$

(d) When the car is at the top of its path, the track exerts no force on it. The only force acting on it is its weight, which, at this position, is also the centripetal force.

(e) When the car is at the bottom of its path, the force F that the track exerts is the resultant of two forces—(1) a push upward equal to the weight of the car and (2) a centripetal force mv_2^2/R to keep it moving in the circle; hence

$$F = mg + \frac{mv_2^2}{R};$$

but $$v_2^2 = 5gR,$$

$$F = mg + \frac{m \times 5gR}{R},$$

which yields $$F = 6mg,$$

so that $$F = 6 \times 0.5 \text{ lb} = 3 \text{ lb}.$$

Thus at the bottom of the path, the track must exert a force equal to six times the weight of the car, providing the car started with the minimum safe speed at the top of the vertical circle.

6-6   PERIODICITY OF UNIFORM CIRCULAR MOTION

One of the interesting properties of uniform circular motion is that it is periodic; that is, a particle in uniform circular motion traverses a full circumference in a time T. This time T is called the *period* of the motion. The period remains the same no matter how often the motion is repeated.

The relationships between the period and the other quantities used to describe the motion are readily obtainable. Referring to Figure 6–7, the

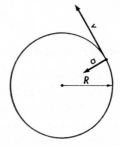

Fig. 6–7   Directions of velocity and acceleration in uniform circular motion.

distance covered by such a particle in one revolution is the length of the circumference, which is $2\pi R$, where R is the radius of the circle. From the definition of the speed of a particle as the distance traversed divided by the time, we get

$$v = \frac{2\pi R}{T},$$ **(8)**

from which

$$T = \frac{2\pi R}{v}.$$ **(9)**

The greater the speed of the particle, the shorter is the period of the motion. The period is expressed in units of time, usually in seconds.

We have already shown that the acceleration of a particle in uniform circular motion is

$$a = \frac{v^2}{R}.$$ **(4)**

Substituting the value of v from Equation (8) yields

$$a = \frac{4\pi^2 R}{T^2}$$ **(10)**

for the relationship between the acceleration and the period for uniform circular motion.

Illustrative Example. A small car moves around a circular track once every 8 sec. The radius of the track is 3 m. Determine (a) the speed of the car and (b) its centripetal acceleration.

Substituting $T = 8$ sec and $R = 300$ cm in Equation (8) yields

$$v = \frac{2\pi \times 300 \text{ cm}}{8 \text{ sec}} = 235 \text{ cm/sec}.$$

The acceleration can be obtained from Equation (10), which yields

$$a = \frac{4\pi^2 \times 300 \text{ cm}}{64 \text{ sec}^2},$$

so that $\qquad\qquad a = 185 \text{ cm/sec}^2.$

6-7 PLANETARY MOTION

One important type of periodic motion which has been studied and recorded for centuries is that of the bodies constituting the solar system. Theories concerning the solar system have changed with the centuries, and to a certain extent these changes mirror man's intellectual progress. Among the early theories which held sway for many centuries was that associated with the name of Claudius Ptolemy (c. A.D. 150) and known as the *geocentric* theory. This theory was reasonably successful in explaining and predicting planetary motion with the degree of accuracy then possible of attainment. In the geocentric theory, the earth was assumed to be at the center of the universe, and the sun and the planets moved around it in complicated paths.

Several centuries before Ptolemy, Aristarchus of Samos (c. 310–230 B.C.) proposed a theory in which the sun was fixed at the center of the universe and the earth revolved around the sun in a circular orbit. He also recognized that the stars appeared "fixed" in position, because their distances from the sun were tremendous in comparison with the distance of the earth from the sun. Very few of the early astronomers accepted this *heliocentric* theory of the universe; from the second century until the sixteenth century, only the geocentric theory of Ptolemy was taught and used. In the latter century, Nicholas Copernicus (1472–1543) revived and extended the heliocentric theory of Aristarchus and thus started a revolution in scientific thought which was carried forward by Kepler, Galileo, and Newton. In the heliocentric theory of Copernicus (see Figure 6–8), the sun was considered at the center of the universe, the planets revolved around the sun in circular orbits, and the fixed stars were assumed to lie in a sphere surrounding the solar system.

The heliocentric theory was not readily accepted by scientists of that period.   Tycho Brahe (1546–1601), a famous Danish astronomer, made very careful and accurate measurements of the motions of the planets and the sun.   He had never become convinced of the correctness of the Copernican hypothesis, but his extensive and careful measurements which he bequeathed to another astronomer, John Kepler (1571–1630), laid the foundations of modern astronomy.   It may be noted here that Brahe's observations were made without the aid of telescopic instruments.

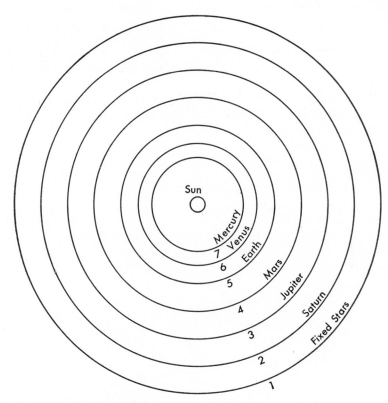

Fig. 6–8   Orbits of the planets and the fixed stars in the heliocentric theory of the universe according to Copernicus.

Kepler, from his study of the data accumulated by Tycho Brahe, deduced three laws which accurately describe the motions of the planets around the sun.   Kepler's three laws are

(a) Each planet moves around the sun in an elliptic path (or orbit) with the sun at one focus of the ellipse.

(b) As the planet moves in its orbit, a line drawn from the sun to the planet sweeps out equal areas in equal intervals of time (see Figure 6–9).

(c) The squares of the periods of the planets are proportional to the cubes of their mean distances from the sun.

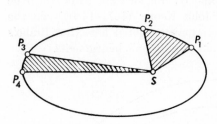

FIG. 6-9 The path of a planet about the sun S is an ellipse. P_1, P_2, P_3, P_4 represent positions of a planet in its orbit at different times. The speed of a planet in its orbit is such that an imaginary line joining the sun and the planet would sweep out equal areas in equal intervals of time. For example, area SP_1P_2 is equal to area SP_3P_4.

It can be seen that the simplified picture of the planetary system proposed by Copernicus is not sufficiently accurate; however, the elliptical

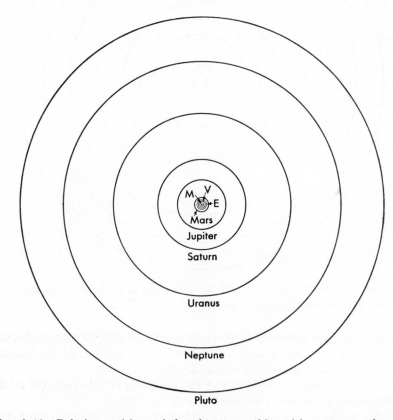

FIG. 6-10   Relative positions of the planetary orbits with respect to the sun. Drawn to scale. The sun is at the center; M is the orbit of mercury; V, that of Venus; and E, that of the earth.

orbits of the planets are not far removed from circles. In Figure 6–10, the planetary orbits are represented as circles merely to show their relative positions with respect to the sun. Kepler's third law can be put in mathematical form as follows: if r_1 is the average distance (or radius in Figure 6–10) of one planet from the sun, and r_2 is the average distance of another planet from the sun, then

$$\frac{T_1^2}{T_2^2} = \frac{r_1^3}{r_2^3} , \qquad \text{(11)}$$

where T_1 is the period of revolution of the first planet and T_2 that of the second planet. It can be seen from the third law that the farther from the sun a planet is, the longer is its period.

6-8 NEWTON'S LAW OF UNIVERSAL GRAVITATION

Although Kepler's laws give an adequate description of the motions of the planets, they do not give a physical explanation of the cause of the motion. Newton, having introduced the concept of force into mechanics, now applied this concept to help explain the cause of the motions of the planets around the sun. He developed the *law of universal gravitation* which states that *any two bodies in the universe attract each other with a force which is directly proportional to the product of the masses of the two bodies and inversely proportional to the square of the distance between them.*
Stated in mathematical form, this law becomes

$$F \propto \frac{Mm}{r^2} ,$$

where M is the mass of one body, m is the mass of the other body, r is the distance between them, and F is the force that one body exerts on the other. This law can be put in the form of an equation by replacing the proportionality sign by an equals sign and a constant of proportionality, thus

$$F = G_0 \frac{Mm}{r^2} , \qquad \text{(12)}$$

where G_0 is the constant of proportionality and is known as the *universal constant of gravitation.*
Newton's law of universal gravitation, when combined with his laws of motion, predicts the motions of the planets with great accuracy. There is the interesting story of the discovery of the planet Neptune to attest to the accuracy of Newton's laws. When it was observed that the motion of the planet Uranus varied slightly from the predictions based upon Newton's law of gravitation, it was assumed that this variation was produced by the

gravitational attraction of another, then unknown, planet. Newton's laws were then used to calculate the position of this new planet; it was looked for and found at about the calculated position. This newly discovered planet was called Neptune.

Newton's law of universal gravitation is applicable to all particles in the universe. In order to be able to use it in the form given by Equation (12), it is necessary to evaluate the gravitational constant G_0. Its numerical value will depend upon the particular system of units used. We can give it a simple physical interpretation, no matter what system of units is used, by imagining two unit masses placed a unit distance apart; that is, $M = 1$, $m = 1$, and $r = 1$. The force F_1 with which two such masses attract each other is, from Equation (12),

$$F_1 = G_0 ;$$

that is, G_0 can be interpreted as the force with which two unit masses will attract each other when placed a unit distance apart.

The first experimenter to evaluate G_0 was Henry Cavendish (1731–1810); it has also been determined by C. V. Boys and more recently by Paul R. Heyl. One method of determining the gravitational constant G_0 makes use of a very delicate torsion balance, such as that sketched in Figure 6–11. This consists of a fine elastic fiber AB suspended from some

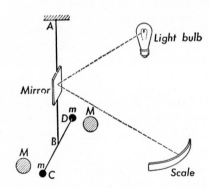

Fig. 6–11   Method of determining the gravitational constant G_0, using a delicate torsion balance.

support at A; a small, stiff metal rod CD is fastened to B. Two equal metal spheres, usually silver or gold, each of mass m, are mounted on the ends C and D. Two much more massive spheres made of lead are placed near the small spheres, one in front of the sphere at D, the other behind the sphere at C. Each of these lead spheres has a mass M. The force of attraction between each lead sphere and the small metal sphere near it produces a torque about AB as an axis; the two torques are in the same direction and cause the fiber to twist through a small angle. The angle of twist can be measured by reflecting a beam of light from a small mirror attached to the fiber onto a scale. By shifting the positions of the large lead spheres so that one is now behind D and the other in front of C, the fiber is made to twist in the opposite direction. From a knowledge of the torque required to produce a given angular twist of the fiber obtained in a separate experiment, the force F that each lead sphere of mass M exerts on the small metal sphere of mass m can be computed. The distance r between the centers of the spheres is also measured. Putting these data in Equation (12) will give the value of the constant G_0 of universal gravitation.

The value of G_0 determined experimentally is, in cgs units,

$$G_0 = 6.670 \times 10^{-8} \text{ dyne cm}^2/\text{gm}^2.$$

Illustrative Example. Determine the force of attraction between a lead sphere whose mass is 2,000 gm and a gold sphere whose mass is 4 gm when placed 6 cm apart.

Using Equation (12) and setting $M = 2,000$ gm, $m = 4$ gm, $r = 6$ cm, and $G_0 = 6.67 \times 10^{-8}$ dyne cm^2/gm^2, we get

$$F = 6.67 \times 10^{-8} \frac{\text{dyne cm}^2}{\text{gm}^2} \times \frac{2,000 \text{ gm} \times 4 \text{ gm}}{36 \text{ cm}^2},$$

from which
$$F = 1.48 \times 10^{-5} \text{ dyne}.$$

6-9 THE GRAVITATIONAL FIELD

The force that exists between two particles because of their masses acts no matter how far apart these masses may be. There is another way of thinking about gravitational forces and that is to imagine that in the space all around a particle of mass M there exists a *gravitational field*. Whenever any other particle finds itself in this gravitational field, it will experience a force F given by Equation (12)

$$F = G_0 \frac{Mm}{r^2},$$

where r is the distance between the two masses. We can define a new term called the *intensity of the gravitational field at any point* in space as *the ratio of the force F which acts on a particle at this point to the mass m of the particle situated there.* Let us denote the intensity by the letter I; then

$$I = \frac{F}{m}, \tag{13}$$

and, putting in the value of F from Equation (12),

$$I = \frac{G_0 M}{r^2}. \tag{14}$$

Equation (14) shows that the intensity of the gravitational field varies inversely as the square of the distance from the particle of mass M. The intensity I is a vector quantity; its direction is that of the force F which acts on a particle placed anywhere in the field, and, since the force is always one of attraction, its direction is toward the mass M. We can develop a graphical method for representing the gravitational field so that it will show at a glance both the magnitude and direction of the field intensity. This is illustrated in Figure 6–12, in which radial lines are drawn converging upon the mass M; a scale can be chosen so that the number of lines passing perpendicularly through a unit area at any point such as P will be proportional to the intensity I at that point.

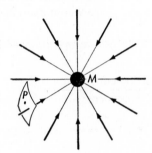

FIG. 6–12 Radial gravitational field around a small concentrated mass M. The number of lines of force through a unit area at P is proportional to the intensity I of the gravitational field at P.

An interesting case is that of the earth's gravitational field. Newton was the first to prove that the field outside a spherical mass is identical with that of a mass concentrated at the center of the sphere. Hence, at points outside the earth's surface, the gravitational field intensity is given by Equation (14). However, we have been using the term weight of a particle to describe the force which the earth exerts on a mass m placed anywhere in its field. The intensity of the earth's gravitational field I_e is, therefore,

$$I_e = \frac{W}{m} = g. \tag{15}$$

The term which we have been calling the acceleration of a freely falling body is identical with the intensity of the earth's gravitational field.

Comparing Equations (14) and (15), we find that

$$g = G_0 \frac{M}{r^2} \qquad (r \geq R), \tag{16}$$

in which M is now the mass of the earth and r is the distance of a point from the center of the earth. Equation (16) holds only for points outside the earth, that is, for distances greater than the radius R of the earth. For a point very close to the surface of the earth we may set $r = R$.

Equation (16) shows that the value of g, the intensity of the earth's gravitational field, and also the acceleration of a freely falling body varies inversely as the square of the distance from the center of the earth. Hence, g varies with altitude; that is, g decreases as the altitude increases.

Equation (16) can be used to determine the mass of the earth. Setting $g = 980$ cm/sec^2, $G_0 = 6.70 \times 10^{-8}$ dyne cm^2/gm^2, and $r = R = 6{,}380$ km $= 6.380 \times 10^8$ cm, and solving for M, we get

$$M = \frac{gR^2}{G_0}$$

$$= \frac{980 \ \dfrac{\text{cm}}{\text{sec}^2} \times (6.38 \times 10^8 \ \text{cm})^2}{6.67 \times 10^{-8} \ \text{dyne cm}^2/\text{gm}^2},$$

from which $\qquad M = 5.98 \times 10^{27}$ gm.

Illustrative Example. With the development of modern high-speed rockets, it is interesting to inquire what speed a particle should have in order that it become a satellite of the earth, that is, travel in an approximately circular path around the earth.

Any particle traveling with a speed v on a circular path of radius R has an acceleration toward the center of the circle

$$a = \frac{v^2}{R} \cdot \tag{4}$$

If it is traveling in the earth's gravitational field, then $a = g$, so that

$$g = \frac{v^2}{R},$$

from which $\qquad v = \sqrt{gR}. \tag{17}$

Near the surface of the earth $R = 4{,}000$ miles and

$$g = 32 \ \text{ft/sec}^2 = \frac{32}{5{,}280} \ \text{mi/sec}^2;$$

substituting these values in Equation (17) yields

$$v = \sqrt{\frac{32 \ \text{mi}}{5{,}280 \ \text{sec}^2} \times 4{,}000 \ \text{mi}},$$

$$v \doteq 5 \ \text{mi/sec}.$$

At the position of the moon, the value of g is much less than near the surface of the earth.   The moon is approximately 240,000 miles from the center of the earth.   This distance is about 60 times the radius of the earth.   Hence the value of the gravitational field at the position of the moon g_m is less than the value of g at the surface of the earth by a factor of $(1/60)^2$.   But since the radius of the circular path R_m has been increased by a factor of 60 over that near the surface of the earth, we have

$$g_m R_m = \frac{g}{(60)^2} \times 60R$$

or
$$g_m R_m = \frac{gR}{60} .$$

The velocity v_m of a satellite at the distance of the moon from the earth should therefore be

$$v_m = \sqrt{g_m R_m} = \frac{v}{\sqrt{60}} = 0.64 \text{ mi/sec.}$$

The comparison of this speed with the average speed of the moon in its orbit is left as an exercise for the student (see Problem 5).

QUESTIONS

1. Sometimes when a car rounds a curve on a level road at a high speed, two of its wheels leave the ground.   Which two wheels remain on the ground?

2. An aviator makes a quick turn in coming out of a power dive.   On the assumption that the airplane is moving in a circular path at this instant, its central acceleration has been determined as $6.9g$.   Discuss the meaning of this term.   How big a force is exerted on the pilot if his weight is 175 lb?

3. A boy swings a pitcher of water in a vertical circle so that the open end of the pitcher faces downward at the top of the circle.   Discuss the motion of the pitcher and the water.   Is there any minimum speed that the pitcher must have at the top of the circle so that the water will not spill out?

4. An aviator loops the loop in an airplane; that is, he travels in a vertical circle with the bottom of the plane always on the outside of the circle.   Analyze the forces acting on the aviator when he is (a) at the top of the circle, (b) halfway down, and (c) at the bottom of the circle.

5. A ball tied to a string is whirled in a horizontal circle on a smooth table with speed v.   If the string should be cut suddenly, discuss the subsequent motion of the ball.   What happens to the string after it is cut?

6. In the so-called "centrifugal" type of clothes drier, the wet clothes are put into a cylinder which has holes drilled in its walls.   This cylinder, with the clothes in it, is then spun rapidly.   Explain the action of this drier.

7. A man is standing in a car.   Toward which side of the car will he tend to move when the car rounds a curve?

8. At what time of the year is the speed of the earth in its orbit (a) greatest, (b) smallest?

9. Compare the speeds of the planets in their orbits relative to their distances from the sun.

10. A glass jar is fastened on a horizontal turntable near its rim, and a candle is placed inside the jar. When the candle is lit, the flame will point in a vertical direction owing to the upward motion of the hot gases formed in the combustion process. If the turntable is set into rotation, in which direction will the flame be deflected—toward or away from the center of the circle? Explain your answer.

11. A train is rounding a curve at a high speed. A man in the train drops a ball. What will be the path of the ball as observed (a) by the man in the train and (b) by an observer who is standing outside at a distance from the train?

PROBLEMS

1. A stone whose mass is 150 gm is attached to a cord 30 cm long and placed on a smooth horizontal table. The stone is then whirled in a circular path with a speed of 40 cm/sec. Determine the tension in the cord.

2. A car weighing 3,600 lb rounds a curve of 900 ft radius at a speed of 40 mi/hr. What force must the ground exert on the tires to keep this car moving in this circular path? In what direction is this force?

3. A train of cars, each weighing 20 tons, rounds a curve at a speed of 60 mi/hr. What lateral force is exerted on the wheels of each car if the radius of the curve is 1,200 ft?

4. A small car weighing 2 lb takes 12 seconds to go around a circular track whose radius is 5 ft. Determine (a) the acceleration of this car and (b) the centripetal force which acts on it. (c) What is the reaction to this force?

5. Assume that the moon is moving in a circular path of 240,000 miles radius about the earth. The period of revolution is $27\frac{1}{2}$ days. Calculate the acceleration of the moon.

6. An automobile weighing 3,200 lb rounds a curve of 800 ft radius at a speed of 60 mi/hr. (a) What force must the ground exert on the tires to keep the car moving in this circular path? (b) What is the minimum value for the coefficient of friction between the tires and the road in order that there be no skidding?

7. Determine the angle at which a road should be banked if the radius of the curve is 1,600 ft and if it is to supply the necessary centripetal force to a car traveling at 60 mi/hr; the centripetal force is to be the horizontal component of the normal force of the road on the car.

8. A small car whose mass is 75 gm moves on the inside of a vertical circular track, as in Figure 6–5. The radius of this circle is 120 cm. (a) Determine the minimum speed that the car must have at the top of the circular track in order to move in this circular path. (b) Assuming that it has this minimum safe speed at the top of the track, determine its speed at the bottom of the track. What is the force that the track exerts on the car (c) at the top of the track, (d) at the bottom of the track?

9. An airplane is diving at 600 mi/hr; the pilot pulls it out of this dive

by moving in the arc of a vertical circle.   (a) Determine the minimum radius of this circle if his acceleration is not to exceed $7g$ at the lowest point.   (b) Determine the force which acts on a pilot who weighs 180 lb.

10. The period of Jupiter is 11.86 years.   Determine its distance from the sun with the aid of Kepler's third law.

11. Assuming the earth to move around the sun in a circular orbit of radius 92,900,000 miles with a period of 365.3 days, compute (a) the speed of the earth in its orbit, and (b) the acceleration of the earth relative to the sun.   (c) The mass of the earth is 5.98×10^{24} kg.   Determine the gravitational force between the sun and the earth.

12. Determine the ratio of the force of the sun on the moon to that of the earth on the moon, given the following data: distance of the sun from the moon is 92,500,000 miles; distance of the earth from the moon is 240,000 miles; mass of the sun is 332,000 times the mass of the earth.

7

Harmonic
Motion

7-1 SIMPLE HARMONIC MOTION

An extremely important type of periodic motion of a particle is one in which *the acceleration* a *of the particle is proportional to its displacement* x *from its equilibrium position and is opposite in direction to the displacement;* that is,

$$a \propto -x$$

or

$$a = -cx, \qquad\qquad (1)$$

where c is a constant of proportionality. The minus sign is used to show that the direction of the acceleration is always opposite to the direction of the displacement of the particle. The type of motion defined by Equation (1) is called *simple harmonic motion.*

A common example of simple harmonic motion is the motion of a body attached to one end of a helical spring which is suspended from some fixed support O (see Figure 7–1). When a body of mass m is attached to this spring and lowered slowly, it will come to rest at some point C, at which position it is in equilibrium under the action of two forces—its weight mg downward and the pull of the spring F_1 upward. Suppose we now pull the mass down a distance x below C. To hold it there, we shall have to exert a force $F = kx$, where k is the constant of the spring (see Section 2–1). The spring will exert an equal force in the upward direction, that is, a force

$$F = -kx. \qquad\qquad (2)$$

The distance x is called the *displacement* of the body from its equilibrium position C, and the minus sign indicates that the force which the spring exerts on it is opposite to the displacement.

If we now release the body, it will no longer be in equilibrium, and the unbalanced force acting on it will be $F = -kx$. As the body returns to its equilibrium position, its displacement becomes smaller, and so does the

151

unbalanced force F. At the equilibrium position, $F = 0$, but the motion does not stop. From Newton's first law, we know that the body will continue to move in the same direction with the same speed unless an unbalanced force acts on it. As it moves above C, it is again displaced from its equilibrium position, and the unbalanced force $F = -kx$ acts on it; the direction of this force is again opposite to the displacement and decreases the speed of the body.

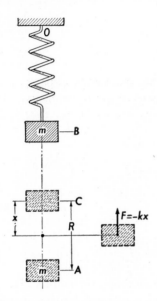

FIG. 7–1   A body of mass m attached to a helical spring. C is its equilibrium position. When the body is pulled down to A and released, it will vibrate from A to B and back to A, repeating this motion periodically; x is the displacement of the body at a point in its path.

If originally the body attached to the spring was pulled down to position A, a distance R below C, it would move upward beyond C to a position B at a distance almost equal to R. If there were no losses due to air resistance and internal friction in the spring, the distances AC and BC would be equal. After the body has reached point B and stopped, it will return through C to A and then back again through C to B and keep up this motion indefinitely. If we time this motion, we shall find that the motion is periodic, that is, that the time to execute a complete vibration, going from A to B and back to A, is always the same.

We can apply Newton's second law

$$F = ma$$

in discussing the motion of this particle. The unbalanced force acting on this particle is, from Equation (2)

$$F = -kx. \tag{2}$$

Equating these two expressions for the force on the particle, we get

$$ma = -kx,$$

from which

$$a = -\frac{k}{m}x. \tag{3}$$

Equation (3) shows that the acceleration of this particle is directly proportional to the displacement from its equilibrium position and is always opposite in direction to that of the displacement. Equation (3) is identical with Equation (1), the defining equation of simple harmonic motion with the constant of proportionality $c = k/m$ for this specific case.

Illustrative Example. A spring whose natural length, when hung from a fixed point O, is 40 cm has a 50-gm mass attached to its free end. When this mass is at the equilibrium position C, the length of the spring is 45 cm. The mass is then pulled down a distance of 6 cm and released. Determine (a) the constant of the spring, (b) its acceleration at the 6-cm point, (c) its acceleration when it has reached a point 2 cm above C, and (d) the unbalanced force which acts on it at the 2-cm point.

(a) Since the length of the spring was increased from 40 to 45 cm by hanging the 50-gm mass on it, the weight mg of this mass produced an extension of 5 cm in the length of the spring;

hence

$$mg = kx,$$

so that

$$50 \text{ gm} \times 980 \frac{\text{cm}}{\text{sec}^2} = k \times 5 \text{ cm},$$

from which

$$k = 9{,}800 \frac{\text{dynes}}{\text{cm}}.$$

(b) The acceleration of the body is given by Equation (3)

$$a = -\frac{k}{m}x. \tag{3}$$

At the 6-cm point, $x = 6$ cm, so that

$$a = -\frac{9{,}800 \text{ dynes/cm}}{50 \text{ gm}} \times 6 \text{ cm}$$

or

$$a = -1{,}176 \frac{\text{cm}}{\text{sec}^2}.$$

(c) At a distance of 2 cm above C, $x = 2$ cm;

hence

$$a = -\frac{9{,}800 \text{ dynes/cm}}{50 \text{ gm}} \times 2 \text{ cm},$$

so that
$$a = -392 \ \frac{\text{cm}}{\text{sec}^2}.$$

(d) The unbalanced force which acts on the mass is given by the equation

$$F = -kx, \tag{2}$$

so that
$$F = -9,800 \ \frac{\text{dynes}}{\text{cm}} \times 2 \text{ cm,}$$

from which
$$F = -19,600 \text{ dynes.}$$

7-2 PERIOD OF SIMPLE HARMONIC MOTION

To determine the period of a particle in simple harmonic motion directly from Equation (3) involves a type of mathematics which is beyond the scope of this book. One method of circumventing this difficulty is to make use of a simple relationship which exists between a particle in simple harmonic motion and another particle in uniform circular motion, both having the same period. It will be shown that simple harmonic motion is the projection of uniform circular motion on a line in the plane of the circle. For convenience, we shall take this line to coincide with a diameter of the circle.

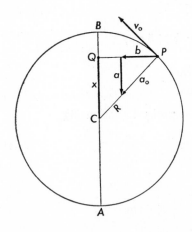

Fig. 7-2 Projection of the motion of particle P on a diameter of the circle. a_0 is the acceleration of P; a is the acceleration of Q, the projection of P on the diameter AB.

Let us consider a particle P moving with uniform circular motion, as shown in Figure 7-2. Let us call its velocity v_0 and its acceleration a_0. Its acceleration is directed toward the center C of the circle of radius R. To project this motion on a vertical diameter AB, draw a perpendicular from the particle P onto this diameter to point Q; the particle moving with simple harmonic motion is, at this instant, situated at Q. As the particle

P moves around the circular path, the particle Q moves up and down the diameter AB. No matter where P is, its projection on the diameter determines the position of Q. The velocity of the particle at Q is the projection of the velocity of P on AB, and the acceleration of the particle at Q is the projection of the acceleration of P on AB.

Let us first determine the acceleration a of the particle at Q. To do this, we resolve the acceleration a_0 of the particle P into two components, one of which is parallel to AB; we shall call this component a. Now we know, from Equation (4) of Chapter 6, that

$$a_0 = -\frac{v_0^2}{R}. \tag{4}$$

The minus sign is used here to indicate that a_0 is directed toward the center, while the radius R is measured outward from the center. The triangles PQC and aba_0 are similar; hence

$$\frac{a}{a_0} = \frac{x}{R},$$

where $x = QC$ and is the displacement of the particle at Q.

Substituting the value of a_0 from Equation (4) into the above equation yields

$$a = -\frac{v_0^2}{R^2} x. \tag{5}$$

From Equation (5), we see that since v_0 and R are constant, the acceleration of the particle at Q is directly proportional to its displacement x and opposite in direction. Hence, the particle at Q is moving with simple harmonic motion.

We have already shown in Equation (8) of Chapter 6 that the period T of a particle in uniform circular motion with speed v_0 is

$$T = \frac{2\pi R}{v_0}. \tag{6}$$

From this equation, we get

$$\frac{v_0}{R} = \frac{2\pi}{T}.$$

Substituting this expression for v_0/R into Equation (5) yields

$$a = -\frac{4\pi^2}{T^2} x. \tag{7}$$

The period T is the same for the particle in simple harmonic motion as for the particle in uniform circular motion. Solving Equation (7) for T, we get

$$T = 2\pi\sqrt{-\frac{x}{a}} \tag{8}$$

for the period of a particle in simple harmonic motion.

The period as given by Equation (8) is always real; this can be seen if we put in the value of x/a from Equation (1), which yields

$$T = \frac{2\pi}{\sqrt{c}} \tag{9}$$

as a general equation for the period of a particle in simple harmonic motion.

For the case of a particle of mass m attached to a spring of constant k, we know that $c = k/m$; substituting this value into Equation (9) yields

$$T = 2\pi\sqrt{\frac{m}{k}} \tag{10}$$

for the period of vibration of a particle attached to a spring.

Illustrative Example. A particle whose mass is 30 gm is attached to a spring which has a constant $k = 2{,}400$ dynes/cm. Determine its period of vibration.

The period of vibration of the particle attached to the spring is

$$T = 2\pi\sqrt{\frac{m}{k}} \cdot \tag{10}$$

Substituting $m = 30$ gm and $k = 2{,}400$ dynes/cm,

we get
$$T = 2\pi\sqrt{\frac{30 \text{ gm}}{2{,}400 \text{ dynes/cm}}},$$

from which
$$T = \frac{2\pi}{\sqrt{80}} \text{ sec}$$

or
$$T = 0.70 \text{ sec.}$$

Illustrative Example. A cylinder weighing 4 lb is hung from a very stiff spring whose elastic constant is 24 lb/in. Determine (a) the period of vibration of this cylinder and (b) its acceleration when its displacement is 3 in.

The mass of this cylinder is

$$m = \frac{4 \text{ lb}}{32 \text{ ft/sec}^2} = \tfrac{1}{8} \text{ slug.}$$

In order to avoid having the units inches and feet in the same equation, let us express k in pounds per foot thus:

$$k = 24 \times 12 \text{ lb/ft}$$
$$= 288 \text{ lb/ft,}$$

and
$$x = \tfrac{3}{12} \text{ ft} = 0.25 \text{ ft.}$$

(a) The period can be determined by substituting the above values of m and k into Equation (10)

$$T = 2\pi \sqrt{\frac{m}{k}},$$

yielding
$$T = 2\pi \sqrt{\frac{\tfrac{1}{8} \text{ slug}}{288 \text{ lb/ft}}},$$

from which
$$T = 0.13 \text{ sec.}$$

(b) The acceleration can be found with the aid of Equation (3); thus:

$$a = -\frac{k}{m} x,$$

and, substituting values for k, m, and x, we get

$$a = -\frac{288 \text{ lb/ft}}{\tfrac{1}{8} \text{ slug}} \times 0.25 \text{ ft,}$$

from which
$$a = -576 \text{ ft/sec}^2.$$

The same result could have been obtained by using Equation (7).

7-3 PROPERTIES OF SIMPLE HARMONIC MOTION

A term often used in discussing simple harmonic motion is the *frequency of vibration* of the particle which is defined as *the number of vibrations per unit time*. Since T is the time for 1 vibration, the frequency of vibration f is the reciprocal of the period, or,

$$f = \frac{1}{T}.$$

(11)

Eliminating T between Equations (8) and (11), we get, for the frequency of vibration,

$$f = \frac{\sqrt{c}}{2\pi} .$$

(12)

For the case of a particle of mass m attached to a spring of constant k, the frequency of vibration becomes

$$f = \frac{1}{2\pi} \sqrt{\frac{k}{m}} .$$

(13)

Figure 7–3 shows the path of a particle in simple harmonic motion. As the particle moves in its path from A through C to B and then back through C to A to complete 1 vibration, its displacement x passes through a series of

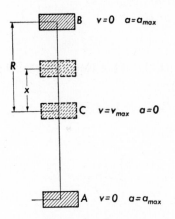

FIG. 7–3   Path of a body in simple harmonic motion showing the values of the velocity and the acceleration at the center and at the ends of the path.

values from a maximum at A to zero at C to a maximum again at B. Let us call the value of the maximum displacement R; the maximum displacement is called the *amplitude* of the motion. It will be observed that the equations for the period and frequency do not contain the amplitude of the motion; hence the period and frequency of a particle in simple harmonic motion are independent of the amplitude.

The velocity of a particle in simple harmonic motion can be obtained with the aid of the reference circle (see Figure 7–4). If v_0 is the velocity of the particle at P in uniform circular motion, then the velocity v of the particle at Q in simple harmonic motion is the component of v_0 parallel to the diameter AB.

Since the triangle v, v_1, v_0 is similar to the triangle PQC, we have

$$\frac{v}{v_0} = \frac{\sqrt{R^2 - x^2}}{R}.$$

From the definition of the period, we know that

$$T = \frac{2\pi R}{v_0};$$

hence

$$v = \frac{2\pi}{T} \sqrt{R^2 - x^2}, \tag{14}$$

or, in terms of the frequency $f = 1/T$,

we have

$$v = 2\pi f \sqrt{R^2 - x^2}. \tag{15}$$

Equation (15) shows that the velocity is a maximum when the displacement $x = 0$, that is, at point C, and the velocity is zero when $x = R$, that is, at points A and B.

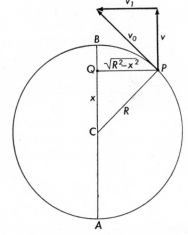

FIG. 7–4   The velocity v of the particle at Q moving with simple harmonic motion is the vertical component of the velocity v_0 of the particle at P moving with uniform circular motion.

There is a simple graphical method of representing simple harmonic motion. This graph can be obtained by fastening a needle or stylus to the end of a spring to which the vibrating particle is attached. If, as the particle and the stylus move up and down, a piece of waxed paper held close to the stylus is moved horizontally from left to right, an impression will be left on the waxed paper similar to the curve shown in Figure 7–5. This curve is a graph of the displacement x against the time t. The time axis is obtained by drawing a horizontal line between the extremes of the curve.

The amplitude of the motion is R. The period T is the time elapsed during the motion of the particle from one position such as A to the next similar position C, or between B and D, or between E and H. The motion of the particle at the time A as it goes through the position of maximum displacement is said to be in the same *phase* as its motion at the time C. Similarly, at times B and D, the motions are in phase. The motions are in phase at times E and H; at each of these instants of time, the particle is moving upward through the equilibrium position. But at times E and G the motions are *out of phase* by half a period; at the time E the particle is moving upward through its equilibrium position, while at time G it is moving downward through its equilibrium position.

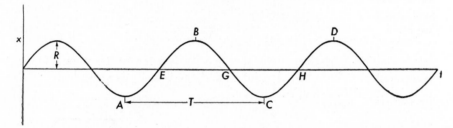

FIG. 7–5   Graph of the displacement x against the time t of a particle in simple harmonic motion. T is the period and R the amplitude of the motion.

Illustrative Example. A particle attached to a spring has a frequency of 4 vibrations/sec and an amplitude of 6 cm. Determine (a) the period of vibration, (b) the maximum velocity of the particle, (c) the velocity of the particle when its displacement is 2 cm, (d) the acceleration of the particle when its displacement is 2 cm, and (e) its maximum acceleration.

(a) The period of vibration is the reciprocal of the frequency; hence, from Equation (11),

$$T = \tfrac{1}{4} \text{ sec} = 0.25 \text{ sec.}$$

(b) The velocity of the particle at any position is given by Equation (15)

$$v = 2\pi f \sqrt{R^2 - x^2}.$$

The velocity is a maximum at the center where $x = 0$; hence, from Equation (15),

$$v_{\max} = 2\pi f R,$$

and, substituting the values $\quad f = 4\ \dfrac{\text{vib}}{\text{sec}}, R = 6 \text{ cm,}$

we get $\qquad v_{\max} = 2\pi \times 4\ \dfrac{\text{vib}}{\text{sec}} \times 6 \text{ cm,}$

so that $$v_{max} = 151 \frac{cm}{sec}.$$

(Note: The term *vibrations* has no physical dimensions; hence vibrations/sec is equivalent to 1/sec.)

(c) The velocity when $x = 2$ cm is obtained by substituting this value in Equation (15), obtaining

$$v_2 = 2\pi \times 4 \frac{vib}{sec} \sqrt{(36 - 4) \, cm^2}$$

or $$v_2 = 8\pi \sqrt{32} \, cm/sec,$$

from which $$v_2 = 142 \, cm/sec.$$

(d) The acceleration can be obtained from Equation (7)

$$a = -\frac{4\pi^2}{T^2} x.$$

This equation can be rewritten in terms of the frequency f, since $f = 1/T$, so that $$a = -4\pi^2 f^2 x.$$

Substituting $$f = 4 \frac{1}{sec}, \text{ and } x = 2 \text{ cm,}$$

we get $$a_2 = -4\pi^2 \times 16 \frac{1}{sec^2} \times 2 \text{ cm,}$$

from which $$a_2 = -1{,}263 \text{ cm/sec}^2.$$

(e) The maximum acceleration will occur at $x = R = 6$ cm. Since the acceleration is directly proportional to the displacement, the maximum acceleration will be three times the acceleration at the 2-cm point or

$$a_{max} = -3 \times 1{,}263 \text{ cm/sec}^2 = -3{,}789 \text{ cm/sec}^2.$$

7-4 THE SIMPLE PENDULUM

The motion of a pendulum is another interesting example of periodic motion. This property was first discovered by Galileo as a result of his observations of the periodic motions of lamps which were suspended by means of cords. Because of their periodic motion, pendulums are used in the construction of clocks. Although Galileo had designed a pendulum clock, he never actually constructed one. The first pendulum clock was constructed by the Dutch physicist Christian Huygens (1629–1695) in 1657. He also developed the mathematical theory of the pendulum. Newton also studied the motion of a pendulum and experimented with pendulums made of different materials and of different lengths.

We shall simplify the problem by confining our attention to the motion of a *simple pendulum*. A simple pendulum consists of a string of negligible weight, one end of which is attached to some fixed support O; a small ball, called a *pendulum bob*, is attached to the other end of the string (see Figure 7–6). When at rest, the bob is at C vertically below O and is in equilibrium under the action of two forces—its weight mg and the tension S in the string. When pulled aside to some position A and released, it travels in a circular arc through C to a point B on the other side. In moving the pendulum to A, it was actually lifted through a height h. If we make friction effects negligible, point B which it reaches will also be at a height h above C. It will then travel back through C to A, and the motion will be repeated. Both theory and experiment show that the period of the motion does depend upon the length of arc ACB. However, if this arc is made very small, so that it approximates a straight line, then the motion of the pendulum is simple harmonic.

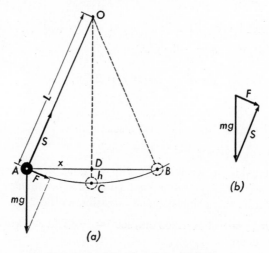

Fig. 7–6   The simple pendulum.

To derive the expression for the period of a simple pendulum, let us consider the forces which act on the bob at the point A. These forces are its weight mg downward and the tension S in the string in the direction AO [see Figure 7–6(a)]. The resultant F of these two forces is shown in Figure 7–6(b). F is perpendicular to S and hence to OA. If we drop a perpendicular from A onto OC, it will intersect it at D. The triangle OAD is similar to the triangle of forces F, mg, S. Hence

$$\frac{F}{mg} = \frac{DA}{AO} = \frac{x}{L},$$

where L is the length of the pendulum and $x = DA$. When the amplitude of the motion is very small, point D will practically coincide with point C, and $DA = CA = x$, the displacement of the particle. Using a minus sign to indicate that the direction of F is opposite to that of x, we get

$$F = -\frac{mg}{L}x. \qquad (16)$$

Using Newton's second law

$$F = ma,$$

we get, for the acceleration of the pendulum bob,

$$a = -\frac{g}{L}x. \qquad (17)$$

Equation (17) shows that the acceleration of the pendulum bob is proportional to its displacement and opposite in direction, when the amplitude of vibrations is small. This motion of the pendulum is therefore simple harmonic.

The period of the pendulum can be found by substituting the value of a/x from Equation (17) into Equation (8), obtaining

$$T = 2\pi\sqrt{\frac{L}{g}}. \qquad (18)$$

Equation (18) shows that the period of a simple pendulum does not depend upon the mass of the pendulum bob. This is in agreement with the results of the experiments of Newton with pendulum bobs of different masses. At any particular place on the earth's surface, the period depends only upon its length L. If a pendulum of known length is taken to different parts of the earth and its period is determined at each place, the value of g can readily be computed. However, actual pendulums used for such determinations are made of rigid bars; these are called physical or compound pendulums. It is possible to determine the equivalent simple pendulum length of a physical pendulum and then use Equation (18) for determining g with it.

Illustrative Example. A simple pendulum is 100 cm long. (a) Determine its period at a place where $g = 980$ cm/sec^2. (b) The measured value of its period at another place is 2.03 sec. Determine the value of g at this place.

(a) The period of the pendulum can be determined with the aid of the equation

$$T = 2\pi\sqrt{\frac{L}{g}}. \qquad (18)$$

Substituting values for L and g in this equation, we get

$$T = 2\pi \sqrt{\frac{100 \text{ cm}}{980 \text{ cm/sec}^2}} = 2.01 \text{ sec.}$$

(b) To determine the value of g, let us solve Equation (18) for g, obtaining

$$g = \frac{4\pi^2 L}{T^2},$$

and, substituting $L = 100$ cm and $T = 2.03$ sec, we get

$$g = \frac{4\pi^2 \times 100 \text{ cm}}{(2.03 \text{ sec})^2},$$

from which $g = 958 \text{ cm/sec}^2.$

QUESTIONS

1. A billiard ball hits the edge of the billiard table perpendicularly, bounces back and strikes the opposite edge, bounces off it, and continues back to the opposite edge, and so forth. Is the billiard ball moving with simple harmonic motion?

2. Analyze the motion of a piston in the cylinder of a steam engine or a gasoline engine to determine whether its motion is simple harmonic.

3. Compare the direction of the acceleration of a particle in simple harmonic motion with that of a particle in uniform circular motion.

4. What is the relationship between the frequency of a particle in simple harmonic motion and its acceleration?

5. What is the effect on the period of the motion of a spring if the mass attached to it is increased so that it is four times the original mass?

6. What is the function of a simple pendulum in a clock?

7. Two pendulums have equal lengths, but the mass of one pendulum bob is four times that of the other. Compare their periods.

8. In an experiment for the determination of g using a simple pendulum, the student is usually advised to keep the length of arc, or the amplitude of the motion, small. Why is this precaution necessary?

PROBLEMS

1. A body whose mass is 800 gm hangs from a vertical spring whose constant is 200,000 dynes/cm. The body is pulled down a distance of 6 cm and released. Determine (a) the period of the motion, (b) the resultant force on the body when at the 6-cm point, and (c) its acceleration at this position.

2. Referring to Problem 1, determine (a) the velocity of the body when its displacement is 3 cm and (b) its maximum velocity.

3. A body which has a mass of 90 gm is attached to a helical spring 25 cm

long and, when lowered gently, stretches it 5 cm. The body is then pulled down an additional 8 cm and released, thus setting it in vibration. (a) What is the constant of this spring? (b) What is its period of oscillation?

4. A body which has a mass of 40 gm is attached to a spring, and this system is then set into vibration. The measured value of the period of this vibration is 0.70 sec. (a) Determine the constant of the spring. (b) Determine the velocity of the body at its equilibrium position if the amplitude is 6 cm. (c) Determine its maximum acceleration.

5. A spring balance is marked with 2-lb intervals every $\frac{1}{4}$ in. A body weighing 12 lb is placed on this balance. Determine (a) the constant of the spring and (b) its period of vibration.

6. When a cylinder whose mass is 4.0 kg is hung from a spring and set into vibration, the frequency is 2.4 vibration/sec. When another cylinder is substituted for the first one, its frequency of vibration is 3.2 vibration/sec. Determine the mass of the second cylinder.

7. What is the period of a simple pendulum 4 ft long when it is oscillating with a small amplitude?

8. Determine the period of a simple pendulum which is 65 cm long.

9. A simple pendulum 1.0 m long having a mass of 300 gm is displaced through an angle of 10° and released. Determine (a) the resultant force acting on it at its position of maximum displacement, (b) its maximum acceleration, and (c) its maximum velocity.

10. (a) Determine the period of vibration of a pendulum 80 cm long at a place where $g = 980$ cm/sec^2. (b) What length of pendulum at the same place will have half this period?

11. (a) Determine the frequency of vibration of a pendulum 50 cm long at a place where $g = 980$ cm/sec^2. (b) What length of pendulum will have twice this frequency at the same place?

12. A so-called "seconds" pendulum has a period of 2.00 sec. Determine the length of a seconds pendulum at a place where $g = 980$ cm/sec^2.

13. A seconds pendulum which kept accurate time at a place where g was 980.0 cm/sec^2 is found to lose 2 min per day at a new location. Find g at this location.

8

Fluids at Rest

8-1 THREE PHASES OF MATTER

From our everyday experience, we have become familiar with the fact that matter occurs in three different forms—*solid, liquid,* and *gas.* Under ordinary conditions, stone, iron, copper, and chalk, for example, are solids; water, oil, and mercury are liquids; and air, hydrogen, and carbon dioxide are gases. Each one of these forms is called a *phase.* The phase of a substance is determined by its temperature and pressure. The study of changes of phase will be considered in Chapter 15. For the present, we shall confine our discussion to the application of the principles of mechanics to bodies which remain in the same phase.

Liquids and gases are sometimes grouped together as *fluids* because they flow very readily upon the application of an external force, while solids do not. A solid has a definite size and a definite shape, and these change only very slightly when subject to external forces. Liquids, on the other hand, although they do possess a definite size or volume, change their shape very readily. Liquids at rest generally take the shape of the containing vessel. If the containing vessel is open to the atmosphere, or if its volume is greater than that of the liquid put into it, there will be a *free surface* at the top of the liquid. A mass of gas differs from a mass of liquid in that it has neither definite size nor definite shape. A mass of gas, no matter how small, will completely fill the container. The volume of the gas is the volume of the container.

8-2 DENSITY

Different substances differ greatly in their physical properties. These properties determine the behavior of the substances under various conditions. A knowledge of these properties acts as a guide when the substance to be used for a special purpose is chosen, or its behavior under various conditions is forecast. Some of these properties, known as the *physical constants* of the substance, can be measured and then tabulated for easy reference. Among these constants is the *density* of each substance.

The *density* of a substance is defined as *the ratio of the mass of a sample of the substance to its volume;* that is,

$$d = \frac{M}{V},$$ (1)

where d is the density of the substance, M the mass of the sample, and V its volume. The densities of solids and liquids vary slightly with changes of temperature and pressure, while the densities of gases vary greatly with changes of temperature and pressure. The temperature and pressure should always be specified when the densities of gases are given. In the cgs system, the densities of substances are expressed in grams per cubic centimeter. The density of water is 1 gm/cm^3, while the density of air at 0°C and atmospheric pressure is 0.001293 gm/cm^3. Table 8–1 gives the densities of some of the more common substances.

Table 8-1 Densities of Some Common Substances

Solids	Density in gm/cm³	Liquids	Density in gm/cm³
Aluminum	2.70	Alcohol	0.79
Brass	8.44–8.70	Ether	0.74
Copper	8.93	Glycerin	1.26
Cork	0.22–0.26	Mercury	13.596
Glass, common	2.4–2.8	Oil, olive	0.92
Glass, flint	2.9–5.9	Oil, paraffin	0.8
Gold	19.3	Water	1.00
Ice	0.917		
Iron	7.03–7.9		Density at 0°C,
Lead	11.34	Gases	760 mm Hg
Osmium	22.5		in gm/cm³
Nickel	8.9		
Platinum	21.50	Air	0.001293
Silver	10.5	Ammonia	0.000771
Tungsten	18.6–19.1	Carbon dioxide	0.001977
Wood, cedar	0.49–0.57	Helium	0.000179
Wood, ebony	1.11–1.33	Hydrogen	0.000090
Wood, elm	0.54–0.60	Oxygen	0.001429
Wood, white pine	0.35–0.50		
Zinc	7.1		

In the fps system, where the pound is used as the unit of mass and the volume is expressed in cubic feet, the density is expressed in pounds mass per cubic foot. The density of water is 62.4 lb-m/ft^3. If the density of the substance is known in grams per cubic centimeter, its value in pounds mass per cubic foot can be obtained by multiplying that value by 62.4.

In the British engineering system, the slug is the unit of mass, and the density is expressed in slugs/ft^3. Since 1 cu ft of water weighs 62.4 lb, its mass is 62.4/32.17 slugs or 1.94 slugs. Hence the density of water in this system is 1.94 slugs/ft^3, and the density of any other substance in the British engineering system can be obtained by multiplying its value in Table 8–1 by 1.94.

8-3 PRESSURE

There is a difference in the manner in which a force is applied to a fluid and the way it is applied to a solid. A force can be applied to a single point of a solid, but it can be applied only over a surface in the case of a fluid. In a discussion of the results of the application of forces to fluids, it is therefore convenient to introduce a new term called *pressure*. If a force F is applied to the surface of a fluid and acts over an area A perpendicular to it, then the pressure P is defined as

$$P = \frac{F}{A}. \tag{2}$$

The pressure may be expressed in dynes per square centimeter, in pounds per square foot, in pounds per square inch, or in any other appropriate set of units.

8-4 PRESSURE DUE TO WEIGHT OF A LIQUID

Suppose that a cylindrical jar of cross-sectional area A is filled with a liquid to a level a distance h from the bottom, as shown in Figure 8–1. If W is the weight of the liquid, then the pressure P on the bottom of the jar is, from Equation (2),

$$P = \frac{W}{A}.$$

The volume V of the liquid can be expressed as

$$V = Ah.$$

If d is the density of the liquid, and M its mass, then, from Equation (1),

$$d = \frac{M}{V},$$

or
$$M = Vd = Ahd.$$

Now $W = Mg,$

so that $W = Ahdg.$

Substituting this value of W in the equation for the pressure, we get

$$P = \frac{Ahdg}{A},$$

so that $\boxed{P = hdg.}$ **(3)**

Equation (3) shows that the pressure at the bottom of the vessel depends upon the height of the liquid above it, the density of the liquid, and
the value of g at that place. This equation also shows that the pressure
does not depend upon the area of the base or upon the shape of the vessel.

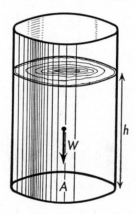

Fig. 8–1 Pressure on the base of a
cylindrical jar produced by the
weight of the liquid it contains.

This latter can be demonstrated with the aid of a series of vessels which
have different shapes but whose bases have the same cross-sectional area.
Three such vessels are shown in Figure 8–2. Each vessel is fitted with a
brass screw thread at the bottom so that it can be mounted on a pressure
gauge. When these vessels are filled to the same level with a liquid such as
water, the pressure readings will be found to be the same in all three cases.

Equation (3) gives the pressure not only at the bottom of the liquid
but at any point in the liquid. The height h in this equation is then interpreted as the height of liquid above the point in question. To verify this,
just imagine any horizontal surface of area A in the liquid; this surface
supports the weight of a cylindrical column of height h and area A. Using
the same analysis as that used in deriving Equation (3), we find that the
pressure on this surface is hdg.

Pressure is the ratio of a force to the area of the surface over which it
acts, the direction of the force being perpendicular to the surface. If we

imagine a small area at any point in the liquid where the pressure is P, there is a force acting on this small area at right angles to it. This is so no matter how the surface is oriented. If the vessel is cylindrical, the force produced by the pressure of the liquid acts horizontally on the sides of the cylinder. Since the pressure increases uniformly from zero at the top to its largest value at the bottom, the force on the sides also increases uniformly from the top of the liquid to the bottom.

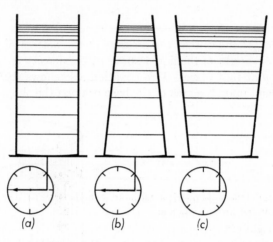

FIG. 8–2   Pressure at the bottom of a vessel is independent of the shape of the vessel; it depends only upon the height of the liquid and its density. Here jars are filled to the same level with the same liquid; pressure gauges attached show identical readings.

Each of the vessels in Figure 8–2 contains a different quantity of water, but the level in each is at the same height h above the bottom, and the pressure at the bottom is the same in each one. It may appear surprising that different weights of liquids can produce the same pressure, but the paradox disappears if we analyze the forces which act on the bottom of each vessel. In the cylinder of Figure 8–2(a), the weight of the cylindrical column of water of area A is the only force acting downward on the bottom. The liquid also exerts forces on the walls of the cylinder, and these walls in turn exert equal forces in the opposite direction on the water. But since the walls are vertical, the forces are horizontal and have no components in the vertical direction. But in Figure 8–2(b), the walls flare inward and exert forces which have vertical components directed downward. Although the weight of water in this vessel is less than that in the cylinder, it can be shown that the vertical component of the force exerted by the walls is just equal to the difference between these weights. Hence the force on the bottom of this vessel is equal to that on the bottom of the cylindrical vessel. When the sides of the vessel flare outward as in Figure 8–2(c), it is easy to see that they contribute a force which has a vertical component upward to support the weight of water which is in excess of that of a cylinder of cross-sectional area A. Hence the force on the bottom of this vessel is also equal to that of a cylindrical column of water of height h and cross-sectional area A.

Another consequence of the fact that the pressure at any point in a given liquid depends only upon the height of liquid above that point is that if some liquid is poured into a series of connected vessels, such as those shown in Figure 8–3, the level of the liquid will be the same in each

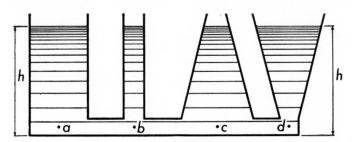

FIG. 8–3   The level of a liquid in a series of connected vessels is the same in each vessel if the liquid is at rest.

vessel. If we consider such points as a, b, c, and d in the connecting tubes when the liquid is at rest, the force due to the liquid to the right of each point must be equal to the force due to the liquid at the left of the point; otherwise there will be a flow of liquid in the direction of the greater force.

The pressure, as given by Equation (3), is usually expressed in dynes/cm^2, or lb/ft^2, or lb/in.^{2}. Frequently, however, the pressure is expressed simply as the height of a column of liquid which produces it, such as a pressure of 2 in. of water, or a pressure of 30 in. of mercury, or a pressure of 760 mm of mercury. Whenever necessary, these values can always be converted to the more appropriate ones by means of Equation (3).

Illustrative Example. Determine the pressure at the bottom of a column of mercury 70 cm high.

The pressure can be found with the aid of Equation (3)

$$P = hdg, \tag{3}$$

with $h = 70$ cm, $d = 13.60$ gm/cm^3, and $g = 980$ cm/sec^2. Substituting these values in Equation (3), we get

$$P = 70 \text{ cm} \times 13.6 \, \frac{\text{gm}}{\text{cm}^3} \times 980 \, \frac{\text{cm}}{\text{sec}^2}$$

$$= 933{,}000 \text{ dynes/cm}^2,$$

or

$$P = 9.33 \times 10^5 \text{ dynes/cm}^2.$$

Illustrative Example. A dam is built to impound water in a reservoir. The level of the water is 20 ft above the bottom of the dam. Determine (a) the pressure 5 ft below the surface, (b) 20 ft below the surface. Assuming the face of the dam to be vertical and 60 ft across, determine (c) the force on the dam.

The pressure at any level is given by Equation (3)

$$P = hdg. \tag{3}$$

Since h is given in feet, d must be in slugs/ft^3. For the case of water

$$d = \frac{62.4}{32.17} \text{ slugs/ft}^3$$

and

$$dg = \frac{62.4}{32.17} \frac{\text{slugs}}{\text{ft}^3} \times 32.17 \frac{\text{ft}}{\text{sec}^2}$$

$$= 62.4 \text{ lb/ft}^3.$$

(a) At $h = 5$ ft,

$$P = 5 \text{ ft} \times 62.4 \frac{\text{lb}}{\text{ft}^3},$$

so that

$$P = 312.0 \frac{\text{lb}}{\text{ft}^2}.$$

(b) At $h = 20$ ft,

$$P = 20 \text{ ft} \times 62.4 \frac{\text{lb}}{\text{ft}^3}.$$

so that

$$P = 1{,}248 \text{ lb/ft}^2.$$

(c) Since the pressure varies uniformly from zero at the top of the water to 1,248 lb/ft^2 at the bottom, the force against the dam will also vary uniformly from the top of the water surface to the bottom. The total force against the wall can be determined by considering the *average* pressure to act over the entire area A of the wall. In this case the average pressure is half its largest value; that is, $P_{av} = 624$ lb/ft^2. The area A over which this pressure acts is

$$A = 20 \text{ ft} \times 60 \text{ ft}$$

$$= 1{,}200 \text{ ft}^2,$$

and the total force acting on this dam is

$$F = P_{av}A,$$

so that

$$F = 624 \frac{\text{lb}}{\text{ft}^2} \times 1{,}200 \text{ ft}^2,$$

from which $\qquad\qquad\qquad F = 748,800 \text{ lb}$

or $\qquad\qquad\qquad\qquad F = 374 \text{ tons.}$

8-5 PRESSURE IN A CONFINED LIQUID

In addition to the pressure due to its weight, a confined liquid may be subjected to an additional pressure by the application of an external force. Suppose the liquid is in a cylinder, as shown in Figure 8–4, and that a tight-fitting piston is placed on the surface of the liquid. If a force F is applied to the piston, it will remain practically in the same position since the compressibility of liquids is very small. If A is the area of the piston, this external force produces a pressure $P = F/A$ in the liquid. This additional pressure is transmitted throughout every part of the liquid and acts on all surfaces in contact with the liquid. This is sometimes known as *Pascal's principle* and may be stated as follows:

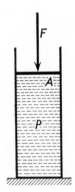

Fig. 8–4   A pressure P is produced in a confined liquid by the application of a force F on a piston of area A in contact with the liquid.

Whenever the pressure in a confined liquid is increased or diminished at any point, this change in pressure is transmitted equally throughout the entire liquid.

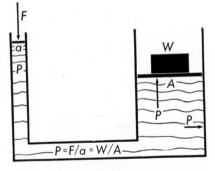

Fig. 8–5   Hydraulic press. The pressure P is the same everywhere throughout the liquid, if the pressure due to the weight of the liquid is negligible.

There are many practical applications of this principle. The operation of the hydraulic press is based upon this principle. The hydraulic press, which is sketched in Figure 8–5, consists essentially of two connected cylinders, one of small cross-sectional area a, the other of large cross-sectional area A, each fitted with a piston. A liquid, usually oil or water, is supplied to it from a reservoir. By exerting a force F on the small piston, the additional pressure produced is $P = F/a$. This pressure is transmitted throughout the liquid and hence acts on the larger piston of area A. The force that can be exerted by this piston is then PA. If this hydraulic press is designed to lift a weight W, then

$$W = PA = F\frac{A}{a},$$

or

$$\boxed{\frac{W}{F} = \frac{A}{a}.}$$ (4)

The weight that can be lifted with the aid of a hydraulic press by the application of a force F is multiplied in the ratio of the areas of the two pistons.

There are many other practical applications of Pascal's principle. Most automobiles are now equipped with hydraulic brakes. By pushing down on the brake pedal, the driver exerts a force on the piston of a cylinder containing a light oil. This force produces an increase in pressure which is transmitted equally through hollow tubes to the brakes.

8-6   BALANCED COLUMNS OF LIQUID

A convenient method for comparing the densities of two liquids is shown in Figure 8–6. Some mercury is first poured into the U-tube to pre-

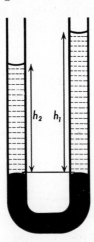

Fig. 8–6   Balanced columns of liquid of different densities; the heights of the two columns are in the inverse ratio of the densities of the liquids.

vent the two liquids from mixing. One of the liquids, say alcohol, is poured in on the right side and the other liquid, say water, is poured in on the left side and adjusted until the level of mercury is the same in both tubes.

Since the pressure on each mercury surface is now the same, we can write, from Equation (3),

$$P = h_1 d_1 g = h_2 d_2 g,$$

from which
$$\boxed{\frac{h_1}{h_2} = \frac{d_2}{d_1}.}$$
(5)

Equation (5) shows that the heights of the two columns are in the inverse ratio of their densities. Thus the alcohol will stand at a higher level than the water.

8-7 ARCHIMEDES' PRINCIPLE

The fact that some objects float in water while others sink to the bottom has been known for centuries; Archimedes (287–212 B.C.) was the first to discover the principle underlying these phenomena. To understand Archimedes' principle, it is necessary to consider the forces acting on a body totally immersed in a liquid. It will be convenient to use a glass cylinder with graduations on it indicating the volume of the liquid at different levels. Suppose that liquid is poured into the cylinder and its

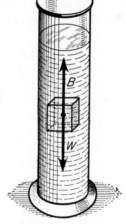

FIG. 8-7 Buoyant force on a block immersed in a liquid.

volume is noted. Now let us take some regularly shaped object of known volume V and immerse it in the liquid, as shown in Figure 8–7. The liquid will rise to a new level and will show that the body displaces a volume of liquid V equal to its own volume.

Let us now consider the forces acting on this body when it is immersed in the liquid. There is, of course, the weight W of the body pulling it down. There is also an additional force B acting upward on this body. This can be understood by imagining the volume now occupied by the body to be occupied instead by an equal volume of liquid. This volume of liquid would have been in equilibrium, which means that its weight must have been supported by the action of the rest of the liquid. This support comes from the difference in pressure between the top and bottom of this volume. Hence, no matter what material occupies this volume, there will be a force upward on it equal to the weight of the liquid displaced. This upward force B exerted by the rest of the liquid is known as the *buoyant force.*

Archimedes' principle is a generalization of the result obtained above: it states that *any object partly or completely immersed in a fluid is buoyed up by a force equal to the weight of the fluid displaced.* This principle is applicable to both liquids and gases.

The question that still remains to be answered is whether the body which is completely immersed in the liquid will go up or down. The result depends upon the difference between the weight of the body and the buoyant force due to the liquid. If the weight W of the body is greater than that of an equal volume of liquid, the resultant force on it will be downward, and the body will sink to the bottom. If its weight W is less than the weight of liquid displaced, the resultant force will be upward; the body will be forced upward, and part of its volume will rise above the surface so as to establish equilibrium. Equilibrium will be established when the weight of liquid displaced becomes equal to the weight of the body; it floats with part of it below and part of it above the surface of the liquid.

A ship afloat, for example, displaces its own weight of water. The weight of a ship is frequently expressed in terms of the weight of water it displaces. Thus there are ships of 10,000 tons displacement, 15,000 tons displacement, and so forth. Of course, as the ship is loaded with fuel, freight, and passengers, it displaces a correspondingly greater amount of water, and more of it is submerged in the water. There is usually a definite water line marked on a ship indicating the limit to which a ship may be submerged and still be safe.

A submarine is designed so that it can take water into specially built tanks to make its weight greater than the weight of the volume of water equal to its own volume. It then submerges completely and may, if necessary, rest on the bottom of the ocean. To enable the vessel to rise to the surface, water is forced out of the tanks with the aid of pumps.

Illustrative Example. A cylinder of brass 6 cm high and 4 cm^2 in cross-sectional area is suspended in water by means of a string so that its upper surface is 7 cm below the surface of the water, as shown in Figure 8–8. Determine (a) the force acting on the top of the cylinder, (b) the force acting on the bottom of the cylinder, (c) the buoyant force acting on this cylinder

(a) The force F_1 acting on the top of the cylinder is that due to the pressure of the water above it and is

$$F_1 = P_1A,$$

and, since $$P_1 = h_1dg$$

$$= 7 \text{ cm} \times 1 \frac{\text{gm}}{\text{cm}^3} \times 980 \frac{\text{cm}}{\text{sec}^2}$$

$$= 6{,}860 \frac{\text{dynes}}{\text{cm}^2},$$

therefore $$F_1 = 6{,}860 \frac{\text{dynes}}{\text{cm}^2} \times 4 \text{ cm}^2,$$

so that $$F_1 = 27{,}440 \text{ dynes}.$$

This force pushes down on the cylinder.

(b) The force F_2 acting on the bottom of the cylinder is that due to the pressure produced by the column of water above it. This column is 6 cm + 7 cm = 13 cm high.

Calling this pressure P_2, we get

$$P_2 = h_2dg$$

$$= 13 \text{ cm} \times 1 \frac{\text{gm}}{\text{cm}^3} \times 980 \frac{\text{cm}}{\text{sec}^2}$$

or $$P_2 = 12{,}740 \text{ dynes/cm}^2.$$

Since $F_2 = P_2A,$

$$F_2 = 12{,}740 \frac{\text{dynes}}{\text{cm}^2} \times 4 \text{ cm}^2,$$

or $$F_2 = 50{,}960 \text{ dynes}.$$

This force F_2 acts upward on the cylinder.

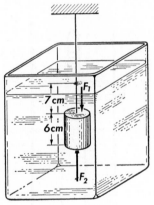

FIG. 8–8

(c) The buoyant force B is the net force upward caused by the difference in pressures in the liquid. The forces which act on the walls of the cylinder are all directed horizontally and their resultant is zero, as can be seen from the symmetry of the figure. Therefore the buoyant force is simply the difference between the two vertical forces F_1 and F_2; thus

$$B = F_2 - F_1,$$

or $$B = 50{,}960 \text{ dynes} - 27{,}440 \text{ dynes},$$

so that $$B = 23{,}520 \text{ dynes}$$

and acts upward.

It is interesting to compare this buoyant force with the weight of water displaced. The volume of the cylinder is $h \times A = 6$ cm $\times 4$ cm$^2 = 24$ cm^3. This is also the volume of water displaced. The weight of this displaced water is

$$w = mg$$

$$= dVg$$

$$= 1\,\frac{\text{gm}}{\text{cm}^3} \times 24\ \text{cm}^3 \times 980\,\frac{\text{cm}}{\text{sec}^2},$$

or $$w = 23{,}520 \text{ dynes.}$$

As expected, this is the same as the buoyant force on the cylinder.

8-8 SPECIFIC GRAVITY

From what has gone before, it appears that the ratio of the weight of a body to the weight of an equal volume of water will determine whether the body sinks or floats. This ratio is termed the *specific gravity* of the body. If its specific gravity is greater than 1, the body will sink; if it is less than 1, it will float. *The specific gravity is also the ratio of the density of the body to the density of water.* Since it is a ratio, the specific gravity is represented by a pure number and is the same no matter what system of units is used. Since the density of water in the cgs system is 1 gm/cm^3, the specific gravity of a substance has the same numerical value as its density in the cgs system.

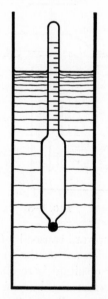

FIG. 8–9   Hydrometer.

Specific gravities of liquids are frequently measured with *hydrometers*. A hydrometer is usually made in the form of a cylinder with a bulb at one end, as shown in Figure 8–9; some mercury or lead shot is placed in this bulb so that the hydrometer will float upright at some definite level when placed in water. If this hydrometer is now placed in a denser liquid, it will rise to a higher level; if it is placed in a less dense liquid, it will sink to a lower level. The specific gravity is usually marked on a scale on the hydrometer so that it can be read directly. Some hydrometers designed for use with special liquids have completely arbitrary scales conventionally used with those liquids. An example of the latter is the so-called "proof scale" used on hydrometers to test the percentage of alcohol in liquor. On such a scale, "100 proof" means 50 per cent alcohol content.

Illustrative Example. A block of aluminum is attached to a spring balance. When suspended in air, the spring balance reads 250 gm. When the aluminum block is lowered until it is completely immersed in water, the spring balance reads 160 gm. When the aluminum block is lowered until it is completely immersed in alcohol, the spring balance reads 180 gm. Determine (a) the specific gravity of aluminum, (b) the specific gravity of alcohol.

At any one place the mass of a substance is directly proportional to its weight, and since, in determining specific gravities of substances, we need only the ratios of their weights, we can use the masses of the substances in grams instead of converting them to dynes.

(a) The buoyant force provided by the water is the difference between the weight of the aluminum block in air and its weight when immersed in water; that is,

$$B = 250 \text{ gm} - 160 \text{ gm} = 90 \text{ gm.}$$

The aluminum block thus displaces 90 gm of water. Its specific gravity S_G, which is the ratio of the weight of the aluminum to the weight of an equal volume of water, is thus

$$S_G = \frac{250}{90} = 2.78.$$

(b) The amount of alcohol displaced by the aluminum block is

$$250 \text{ gm} - 180 \text{ gm} = 70 \text{ gm.}$$

The volume of 70 gm of alcohol is the same as that of 90 gm of water, since each is equal to the volume of the aluminum block; hence the ratio of their weights is the specific gravity of the alcohol; that is,

$$S_G = \frac{70}{90} = 0.78.$$

8-9 ATMOSPHERIC PRESSURE

The atmosphere is a layer of air surrounding the earth; its thickness has been estimated at about 500 or 600 miles. Since air has weight, this layer of air produces a pressure. This pressure can be measured by an adaptation of the balanced-column method, that is, balancing the pressure due to the column of air above us against the pressure produced by a column of mercury. A simple way of doing this is to take a glass tube about 3 ft long, closed at one end, and fill it completely with clean mercury. The open end is closed temporarily by placing the thumb over it. The tube is then inverted, and the end is placed in an open dish of mercury. When the thumb is removed, the column of mercury will drop slightly and come to equilibrium at a height of about 30 in. above the open level in the dish, as in Figure 8–10. The atmosphere exerts a pressure P on the open surface of mercury in the dish, and this is transmitted to the liquid in the tube.

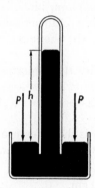

This pressure is balanced by the pressure due to the mercury in the tube at a height h above the open surface in the dish. This pressure is therefore

$$P = hdg, \qquad (3)$$

where d is the density of mercury. The instrument used for measuring atmospheric pressure is called a *barometer*.

Fig. 8–10   Mercury barometer.

At any one place, atmospheric pressure varies slightly from day to day. For scientific work, standard atmospheric pressure is defined as the pressure equivalent to that produced by a column of mercury 76 cm high at 0°C. This height corresponds to 29.92 in. The density of mercury at 0°C is, from Table 8–1, 13.60 gm/cm^3; substituting this value into Equation (3), we get

$$P = 76 \text{ cm} \times 13.60 \, \frac{\text{gm}}{\text{cm}^3} \times 980 \, \frac{\text{cm}}{\text{sec}^2},$$

from which $\qquad P = 1{,}013{,}000 \, \dfrac{\text{dynes}}{\text{cm}^2}.$ \hfill (6)

This pressure can also be expressed as

$$P = 14.70 \, \frac{\text{lb}}{\text{in.}^2} \qquad (7)$$

8-10 BAROMETERS

There are two types of barometers in general use: the liquid type of barometer using a column of mercury, and the nonliquid or *aneroid* type of barometer. The liquid type is the standard one; it is provided with a scale for measuring the height of the mercury column above the level of the mercury in the reservoir. Since the scale is permanently attached to the instrument, a leather piston and a screw are provided for adjusting the level in the reservoir to the zero on the scale.

The aneroid barometer consists of a partially evacuated pillbox made of corrugated metal, as shown in Figure 8–11. The difference between the pressure inside the chamber and the atmosphere is balanced by a steel

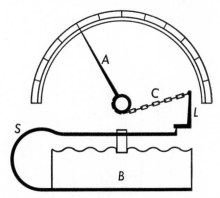

Fig. 8–11 Aneroid barometer. *B* is a box containing air at reduced pressure, *S* is a spring, *L* a lever, *C* a chain, and *A* a pointer.

spring. As the atmospheric pressure changes, the upper surface of this pillbox moves up or down. This motion is magnified by means of a lever which moves a pointer over a scale. The aneroid barometer must be calibrated by means of a standard mercury barometer.

8-11 VARIATION OF ATMOSPHERIC PRESSURE WITH ALTITUDE

As we ascend into the atmosphere, the weight of the air above the higher levels is less than at sea level. Hence the pressure recorded on the barometer is less at the higher altitude. Atmospheric pressure decreases about 1 in. for every 1,000 ft of elevation. Figure 8–12 is a graph showing the relationship between the barometric pressure, expressed in inches of mercury, and the elevation above sea level, expressed in thousands of feet. The values of the pressure are average values during winter and summer over the United States. With the aid of this graph, aneroid barometers can be calibrated in terms of altitude; when so calibrated, they are called *altimeters*.

Not only is the pressure less at higher elevations, but also, because air is compressible, its density decreases with elevation. For this reason one cannot use Equation (3) for calculating the height of the atmosphere. Other phenomena, such as the height at which meteors are observed and at which the aurora borealis (northern lights) occurs, are used for estimating the height of the atmosphere.

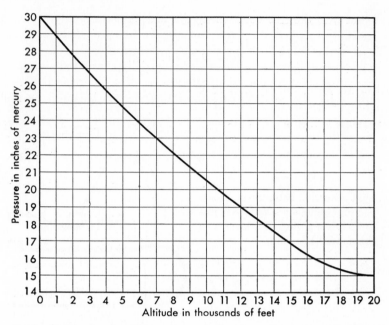

Fig. 8–12 Graph showing the pressure of the atmosphere as a function of the elevation above sea level.

8-12 COMPRESSIBILITY OF GASES: BOYLE'S LAW

The compressibility of gases was first studied by Robert Boyle (1627–1691). Suppose we have a mass of gas in a cylinder with a tight-fitting piston, on which a force F is exerted producing a pressure $P = F/A$, where A is the area of the piston, as shown in Figure 8–13. The gas will be subject to this pressure and will occupy a volume V determined by the distance of the piston from the end of the cylinder. By increasing the force on the piston to a new value F_1, the pressure on the gas will be increased to a new value P_1. It will be observed that the piston will descend, decreasing the volume of the gas. Unless precautions are taken, the temperature of the gas will also increase. This can be avoided by surrounding the cylinder with a water jacket, or else by waiting until the gas has cooled to room temperature. If the new volume V_1 is measured at the same temperature as the original volume V, it will be found that

$$\frac{V_1}{V} = \frac{P}{P_1}. \qquad \text{(8)}$$

Or, stated in words, at constant temperature the volume of a mass of gas varies inversely as the pressure.

A more convenient form for the equation is

$$P_1 V_1 = PV = \text{constant};$$ (9)

that is, *the product of the pressure and the volume of an enclosed gas at constant temperature remains constant.* This statement is known as *Boyle's law.* For example, 1.293 gm of air occupy a volume of 1,000 cm^3 at a pressure of 1 atm at 0°C. If the pressure is increased to 2 atm and the temperature kept at 0°C, then the volume occupied by this gas will be 500 cm^3.

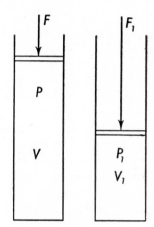

Fɪɢ. 8–13   Gas in a cylinder is compressed by increasing the force on the piston, that is, by increasing the pressure of the gas.

Since the density of a gas varies inversely with the volume, a decrease in volume means an increase in density. Hence, when the pressure in a mass of gas is increased, its density is also increased in the same ratio. Thus Boyle's law may also be written as

$$\frac{P}{P_1} = \frac{d}{d_1},$$ (10)

in which d is the density of the gas at pressure P, and d_1 is the density of the gas at pressure P_1.

In the above example, by doubling the pressure of the air, its density was doubled.

Illustrative Example.   A steel tank contains 2 cu ft of oxygen at a gauge pressure of 200 lb/in.^{2}. What volume will this gas occupy at the same temperature at atmospheric pressure?

The gauge pressure reading is the difference between the pressure of the gas in the cylinder and the pressure of the atmosphere. Hence the pressure P_1 of the oxygen in the cylinder is 214.7 lb/in.^{2}; the pressure P

of the atmosphere is taken as 14.7 lb/in.^{2}. Using Boyle's law in the form $P_1V_1 = PV$ and substituting numerical values, we get

$$214.7 \, \frac{\text{lb}}{\text{in.}^2} \times 2 \, \text{ft}^3 = 14.7 \, \frac{\text{lb}}{\text{in.}^2} \times V,$$

from which $$V = 29.2 \, \text{ft}^3.$$

8-13 ARCHIMEDES' PRINCIPLE APPLIED TO GASES

We can think of ourselves and all objects on the earth as situated at the bottom of an ocean of air. Every object in this ocean is buoyed up by a force equal to the weight of air it displaces. If this buoyant force is greater than the weight of the object, it will rise. Balloons are made by filling a flexible bag with a gas such as hydrogen or helium which is less dense than air. The balloon will rise if its total weight is less than the weight of the air it displaces. As it rises, the density of the atmosphere becomes smaller, and, if the volume of the balloon does not change, the buoyant force on it becomes smaller. The balloon will stop rising at the level at which the buoyant force equals the weight of the balloon.

As the balloon rises, the pressure of the gas inside the flexible bag becomes greater than the atmospheric pressure. This difference in pressure causes the bag to expand, displacing a greater quantity of air and increasing the buoyant force. For the balloon to descend, valves must be provided to allow some of the gas to escape so that the volume of the balloon is decreased. It is quite a common practice to send up a set of instruments attached to one or more small balloons. Meteorological stations send up radiosondes regularly. These radiosondes contain instruments which measure the pressure, temperature, and relative humidity of the atmosphere, and a radio transmitter which sends signals to a receiving station on the ground. They rise until the difference between the pressures inside and outside the balloon causes the bag to burst. When this happens, a parachute attached to the instrument box opens so that the radiosonde falls slowly. Most of the instrument boxes are later recovered. Some of these balloons have gone up to heights of 130,000 ft, while manned balloons have gone up as high as 72,000 ft.

8-14 PRESSURE GAUGES: MANOMETERS

Of the many different types of pressure gauges in use, two simple ones will be described here. The one known as the *open-tube manometer* is illustrated in Figure 8–14 and consists essentially of a bent tube with both arms vertical. One end A is open to the atmosphere, and the other end B

is connected to the vessel in which the pressure is to be measured. The tube is partially filled with a liquid of density d. When the top of the column of liquid in the open tube A is at a height h above the level of the column of liquid in tube B, the pressure P in the vessel connected to B is

$$P = P_a + hdg, \qquad \text{(11)}$$

where P_a is the atmospheric pressure. If the level of the liquid column in B is higher than that in A, the pressure in the vessel connected to B is less than atmospheric pressure by an amount hdg. Liquids of different densities can be used for different pressure ranges.

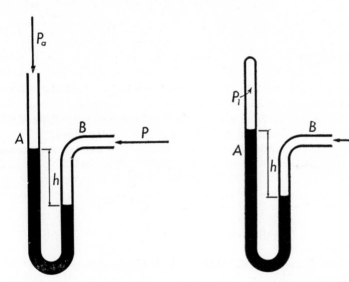

FIG. 8–14   Open-tube manometer.   FIG. 8–15   Closed-tube manometer.

The second type of pressure gauge used for higher pressures, is known as the *closed-tube manometer* and is sketched in Figure 8–15. The end of the tube A is closed, and the space between the top of the liquid level and the end of the tube usually contains a gas. The pressure in the vessel connected to B is then

$$P = hdg + P_1, \qquad \text{(12)}$$

where h is the difference in levels of the liquid columns in A and B, and P_1 is the pressure of the gas above the column in A. The value of P_1 has to be determined by experiment, and the gauge is calibrated to yield the pressure P for any level of the liquid column.

1. Using Archimedes' principle, prove that the specific gravity of a solid is equal to the weight of the solid divided by its apparent "loss of weight" in water.

2. A steel battleship is sunk in the ocean where the depth is about 5 miles. How far down will the ship go?

3. Make a guess as to the weight of the air contained in your classroom. Check this guess by calculating the weight of the air in the room.

4. Consider a cube placed in a liquid with one surface at some distance h below the level of the liquid. Calculate the force on the top surface and on the bottom surface of the cube and show that the buoyant force is equal to the weight of the liquid displaced no matter what the value of h is.

5. Compare the highest altitude reached by a balloon with the estimated height of the atmosphere.

6. Explain why a balloon can float at a definite level in the atmosphere while a submarine cannot float at a definite level below the surface of the ocean.

7. Why is a radiosonde sent up with many small balloons instead of with one large balloon.?

8. Make an estimate of the surface area of your body and calculate the total force exerted by the atmosphere on you.

9. A physician measuring a patient's blood pressure notes it as 125–88. What do these numbers mean in terms of the pressure of the blood?

10. A man holds a bottle of club soda in his hand and watches the formation of a bubble of gas in the liquid. He drops the bottle. Will the bubble rise in the liquid while it is falling with an acceleration g? Explain your answer.

11. A glass tumbler is filled to the brim with water, and a thin aluminum disk is placed on top of the glass. The glass is inverted, the disk being held in place. The hand supporting the disk is then removed. The disk remains pressed against the glass. Explain. Try this experiment; use any light material for a cover if aluminum is not available.

12. Water is poured into a glass tumbler until it is about three fourths full. A thin aluminum disk is placed over the glass, and the glass is inverted. If the disk is no longer supported by the hand, will it fall down? Try this experiment using a light disk of any material if aluminum is not available.

13. An empty glass tumbler is inverted and pushed down into a dish of water. Will the water level inside the tumbler be the same as outside the glass? Explain. Try this experiment.

1. A block of metal weighs 12 lb in air, 10.5 lb when immersed in water, and 10.8 lb when immersed in a certain liquid. Determine (a) the density of the metal and (b) the density of the liquid.

2. A metal sphere whose mass is 42 gm is attached to one arm of an equal-arm balance by means of a string. When the sphere is completely immersed in water a mass of 28 gm is sufficient to balance it. Determine (a) the volume of the sphere and (b) the density of the metal.

3. A block of wood whose mass is 90 gm has a hole drilled in it removing 8 gm of wood. The specific gravity of the wood is 0.6. The hole in the wood is filled with lead. Will this block sink or float when placed in water?

4. A raft is made in the form of a rectangular box 8 ft by 10 ft by 4 ft deep. The raft weighs 2,500 lb. (a) How deep will this raft go when placed in fresh water? (b) What load can this raft carry without sinking? (c) What is the total force on the bottom of the raft when so loaded?

5. A beaker partially filled with water is placed on a scale pan and found to have a mass of 450 gm. A string is attached to a stone and held so that the stone is completely submerged in the water but does not touch the beaker at any point. The scale now reads 550 gm. When the string is released and the stone rests on the bottom of the beaker, the scale reads 620 gm. Determine (a) the mass of the stone, (b) the density of the stone, and (c) the tension in the string.

6. A cube of iron 4 cm on edge is placed in a dish of mercury. The density of this iron is 7.5 gm/cm^3. (a) How much of this cube is immersed in the mercury? (b) If water is poured over the mercury to a depth of 5 cm, what will be the depth of the iron in the mercury?

7. A piece of concrete weighing 150 lb has a specific gravity of 2.5. A block of wood of specific gravity 0.5 is to be fastened to the concrete block so that, when placed in water, they will both float almost completely submerged. What is the maximum weight of wood that may be used?

8. A glass tube 130 cm long and closed at one end is sunk, open end down, to the bottom of the ocean. When it is drawn up, a marker indicates that the water had risen to a point 5 cm from the top. Calculate the depth of the ocean at this spot.

9. A vertical cylinder, closed at the bottom, contains air at room temperature. A piston weighing 30 lb is placed in the open end and comes to rest with its face 12 in. from the bottom of the cylinder. The area of the piston face is 100 sq in. A load of 900 lb is now placed on the piston. Determine how far above the bottom of the cylinder the piston face is when equilibrium is established.

10. A bubble of air rising from the bottom of a lake has four times as large a volume when near the surface as it had at the bottom. If the barometric pressure is 76 cm, how deep is the lake?

11. An airtight bag is filled with air while lying on the shore of a lake. It is then lowered under water by means of a rock tied to it with a string. At what depth will the volume be one half as much as it was before immersion?

12. A U-tube contains mercury at the bottom. Glycerin is poured into one arm to a height of 20 cm. How high a column of water must be poured into the other arm to bring the mercury to the same level in both arms?

13. What is the atmospheric pressure in dynes per square centimeter when the barometer reading is 77 cm?

14. As an airplane rises, its barometer reading drops from 30 in. to 16 in. Determine the altitude of the plane above its starting point.

15. The pistons of a hydraulic press have diameters of 2 in. and 10 in., respectively. A force of 30 lb is applied to the smaller piston. (a) What is the pressure developed by the application of this force? (b) What weight can be lifted by the larger piston as a result of this force?

16. A glass tube 1 cm² in cross-sectional area and 40 cm long is fitted into the top of a cylindrical bottle 20 cm high and 10 cm² in cross-sectional area. The bottle and tube are filled with water. (a) What is the mass of water in this system? (b) What is the pressure on the top surface of the bottle? (c) What is the pressure on the bottom of the bottle? (d) What is the force exerted by the liquid on the bottom of the bottle?

17. Hoover Dam is 1,180 ft long and 726 ft high. (a) What is the pressure at the bottom of the dam when the reservoir behind it is full? (b) Assuming the face of the dam to be a plane rectangle, determine the force pushing against the dam.

18. A diving bell is a cylinder open only at one end; it is submerged in water with its open end down, and it is large enough so that men can work in it. If a diving bell is 6 ft in diameter and 9 ft high and is submerged so that the lower end is 24 ft below the surface of the water, how high will the water rise in it?

19. An open-tube manometer containing water has one end connected to a city gas supply outlet. The difference in levels in the two arms of the tube is 2.0 in. Determine the pressure of the gas.

20. The gauge pressure of the air in a tire is 30 lb/in.². If the volume of the tire is 1 cu ft, what volume will this air occupy at atmospheric pressure? Assume atmospheric pressure to be 15 lb/in.².

21. The gauge pressure of the air in a tire is 24 lb/in.². Additional air is put into this tire until the gauge pressure is 30 lb/in.². Assuming the volume of the tire remains the same, determine the change in density of the air in the tire. Assume atmospheric pressure is 15 lb/in.².

22. A balloon is partly inflated with 4,000 cu ft of hydrogen when the temperature is 0°C. (a) Determine the buoyant force on the balloon. (b) What is the total load that the balloon can lift? (c) If the balloon rises 11,000 ft above sea level, determine the new volume of the hydrogen, assuming the balloon capable of this expansion.

9

Fluids in Motion

9-1 STEADY FLOW OF LIQUID

When a liquid flows through a pipe in such a way that it completely fills the pipe and as much liquid enters one end of the pipe as leaves at the other end in the same time, then the liquid is said to *flow at a steady rate*. At any point in the liquid, the motion does not change with time; as a small volume of liquid leaves that point, another particle comes to it and moves with the same velocity that the preceding particle had there. The path of any particle of liquid as it moves through the pipe is known as a *streamline*. We can map the flow of liquid through the pipe by drawing a series of stream-lines following the paths of the particles of liquid, as shown in Figure 9–1; these lines will be close together where the liquid is moving rapidly and farther apart in regions of the pipe where the liquid is moving slowly.

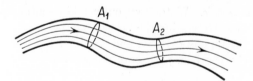

FIG. 9–1   Streamlines of a liquid flowing through a pipe at a steady rate.

Since the liquid is incompressible and there are no places in the pipe in which the liquid can be stored, the volume of liquid which flows through any cross-sectional area perpendicular to the streamlines in any interval of time must be the same everywhere in the pipe. The small volume of liquid ΔV, which flows through a small distance Δs past a point where the cross-sectional area of the pipe is A, is

$$\Delta V = A \, \Delta s.$$

If this flow takes place in a short time interval Δt, then the rate of flow Q, or the quantity of liquid which flows through this area per unit time, is

$$Q = \frac{\Delta V}{\Delta t},$$

so that
$$Q = \frac{A \, \Delta s}{\Delta t}$$

or
$$Q = Av, \tag{1}$$

where $v = \Delta s / \Delta t$ is the velocity of the liquid at this point.

Consider two typical areas A_1 and A_2 perpendicular to the streamlines. The volume of liquid Q passing through area A_1 in unit time is simply

$$Q = A_1 v_1,$$

where v_1 is the velocity of the liquid at this point. Similarly the volume of liquid passing through A_2 in unit time is

$$Q = A_2 v_2.$$

Since these two quantities must be equal for steady flow, we have

$$Q = A_1 v_1 = A_2 v_2, \tag{2}$$

from which
$$\boxed{\frac{v_1}{v_2} = \frac{A_2}{A_1}.} \tag{3}$$

This equation states that the velocity of the liquid at any point in the pipe is inversely proportional to the cross-sectional area of the pipe. The liquid will be moving slowly where the area is large and will be moving rapidly where the area is small.

Illustrative Example. Water flows out of a horizontal pipe at the steady rate of 2 cu ft/min. Determine the velocity of the water at a point where the diameter of the pipe is (a) 1 in. and (b) $\frac{1}{2}$ in.

The area A_1 of the 1-in. portion of the pipe is

$$A_1 = \frac{\pi \times 1}{4 \times 144} \text{ ft}^2 = 0.0055 \text{ ft}^2,$$

and the area of the $\frac{1}{2}$-in. pipe is

$$A_2 = 0.0014 \text{ ft}^2;$$

also
$$Q = 2 \frac{\text{ft}^3}{\text{min}} = \frac{2}{60} \frac{\text{ft}^3}{\text{sec}}.$$

Using Equation (1), we get for the velocity through the 1-in. pipe

$$\frac{2}{60} \frac{\text{ft}^3}{\text{sec}} = 0.0055 \text{ ft}^2 \times v_1,$$

from which
$$v_1 = 6.10 \frac{\text{ft}}{\text{sec}}.$$

From Equation (3), the velocity of the water through the $\frac{1}{2}$-in. pipe is four times that through the 1-in. pipe, so that

$$v_2 = 24.4 \, \frac{\text{ft}}{\text{sec}} \, .$$

9-2   KINETIC ENERGY OF A LIQUID

A quantity of liquid of mass m moving with velocity v possesses kinetic energy $\frac{1}{2}mv^2$. It acquires this energy as a result of work done on it by external forces. For example, consider the case of a liquid flowing out of a tank which is filled to a height h and open to the atmosphere, as illustrated in Figure 9–2. Suppose that the liquid flows out of the bottom of the tank

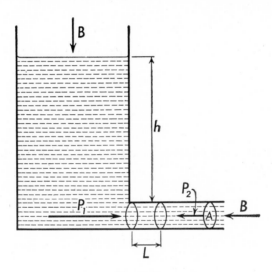

FIG. 9–2

through a horizontal pipe of cross-sectional area A. Let us focus our attention on a small volume of liquid V which has just entered this pipe. There are two forces acting on this small cylinder of liquid: one to the right, owing to the pressure p_1 of the liquid in the tank, and the other to the left, because of the pressure p_2 of the liquid in the pipe. Since each of these pressures acts on an area A, the resultant force F acting on this cylinder is

$$F = (p_1 - p_2)A. \tag{4}$$

Suppose that the length of this cylinder of liquid is L. The work done by the force in pushing this liquid from the tank into the pipe is

$$\mathcal{W} = FL = (p_1 - p_2)AL. \tag{5}$$

But AL is the volume V of the liquid. Hence

$$\mathcal{W} = (p_1 - p_2)V. \tag{6}$$

Thus the work done in forcing the liquid into the pipe is the difference of pressure multiplied by the volume of the liquid. It is this work which gives the liquid its kinetic energy; hence we may write

$$(p_1 - p_2)V = \tfrac{1}{2}mv^2. \tag{7}$$

In the above case, the pressures can be evaluated. The pressure p_2 is due to the pressure of the atmosphere B on the open end of the pipe, while the pressure p_1 is due to the pressure of the atmosphere B plus that due to the height h of the liquid above the pipe. The difference between these two pressures is

$$p_1 - p_2 = hdg, \tag{8}$$

where d is the density of the liquid. Putting this into Equation (7), we get

$$hdgV = \tfrac{1}{2}mv^2; \tag{9}$$

hence
$$\boxed{v^2 = 2gh.} \tag{10}$$

Equation (10), sometimes called *Torricelli's theorem*, states that the speed of the liquid coming out of a tank filled to a height h above the opening is exactly the same as if the liquid had fallen through the same height. If the pipe were provided with an outlet directed vertically upward, the

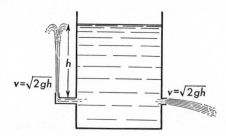

Fig. 9-3   Velocity of efflux of a liquid depends only upon the height of the liquid above the orifice.

liquid would rise to a height h equal to the level of the liquid in the tank (see Figure 9–3). In this discussion we have neglected the effect of friction in the pipe. If friction, or rather viscosity, is taken into consideration, the velocity with which the liquid comes out of the tank will be less than that given by Equation (10).

9-3 BERNOULLI'S THEOREM

There is a very important relationship between the pressure at any point in a moving fluid and the velocity of the fluid at that point. This relationship can be derived most conveniently by considering the steady flow of an incompressible liquid through a frictionless horizontal pipe of varying cross section, illustrated in Figure 9–4. The path of a small volume

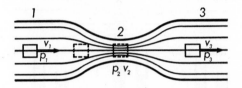

FIG. 9–4   Steady flow of a liquid through a nonuniform horizontal pipe.

of liquid is along a streamline. As it moves from region 1 to region 2 along the streamline, its velocity increases from v_1 to v_2; its kinetic energy therefore also increases. If the pressure in region 1 is p_1 and the pressure in region 2 is p_2, the work done on this small volume V is, from Equation (6),

$$\mathcal{W} = (p_1 - p_2)V.$$

Neglecting the small change in level along the streamline, we find that the work done by this pressure difference produces the change in kinetic energy of this small volume of liquid. If m is the mass of this small volume, its kinetic energy at position 1 is $\frac{1}{2}mv_1^2$ and at position 2 is $\frac{1}{2}mv_2^2$, so that the

change in kinetic energy $= \frac{1}{2}mv_2^2 - \frac{1}{2}mv_1^2.$

Equating this to the work done on this small volume, we get

$$(p_1 - p_2)V = \tfrac{1}{2}mv_2^2 - \tfrac{1}{2}mv_1^2,$$

or $\qquad\qquad\qquad p_1 - p_2 = \tfrac{1}{2}dv_2^2 - \tfrac{1}{2}dv_1^2,$

since d is m/V.
Rearranging terms, we get

$$\boxed{p_1 + \tfrac{1}{2}dv_1^2 = p_2 + \tfrac{1}{2}dv_2^2.} \qquad\qquad \text{(11)}$$

Equation (11) gives the relationship between the pressure and the velocity at any point along a streamline of a fluid in steady motion. The quantity $p + \frac{1}{2}dv^2$ remains constant at constant level. This is a mathematical statement of *Bernoulli's theorem.* An analysis of this equation shows that in the region where the velocity is small, the pressure is large; while in the region where the velocity is large, the pressure is small. This theorem can be verified experimentally by attaching pressure gauges or manometers at various points along the pipe. Figure 9–5 shows three pressure gauges: at points 1 and 3, the pressures are the same since the cross-sectional areas are equal; at point 2, the pressure is less than at 1 and 3 since the area here is smaller and the kinetic energy of the water is greater.

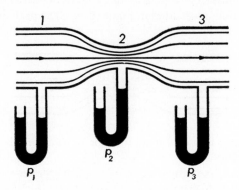

FIG. 9–5   The pressure in the narrow portion of the pipe is less than in the wide portion.

Although Bernoulli's theorem has been derived for the steady flow of an incompressible liquid, it can be applied to the steady flow of gases. There are many practical devices whose operation is based upon Bernoulli's theorem. Among these are the aspirator or filter pump, the atomizer or sprayer, and the rotor ship. Of the highest importance is its application to the design of the wings of an airplane so that the pressure on the top of the wing will be less than on the bottom of the wing, thus providing the force necessary to sustain the airplane in flight.

Illustrative Example. The horizontal pipe sketched in Figure 9–6 is known as a *Venturi tube;* the constricted region is known as the throat of

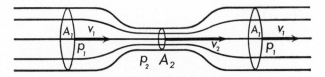

FIG. 9–6   The Venturi tube.

the tube. Suppose that water is flowing through a Venturi tube at the rate of 100 cu ft/min. The pressure in the wide portion is 15 lb/sq in. and the diameter is 6 in. Determine the pressure in the throat of the tube if its diameter is 3 in.

The area of the tube A_1 is

$$A_1 = \frac{\pi}{16} \text{ ft}^2.$$

The area of the throat is

$$A_2 = \frac{\pi}{64} \text{ ft}^2.$$

The velocity v_1 in the tube is, from Equation (1),

$$\frac{100 \text{ ft}^3}{60 \text{ sec}} = \frac{\pi}{16} \text{ ft}^2 \times v_1,$$

so that

$$v_1 = 8.5 \frac{\text{ft}}{\text{sec}},$$

and the velocity in the throat of the tube is

$$v_2 = 4 \times 8.5 \frac{\text{ft}}{\text{sec}} = 34 \frac{\text{ft}}{\text{sec}}.$$

In applying Equation (11), it is essential that a consistent set of units be used. Now

$$p_1 = 15 \frac{\text{lb}}{\text{in.}^2} = 15 \times 144 \frac{\text{lb}}{\text{ft}^2} = 2{,}160 \frac{\text{lb}}{\text{ft}^2},$$

and

$$d = \frac{62.4}{32} \frac{\text{slugs}}{\text{ft}^3}.$$

Solving for p_2 from Equation (11), we get

$$p_2 = p_1 + \tfrac{1}{2} dv_1^2 - \tfrac{1}{2} dv_2^2.$$

Substituting numerical values, we get

$$p_2 = 2{,}160 + \tfrac{1}{2} \frac{62.4}{32} \times (8.5)^2 - \tfrac{1}{2} \frac{62.4}{32} \times (34)^2,$$

$$p_2 = 2{,}160 + 70 - 1{,}130 = 1{,}100 \frac{\text{lb}}{\text{ft}^2},$$

or

$$p_2 = \frac{1{,}100 \text{ lb}}{144 \text{ in.}^2} = 7.64 \frac{\text{lb}}{\text{in.}^2}.$$

The Venturi tube has several practical applications. If manometers or pressure gauges are placed at the throat and at the wide portion of the tube, the difference in pressures between these two regions and a knowledge of the cross-sectional areas can be used to measure the rate of flow of a fluid. Used in this way, it is called a *Venturi meter*. Wind tunnels designed for experiments with models of airplanes are also built in the shape of a Venturi tube (see Figure 9–7).

Fig. 9–7 Supersonic wind tunnel. Wind velocities from 1.5 to 5 times the velocity of sound can be obtained by the use of appropriate nozzles. The photograph shows the wind tunnel with the nozzle installed which can produce a wind velocity 3 times the velocity of sound; the near side wall not yet installed. (Courtesy of Supersonics Laboratory, Aeronautical Engineering Department, Princeton University; sponsored by the Office of Naval Research.)

9-4 LIFT OF AN AIRPLANE

With a properly designed wing surface, the motion of the air will be along streamlines in the neighborhood of the surface of the wing. This is more likely to be the case when the angle between the wing and its direction of motion through the air is small; this is usually called a low *angle of attack*. The motion of the air past a wing at different angles of attack is illustrated in the photographs reproduced in Figure 9–8. Smoke was used to make the flow of air visible. The streamlines above the wing are crowded together closely because the air is moving more rapidly than below the wing. According to Bernoulli's theorem, since the air is moving more rapidly above the wing than below, the pressure above the wing is less than the pressure below it. The pressure below the wing is usually the pressure of the undisturbed atmosphere at that level, while the pressure above the wing is less than atmospheric. It is this difference in pressure which supplies the lifting force when the angle of attack is low.

Fig. 9–8   Smoke is used in the NACA smoke tunnel at Langley Field, Virginia, to make the flow of air visible, as illustrated in these photographs. Note the smoothness of the air flow in the lower pictures. When the angle of attack has been increased to 10°, the air flow begins to separate from the upper surface of the airfoil (center view); and when the angle is increased to 30°, the flow separates completely from the upper surface. Turbulence behind the trailing edge of the airfoil may be observed in this picture. (Reproduced from *Journal of Applied Physics*, August, 1943, with permission from the National Advisory Committee for Aeronautics.)

At higher angles of attack, the streamlines do not follow the wing surfaces very closely, and turbulence of the air sets in, particularly near the rear of the wing. Wherever turbulence sets in, the pressure is not reduced below atmospheric pressure. At very high angles of attack, the wing acts more nearly like a sail. The lifting effect in this case is due to the force exerted on the wing as the air is deflected from it.

An idea of the magnitude of the lifting effect caused by the streamline motion of the air at low angles of attack can be obtained from the following data. The measured value of the pressure on the top of a wing was found to be 14.55 lb/sq in. while the pressure on the bottom of the wing was 14.70 lb/sq in. The difference is 0.15 lb/sq in. or 21.6 lb/sq ft. If the wing has a spread of 40 ft and a width of 8 ft or an area of 320 sq ft, the lifting force would be 6,900 lb.

One of the factors determining the lift of an airplane is the speed of the air relative to the plane and is called the *air speed*. In taking off, the airplane should be headed into the wind to provide greater air speed. The angle of attack is very small while the plane is running along the ground, so that the entire lift is due to the Bernoulli effect. Once the plane is off the ground, the angle of attack is increased to provide a higher rate of climb. The lift in this case is due partly to the Bernoulli effect and partly to the force of the air against the wing as it is deflected from its lower surface.

9-5   PITCHING A CURVE BALL

Bernoulli's theorem can be used to explain the curving of a baseball. When the ball is pitched it not only is thrown forward but also is given a spin. Suppose that the ball is thrown to the left and given a spin in a clockwise direction, as shown in Figure 9–9. If it were not for the spin,

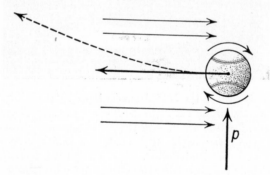

Fig. 9–9   Curving of the path of a baseball is produced by giving it a spin when pitching it.

the air speed would be the same at the top and bottom and would be equal in magnitude and opposite in direction to the velocity of the ball. But, because of the spin of the ball, the air near its surface is forced around in the direction of spin. This means that the speed of air on top of the ball is greater than at the bottom. This will create a difference in pressure between top and bottom, with the greater pressure on the bottom. There will thus be a force upward causing the ball to deviate from the usual path. If we are looking down on the ball as it moves forward, this force will produce a deflection to the right. If the direction of spin is reversed, the ball will be deflected to the left.

9-6 FLUID FRICTION; VISCOSITY

When a fluid, either a liquid or a gas, is set into motion, different parts of the fluid move with different velocities. For example, if a jar of water is tilted so that the water starts flowing out, the top layer of the water moves over the lower portion of water. Just as there is friction when one surface of a solid slides over another, so there is friction when one layer of a fluid slides over another. This friction in fluids is called *viscosity*. When a fluid flows through a cylindrical pipe, for example, the part of the fluid which is in contact with the pipe adheres to it and remains at rest. We may think of the rest of the fluid as divided into concentric cylindrical layers. The cylindrical layer next to the stationary layer of fluid moves slowly past it. The next inner cylindrical layer moves with greater velocity, and the velocity of each succeeding inner layer increases as we go toward the center. A difference in pressure between the two ends of the pipe is needed to maintain a steady flow through it and oppose the force due to the viscosity of the fluid. One method for measuring the viscosity of the fluid is to determine the volume of fluid flowing in unit time through a pipe of given diameter under a known difference of pressure. The greater the viscosity, the smaller is the volume of fluid flowing through the pipe in unit time. For example, glycerin at 20°C has a viscosity 850 times that of water at 20°C, while the viscosity of water is about 55 times that of air at 20°C. There is, however, one important distinction between the viscosity of a liquid and that of a gas: the viscosity of a liquid decreases with a rise in temperature, while the viscosity of a gas increases with a rise in temperature.

The resistance experienced by a solid in moving through a fluid is due essentially to the viscosity of the fluid. A certain amount of the fluid adheres to the surface of the solid and moves with it. There is relative motion between this layer of fluid and the layer adjacent to it. The latter, in turn, moves relative to the next outer layer, and so on until we come to a layer of fluid which remains at rest. An additional cause of the resistance experienced by objects moving through fluids is the turbulence set up in the fluid. In this case the fluid can no longer be considered as made up of layers; these layers are broken up, forming eddies and sometimes waves.

9-7 THE SIPHON

A siphon is a bent tube used for transferring a liquid from one vessel to another one at a lower level. Figure 9–10 shows a siphon in operation.

Liquid is flowing through the bent tube from A to B in the direction of the arrows and will continue to flow as long as there is a difference in levels between A and B. To understand the operation of the siphon let us imagine that A and B are at the same level and that the bent tube is filled with liquid; in this case there will be no flow of liquid. If the level of B is now lowered so that it is at a distance H from the top of the bend while the level

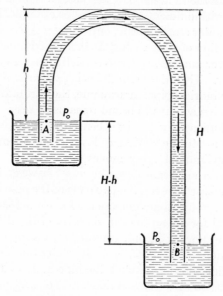

Fig. 9-10   Operation of a siphon.

of A remains at a distance h below the top, liquid will flow from left to right. To prevent the flow, we would have to supply an external force on the lower surface sufficient to produce an additional pressure equal to that produced by a column of liquid of height H-h. But this is simply the difference in the lengths of the columns of liquids in the two arms of the siphon. When there is no additional external force, liquid flows through the siphon because the column of liquid in the longer arm, being heavier than the column of liquid in the shorter arm, pulls the liquid over the bend in the tube.

Another way of considering the action of a siphon is to imagine it already full of liquid and a valve placed at the highest point to stop the flow of liquid. Consider the pressures on the two sides of this valve. The pressure P_L on the left side will be that due to the atmosphere less that due to the column of liquid of height h, or

$$P_L = P_0 - hdg,$$

where d is the density of the liquid. Similarly the pressure P_R on the right side of the valve will be

$$P_R = P_0 - Hdg.$$

The difference in pressure on the two sides of the valve will be

$$P_L - P_R = (H - h)dg, \qquad (12)$$

producing a force towards the right. If the valve is opened or removed, the liquid will flow from left to right and will continue to flow as long as there is a difference in pressure.

There are various methods for starting the motion of a liquid through a siphon. They all depend upon getting a continuous column of liquid from A over the bend of the siphon toward B. One method is first to fill the tube with the same kind of liquid that is to be transferred, then, keeping the two ends closed, to invert the siphon and put the end of one tube in one vessel, and then to open both ends. Another method of starting the operation of a siphon is to insert one arm of the siphon in the liquid and then to reduce the pressure at the other end by an amount sufficient to have the liquid forced over the bend from A toward B.

It will be noted that the pressure of the atmosphere P_0 does not appear in Equation (12). Hence, once the siphon has been started, it should be possible to keep it operating even if P_0 is reduced to practically zero. The column on the right, being heavier than that on the left, can pull the liquid over the bend, providing the cohesive forces between the molecules of the liquid are sufficiently large and there are no bubbles of air or vapor to break the column. In ordinary operation, liquids, particularly water, are never free of air bubbles so that it would be practically impossible to operate such a siphon in a vacuum.

9-8 LIQUID PUMPS

There are several different designs of pumps used for transferring liquids from one container to another. One of the simplest is the *lift pump* sketched in Figure 9–11, commonly used for pumping water out of a well. It consists of a metal barrel or cylinder C and a narrower, long cylindrical pipe D which extends into the water. There is a valve A at the bottom of cylinder C and another valve B in the piston P. At the start of the operations, the piston is near the bottom of the cylinder. By pushing down on the lever L, the piston P is raised. The volume of the air between P and A is increased and its pressure decreased below that of the atmosphere; the valve B is kept closed by the pressure of the atmosphere above it. As the pressure above A is reduced, water is pushed through it into cylinder C by the pressure of the atmosphere on the water in the well. On the down-stroke, any air remaining below the piston is compressed and goes out through valve B. As the piston moves through the water, the water flows through valve B, valve A being kept closed by the weight of water above it. At the end of the downward stroke, most of the water is above the piston. On the upward stroke, the water above the piston is lifted and flows out

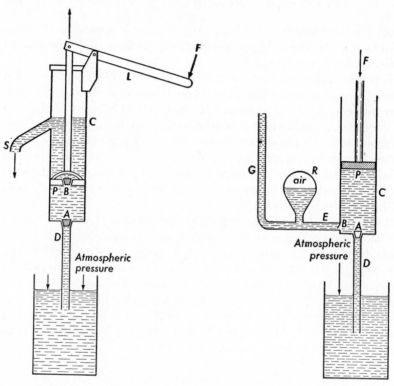

FIG. 9–11 Lift pump.   FIG. 9–12 Force pump.

through the spout S; at the same time, atmospheric pressure forces water up the pipe D and through valve A. On the downstroke of the piston, the water flows through valve B; on the upstroke, it is lifted and flows out of the spout S again.

Since the water is pushed through valve A by the pressure of the atmosphere, the height of this valve above the level of the water in the well should not exceed about 30 ft; that is, it should be less than the height of a column of water that can be supported by atmospheric pressure. Once the water gets above valve A, the height to which it can be lifted depends upon the length of the barrel C.

The *force pump* sketched in Figure 9–12 differs from the lift pump in that the piston P is solid and the valve B is now located near the bottom of the cylinder, separating it from the exit tube E. During the upward stroke of the piston, water is forced through valve A into the cylinder by the pressure of the atmosphere on the water in the well; valve B remains closed. On the downward stroke of the piston, valve A is closed, and water is forced through valve B into the exit tube E and into the vertical pipe G. The height to which water can be raised depends upon the pressure produced on the downstroke of the piston. An air chamber R is usually attached to the exit tube for smoother operation of the pump. Water entering this chamber traps some air in it and compresses it. On the upstroke of the piston, when valve B is closed, there is sufficient pressure inside R to force the water out of it and into the vertical pipe G. On the downward stroke, some water again enters this air chamber, compressing the air once more. It is then sent into the pipeline on the upstroke of the piston. The flow of water in G is thus fairly continuous.

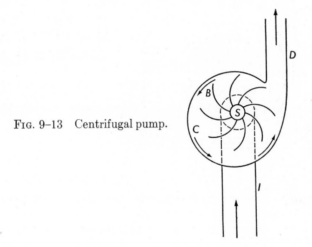

Fig. 9–13   Centrifugal pump.

In the *centrifugal pump* sketched in Figure 9–13, a set of curved blades B are attached to a shaft S and rotated by means of an electric motor. The liquid is whirled around by the rotating blades into the outer part of the chamber C and out through the discharge pipe D. As the liquid moves to the outer part of the chamber C, the pressure near the center is reduced, permitting liquid at lower pressure to flow in through the intake pipe I. There are no valves in the centrifugal pump. Their simplicity and ease of operation have given centrifugal pumps wide use wherever a large, continuous supply of liquid is needed. Centrifugal pumps are also widely used for pumping gases, for example, as blowers for furnaces and as exhaust fans in vacuum cleaners.

9-9 VACUUM PUMPS

A great deal of modern scientific and industrial progress can be traced to the development of good, high-speed vacuum pumps. These can be classified into two general types, mechanical pumps and molecular or diffusion pumps. The latter will be considered in Chapter 15. A common type of mechanical vacuum pump, known as a rotary oil pump, is sketched schematically in Figure 9–14. *D* is a cylindrical drum which is mounted

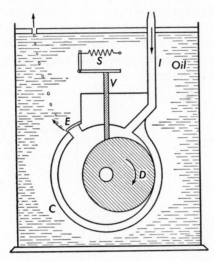

Fig. 9–14   Rotary oil pump.

eccentrically (off center) and rotates within the larger cylinder *C*, making contact with it along its inner surface. The vessel to be pumped out is connected to the intake pipe *I*. A vane *V* is pressed against the rotating drum by means of a spring and serves to separate the regions of high and low pressure. The whole mechanism is immersed in oil, which serves as both a seal and a lubricant.

As the drum *D* rotates, the space near the intake pipe *I* is increased in volume, while the space near the exhaust valve *E* is decreased in volume. Thus the pressure on one side is reduced so that air flows from the vessel to be exhausted into the intake pipe, while the pressure on the other side is increased and the entrapped air is pushed out through the exhaust valve *E*. Pressures as low as 0.001 mm of mercury can be produced fairly rapidly with these rotary pumps. When much lower pressures are needed, as in the production of x-ray tubes and other high-vacuum devices, these rotary pumps are used as *fore pumps* in connection with diffusion pumps (see Chapter 15).

9-10   THE CENTRIFUGE

A centrifuge is a machine designed to rotate a liquid at high speed and thus produce a more rapid separation of the particles suspended in the liquid than would occur if it were allowed to stand and be acted upon by the earth's gravitational field. In some types of centrifuge, such as the cream separator, the separated constituents flow out continuously during its operation. In other types, the rotational motion is stopped after a certain time has elapsed, and the separated constituents are then removed.

To understand the operation of a centrifuge, consider a particle of mass m and weight W placed in a liquid; this particle will experience a buoyant force B equal to the weight of liquid displaced by it. If m_0 is the mass of the displaced liquid, the buoyant force $B = m_0 g$, and, since $W = mg$, the difference between these forces is

$$W - B = (m - m_0)g. \tag{13}$$

If W is greater than B, the particle will move down in the direction of g. Its motion will be opposed by a resisting force owing to the viscosity of the liquid. To increase the motion downward, it will be necessary to increase the difference between W and B. An examination of Equation (13) shows that the only way this can be done is to put the system in a region where g has a larger value. In our discussion of circular motion (Section 6–4), we showed that a particle in a rotating system experiences an effect equivalent to that of a gravitational field directed away from the center;

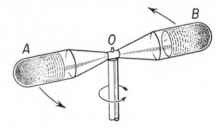

FIG. 9–15 The centrifuge. Tubes A and B are whirled around in a circular path about an axis through O. Particles of greatest density go to ends of tubes farthest removed from O.

this effect is an acceleration which is independent of the mass of the particle. The magnitude of this acceleration is $a = v^2/R$, where v is the speed of the particle and R is its distance from the axis of rotation. By making the speed v large enough, we can produce any desired value of a equivalent in effect to cg, where c is a number greater than one. Hence, if a liquid is put into a tube such as that shown in Figure 9–15 and the tube is rotated at high speed, the particles in the liquid will separate out very rapidly. Those particles which are denser than the liquid will be found at the bottom, that is, farthest removed from the axis of rotation O. Those particles which are less dense than the liquid will be found near the top of the liquid, that is, closest to the axis of rotation.

Illustrative Example. A liquid containing some solid particles is poured into the cup of a centrifuge. It is then rotated by means of an electric motor at a constant speed of 6,000 rpm. Determine the acceleration of a particle at a distance of 12 cm from the axis of rotation. Express this acceleration in terms of g.

A particle revolving at 6,000 rpm makes 100 rps. The period of this motion $T = 0.01$ sec $= 10^{-2}$ sec. The acceleration of a particle moving with uniform speed in a circle is given by Equation (10) of Chapter 6:

$$a = \frac{4\pi^2 R}{T^2}.$$

Substituting the values $R = 12$ cm, $T = 10^{-2}$ sec, we get

$$a = \frac{4\pi^2 \times 12 \text{ cm}}{10^{-4} \text{ sec}^2}$$

or $\qquad a = 474 \times 10^4$ cm/sec^2.

Taking $\qquad g = 980$ cm/sec^2,

we get $\qquad a = \dfrac{474 \times 10^4}{980}\, g,$

so that $\qquad a = 4{,}840g.$

Some modern centrifuges are being operated at speeds of about 20,000 rps. A few experimental models have been operated at speeds as high as 50,000 rps.

QUESTIONS

1. Suppose water were flowing in a frictionless horizontal pipe of uniform cross section open at one end. What would the pressure be at every point in the pipe?

2. Why is a difference in pressure usually necessary to force a liquid through a horizontal pipe of uniform cross section?

3. There is a steady flow of a liquid through a horizontal pipe of nonuniform cross section. Does a typical small volume of the liquid remain in equilibrium as it flows through this tube?

4. Discuss the forces acting on a small volume of liquid as it flows through a tube of nonuniform cross section.

5. If a ball is placed in a funnel and a stream of air is blown through the stem of the funnel against the ball, the ball will remain in the funnel. Account for this fact on the basis of Bernoulli's theorem.

6. Examine a Bunsen burner or other gas burner used in the laboratory

and see how it is constructed to get air to mix with the stream of gas. Is Bernoulli's principle applicable?

7. Explain how you would pitch a ball to produce (a) an outcurve and (b) a drop.

8. Hold two sheets of paper loosely and blow air between them. Instead of separating, the two sheets will come together. Explain this on the basis of Bernoulli's principle.

9. What effect would an increase in elevation have on the difference in pressure on the two surfaces of an airplane wing? Justify your answer in terms of the mathematical statement of Bernoulli's theorem given by Equation (11).

10. Compare the operation of a force pump with that of a hydraulic press. What factor determines the height to which water can be lifted by a force pump?

11. Is it possible to siphon water out of the bottom of a tank 40 ft deep if it is mounted on a 50-ft tower?

12. Will a siphon work in a vacuum? Explain your answer.

13. A tank of water is filled to a height H by letting the water flow in from a faucet at that level. Compare the kinetic energy of the water as it enters with the final potential energy of the water in the tank. Account for any difference between them.

PROBLEMS

1. Water flows through a horizontal pipe of varying cross section at the rate of 4 cu ft/min. Determine the velocity of the water at a point where the diameter of the pipe is (a) 1.5 in. and (b) 2 in.

2. Oil flows through a 12-in. pipeline with a speed of 3 mi/hr. How many gallons of oil are delivered per day by this pipeline? (1 gal. = 231 cu in.)

3. At a place in a pipeline where the diameter is 6 in., the speed of a steady stream of water is 12 ft/sec. (a) What will be the speed of the water in that portion of the pipeline where the diameter is 4 in.? (b) At what rate, in cubic feet per minute, is water being delivered by this pipeline?

4. A water storage tank is filled to a height of 16 ft. (a) With what speed will water come out of a valve at the bottom of the tank, if friction is negligible? (b) To what height will this water rise if the opening in the valve is directed upward?

5. How much work is done in forcing 25 cu ft of water through a pipe if the difference in pressure between the two ends of the pipe is 50 lb/in.²?

6. Water flows steadily through a Venturi tube at the rate of 40 cu ft/min. At a place where the diameter of the tube is 4 in., a pressure gauge reads 15 lb/in.². Determine the pressure in the throat of the tube where the diameter is 2 in.

7. Gauges attached to a tube in which water is flowing steadily show a pressure of 25 lb/in.² where the diameter of the tube is 4 in. and a pressure of 20 lb/in.² where the diameter of the tube is 3 in. (a) Determine the velocity of the liquid in the wider portion of the tube. (b) Determine the quantity of water per second flowing through this tube.

8. Oil of specific gravity 0.9 flows through a tube 3 cm in diameter at a

pressure of 1.5×10^6 dynes/cm². At one portion, the tube narrows down to 2 cm diameter, and the pressure drops to 10^6 dynes/cm². (a) Determine the velocity of the oil in the wider portion of the tube. (b) Determine the rate at which oil flows through this tube.

9. In a wind-tunnel experiment, the pressure on the upper surface of a wing was 13.05 lb/in.², while the pressure on the lower surface was 13.20 lb/in.². Determine the lifting force of a wing of this design if it has a spread of 50 ft and a width of 9 ft.

10. A monoplane weighing 14,000 lb has a wing area of 600 sq ft. (a) What difference in pressure on the two sides of the wing surface is required to maintain this plane in level flight? (b) If the plane is flying at a level of 13,000 ft and the pressure on the lower wing surface is 9.0 lb/in.², determine the pressure on the upper wing surface.

11. The lower end of a siphon is 8 ft below the level of the water surface in the tank. (a) Determine the speed with which water flows out of the open end. (b) If the cross-sectional area of the siphon is 2.5 in.², determine the rate at which water is siphoned out.

12. The pressure in the cylinder of a force pump is 45 lb/in.² above atmospheric pressure. Determine the height to which water may be lifted by this pump.

13. A centrifugal pump is operated by an electric motor. Water is pumped to a height of 90 ft and comes out of the nozzle at the rate of 2 ft³/sec. Determine the power needed to operate the pump, neglecting friction.

14. The level of water in a tank is 500 cm above the ground. Water flows out of this tank in a horizontal direction through a valve located 400 cm below the surface. Determine (a) the velocity with which the water escapes, neglecting friction, (b) the distance from the valve where the water strikes the ground, and (c) the velocity of the water when it reaches the ground.

15. Water falls from a height of 120 ft and drives a water turbine. If the rate of flow of water is 480 ft³/min, determine the maximum power that can be developed by this turbine.

10

Properties of Matter

10-1 INTERNAL FORCES

When a system is subjected to external forces, it generally undergoes a change in size or shape or both. We have thus far touched very lightly on such changes; for example, we have considered the change in length of an elastic spring and the change in volume of a gas when such systems were subjected to varying pressures. The changes produced in a system by the action of external forces depend upon the physical properties of the material of which the system is composed. A study of the properties of matter leads to information which is of practical value to both the physicist and the engineer, and also gives us some information about the internal forces which act between the constituent parts of the substance. In the final analysis these physical properties must be explicable in terms of the forces between the molecules of the substance and, in some cases, between the atoms of the substance.

We have so far discussed only one type of force which exists between particles—the gravitational attraction of two particles because of their masses. However, gravitational forces are much too small to account for the observed properties of substances. Furthermore we frequently encounter cases in which a force of repulsion is needed to explain the phenomena, whereas gravitational forces are always forces of attraction. One other fact worth noting here is that the forces which act between molecules produce their effect only over very short distances, that is, distances of the order of molecular diameters. These are called *short-range forces*. These short-range forces are undoubtedly of electrical origin. As we proceed with our study of physics, we shall study the forces between electrically charged particles and show how these are thought to be related to the structure of matter.

At present, there are 101 different elements known. A chemical analysis of any substance will show that it is composed of one or more of these elements. If the substance is a chemical compound, the elements composing it always occur in a definite ratio of their weights. More complex substances consist of several or many compounds. The smallest constituent of a chemical compound is the *molecule;* it is the fundamental structural unit of the compound. A molecule is composed of one or more atoms held together by the short-range forces due to their electrical charges. As we shall show, an atom of an element consists of a very small

Fɪɢ. 10–1   Photograph of a large quartz crystal grown at the Bell Telephone Laboratories.   (Courtesy of Bell Telephone Laboratories.)

but massive *nucleus* surrounded by a suitable number of *electrons.* The nucleus consists of two kinds of particles: *neutrons,* which are neutral particles, and *protons,* which are positively charged electrically. Every atom of any one element has exactly the same number of protons in its nucleus. This number is the *atomic number* of the element and can have one of the values from 1 to 101, inclusive. In the normal state of the atom, the atomic number also represents the number of electrons outside the nucleus. Most of the chemical properties of an element can be explained in terms of the arrangement and behavior of the electrons in the atoms.   The electrons exert forces of repulsion on each other and forces of attraction on positively charged nuclei.   When a molecule is formed with two or more atoms, there is a change in the electronic arrangement, and a new arrangement of charges is produced.   This rearrangement is brought about by the short-range forces which act between the atoms.

When the substance is in the solid phase, the forces which exist between atoms and molecules cause them to form definite geometrical patterns;   these show up as the crystalline structure.   Sometimes these crystals grow to a fairly large size as in the case of rock salt or quartz (see Figure 10–1).   Sometimes the crystals are very small and can be seen only with the aid of a microscope.   Most metals consist of such microcrystals. Even in the liquid phase, there is a definite grouping of the atoms and molecules, although individual atoms and molecules often change places. The arrangement of the atoms and molecules of a substance can be determined by means of x-ray analysis.

In the gaseous phase, the molecules are comparatively far apart so that the forces they exert on each other are extremely small.   As a matter of fact, in the so-called "ideal gas," it is assumed that the molecules exert no forces on each other except during the instant of collision.   We shall return to a more detailed consideration of the ideal gas in Section 14–3.

10-2   ELASTICITY

When the substance is subjected to the action of external forces, it may undergo a change in size or shape.   If, after these forces are removed, the substance returns to its original size and shape, the substance is said to be *elastic*.   In order to make quantitative measurements of the elastic properties of a substance, we find it convenient to introduce two new terms: these are (a) *stress* and (b) *strain*.

Stress is defined as *the ratio of the internal force* F, *brought into play when the substance is distorted in any way, to the area* A *over which this force acts.*

Thus
$$\text{Stress} = \frac{F}{A} \cdot \tag{1}$$

In the cgs system, the stress is expressed in dynes per square centimeter; in the British Engineering system, in pounds per square foot. In most engineering practice, the stress is expressed in pounds per square inch.

Strain is defined as *the ratio of the change in size or shape to the original size or shape.*   As a ratio, strain has no physical dimensions; that is, it is a numeric.   Methods of expressing the strain will be given in the discussion of the various cases.

The relationship between stress and strain was first given by Robert Hooke (1635–1703) and is known as *Hooke's law*. *Hooke's law states that, for an elastic body, the ratio of the stress to the strain produced is a constant,* or

$$\frac{\text{Stress}}{\text{Strain}} = K, \tag{2}$$

where K is called the *modulus of elasticity*. The units for K are the same as those for stress, since strain is expressed as a pure number.

10-3 TENSILE STRESS AND STRAIN

As an example of the stress set up inside a substance, let us consider the increase in the length of a rod produced by the action of two forces, each equal to F, applied at the ends of the rod, as shown in Figure 10–2(a). These forces are applied by means of clamps C_1 and C_2 attached to the ends of the rod.

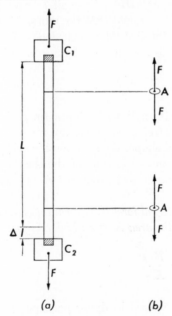

FIG. 10–2   Tensile stress in a rod.

(a)   (b)

If L is the original length of the rod and if Δl is the increase in length produced by the application of the forces F, then the strain produced is

$$\text{Strain} = \frac{\text{increase in length}}{\text{original length}} = \frac{\Delta l}{L}. \tag{3}$$

To determine the stress in the rod, let us take any cross-sectional area A through the rod and consider the forces which act on it [see Figure 10–2(b)]. The entire rod is in equilibrium under the action of the two external forces, each of magnitude F but in opposite directions, so as to extend the rod. These forces produce a *tension* inside the rod. If we consider a cross-sectional area A near the clamp C_2, it is acted upon by the external force F downward, and, since it is in equilibrium, it must also be acted upon by a force F upward exerted by that part of the rod which is immediately above this area. If we take any other parallel cross-sectional area A, it will be acted upon by a force downward equal to F exerted by that part of the rod below it and another force upward also equal to F exerted by that part of the rod above it. The effect of these two forces is to tend to separate the rod across this section; it is opposed by the forces of attraction between the molecules on the two sides of this section. The stress in the rod is the ratio of one of these forces F to the cross-sectional area A, or

$$\text{Stress} = \frac{F}{A}. \tag{1}$$

This type of stress is called a *tensile stress*.

If the material of the rod is elastic, then we know, from Hooke's law, that

$$\frac{\text{Stress}}{\text{Strain}} = K. \tag{2}$$

Putting in the values of the stress and strain found above and replacing the letter K by Y, we get

$$\boxed{\frac{F/A}{\Delta l/L} = Y.} \tag{4}$$

Y is called *Young's modulus*, after Thomas Young (1773–1829), who devised careful experiments for the determination of ratio of stress and strain. The values of Y for several substances are listed in Table 10–1.

The extent to which a substance remains elastic as the tensile stress is increased can be determined only by experiment. Figure 10–3 shows the results of a typical experiment on a metallic rod. In this figure, the stress is plotted as ordinate and the strain as abscissa. This curve is obtained by exerting a force, measuring the strain, and then removing this force. If the rod returns to its original length, then it is elastic. The straight-line portion of this curve from O to E represents the values of stress and strain for which the rod remained elastic. The curved portion from E to B represents the values of stress and strain for which the rod is no longer elastic. For example, if a stress of value CD is applied to the rod, then, when this

Table 10-1 Elastic Constants of Some Solids

Material	Young's Modulus		Shear Modulus		Bulk Modulus	
	in dynes/cm² $\times 10^{11}$	in lb/in.² $\times 10^{6}$	in dynes/cm² $\times 10^{11}$	in lb/in.² $\times 10^{6}$	in dynes/cm² $\times 10^{11}$	in lb/in.² $\times 10^{6}$
Aluminum, rolled	6.96	10.1	2.37	3.44	7.	10.
Brass	9.02	13.1	3.53	5.12	6.1	8.5
Copper, rolled	12.1 – 12.9	17.5 – 18.6	4.24	6.14	14	21
Duralumin	6.89	10.0	2.75	3.98		
Iron, cast	8.4 – 9.8	12–14	. . .	. . .	9.6	14
Glass, crown	6.5 – 7.8	9.5 – 11.3	2.6 – 3.2	3.8 – 4.7		
Lead	1.47 – 1.67	2.13 – 2.42	0.54	0.78	0.8	1.1
Nickel	20.0 – 21.4	29.0 – 31.0	7.06–7.55	10.24–10.95		
Platinum	16.67	24.18	6.42	9.32		
Silver, hard drawn	7.75	11.24	2.00	3.77		
Steel annealed	20.0	29.0	8.11	11.76	16	23
Tin	3.92 – 5.39	5.69 – 7.82	1.67	2.42		
Tungsten, drawn	35.5	51.5	14.8	21.5		

stress is removed, it is found that the rod does not return to its original length. It is said to have a permanent set. The point E is called the *elastic*

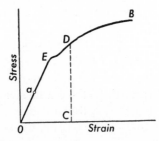

FIG. 10–3 Stress-strain curve for a ductile material.

limit of the material. At point B, the stress was great enough to break the rod. The value of this stress is known as the *breaking strength* of the material.

A very simple and instructive experiment to demonstrate the above properties of a metal can be performed by attaching one end of a long copper wire to a support in the ceiling and hanging a weight of, say, 1 lb on the other end. (Number 16 B. & S. gauge wire will do.) (See Figure 10–4.) A yardstick mounted in a base is placed on the floor, and a pointer near the top of the yardstick is set opposite a reference mark on the wire. Additional weights of 1 lb are then added to the wire, and its elongation is noted. At first this elongation will be small but observable. The additional weights can be removed to see whether the wire returns to its original length.

After about 6 lb. have been added to the wire, the increase in length for each additional pound weight will become more and more marked when the elastic limit is passed. With sufficient weights, the breaking strength will finally be reached.

Illustrative Example. A piece of No. 16 B. & S. gauge copper wire 3 ft long is suspended from a rigid support and supports a load of 8 lb. Determine (a) the stress in the wire, (b) the increase in length produced by the 8-lb load, and (c) the strain produced.

Fig. 10–4 Demonstration of stress versus strain using a long copper wire AB attached to support S in ceiling. W is load put on wire, D is a yardstick in a holder, and P is a movable pointer.

(a) A wire of No. 16 B. & S. gauge has a diameter of 0.05082 in. and a cross-sectional area of 0.00203 in.^{2}. The stress in this wire is, from Equation (1),

$$\text{Stress} = \frac{F}{A} = \frac{8 \text{ lb}}{0.00203 \text{ in.}^2} = 3{,}950 \text{ lb/in.}^2.$$

(b) The increase in length can be determined by solving Equation (4) for Δl.

Now
$$Y = \frac{F/A}{\Delta l/L};$$
(4)

hence
$$\Delta l = \frac{F}{A} \times \frac{L}{Y}.$$

The value of Young's modulus for copper is given in Table 10–1 and is

$$Y = 17.5 \times 10^6 \text{ lb/in.}^2.$$

Substituting this value for Y in the equation for the increase in length of the wire, for F/A the value determined in (a), and for L the value 36 in., we get

$$\Delta l = 3{,}950 \frac{\text{lb}}{\text{in.}^2} \times \frac{36 \text{ in.}}{17.5 \times 10^6 \frac{\text{lb}}{\text{in.}^2}},$$

from which $\qquad \Delta l = 0.008$ in.

(c) The strain produced in the wire is, from Equation (3),

$$\text{Strain} = \frac{\Delta l}{L}. \qquad \qquad \text{(3)}$$

Hence $\qquad \qquad \text{Strain} = \dfrac{0.008 \text{ in.}}{36 \text{ in.}},$

or $\qquad \qquad \text{Strain} = 0.00022 = 2.2 \times 10^{-4}.$

The strain, or the fractional change in length, is about 2 parts in 10,000.

10-4 COMPRESSIVE STRESS AND STRAIN

If the ends of a rod of some material are subjected to the action of two forces, each of magnitude F but directed so as to diminish its length, the rod is said to be under *compression*, and the stress inside the rod is a *compressive stress* [see Figure 10–5(a)]. If we consider the forces which act across any

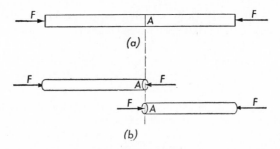

Fig. 10–5 (a) Rod put under compression by action of two external forces each equal to F. (b) Any cross section A is acted upon by an internal force F to the left due to the section of rod on the right, and by an internal force F to the right due to the section of rod on its left.

cross-sectional area A, that part of the rod to the right of this area exerts a force F toward the left, while that part to the left of this area exerts a force to the right [see Figure 10–5(b)]. The compressive stress in the rod is the ratio of either one of these forces to the area over which it acts; that is,

$$\text{Compressive stress} = \frac{F}{A}.$$

The molecular forces brought into play by the action of the external forces must be forces of repulsion, and these are of an electrical nature.

The strain produced by the compressive stress is the ratio of the decrease in length Δl to the original length L; that is,

$$\text{Compressive strain} = \frac{\Delta l}{L}.$$

If the material of which the rod is made is elastic, then experiment shows that, within the elastic limit, the ratio of compressive stress to compressive strain, or Young's modulus for compression, is identical in value to Young's modulus for tension for the same material.

Illustrative Example. A steel shaft 8 in. in diameter is part of a hydraulic press. The shaft is 10 ft long. It is used to support a car weighing 3,200 lb. Determine (a) the compressive stress in this shaft, (b) the strain in it, and (c) the decrease in its length produced by this stress.

(a) The cross-sectional area of this shaft is

$$A = \frac{\pi D^2}{4} = \frac{\pi}{4} \times 64 \text{ in.}^2 = 16\pi \text{ in.}^2,$$

so that $\qquad\qquad A = 50.1 \text{ in.}^2.$

The compressive stress is therefore

$$\frac{F}{A} = \frac{3,200 \text{ lb}}{50.1 \text{ in.}^2} = 63.6 \text{ lb/in.}^2.$$

(b) The compressive strain can be found from Equation (4)

$$Y = \frac{F/A}{\Delta l/L},$$

so that $\qquad\qquad \dfrac{\Delta l}{L} = \dfrac{F}{A} \times \dfrac{1}{Y}.$

Taking the value of Young's modulus for steel to be $Y = 29 \times 10^6 \text{ lb/in.}^2$, we get

$$\frac{\Delta l}{L} = \frac{63.6}{29 \times 10^6} \doteq 2.2 \times 10^{-6}.$$

(c) The change in length Δl is, from the above equation,

$$\Delta l = 2.2 \times 10^{-6} \times 10 \text{ ft}$$
$$= 2.2 \times 10^{-5} \text{ ft}.$$

This is a practically insignificant amount.

10-5 VOLUME CHANGE: BULK MODULUS

In both compressive and tensile stresses, the stress acts along one direction in the body and produces a change in only one dimension. The change produced in the cross-sectional area of a rod under compression or tension is practically negligible. To produce equal strains in all three dimensions of a homogeneous solid, it is necessary to have equal stresses along these three directions. The simplest method of doing this is to subject the solid to a uniform hydrostatic pressure P, as shown in Figure 10–6. The solid is

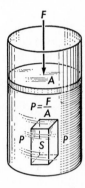

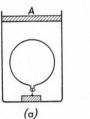

FIG. 10–6 Hydrostatic pressure $P = F/A$ used to produce a change in volume of the solid S immersed in the liquid.

FIG. 10–7 Demonstration of a volume change of a gas in a balloon by the application of additional hydrostatic pressure $P = F/A$. The volume change is Ad.

placed in some liquid in a jar with a tight-fitting piston of area A. By applying an external force F to the piston, an increased pressure $P = F/A$ is transmitted uniformly throughout the liquid. This increased pressure P is usually called *hydrostatic pressure* irrespective of the nature of the liquid. This hydrostatic pressure is the same on all sides of the solid and is also the stress inside the solid. If we call V the volume of the solid and ΔV the change in its volume produced by the stress P, then, from Hooke's law,

$$\frac{\text{Stress}}{\text{Strain}} = \frac{P}{\Delta V/V} = K.$$

Since an increase in pressure always produces a decrease in volume, the modulus K for volume change will always be a negative number. To avoid having a negative number let us define the *bulk modulus* $B = -K$, so that

$$B = -\frac{P}{\Delta V/V}. \tag{5}$$

Not only solids but also liquids and gases undergo volume changes when subjected to changing pressures.   Equation (5) is also applicable to liquids and gases.   Table 10–1 lists values of the bulk modulus for several solids, and Table 10–2 lists them for a few liquids.

Table 10-2   Bulk Modulus of Liquids

Material	in dynes/cm^2 $\times 10^{11}$
Carbon disulphide	0.1 5
Ethyl alcohol	0.0 9
Glycerin	0.4 5
Mercury	2.6
Nitric acid	0.0 3
Water	0.2 3

The volume change of a gas when subjected to hydrostatic pressure can be demonstrated very simply by taking a balloon filled with air and submerging it in water contained in a glass cylinder with a tight-fitting piston.   The balloon can be kept submerged by tying a piece of lead to it [see Figure 10–7(a)].   The hydrostatic pressure can be increased by any desired amount P by applying a force F to the piston of area A.   The decrease in volume of the balloon can be readily observed, and, if a measure of the change in volume is desired, it is merely necessary to measure the distance d through which the piston has been moved [see Figure 10–7(b)].

Illustrative Example.   A piece of copper 3 cm by 4 cm by 4 cm is placed in a steel cylinder filled with oil.   The pressure of this oil is increased from 1 atm to 101 atm.   Determine (a) the stress, (b) the strain, and (c) the change in volume of the copper.

(a) The stress P is the same as the increase in the hydrostatic pressure, and this is

$$P = (101 - 1) \text{ atm} = 100 \text{ atm},$$

and, since

$$1 \text{ atm} = 1.013 \times 10^6 \frac{\text{dynes}}{\text{cm}^2},$$

therefore

$$P = 1.013 \times 10^8 \frac{\text{dynes}}{\text{cm}^2}.$$

(b) To determine the strain produced, let us solve Equation (5) for $\Delta V/V$, obtaining

$$\frac{\Delta V}{V} = -\frac{P}{B}.$$

The value of the bulk modulus of copper, as given in Table 10–1, is

$$B = 14 \times 10^{11} \frac{\text{dynes}}{\text{cm}^2}.$$

Hence $\qquad\qquad$ Strain $= \dfrac{\Delta V}{V} = -\dfrac{1.013 \times 10^8}{14 \times 10^{11}},$

so that $\qquad\qquad \Delta V/V = -7.24 \times 10^{-5}.$

(c) The change in volume is

$$\Delta V = -7.24 \times 10^{-5} \times V.$$

Now $\qquad\qquad V = 3 \times 4 \times 4 \text{ cm}^3 = 48 \text{ cm}^3.$

Hence $\qquad\qquad \Delta V = -7.24 \times 10^{-5} \times 48 \text{ cm}^3,$

from which $\qquad\qquad \Delta V = -3.47 \times 10^{-3} \text{ cm}^3.$

The volume of the copper is thus decreased by about 0.0035 cm^3.

Illustrative Example. The pressure on 500 cm^3 of water contained in a steel cylinder is increased from almost zero to 1,000 atm. The temperature of the water is maintained at 20°C; its bulk modulus is $B = 23 \times 10^9$ dynes/cm^2. Determine (a) the strain produced, and (b) the change in volume of the water.

(a) The strain can be obtained by solving Equation (5) for $\Delta V/V$, obtaining

$$\Delta V/V = -\frac{P}{B}.$$

Since $\qquad\qquad 1 \text{ atm} = 1.013 \times 10^6 \text{ dynes/cm}^2,$

a pressure of 1,000 atm is

$$P = 1.013 \times 10^9 \text{ dynes/cm}^2.$$

Hence $\qquad\qquad \Delta V/V = -\dfrac{1.013 \times 10^9}{23 \times 10^9},$

so that the strain is

$$\Delta V/V = -4.4 \times 10^{-2}.$$

Thus an increase in pressure of 1,000 atm produces a change in the volume of water of 4.4 per cent.

(b) The change in volume of 500 cm^3 is, from the value of the strain produced,

$$\Delta V = -500 \text{ cm}^3 \times 4.4 \times 10^{-2},$$

so that $\qquad\qquad \Delta V = -22.0 \text{ cm}^3.$

Illustrative Example. Show that if a gas which obeys Boyle's law undergoes small pressure changes at constant temperature, its bulk modulus is equal to the pressure of the gas.

The bulk modulus is given by

$$B = -\frac{P}{\Delta V/V}, \tag{5}$$

where P is the *change in pressure* of the gas and ΔV the *change in its volume*. Let us assume that the pressure of the gas is changed by a small fraction, say 1 per cent, so that if P_1 was the original pressure, the change in pressure will be

$$P = 0.01 P_1.$$

From Boyle's law we know that if the pressure is increased by 1 per cent, the volume will be decreased by 1 per cent. Now $\Delta V/V$ is the fractional change in volume; hence

$$\Delta V/V = -0.01.$$

The minus sign is used to show that there was a decrease in volume.

Substituting the above values for P and $\Delta V/V$ in Equation (5), we get

$$B = \frac{-0.01P_1}{-0.01} = P_1.$$

Thus when the change in pressure is very small, the bulk modulus of a gas which follows Boyle's law is equal to the initial pressure.

From the above analysis, it can be seen that if the pressure of a gas is changed by any amount while the temperature is kept constant, the bulk modulus will vary and, at any stage of the process, will be equal to the pressure of the gas at that stage.

10-6 SHEARING STRESS AND STRAIN

It is possible to produce a change in the shape of a solid without changing its volume. Such a distortion is called a *shear*. A simple method of producing a shear is illustrated in Figure 10–8(a). If we take a rectangular solid and apply a force F along its top surface and an equal force F acting in the opposite direction along its bottom surface, the rectangular surfaces such as $BCDE$ at right angles to the top and bottom surfaces will be distorted into parallelograms such as $B'C'DE$, whose angles are not right angles. If we imagine the solid as made up of a series of layers parallel to the top and bottom surfaces, each of area A, then the effect of the shear is to cause one layer to slide with respect to another layer just as the blades of a pair of shears slide past each other.

The *shearing stress* set up in the solid is the ratio of the force F to the area A of the surface over which it acts. Each layer parallel to the top and bottom surfaces is acted upon by two forces, as shown in Figure 10–8(b), the layer above it exerting a force to the right, and the layer below

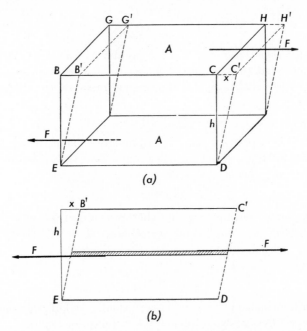

(a)

(b)

FIG. 10–8   (a) Shearing stress set up in a solid by parallel forces F acting on top and bottom surfaces each of area A. Rectangle $BCDE$ is distorted into parallelogram $B'C'DE$. No change in the volume of the solid. (b) Shaded area is section of layer in the solid parallel to top and bottom surfaces. Shearing strain is x/h.

it exerting a force to the left. These forces between the molecules of the layers oppose the sliding of one layer with respect to another. If the applied force becomes too great, the solid will be sheared; that is, it will be separated into two parts, with the surfaces of separation parallel to the direction of the applied force.

The shearing strain produced is measured by the ratio of the distance x through which the top surface has been moved relative to the bottom surface, to the height h, that is, the distance between the two surfaces. Thus

$$\text{Shearing strain} = \frac{x}{h}.$$

It will be noted that the tangent of the angle $B'EB$ is x/h.

Applying Hooke's law, we get for the *shear modulus M*

$$M = \frac{F/A}{x/h} \cdot$$ (6)

The shear modulus is sometimes called the *modulus of rigidity*. Some values of the shear modulus are listed in Table 10–1.

Illustrative Example. Two clamps are fastened near the ends of a rectangular steel rod 5 in. long. The rectangular cross section of the rod has an area of 2.5 in.^{2}. A force of 800 lb is exerted on each of these clamps parallel to this area but in opposite directions. Determine (a) the shearing stress, (b) the shearing strain, and (c) the relative displacement of the top surface with respect to the bottom surface.

(a) The shearing stress is

$$\frac{F}{A} = \frac{800 \text{ lb}}{2.5 \text{ in.}^2} = 320 \text{ lb/in.}^2.$$

(b) The shearing strain can be found by solving Equation (6) for x/h, obtaining

$$\frac{x}{h} = \frac{F}{A} \cdot \frac{1}{M} \cdot$$

The shearing modulus of steel, listed in Table 10–1, is

$$M = 11.8 \times 10^6 \frac{\text{lb}}{\text{in.}^2} ;$$

hence

$$\frac{x}{h} = \frac{320}{11.8 \times 10^6} = 27.2 \times 10^{-6}.$$

(c) Since $h = 5$ in.,

$$x = 5 \text{ in.} \times 27.2 \times 10^{-6},$$

so that

$$x = 136 \times 10^{-6} \text{ in.} = 1.36 \times 10^{-4} \text{ in.}$$

for the relative displacement of the two surfaces.

10-7 COHESION AND ADHESION

The fact that molecular forces have a short range would lead us to expect some distinctive types of phenomena to be observable at the surfaces of substances. Conversely, the appearance of these surface phenomena should lead to information about these molecular forces. For example, if we take two pieces of metal, each with an accurately plane surface, and bring them together, there will be no observable force between them until the two surfaces are placed in very good contact. Once they are placed in good contact, a very great force will be required to pull them apart. This experiment shows that the forces between the molecules in the two surface layers have a very short range of effectiveness. The above experiment can be readily performed with two pieces of steel with clean plane surfaces, or with two pieces of lead with clean plane surfaces. The force of attraction acting between molecules of the same material is sometimes called *cohesion.*

If some water is poured into a glass vessel, the free surface of the water will be a level surface, that is, horizontal, except at the region of contact with the glass; at this region, the water will be seen to cling to the glass for a short distance above the level surface (see Figure 10–9). This phe-

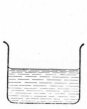

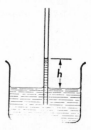

FIG. 10–9   Free surface of water in a   FIG. 10–10   Level of water in a capil-
   glass jar is level (horizontal) ex-   lary tube is at a height *h* above
   cept near the glass.   level in the large vessel.

nomenon can be accentuated by immersing a glass tube with a narrow bore, a so-called "capillary tube," into the water (see Figure 10–10). The level of the water inside the capillary tube will be found to be considerably higher than the level in the larger jar. Furthermore, an examination of the surface of the water in the capillary tube shows that it is not plane but is concave upward.

The above experiment can be repeated with a variety of capillary tubes of different materials and a variety of liquids. In many cases, the liquid will be found to rise in the capillary tube to a level above that in the liquid outside the tube. In some cases, the level in the capillary will be lower than that outside the tube. For example, if a glass capillary tube is immersed in mercury contained in a larger dish, the level of the mercury will be lower in the capillary tube than outside the tube (see Figure 10–11). If a glass U-tube is constructed with one arm about 1 cm in diameter and the other about 0.2 cm in diameter, and mercury is poured into the tube, the level in the narrower tube will be lower than that in the wider tube [see Figure 10–12(a)]. If water is poured into such a U-tube, the level of water will be higher in the narrower tube, as shown in Figure 10–12(b).

One method of accounting for the behavior of liquids in capillary tubes is to assume that there are forces of attraction, also of short range, between the molecules of the liquid and the molecules of the solid at the surface of contact. This type of attractive force between molecules in the surface of one substance for those in the surface of another substance

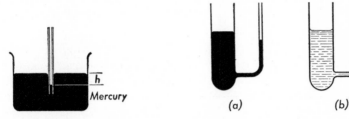

Fig. 10–11   Level of mercury in a glass capillary tube is at a level *h* below that in the large vessel.

Fig. 10–12   (a) **U-tube** containing mercury. (b) **U-tube** containing water.

is called *adhesion,* to distinguish it from the force of cohesion between like molecules. If the force of adhesion is greater than the force of cohesion, the liquid will cling to the solid surface; that is, it will wet the solid. Water and glass, and oil and glass are examples of liquids which wet the solids.

The angle between the liquid surface and the solid surface at the region of contact is an indication of the relative values of the forces of cohesion and adhesion. This angle is known as the *angle of contact.* For water and

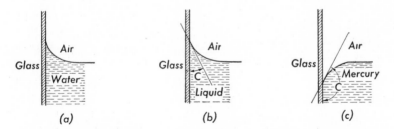

Fig. 10–13   Angles of contact. (a) 0° between water and glass; (b) angle of contact $C < 90°$ between a liquid and glass; (c) angle of contact $C > 90°$ between mercury and glass.

glass, the angle of contact is zero degrees [see Figure 10–13(a)]. For some other liquid, the angle of contact will have some value *C*, as shown in Figure 10–13(b). In this case, the relative value of the force of adhesion to that of cohesion is not so great as in the case of water and glass. If the force of cohesion is much greater than the force of adhesion, as in the case of mercury and glass, the angle of contact C is greater than 90°.   For mercury and glass, $C = 139°$.

Table 10-3   Contact Angles

Liquid	Tube	Angle, Degrees
Alcohol	Glass	0
Ether	Glass	0
Glycerin	Glass	0
Mercury	Glass	139
Water	Glass	0
Water	Paraffin	107

10-8   SURFACE TENSION

We have seen that the liquid inside a capillary tube has a curved surface, and if the tube is circular the liquid surface is spherical.   The interesting phenomena associated with liquid surfaces can be most easily explained by introducing the concept of *surface tension*.   If we reconsider the case of water in a glass capillary tube, we find that there is a force upward around the circular region of contact between the glass and the water.   The liquid surface behaves as though it is under tension, with the pull everywhere tangential to the surface.   If we take a small section of such a liquid surface and imagine a line AB in it (see Figure 10–14), this line will experience a pull to the right produced by the surface to its right, and it will experience an equal pull to the left produced by the surface to the left of it.

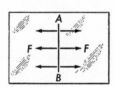

FIG. 10–14   Any line AB in a surface is acted on by equal forces F at right angles to AB produced by the surfaces on either side.

If F is the force due to either part of the surface and L is the length of the line AB, the ratio of F to L is called the *surface tension S;* thus

$$S = \frac{F}{L} \cdot$$

(7)

The surface tension S acts at right angles to any line imagined in the surface.   The surface tension is usually expressed in dynes per centimeter.

That a liquid surface behaves as though it is under tension can be demonstrated in a variety of experiments.   Let us construct a rectangular wire frame having one side movable; this can be done by curving the ends of a wire AB so that it slides easily on two legs of the frame [see Figure 10–15(a)]. We can pick up a film on this frame by dipping it in a soap solution. This film will have two rectangular surfaces. The film will tend to contract, and, since AB is movable, it will pull this wire toward CD with some force F. As the surface contracts, the thickness of the film will increase; that is, molecules will leave the surface and enter the liquid between the two surfaces.

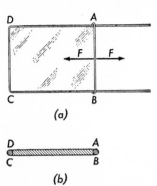

(a)

(b)

Fɪɢ. 10–15   (a) Wire frame with movable slide AB used to measure the surface tension of a film in the frame $ABCD$.   (b) Shows the thickness of the film.

To keep the wire AB in equilibrium, a force F to the right has to be applied to it. This force can be used to measure the surface tension. If l is the length of the wire, the length of the surface which exerts this force F is $2l$, since there are two surfaces to this film. The surface tension S is therefore

$$S = \frac{F}{2l}.$$

If the surface area is increased by moving the wire AB through a distance x, the work done is

$$\mathcal{W} = Fx,$$

and, since

$$F = 2lS,$$

therefore

$$\boxed{\mathcal{W} = S \times 2lx.} \tag{8}$$

Now $2lx$ is the increase in the surface area of the film; setting $2lx = A$ and solving Equation (8) for S, we get

$$\boxed{S = \frac{\mathcal{W}}{A}.} \tag{9}$$

The surface tension thus represents the work done per unit area in increasing the area of the film.

Another simple experiment to illustrate the contractile force of a film is to dip a metal frame, with a looped piece of thread loosely tied to it, into a soap solution. When taken out of the solution, a soap film will be stretched across the circular frame, and the looped thread will be collapsed in it [see Figure 10–16(a)]. If we now take a heated needle and puncture the film inside the loop, the contractile force of the film on the outside of

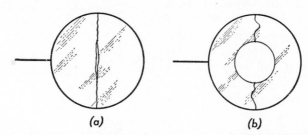

(a)   *(b)*

FIG. 10–16   A circular wire frame with a loop of thread loosely tied to it.   (a) A soap film on the wire frame with loop in it.   (b) Film inside loop broken. Soap film on the outside of the loop pulls at right angles to it giving it circular shape.

the loop will stretch it into a circular shape [see Figure 10–16(b)].   The circular shape is due to the fact that the surface tension acts at right angles to every part of the looped thread.

The contractile force in the surface of a liquid is the cause of the spherical shape of a liquid drop.   A simple experiment to show the formation of a spherical drop can be performed by preparing a solution of alcohol and water which has the same density as some heavy engine oil. The oil will not mix with this solution.   If the oil is now introduced into the middle of this solution by letting it flow out of a glass tube placed there, the oil will assume a spherical shape and remain suspended in the solution (see Figure 10–17).   The contractile force in the surface makes it

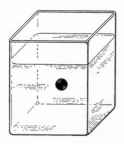

FIG. 10–17   Spherical shape of drop of oil suspended in an alcohol solution of equal density.

assume the smallest possible area consistent with its volume.   The shape of such a surface is spherical.

The surface tension of a liquid depends upon the nature of the liquid and the nature of the substance on the outside of the liquid surface, that is, whether it is air or the vapor of the liquid itself.   The values of the surface tensions of some liquids are given in Table 10–4. The surface tension depends upon the temperature of the system, decreasing as the temperature rises.

Table 10-4   Surface Tension

Liquid in Contact with Air	Temperature in °C	Surface Tension in dynes/cm
Ethyl alcohol	20	22.3
Water	0	75.6
	20	72.8
	60	66.2
	100	58.9
Mercury	25	473
Olive oil	20	32
Glycerin	20	63.1
Soap solution		26

10-9 CAPILLARITY

We have already shown that if a capillary tube is inserted into a liquid, the levels inside and outside the tube will differ by an amount h. In some cases, the liquid will be higher in the capillary tube; in other cases, it will be lower, depending upon the relative values of the forces of adhesion and cohesion.

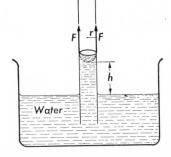

Fɪɢ. 10–18   Force F acting on surface film in capillary tube when the contact angle is zero.

The concept of surface tension enables us to obtain a simple relationship between the difference in levels h inside and outside the capillary tube and the radius r of this tube. Let us take the case of a liquid such as water, which rises in the tube to a height h above the water outside the tube (see Figure 10–18). The contact angle between the water and the glass is 0°. The force F acting upward along the circle of contact between the water and the glass must be equal to the force F caused by the surface tension S in the water. The force F can be evaluated by considering the surface tension S as acting along the circumference of the circle of contact $2\pi r$, so that

$$F = S \times 2\pi r.$$

This upward force supports the weight of the column of water of height h. If d is the density of the liquid, the mass m of this liquid is

$$m = d \times \pi r^2 h,$$

since $\pi r^2 h$ is the volume of this column of liquid. Its weight W is

$$W = mg = \pi r^2 dgh.$$

Equating the upward force F to the weight of the column of liquid, we get

$$2\pi r S = \pi r^2 dgh,$$

from which
$$h = \frac{2S}{rdg}.$$
(10)

Thus the height to which water will rise in a capillary tube varies inversely as the radius of the tube. This is known as *Jurin's law.*

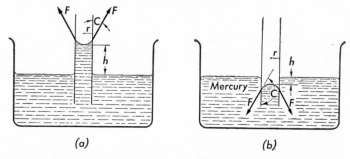

(a)   (b)

FIG. 10–19   Surface tension forces in capillary tubes (a) when contact angle C is less than 90°, (b) when contact angle C is greater than 90°.

If the contact angle is not zero but has some value C, then the upward force is the vertical component of F and is therefore

$$F \cos C = 2\pi r S \cos C = \pi r^2 hdg,$$

so that
$$h = \frac{2S \cos C}{rdg}.$$
(11)

The same analysis will hold if the surface in the capillary is depressed by an amount h (see Figure 10–19). In this case, the vertical component of the force F, that is, $F \cos C$, acts downward and is opposed by the force due to the difference in pressure between the liquid outside the tube and that inside the tube. This difference in pressure is due to a column of liquid of height h and is hdg. The force exerted by such a column is $\pi r^2 hdg$, where πr^2 is the cross-sectional area of the tube. Therefore

$$2\pi r S \cos C = \pi r^2 hdg,$$

and
$$h = \frac{2S \cos C}{rdg},$$

which is the same as Equation (11). When the angle of contact is greater than 90°, the value of its cosine is a negative number; hence h will be negative, indicating that the level is depressed in the capillary tube.

Illustrative Example. Two glass capillary tubes, each 1 mm in radius, are put into two different liquids, one in water and the other in mercury. Compare the liquid levels in the two tubes.

Let us take the level of the liquid outside each capillary tube as the zero reference level. From Equation (11), the level of the liquid inside the capillary will differ from that outside by an amount

$$h = \frac{2S \cos C}{rdg}. \tag{11}$$

For the case of water, $C = 0°$, hence $\cos C = 1$; $S = 73$ dynes/cm; $r = 0.1$ cm, $d = 1$ gm/cm^3, and $g = 980$ cm/sec^2. Letting $h = h_1$ for water, we get

$$h_1 = \frac{2 \times 73 \text{ dynes/cm}}{0.1 \text{ cm} \times 1 \text{ gm/cm}^3 \times 980 \text{ cm/sec}^2},$$

from which
$$h_1 = \frac{146}{98} \text{ cm} = 1.5 \text{ cm}.$$

For the case of mercury, $C = 139°$, hence $\cos C = \cos 139° = -\cos 41° = -0.755$; $S = 473$ dynes/cm; $r = 0.1$ cm, $d = 13.6$ gm/cm^3, and $g = 980$ cm/sec^2. Letting $h = h_2$ for mercury, we get

$$h_2 = -\frac{2 \times 473 \text{ dynes/cm} \times 0.755}{0.1 \text{ cm} \times 13.6 \text{ gm/cm}^3 \times 980 \text{ cm/sec}^2},$$

from which $h_2 = -0.536$ cm.

10-10   PRESSURE AND CURVED SURFACES

From our study of hydrostatics, we know that if a liquid is at rest in a series of connected vessels, the pressure at any one level must be the same in all the vessels, and the pressure at a higher level is less than that at a lower

level by an amount equal to hdg, where h is the difference in levels.   Let us
apply this rule to a liquid in a capillary tube which is connected to a much
larger vessel (see Figure 10–20).   The atmospheric pressure P_0 acts on the

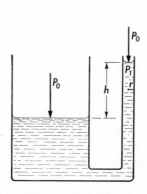

FIG. 10–20   Pressure P_1 under convex   FIG. 10–21   Relationship between ra-
surface is less than pressure P_0 dius R of spherical surface, radius
over concave surface. r of the capillary tube, and contact
                                             angle C. $r = R \cos C$.

open surfaces in the two vessels.   If the liquid surface in the capillary is at a
height h above that in the larger vessel, then the pressure P_1 just under the
curved surface must be less than the pressure P_0 outside it by an amount
equal to the pressure of the column of liquid of height h; that is,

$$P_0 - P_1 = hdg. \tag{12}$$

Now the height h is related to the surface tension S and the radius of the
capillary tube r by

$$h = \frac{2S \cos C}{rdg}. \tag{11}$$

From Equation (11), we get

$$hdg = \frac{2S \cos C}{r};$$

hence $$P_0 - P_1 = \frac{2S \cos C}{r}. \tag{13}$$

The pressure on the convex side of the surface is thus less than the pressure on the concave side.

In the special case where the surface is spherical, such as that shown in
Figure 10–21, the pressure difference is simply related to the radius of the
sphere.   The relationship between the radius r of the tube and the radius

R of the spherical surface can be obtained very readily with the aid of Figure 10–21. O is the center of the sphere, $OA = R$, and, since AB is tangent to the sphere, it is perpendicular to OA. Hence the angle between R and r is equal to the contact angle C, so that

$$r = R \cos C. \tag{14}$$

Substituting this value for r in Equation (13) yields

$$P_0 - P_1 = \frac{2S}{R}. \tag{15}$$

Thus the difference in pressure on the two sides of a spherical surface due to the surface tension depends inversely upon the radius of the sphere. P_0 is the pressure on the concave side of the surface, and P_1 is the pressure on the convex side. The above result holds for a whole sphere as well as for any portion of it. Thus, if an air bubble is formed in the water, the pressure inside exceeds that outside by $2S/R$.

In the case of a soap bubble blown in air, the pressure difference is practically twice as great; that is, it is $4S/R$, since a soap bubble has two spherical surfaces: one of radius R_1, the other of radius R_2 (see Figure 10–22). Since the thickness of the soap film is very small, the difference

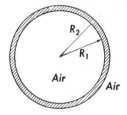

Fig. 10–22 A soap bubble has two spherical surfaces whose radii R_1 and R_2 differ very slightly.

between R_1 and R_2 is negligible, so that the excess pressure inside is practically $4S/R$, where R is the average radius of the soap bubble and S is the surface tension of the soap solution.

The smaller the soap bubble, the greater is the pressure inside it. This can be demonstrated with a very simple experiment using the apparatus sketched in Figure 10–23. A long glass tube has a three-way stopcock at its center. One end of the glass tube A is dipped into a soap solution, and a film is formed on it. The stopcock is then turned so that air blown into it goes only to the film at A, blowing it out into a soap bubble of small size. The stopcock is then turned so that side A is closed and side B is open. The above process is repeated, and a larger soap bubble is blown on B. The stopcock is now turned so as to connect A and B but is shut off from the outside. Air will flow from A to B, since the pressure inside A is greater than that inside *B*. The larger bubble will thus get larger, and the smaller bubble will get smaller; equilibrium can be reached only when the curvatures of the two surfaces become equal; the smaller bubble will then consist of only a small section of a large sphere equal in radius to that of the large bubble.

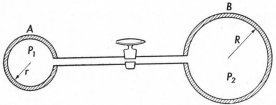

Fig. 10–23   Two soap bubbles of different radii blown at the ends of a glass tube. Smaller soap bubble will get still smaller, and larger one will get still larger.

Illustrative Example.   Determine the excess pressure inside a small raindrop 3 mm in diameter.

Since the raindrop is a sphere with a single surface, the excess pressure ΔP inside the sphere is, from Equation (15),

$$\Delta P = \frac{2S}{R}.$$

Using the values $S = 73$ dynes/cm, and $R = 0.15$ cm, we get

$$\Delta P = \frac{2 \times 73 \text{ dynes/cm}}{0.15 \text{ cm}},$$

so that $\Delta P = 973$ dynes/cm^2.

10-11 PHENOMENA ASSOCIATED WITH SURFACE TENSION

There are many phenomena associated with surface tension, a few of which will be described here. For example, if a drop of oil is allowed to fall on a large clean surface of water, the oil will spread out over this surface until it is 1 molecule thick; it forms a monomolecular layer. If the volume of the original oil drop is known and if the area of the monomolecular layer is measured, its thickness can be computed. This thickness will then give us one dimension of the oil molecule. Studies of the structure of oil molecules by means of x-rays show that they are not spherical but have one long dimension and two shorter dimensions. In a monomolecular layer, the molecules stand on end, so that a measure of the thickness of the oil film will yield the longest dimension.

If two small wooden matchsticks are floated near each other on the surface of water, they will be pulled toward each other. The liquid between the matchsticks is raised to a level higher than the rest of the surface by the surface tension; the pressure in the liquid between the sticks is thus decreased to a value less than atmospheric pressure. If a drop of alcohol is placed between them, the two matchsticks will be pulled apart. The effect of the alcohol is to decrease the surface tension; that is, the surface tension of the solution of alcohol in water is less than that of pure water. The difference in the surface tensions of the two sides of each stick supplies the forces which pull them apart.

When small pieces of camphor are dropped onto a clean surface of water, these drops will perform very erratic motions. Although camphor is soluble in water only to a very slight extent, wherever it is dissolved, the surface tension is reduced. Each little piece of camphor will experience forces caused by the different surface tensions around it, and these forces set the particle in motion. The motion will cease when the surface tension becomes uniform and equal to that of the solution of camphor in water.

QUESTIONS

1. Distinguish between short-range forces and gravitational forces between molecules. Compare the magnitudes of the forces between molecules of a substance in the solid phase and in the gaseous phase.

2. For which value of the strain is the stress in a wire equal to Young's modulus of the substance?

3. Distinguish between the elastic limit of a substance and its breaking strength.

4. Two wires, one twice as long as the other, are made of the same material and have the same cross-sectional area. Compare the changes in length of the two wires when they are subjected to the same stress.

5. Two wires made of the same material and of the same length are hung from a suitable beam. The diameter of one wire is twice that of the other. Equal loads are placed on each wire. Compare the strains produced in them.

6. Compare the compressibilities of steel and water; which is more compressible?

7. How does the bulk modulus of a gas differ from that of a liquid?

8. Water can rise to a height h when a capillary tube of a certain diameter is placed in it. Suppose that this tube is inserted into water so that only a height $h/2$ projects above the surface. Will the water run out of the capillary tube? Try this experiment.

9. When a camel's-hair brush is dipped in water, the bristles stay apart. When it is taken out of the water, the bristles come together. Explain this in terms of the surface tension of water.

10. One plate of soup has a uniform layer of liquid fat covering it; another plate of the same kind of soup has small drops of liquid fat floating on top. Which soup is hotter? Explain.

11. A thin steel needle is placed horizontally on the surface of water without

breaking the surface. Explain what forces are acting on this needle. Does Archimedes' principle apply in this case?

12. A capillary tube has a narrow constriction in one part. Some water is drawn into this part of the tube. Will the water stay in the constricted part or flow into the wider part? Explain your answer in terms of the surface tension of the water.

13. A capillary tube has a narrow constriction in one part. Some mercury is drawn into this part of the tube. Will the mercury stay in the constricted part? Explain your answer in terms of the surface tension of mercury.

14. Account for the rise of ink in blotting paper.

15. Account for the rise of oil in the wick of an oil lamp.

16. What is the meaning of the phrase "pouring oil on troubled waters"? Do you know of any cases in which this has been done?

17. Take a narrow-necked bottle and pour water into it until it is about two thirds full. With a little skill, this bottle can be inverted so that, even though the open end is down, the water will not flow out of it. (a) Describe the shape of the water surface at the open end of the bottle. (b) Is the pressure of the air inside the bottle greater, equal to, or less than atmospheric pressure? Explain your answer.

18. Compare the tension of a soap bubble with that of a rubber balloon. Is Hooke's law applicable to the soap film? to the rubber balloon?

19. How can you demonstrate that the force acting to keep two blocks of metal together when their plane surfaces touch is not due to atmospheric pressure acting on them?

PROBLEMS

1. A copper wire 80 cm long and 0.25 cm in diameter is suspended from a rigid framework. A body whose mass is 6 kg is hung at the end of the wire. Determine (a) the stress in the wire and (b) the strain produced.

2. A steel wire 1.5 m long and 0.04 cm in diameter supports a cylinder whose mass is 5.0 kg. Determine (a) the stress in the wire, (b) the strain produced, and (c) the elongation of the wire.

3. A brass wire 3.0 ft long and 0.04 in. in diameter supports a body whose weight is 6 lb. Determine (a) the stress in the wire, (b) the strain produced, and (c) the increase in length of the wire.

4. A brass wire 3.0 m long and 2.0 mm in diameter is suspended from a hook in a beam in the ceiling. A cylinder whose mass is 6.0 kg is hung from the other end. Determine the increase in length of the brass wire.

5. An aluminum wire 200 cm long and 0.4 mm in diameter has a series of cylinders hung from it in succession. Each cylinder has a mass of 100 gm. The measured changes in length expressed in centimeters, as determined by a telescope and scale method, are 0.0014, 0.0029, 0.0042, 0.0056, and 0.0070. Plot a graph with the stress as ordinate and the strain as abscissa; from the slope of this graph, determine Young's modulus for this aluminum wire.

6. A steel rod 6.0 in. long and 0.5 in. in diameter is to be used as a piston in a cylinder to produce a pressure of 2,000 lb/in.^{2}. Determine the decrease in length of the rod produced by this stress.

7. Glycerin is subjected to a pressure of 800 atm. Determine the percentage change in its volume.

8. Determine the bulk modulus of an oil if a volume of 1,000 cm^3 shows a decrease in volume of 0.3 cm^3 when subjected to a pressure of 15 atm.

9. A cube of copper 5 cm on an edge is subjected to two oppositely directed shearing forces along two of its faces. Each force is 9×10^7 dynes. Determine (a) the shearing stress, (b) the shearing strain, and (c) the angle, in degrees, through which the cube has been sheared.

10. Three capillary tubes of diameters 0.5 mm, 1.0 mm, and 1.5 mm, respectively, are supported in a jar of water. Determine the height to which the water will rise in each of these tubes.

11. Three holes of diameters 1.0 mm, 1.5, and 2.0 mm, respectively, are bored in a block of paraffin. The paraffin is partly immersed in water. Determine the level of the water in each hole.

12. A capillary tube 1.0 mm in diameter is placed in a soap solution. The liquid in the tube rises to a height of 0.90 cm above the level of the rest of the surface. Determine the surface tension of this solution, assuming the contact angle to be zero.

13. A soap film is formed on a rectangular frame 2 cm by 8 cm as in Figure 10–15. (a) Determine the force that the film exerts on the shorter wire. (b) If this wire is moved through a distance of 4 cm, determine the amount of work done. Assume that the temperature remains constant in this process.

14. Calculate the excess pressure inside a raindrop which is 4 mm in diameter; assume the temperature to be 20°C.

15. Calculate the excess pressure inside a drop of mercury whose temperature is 25°C and whose diameter is 3 mm.

16. Determine the excess pressure inside a soap film which is 4 cm in diameter; assume the temperature to be 20°C.

17. Two rectangular glass plates are spaced 1 mm apart; they are partly immersed in a dish of water at 20°C, with the plates placed so that the air space between them is in a vertical plane. Determine how high the water will rise in this air space above the level of the water in the dish.

(Note: Consider the forces acting on a surface film 1 cm wide in contact with each plate; balance these forces against the weight of water lifted through a height h.)

18. A hollow glass tube has a soap bubble of 6 cm diameter formed on one end and another soap bubble of 2 cm diameter formed on the other end. Determine the pressure difference at the ends of the tube. Explain what will happen as a result of this pressure difference.

19. Determine the diameter of a capillary tube such that water will rise a height of 100 cm in it above the level outside the tube.

20. Two glass plates, each having a large surface, are clamped together along one edge and separated by spacers a few millimeters thick along the opposite edge to form a wedge-shaped air film. These plates are then placed vertically in a dish of colored liquid. Calling x the horizontal distance measured from the edge where the thickness of the air film is zero, show that the vertical distance y through which the liquid rises in the air space varies inversely as x.

(Note: The thickness of the air film increases as the distance x increases.)

11

Rotational
Motion

11-1 MOTION OF A RIGID BODY

Our previous discussion of motion was confined almost entirely either to the motion of a particle or to the motion of a rigid body in which each particle of the rigid body moved with the same velocity and acceleration as its center of gravity. This motion of a rigid body, in which the velocities of its particles at any instant are parallel to each other, is called a motion of *translation*. During the motion of translation, any line in the body will move so that it always remains parallel to itself throughout the motion. If any line in the body does not remain parallel to itself throughout the motion, then the body has a motion of *rotation*. For example, a rectangular box sliding down an inclined plane has a motion of translation, but when it reaches the bottom of the incline and goes on to the level floor, it has a motion of rotation; if, after it has left the incline completely, it continues to slide on the level floor, it once again has a motion of translation.

It is possible to discuss the motion of a rigid body in terms of the motion of each of its particles, but this is generally a very difficult procedure. Each particle in the rigid body is acted upon by two types of forces: one type is due to the external forces acting upon the rigid body, and the other type is due to the mutual forces of attraction between the particles of the rigid body. However, from Newton's third law, we know that the forces between the particles are equal in magnitude and opposite in direction; hence, when we add up all of the forces acting on the different particles, the resultant of the internal forces will be zero, and the resultant force acting on the rigid body will be the resultant of all the external forces acting on the rigid body. If, in addition, we make the assumption that the internal forces between two particles not only are equal in magnitude and opposite in direction but also act along the same line, then the sum of all the torques due to the internal forces will be zero, and we need consider only the torques due to the external forces. The result of the above analysis is that it will be possible to give an elementary treatment of the simpler types of rotational motion, such as the motion of a body about a fixed axis

238

and the rolling of a wheel, by considering the motions of typical particles in the body, and from these determine the motion of the rigid body.

11-2   MOTION ABOUT A FIXED AXIS

The motion of a flywheel of a steam engine, that of a propeller of an airplane engine, and that of a pulley on its axle are examples of an important type of motion of a rigid body. Each of these bodies rotates about a *fixed axis*. To simplify the discussion, let us consider a uniform disk rotating about a fixed axis passing through its center of gravity C perpendicular to the face of the disk, as shown in Figure 11–1. The motion of this disk may

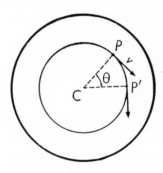

Fig. 11–1   Angle of rotation of a disk.

be described in terms of the motions of each of its individual particles. Each particle P moves in a circular path about the axis of rotation. The velocity v of the particle is, of course, tangent to this circle; the velocity of each particle, however, is different from that of every other particle. While this is a possible mode of description, an examination of the motion will show that a better way to describe it is in terms of the *angle* through which the disk rotates. This may be specified by the angle between two successive positions of a line in the plane of the disk. Consider two successive positions of the line joining point P to the axis of rotation C; call these successive positions CP and CP'. The angle θ between these two lines is the angle through which the *disk* has rotated; every line in the plane of the disk has rotated through the same angle θ in the same interval of time. The angle θ is called the *angular displacement* of the rigid body.

There are several units for expressing the angular displacement of a rigid body; it may be expressed in *degrees,* in the number of *revolutions* it makes, or in the number of *radians* traversed. The radian measure of the angle θ is defined as the length of arc PP' divided by the radius r of the circle, or

$$\theta = \frac{\widehat{PP'}}{r} .$$

(1)

When the length of the arc PP' is equal to the radius r of the circle, θ is equal to one radian. In one complete revolution, the length of arc PP' is $2\pi r$; hence the number of radians in one revolution is 2π. Since there are $360°$ in one revolution,

$$1 \text{ radian} = \frac{360°}{2\pi} = 57.3°.$$

11-3 MOTION WITH CONSTANT ANGULAR SPEED

The *angular speed* of a rigid body is defined as the *angle through which the body rotates divided by the time required to perform the rotation.* The angle through which the body rotates is the same as the angle through which a line in the body, such as CP of Figure 11–1, rotates; this line is in a plane perpendicular to the axis of rotation.

If the motion of the rigid body is one in which a line such as CP traverses equal angles in equal intervals of time, the body is said to be moving with uniform angular motion, or with *constant angular speed*. If θ is the angle through which a body rotates in a time interval t, when rotating with constant angular speed ω, then

$$\omega = \frac{\theta}{t}. \tag{2}$$

When θ is expressed in radians, and t in seconds, the angular speed ω is expressed in radians/sec. Other appropriate units may also be used.

Illustrative Example. The flywheel of a gasoline engine rotates with uniform angular speed of 3,300 rpm (revolutions per minute). Determine its angular displacement, in radians, in 3 sec.

Since there are 2π radians in 1 revolution, the angular speed ω, in radians per second, is

$$\omega = \frac{2\pi \times 3,300}{60} \frac{\text{radians}}{\text{sec}} = 345.4 \frac{\text{radians}}{\text{sec}}.$$

From Equation (2), therefore,

$$\theta = \omega t,$$

so that

$$\theta = 345.4 \frac{\text{radians}}{\text{sec}} \times 3 \text{ sec}$$

and

$$\theta = 1036.2 \text{ radians}.$$

11-4 ANGULAR SPEED AND LINEAR SPEED

The angular speed of every particle of a rigid body is equal to the angular speed ω of the body. But the linear speed v of a particle depends upon its position. A typical particle P moves in a circle of radius r about the point C on the axis as center. From Equation (1), the distance s that the particle moves while the rigid body rotates through an angle θ is

$$s = PP' = \theta r. \tag{3}$$

If we consider a small time interval t, the speed of the particle is, of course,

$$v = \frac{s}{t} = \frac{\theta}{t} r.$$

But

$$\omega = \frac{\theta}{t};$$

therefore

$$\boxed{v = \omega r,} \tag{4}$$

or the linear speed of a particle is the product of its angular speed by its distance from the axis of rotation. From Equation (4), we see that the particles near the rim of the wheel, which rotates about a fixed axis, move with greater linear speed than the particles which are nearer the axis of rotation. The particles on the axis of rotation have zero linear speed; that is, they are at rest.

Illustrative Example. An airplane propeller is rotating with uniform angular speed of 1,800 rpm. The blades of the propeller are 6 ft long. Determine the linear speed of a point (a) 2 ft from the axis and (b) 6 ft from the axis.

Expressing the angular speed in radians per second, we get

$$\omega = \frac{2\pi \times 1,800}{60} \frac{\text{radians}}{\text{sec}} = 188.4 \frac{\text{radians}}{\text{sec}}.$$

(a) Using Equation (4) and letting $r = 2$ ft, we get

$$v = 188.4 \frac{\text{radians}}{\text{sec}} \times 2 \text{ ft} = 376.8 \frac{\text{ft}}{\text{sec}};$$

and, when $r = 6$ ft, we get

(b) $$v = 188.4 \frac{\text{radians}}{\text{sec}} \times 6 \text{ ft} = 1,130.4 \frac{\text{ft}}{\text{sec}}.$$

Note: The unit *radian* has no physical dimensions since it is the ratio of two lengths, as defined by Equation (1); hence a unit such as $\dfrac{\text{radians}}{\text{sec}} \times$ ft is equivalent to the unit ft/sec.

11-5 KINETIC ENERGY OF ROTATION

A rigid body rotating with uniform angular speed ω possesses kinetic energy of rotation. Its value may be calculated by summing up the individual kinetic energies of all of the particles of which the body is composed. Let us consider a typical particle of mass m_1 at distance r_1 from the axis of rotation of a disk which is rotating with uniform angular speed ω, such as that shown in Figure 11–2. Its kinetic energy is $\frac{1}{2}m_1v_1^2$, where

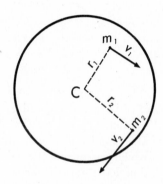

Fig. 11–2   The linear speed of a particle in a rotating disk is proportional to its distance from the fixed axis of rotation.

v_1 is the speed of this particle. Similarly, some other particle of mass m_2 at a distance r_2 from the axis of rotation and moving with linear speed v_2 will have kinetic energy equal to $\frac{1}{2}m_2v_2^2$. There will be a similar term for every particle, and, if we add up all of these kinetic energies, we will get the total kinetic energy $\mathcal{E}$ of the rotating body; that is,

$$\mathcal{E} = \tfrac{1}{2}m_1v_1^2 + \tfrac{1}{2}m_2v_2^2 + \tfrac{1}{2}m_3v_3^2 + \cdots. \tag{5}$$

But
$$v_1 = \omega r_1,$$

$$v_2 = \omega r_2,$$

$$v_3 = \omega r_3 \ldots,$$

so that
$$\mathcal{E} = \tfrac{1}{2}m_1\omega^2 r_1^2 + \tfrac{1}{2}m_2\omega^2 r_2^2 + \tfrac{1}{2}m_3\omega^2 r_3^2 + \cdots,$$

which can be written as

$$\mathcal{E} = \tfrac{1}{2}\omega^2(m_1r_1^2 + m_2r_2^2 + m_3r_3^2 + \cdots). \tag{6}$$

Let us denote the factor in parentheses by the letter I; that is,

$$I = m_1 r_1^2 + m_2 r_2^2 + m_3 r_3^2 + \cdots,$$ (7)

so that the kinetic energy of the rotating body can now be written as

$$\mathcal{E} = \tfrac{1}{2} I \omega^2.$$ (8)

The factor I is called the *moment of inertia* of the rotating body with respect to the axis of rotation. Its defining Equation (7) shows that the value of the moment of inertia depends upon the manner in which the mass is distributed with respect to the axis. Actually, to carry out the summation indicated in Equation (7) is beyond the scope of this book, but its value can frequently be determined indirectly, as will be shown later. The moment of inertia appears in the discussion of the rotational motion of a rigid body in a manner analogous to that in which the term *mass* appears in the discussion of linear motion. As a matter of fact, one can make a rather extensive and useful set of analogies for many of the physical quantities which appear in the mechanics of a particle and the mechanics of a rigid body.

Since the moment of inertia of a body about an axis consists of a sum of terms each of which is the product of a mass by the square of a distance from the axis, the final result will also be expressed as the product of a mass by a square of a distance. That is, it may be written as

$$I = m_1 r_1^2 + m_2 r_2^2 + m_3 r_3^2 + \cdots = Mk^2,$$ (9)

in which M is the mass of the entire body

or $$M = m_1 + m_2 + m_3 + \cdots,$$ (10)

and k is a distance called the *radius of gyration* of the body about the axis. The radius of gyration of a body about an axis can be interpreted as the distance from the axis of rotation at which its entire mass may be concentrated and give the same value for the moment of inertia. If the radius of gyration of a body about any axis is known, its moment of inertia about that axis is obtained by multiplying the mass M of the entire body by the square of its radius of gyration.

The units for moment of inertia are those of mass multiplied by the square of a distance, for example, gm cm^2, or slugs ft^2. If the weight W of the body is given in pounds, its mass M in slugs can be obtained with the aid of the equation $M = W/g$. For most calculations, g may be taken as 32 ft/sec^2.

Illustrative Example. A cylindrical pulley made of wood has a mass of 600 gm and a radius $R = 8$ cm. The moment of inertia of this cylinder about its geometrical axis is given by $I = \frac{1}{2}MR^2$. The pulley is rotating about this axis with an angular speed of 36 radians/sec. Determine (a) the kinetic energy of the pulley and (b) its radius of gyration.

The kinetic energy of the pulley is given by

$$\mathcal{E} = \tfrac{1}{2}I\omega^2,$$

and, since

$$I = \tfrac{1}{2}MR^2,$$

$$\mathcal{E} = \tfrac{1}{4}MR^2\omega^2.$$

Substituting numerical values, we get

(a) $$\mathcal{E} = \frac{1}{4} \times 600 \text{ gm} \times (8 \text{ cm})^2 \times \left(36 \, \frac{\text{radians}}{\text{sec}}\right)^2,$$

from which $\mathcal{E} = 1.27 \times 10^7$ ergs $= 1.27$ joules.

(b) From Equation (9), $I = Mk^2,$

but $$I = \tfrac{1}{2}MR^2;$$

therefore $$k^2 = \frac{R^2}{2},$$

or $$k = \frac{R}{\sqrt{2}},$$

so that $$k = 5.66 \text{ cm}.$$

Illustrative Example. A flywheel of a steam engine weighing 1,500 lb and having a radius of gyration of 2 ft rotates with uniform angular speed of 180 rpm. Determine its kinetic energy.

The kinetic energy of the flywheel is

$$\mathcal{E} = \tfrac{1}{2}I\omega^2,$$

but $$I = Mk^2;$$

therefore $$\mathcal{E} = \tfrac{1}{2}Mk^2\omega^2.$$

Substituting numerical values, we get

$$\mathcal{E} = \frac{1}{2} \times \frac{1,500 \text{ lb}}{32 \text{ ft/sec}^2} \times (2 \text{ ft})^2 \times \left(\frac{2\pi \times 180}{60} \, \frac{\text{radians}}{\text{sec}}\right)^2,$$

which yields

$$\mathcal{E} = 33,310 \text{ ft-lb}.$$

11-6 MOMENTS OF INERTIA

The moments of inertia of a few homogeneous solids of simple geometric shapes are given in Figure 11–3. The mass of each body is called M, and the axis of rotation is a line through the center of gravity in the direction shown in the figure.

It is often necessary to know the moment of inertia of a body about an axis which does not pass through the center of gravity. In the special

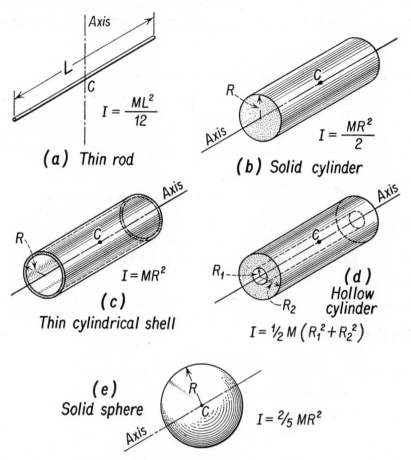

FIG. 11-3   Moments of inertia of some rigid bodies having simple geometrical shapes.

case in which the axis is parallel to the one through the center of gravity, it can be shown that the moment of inertia I about this axis is given by

$$I = I_c + Md^2, \tag{11}$$

where I_c is the moment of inertia about a parallel axis through the center of gravity and d is the distance between the axes. Equation (11) is usually referred to as the *parallel axis theorem* for moments of inertia. Thus the moment of inertia of a homogeneous solid cylinder of mass M and radius R about one of its elements as an axis is

$$I = \tfrac{1}{2}MR^2 + MR^2,$$

or
$$I = \tfrac{3}{2}MR^2,$$

since the distance of an element of a right circular cylinder from its center is $d = R$.

11-7   VECTOR REPRESENTATION OF ANGULAR VELOCITY

There are two possible directions for the rotation of a body about a fixed axis. If we view the motion along the axis, the direction of rotation can be described as clockwise or counterclockwise. The disk of Figure 11–2 is rotating in a clockwise direction as viewed by the reader. For most of

FIG. 11–4   The angular velocity of a body rotating in a counterclockwise direction is represented by a vector coming out of the paper and drawn along the axis of rotation.

our purposes, this description of the motion will be adequate. One may even call one direction, say counterclockwise, positive, and the other direction, clockwise, negative.

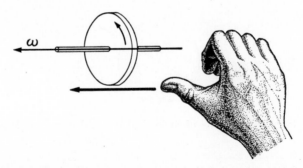

FIG. 11–5   The right-hand rule: if the fingers of the right hand follow the direction of rotation, the thumb will point in the direction in which the arrow should be drawn along the axis of rotation.

The angular velocity ω may also be represented by a vector. The accepted method for doing this is to draw a vector along the axis pointing toward the reader if the motion is counterclockwise, as illustrated in Figure 11–4, and away from the reader if the motion is clockwise. A convenient way of remembering this method of representation is by means of the *right-hand* rule: imagine the right hand held so that the fingers follow the direction of rotation; the thumb will then point in the direction in which the arrow should be drawn along the axis. Figure 11–5 illustrates this. The magnitude of the angular velocity is represented by the length of the arrow drawn to some arbitrary scale.

11-8 ANGULAR ACCELERATION

So far we have limited our discussion of the motion of a rigid body to rotational motion with constant angular velocity. If the angular velocity is not constant, then the body is said to move with an angular acceleration. The *angular acceleration* α of a rigid body is defined as *the ratio of the change in angular velocity $\Delta\omega$ to the time interval Δt during which the change takes place*, or

$$\alpha = \frac{\Delta\omega}{\Delta t}. \tag{12}$$

Another way of stating this is that the angular acceleration is the time rate of change of angular velocity.

Since angular velocity is a vector quantity, it can change either in direction or in magnitude, or in both. In this section we shall limit our discussion to motion with constant angular acceleration about the same axis or a parallel axis, so that only the magnitude of the angular velocity changes. If ω_i is the initial angular velocity of a body about an axis and ω_f is the angular velocity of the body about the same or a parallel axis at the end of a time interval t, then the angular acceleration α of the body is given by

$$\alpha = \frac{\omega_f - \omega_i}{t}, \tag{13}$$

providing the acceleration is constant.

Illustrative Example. The angular velocity of an airplane propeller is increased at a constant rate from 1,800 rpm to 2,200 rpm in 10 sec. Determine its angular acceleration.

(a) We may apply Equation (13) directly with the units as given in the problem and get

$$\alpha = \frac{(2,200 - 1,800)\ \text{rpm}}{10\ \text{sec}} = 40\ \frac{\text{rev}}{\text{min sec}},$$

or (b) we may first express the angular velocities in radians per second and then apply Equation (13).

Now
$$\omega_i = \frac{2\pi \times 1{,}800}{60} \frac{\text{radians}}{\text{sec}},$$

$$\omega_f = \frac{2\pi \times 2{,}200}{60} \frac{\text{radians}}{\text{sec}},$$

so that
$$\alpha = \frac{\dfrac{2\pi}{60}(2{,}200 - 1{,}800)\dfrac{\text{radians}}{\text{sec}}}{10 \text{ sec}} = 4.19 \frac{\text{radians}}{\text{sec}^2}.$$

11-9 ANGULAR ACCELERATION AND LINEAR ACCELERATION

When a rigid body rotates about a fixed axis with constant angular acceleration α, each particle of the body has the same angular acceleration α. But the linear acceleration a of each particle will be different. Since the angular velocity of each particle is changing, its linear velocity is also changing both in magnitude and direction. The linear acceleration a of a particle may be resolved into two components: one component a_t tangent to the path and given by the time rate of change of the speed of the particle,

$$a_t = \frac{v_t - v_i}{t}; \tag{14a}$$

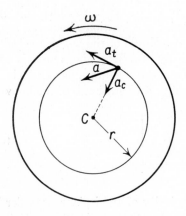

FIG. 11-6   Tangential component a_t and radial component a_c of the linear acceleration a of a particle at a distance r from the axis of rotation.

and the other component a_c directed perpendicular to the velocity and along the radius toward the center of the circle in which the particle is moving, and given by

$$a_c = \frac{v^2}{r}, \tag{14b}$$

in which r is the radius of the circular path (see Figure 11–6). Now, from

Equation (4), we get for any one particle

$$v = \omega r,$$

$$v_i = \omega_i r,$$

$$v_f = \omega_f r.$$

Substituting these values in the equation for the tangential component of the acceleration, we get

$$a_t = \frac{\omega_f - \omega_i}{t}\, r,$$

from which
$$\boxed{a_t = \alpha r,}$$
(15)

and the central or normal component of the acceleration may be expressed in terms of the angular velocity by

$$\boxed{a_c = \frac{v^2}{r} = \omega^2 r.}$$
(16)

Equation (15) shows that the tangential component of the acceleration of a particle is directly proportional to its distance r from the axis of rotation. Equation (16) is a restatement of the fact that a particle which is moving in a circular path has an acceleration directed toward the center of the circle. If the particle is moving with uniform speed in a circle, then the central acceleration is its total acceleration. If its speed is increasing or decreasing while it is moving in a circle, then its total acceleration a is made up of the two components a_t and a_c, and, since these two components are at right angles to each other, we have

$$\boxed{a = \sqrt{a_t^2 + a_c^2}.}$$
(17)

Illustrative Example. A circular pulley 4 ft in diameter is mounted so that it can rotate about an axis passing through its center. One end of a cord which is wound around the pulley is being pulled in a horizontal direction, as shown in Figure 11–7, with an acceleration of 6 ft/sec². Determine (a) the angular acceleration of the pulley and (b), assuming the pulley to have been at rest initially, determine the acceleration of the lowest point B on the rim of the pulley at the end of 10 sec.

(a) The point A at the top of the pulley is the point at which the rope just leaves the pulley. The tangential component of the acceleration a_t of this point is the same as the acceleration of a point on the rope. We can therefore use the acceleration of this point for determining the angular acceleration of the pulley. From Equation (15),

$$\alpha = \frac{a_t}{r} = \frac{6 \text{ ft/sec}^2}{2 \text{ ft}} = 3 \frac{\text{radians}}{\text{sec}^2}.$$

(b) The angular speed of the pulley at the end of 10 sec is, from Equation (13),

$$\omega_f = \omega_i + \alpha t,$$

and, since $\quad\quad \omega_i = 0,$

$$\omega_f = 3 \frac{\text{radians}}{\text{sec}^2} \times 10 \text{ sec} = 30 \frac{\text{radians}}{\text{sec}}.$$

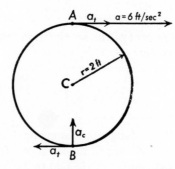

Fɪɢ. 11–7

The linear speed of a point on the rim of the wheel at the end of 10 sec is

$$v_f = \omega_f r,$$

$$v_f = 30 \frac{\text{radians}}{\text{sec}} \times 2 \text{ ft} = 60 \frac{\text{ft}}{\text{sec}}.$$

Since the angular acceleration is clockwise, the lowest point on the rim of the wheel is moving toward the left with a velocity of 60 ft/sec in a circle of radius 2 ft. The two components of its acceleration at this instant are

$$a_t = \alpha r = 6 \frac{\text{ft}}{\text{sec}^2} \quad\quad \text{to the left}$$

and $\quad\quad a_c = \omega^2 r = \left(30 \frac{\text{radians}}{\text{sec}}\right)^2 \times 2 \text{ ft} = 1,800 \frac{\text{ft}}{\text{sec}^2},$

directed toward the center.

11-10 TORQUE AND ANGULAR ACCELERATION

In our discussion of the equilibrium of a rigid body, we found that when the algebraic sum of the moments of all the forces, or the torques, about any

axis is zero, the body is in equilibrium as far as rotational motion is concerned. Referring again to a body capable of rotation about a fixed axis,
we find that if the sum of the torques about this axis is zero, then the body
is in equilibrium. If it is initially at rest, it will remain at rest; or if it is
rotating about this axis with some angular speed ω, it will continue to rotate
about the same axis with uniform angular speed ω unless there is some
external torque acting on it. If there is an external torque G acting on this
body, then it will acquire an angular acceleration α given by

$$G = I\alpha,$$

(18)

where G is the sum of all the external torques about the fixed axis of rotation
and I is the moment of inertia of the body about the same axis. Equation
(18) can be deduced by applying Newton's second and third laws to the
particles forming the rigid body.

In outline, this can be done by considering a typical particle of mass
m_1 anywhere within the rigid body and assuming that it is acted upon by a
force which has a component F_1 tangent to the circular path taken by the
particle. Then, from Newton's second law, we can write

$$F_1 = m_1 a_t,$$

where a_t is the tangential component of its acceleration. The torque G_1
produced by this force is $F_1 r_1$; hence

$$G_1 = F_1 r_1 = m_1 r_1 a_t,$$

but $$a_t = r_1 \alpha;$$

hence $$G_1 = m_1 r_1^2 \alpha,$$

or $$G_1 = I_1 \alpha,$$

(18a)

where I_1 is the moment of inertia of this particle about the axis. The same
analysis can be applied to each particle in the body. Now the sum of all
the forces acting on all the particles should be the total external force on the
rigid body, since the internal forces act in pairs and are equal and oppositely
directed. Furthermore each pair of internal forces acts along the line joining the two particles; hence they produce no resultant torque. Therefore
the torque acting on the entire body must be that produced by the external
forces. Thus, when Equation (18a) is summed up for every particle in the
rigid body, we get Equation (18).

When the mass M of the body is given, then

$$I = Mk^2,$$

and Equation (18) becomes

$$G = Mk^2\alpha.$$ (19)

Illustrative Example. A disk 30 cm in diameter and having a mass of 900 gm is mounted so that it can rotate about a fixed axis passing through

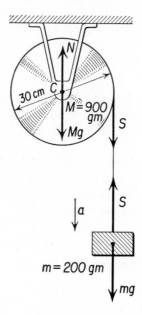

its center, as in Figure 11–8. Its radius of gyration about this axis is 10 cm. A mass of 200 gm hangs from a string which is wound around this disk. Determine (a) the acceleration of the 200-gm mass, (b) the angular acceleration of the disk, and (c) the tension in the string.

Let us consider this problem in two parts. Let us first consider the forces acting on the 200-gm mass. There are just two forces acting on it: its weight *mg* and the pull of the string *S* upward. Since its acceleration *a* is downward, we can write, for Newton's second law,

$$mg - S = ma.$$

Fig. 11–8

Now let us consider the forces acting on the disk. The only force that exerts a torque about the axis of rotation through *C* is the pull of the cord *S*. If *r* is the radius of the disk and *k* its radius of gyration, then Equation (19) becomes

$$Sr = Mk^2\alpha.$$

We have the additional relationship that

$$a = r\alpha.$$

These three equations are sufficient to determine the three unknowns *S*, *a*, and *α*. Eliminating *α* from the last two equations and solving for *S*, we get

$$S = Ma\,\frac{k^2}{r^2}.$$

Substituting this value of *S* in the first equation, we have

$$mg - Ma\,\frac{k^2}{r^2} = ma,$$

and, solving for a, we get

$$a = \frac{m}{m + M\dfrac{k^2}{r^2}}\, g.$$

The numerical values $m = 200$ gm, $M = 900$ gm, $k = 10$ cm, $r = 15$ cm, and $g = 980\, \dfrac{\text{cm}}{\text{sec}^2}$ yield

(a) $$a = \frac{g}{3} = 327\, \frac{\text{cm}}{\text{sec}^2}\cdot$$

(b) Then $$\alpha = \frac{a}{r} = 21.8\, \frac{\text{radians}}{\text{sec}^2},$$

and (c) $$S = 900\text{ gm} \times 327\, \frac{\text{cm}}{\text{sec}^2} \times \frac{4}{9}$$

$$S = 130{,}800 \text{ dynes.}$$

The tension in the cord is thus less than the weight of the 200-gm mass hanging from its end.

Illustrative Example. A body weighing 2 lb hangs from a string wound around the circumference of a pulley 1 ft in diameter. The pulley weighs 8 lb and is free to rotate about a fixed axis passing through its center of gravity. The body, when allowed to fall from rest, traverses 4 ft in 1 sec. Determine (a) the tension in the string and (b) the moment of inertia of the pulley.

Figure 11–9 is similar to the one used in the preceding problem. The acceleration a of the falling weight can be found from the equation

$$s = \tfrac{1}{2}at^2,$$

$$4 \text{ ft} = \tfrac{1}{2}a(1 \text{ sec})^2,$$

so that $a = 8\, \dfrac{\text{ft}}{\text{sec}^2}\cdot$

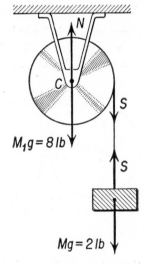

$M_1g = 8\,lb$

$Mg = 2\,lb$

Fig. 11–9

The forces acting on the falling body are its weight Mg downward and the pull of the string S upward, so that

$$Mg - S = Ma.$$

Substituting numerical values, we get

$$2\,\text{lb} - S = \frac{2\,\text{slug}}{32} \times 8\,\frac{\text{ft}}{\text{sec}^2},$$

from which (a) $S = 1.5\,\text{lb}.$

The tension in the string S is the only force which exerts a torque about the axis. If r is the radius of the pulley, then Equation (18) yields

$$Sr = I\alpha$$

and

$$\alpha = \frac{a}{r},$$

so that

$$I = \frac{Sr^2}{a}.$$

Substituting numerical values, we get

$$I = \frac{1.5\,\text{lb} \times (\tfrac{1}{2}\,\text{ft})^2}{8\,\text{ft/sec}^2}$$

$$= \tfrac{3}{64}\,\text{slug ft}^2.$$

11-11 WORK AND ROTATIONAL ENERGY

Whenever a rigid body is set into rotation about an axis, work is done by the torques acting on it to increase its kinetic energy of rotation. Suppose that a force F acts on the rim of a wheel of radius R and rotates the

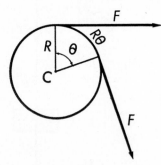

FIG. 11–10 The work done by a constant torque G when it acts through an angle θ is $G\theta$.

body through an angle θ, as in Figure 11–10. If the force F remains tangent to the wheel throughout its displacement $R\theta$, then the work done by this force is

$$\mathcal{W} = FR\theta. \tag{20}$$

But $FR = G;$

therefore

$$\mathcal{W} = G\theta, \tag{21}$$

or the work done by a constant torque G is equal to the product of the torque and the angle through which it acts.

If the torque acts on a rigid body which is rotating about a fixed axis, then, assuming no loss due to friction, the work done by this torque will produce a change in the kinetic energy of the body, given by

$$G\theta = \tfrac{1}{2}I\omega_f^2 - \tfrac{1}{2}I\omega_i^2, \tag{22}$$

in which ω_f is the final angular speed of the body, ω_i is the initial angular speed of the body, and θ is the angle through which the torque acts.

Illustrative Example. The flywheel of a steam engine weighs 500 pounds and has a radius of gyration of 1.5 ft. It is given an angular speed of 150 rpm in 90 rev, starting from rest. Determine the torque, assuming it to be constant, which acted on the flywheel.

The angle θ through which the torque G acted is

$$\theta = 90 \times 2\pi \text{ radians.}$$

The initial angular speed $\omega_i = 0$; the final angular speed is

$$\omega_f = \frac{150 \times 2\pi}{60} \frac{\text{radians}}{\text{sec}} = 5\pi \frac{\text{radians}}{\text{sec}}.$$

The moment of inertia I of the flywheel is

$$I = Mk^2 = \frac{W}{g}k^2,$$

so that

$$I = \frac{500 \text{ lb}}{32 \text{ ft/sec}^2} \times (1.5 \text{ ft})^2.$$

Substituting these values in Equation (22) yields

$$G \times 2\pi \times 90 = \frac{1}{2} \cdot \frac{500 \text{ lb}}{32 \text{ ft/sec}^2} \times 2.25 \text{ ft}^2 \times 25\pi^2 \frac{\text{radians}^2}{\text{sec}^2},$$

from which

$$G = 4{,}340 \text{ lb ft.}$$

11-12 ROLLING MOTION

The motion of a wheel which is rolling along the ground can be considered in one of two ways: either as a rotation of the wheel about an axis through its center of gravity C and an additional motion of the entire wheel with the same velocity as the center of gravity, as shown in Figure 11–11, or as a rotation of the wheel about an *instantaneous axis* through the point of contact O between the wheel and the ground.   A point in the body which is on the instantaneous axis is momentarily at rest.   The instantaneous

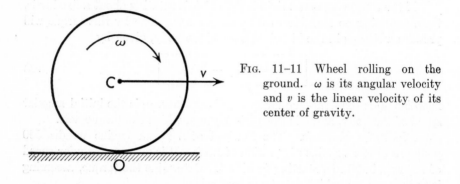

FIG.   11–11   Wheel   rolling   on   the ground. ω is its angular velocity and v is the linear velocity of its center of gravity.

axis itself moves forward as the wheel moves forward, but it always remains parallel to itself and to the axis through the center of gravity.   The angular velocity of the wheel about the instantaneous axis is the same as that about the axis through the center of gravity.

Rolling motion will occur only when there is sufficient friction between the wheel and the ground to prevent slipping.   If there is no slipping, no work is done against friction, and no energy is transformed into heat.   This type of motion can be treated by means of the equations derived in this chapter by considering it as consisting of two types of motion: one a motion of rotation of the body about an axis through its center of gravity, and the other a motion of translation of the entire body with the velocity and acceleration of the center of gravity.   The angular velocity and angular acceleration are calculated by taking the torques and moment of inertia about an axis through the center of gravity.   The linear acceleration and velocity of the center of gravity are then calculated by considering all the forces as though they acted through the center of gravity and by applying Newton's second law of motion to this case.

Illustrative Example.   A solid disk of radius R and mass M rolls, without slipping, down an inclined plane of height h and length L, inclined at an angle ϕ to the horizontal.   Discuss its motion.

There are three forces acting on the disk: its weight Mg, the push N perpendicular to the plane and passing through the center of the disk, and the frictional force F acting parallel to the plane at the point of contact O. Figure 11–12 illustrates this.   The instantaneous axis passes through point O and is perpendicular to the plane of the disk.

It is instructive to consider this problem from the energy point of view.

If the disk rolls down the incline without slipping, there is no energy lost in doing work against the frictional force. If we assume that the disk starts at the top of the incline with zero kinetic energy, its total energy is simply its potential energy Mgh. At the bottom of the inclined plane it has no potential energy but possesses two forms of kinetic energy: kinetic energy

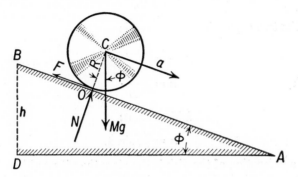

FIG. 11–12   Disk rolling down an inclined plane.

of rotation $\frac{1}{2}I_c\omega^2$ with respect to an axis through its center of gravity, and kinetic energy of translation $\frac{1}{2}Mv^2$, where v is the velocity of its center of gravity. Using the principle of conservation of energy, we get

$$Mgh = \tfrac{1}{2}I_c\omega^2 + \tfrac{1}{2}Mv^2. \tag{23}$$

Now

$$I_c = \tfrac{1}{2}MR^2;$$

hence

$$Mgh = \tfrac{1}{4}MR^2\omega^2 + \tfrac{1}{2}Mv^2,$$

and, since

$$v = R\omega,$$

we get

$$Mgh = \tfrac{3}{4}Mv^2,$$

from which

$$v^2 = \tfrac{4}{3}gh,$$

so that

$$v = \sqrt{\tfrac{4}{3}gh}. \tag{24}$$

It will be noted that the mass of the body does not enter in the equation for the velocity and, further, that the velocity of a body which rolls down an incline of height h is less than it would have been if it had moved down a frictionless plane of the same height. In addition to the linear velocity v of the center of gravity, the disk has an angular velocity

$$\omega = v/R$$

or

$$\omega = \frac{\sqrt{4gh/3}}{R}. \tag{25}$$

To determine the acceleration a of the center of gravity parallel to the plane, we can use the equation

$$v^2 = u^2 + 2as,$$

with $u = 0$ and $s = L$,

so that
$$v^2 = 2aL.$$

Equating the two expressions for v^2 yields

$$\tfrac{4}{3}gh = 2aL,$$

from which
$$a = \tfrac{2}{3}\frac{gh}{L}\,.$$

But
$$h/L = \sin\phi;$$

hence
$$a = \tfrac{2}{3}g\sin\phi. \tag{26}$$

The linear acceleration of the disk is thus less than it would have been had it moved down a frictionless plane with the same angle of inclination.

The angular acceleration of the disk can now readily be determined since

$$\alpha = \frac{a}{R},$$

so that
$$\alpha = \tfrac{2}{3}\frac{g}{R}\sin\phi. \tag{27}$$

The above results could also have been obtained by using Newton's second law for the linear acceleration of the center of gravity thus:

$$Mg\sin\phi - F = Ma; \tag{28}$$

and also by determining the torque about an axis through the center of gravity thus:

$$FR = I_c\alpha. \tag{29}$$

The solutions of these equations of motion, left as an exercise for the student, will yield not only the same values of a and α, and v and ω, as above, but also the value of the frictional force F as

$$F = \tfrac{1}{3}Mg\sin\phi. \tag{30}$$

11-13 ANGULAR MOMENTUM

A rigid body rotating with angular velocity ω about an axis has a definite *angular momentum* about this axis given by

$$\text{angular momentum} = I\omega,$$

where I is the moment of inertia of the body about this axis. To change the angular momentum of the body, an external torque must be applied to the body. The relationship between torque and angular momentum can be obtained by combining Equations (13) and (18)

$$G = I\alpha, \tag{18}$$

$$\alpha = \frac{\omega_f - \omega_i}{t}, \tag{13}$$

from which
$$\boxed{Gt = I\omega_f - I\omega_i.} \tag{31}$$

This equation states that an external torque acting for a time t will produce a change in the angular momentum of the body about the given axis equal to the product of the torque G and the time t during which it acts.

Of particular interest is the case where there is no external torque acting; that is.

$$G = 0;$$

then
$$I\omega_f = I\omega_i = \text{constant.} \tag{32}$$

In this case, there is no change in the angular momentum of the rigid body about its axis; or, the *angular momentum of the system is conserved*. Since angular velocity is a vector quantity, angular momentum is also a vector quantity having the same direction as the angular velocity. A rigid body set spinning about an axis will maintain its direction of rotation as well as its angular speed, providing no external torque acts on it. Flywheels having large moments of inertia are mounted on gasoline engines and steam engines to help maintain a uniform angular speed. Bullets and shells are given rotational motions by being propelled through "rifled" barrels of guns; because of its angular momentum, a spinning bullet or shell will keep spinning about the same axis throughout its flight until it strikes an object. It keeps moving with its nose forward so that it will have greater penetrating power on striking an obstacle. A torpedo maintains its direction of motion through the water because of the angular momentum of the small engine which propels the torpedo through the water.

Probably the most important example of the principle of the conservation of angular momentum is provided by the rotation of the earth on its axis once every 24 hr. This axis is inclined at an angle of 66.5° with respect to the plane of its orbit around the sun. The direction of this axis remains fixed as the earth revolves around the sun, thus giving rise to the seasons.

11-14 ANGULAR SIMPLE HARMONIC MOTION

The analogy between linear and angular motion can be extended to simple harmonic motion by defining *angular simple harmonic motion* as that in which the angular acceleration α of a body is proportional to its angular displacement θ from its equilibrium position and opposite in direction, or

$$\alpha = -c\theta, \tag{33}$$

where c is a constant of proportionality. [Compare this with Equation (1) of Chapter 7.] The motion of the body in this case will be periodic with a period given by

$$T = \frac{2\pi}{\sqrt{c}}.$$

[Equation (9) in Chapter 7]

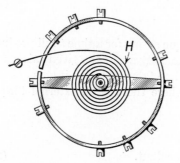

FIG. 11–13   Balance wheel of a watch. H is the hairspring.

An example of angular simple harmonic motion is the motion of the balance wheel of a watch. Such a wheel is mounted on an axle whose ends are pivoted in jeweled bearings. One end of a very fine hairspring is attached to the axle, the other end to the frame (see Figure 11–13). When the wheel rotates through an angle θ from its equilibrium position, the spring exerts a torque G proportional to this angle to return it to its equilibrium position; thus

$$G = -k\theta, \tag{34}$$

where k is the twist or torsional constant of elasticity of the spring.

Since

$$G = I\alpha,$$

we note that

$$\alpha = -\frac{k}{I}\theta.$$

Comparing this with Equation (33), we find that

$$c = \frac{k}{I},$$

so that the period of oscillation of the balance wheel is given by

$$T = 2\pi\sqrt{\frac{I}{k}}. \tag{35}$$

Illustrative Example. The balance wheel of a watch makes 5 vibrations/sec; its moment of inertia is 80 gm cm^2. Determine the torsional constant of the hairspring.

Solving Equation (35) for k yields

$$k = \frac{4\pi^2 I}{T^2}.$$

Now $T = 0.2$ sec, $I = 80$ gm cm^2,

so that $k = \dfrac{4\pi^2 \times 80 \text{ gm cm}^2}{0.04 \text{ sec}^2} = 79{,}200 \text{ dyne cm.}$

11-15 THE GYROSCOPE

We have stressed the fact that the angular momentum of a rigid body about an axis remains constant unless acted upon by some external torque. In the previous sections, we considered the change in the angular momen-

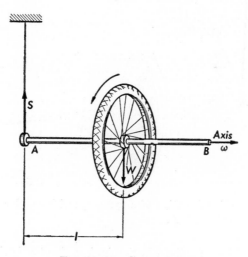

Fig. 11–14   Gyroscope.

tum about the *same axis* produced by the action of an external torque. The more general case in which the torque produces an acceleration about one axis while the body is rotating about a different axis is much beyond the scope of this book. Because of the importance of this type of motion, however, one simple case will be discussed in a qualitative manner. This is the case in which a body is spinning with a large angular momentum about one axis, which we shall call the *axis of spin*, and a steady torque is applied to the body to produce a small acceleration about an axis perpendicular to the axis of spin.

A good demonstration of the motion described above can be presented by mounting a bicycle wheel on an axle which protrudes beyond the hub of the wheel and then supporting one end of this axle in a loop in a string which is suspended from the ceiling, as shown in Figure 11–14. Suppose that the bicycle wheel is given a spin about its axis in the direction shown by the vector ω. (If, as we face the wheel, the arrow points toward us, the motion of the wheel about this axis is counterclockwise.) After the wheel has been given a spin, there are only two forces acting on it: its weight W acting through the center of gravity, and the pull S of the string at A. The torque produced by these two forces about a horizontal axis through A perpendicular to SAB is given by Wl, where l is the distance from the center of gravity to A. This torque is clockwise, as viewed by the reader, and will produce an acceleration α in a clockwise direction about this horizontal axis.

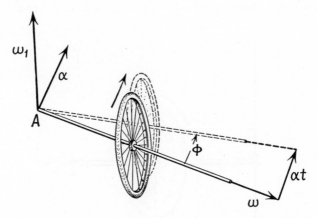

Fɪɢ. 11–15   Precessional motion of a gyroscope with angular velocity ω_1 about a vertical axis through A.

Figure 11–15 shows the wheel spinning about a horizontal axis; its angular velocity ω is shown as a vector along this axis. The angular acceleration α is drawn as a vector at right angles to ω and also in the horizontal plane. As a result of this angular acceleration, the axis of spin will move through an angle ϕ in the horizontal plane with an angular velocity $\omega_1 = \alpha t$, where t is a small time interval. In this new position of the wheel, the torque produces an angular acceleration α equal in magnitude to that in the first position but now directed at right angles to the new axis of spin. This axis will turn through an additional angle ϕ in the horizontal plane in an equal time interval t. Thus the axis of spin will rotate in the horizontal plane which, when viewed from above, will be in a counterclockwise direction about the string through A as an axis. This rotation of the axis is called a motion of *precession*. The rotating wheel is sometimes called a *gyroscope*, and the motion analyzed above is called *gyroscopic motion*.

Any rotating body can be considered a gyroscope. When a torque acts to change the direction of its axis of spin, precessional motion will occur. The motion of a top whose axis of spin is inclined to the vertical is a common example of precessional motion. The propeller of an airplane engine acts like a gyroscope when it is rotating. Whenever the airplane turns in such a way as to change the direction of the axis of spin, the gyroscope will precess, and this motion must be taken into account in making the turn. Many other examples of gyroscopic motion will probably occur to the reader.

QUESTIONS

1. Is the radian a unit in the English or the metric system?

2. Give the analogue in rotational motion for each of the following quantities used in describing linear motion: distance, linear speed, linear acceleration, momentum, mass, force, and kinetic energy.

3. Each of the following equations refers to a particle in linear motion. Write the analogous equation for rotational motion of a rigid body.

$$F = ma$$

$$\mathcal{W} = Fs$$

$$Fs = \tfrac{1}{2}mv_f^2 - \tfrac{1}{2}mv_i^2$$

$$Ft = mv_f - mv_i$$

$$\text{Power} = Fv$$

4. A bicycle wheel rotating about a fixed axis with uniform angular speed is in equilibrium. Any particle in the wheel is therefore moving with uniform circular motion about this fixed axis. Is this particle in equilibrium? If not, what is the force acting on this particle, and in what direction does this force act?

5. Compare the linear acceleration of the center of gravity of a body rolling down a hill inclined at an angle ϕ with the linear acceleration the same body would have in sliding down a frictionless hill having the same inclination.

6. The propeller of an airplane is rotating in a clockwise direction as viewed by the pilot. Which way will the front end of the plane tend to go when this plane makes a right turn?

7. When a car is going forward, the engine and flywheel are rotating counterclockwise as viewed by the driver. In which direction will the car tend to go if the front wheels are suddenly lifted over a bump in the road?

8. Many large ferryboats are driven by large side-wheel paddles. Discuss

the gyroscopic effect produced by the motion of these side wheels when the ferry-boat makes a turn.

PROBLEMS

1. Express the following angles in radian measure: 90°, 180°, and 270°.

2. A flywheel of a steam engine is rotating with a uniform angular speed of 180 rpm. (a) Express this angular speed in radians per second. (b) Determine the linear speed of a point on this wheel which is at a distance of 1.5 ft from the center.

3. The flywheel of a gasoline engine weighs 75 lb and is rotating with an angular speed of 3,300 rpm. The radius of gyration of this flywheel is 5 in. Determine the kinetic energy of this flywheel.

4. A small copper disk of 15 cm radius and 500 gm mass is rotating with an angular speed of 12 radians/sec about an axis through its center perpendicular to the plane of the disk. Determine the kinetic energy of the disk.

5. The fuel supply is shut off from an engine when its angular speed is 1,800 rpm. It stops rotating 12 sec later. Determine its angular acceleration, assuming it to be constant.

6. The angular speed of an automobile engine is increased from 3,000 rpm to 3,600 rpm in 18 sec. (a) Determine its acceleration, assuming it to be uniform; (b) determine the number of revolutions made by the engine in this time.

7. If a rigid body rotating about a fixed axis has a constant angular acceleration α, show that the angle θ through which it rotates in time t is given by $\theta = \omega_i t + \frac{1}{2}\alpha t^2$.

(Hint: Use Equations (2) and (13) with the additional fact that the average angular speed in this case is $\omega = \dfrac{\omega_i + \omega_f}{2}$.)

8. A pulley 6 in. in diameter is mounted so that it can rotate about a fixed axis through its center. The pulley weighs 16 lb and has a radius of gyration of 2 in. A constant force of 3 lb is applied to the rim of the pulley by means of a cord wrapped around it. Determine (a) the angular acceleration of the pulley and (b) the angular speed it has at the end of 10 sec, assuming that the pulley was initially at rest.

9. A wheel having a mass of 1,200 gm and a radius of 8 cm is mounted so that it can rotate about a fixed axis passing through its center. The radius of gyration of the wheel about this axis is 6 cm. A cord is wrapped around the circumference of this wheel, and a mass of 150 gm is attached to its free end. (a) Determine the angular acceleration of the wheel when it is released. (b) Determine the linear acceleration of the 150-gm mass. (c) Determine the tension in the cord.

10. A wheel having a radius of 6 cm is mounted so that it can rotate about a fixed axis passing through its center. A cord wrapped around the circumference of the wheel has a mass of 250 gm attached to its free end. When allowed to fall, the mass takes 8 sec to fall a distance of 100 cm. Determine (a) the angular acceleration of the wheel and (b) its moment of inertia.

11. A solid circular cylinder 2 ft in diameter and weighing 80 lb starts at the top of a rough plane 24 ft long and inclined at an angle of 30° with the horizontal and rolls down without slipping. (a) How much energy did the cylinder have at the top of the hill? (b) How much energy will it have at the bottom of the hill? (c) Determine its angular velocity at the bottom of the hill.

12. Referring to the cylinder of Problem 11, determine (a) its angular acceleration, (b) the linear acceleration of its center of gravity, and (c) the linear velocity of the center of gravity at the bottom of the incline.

13. A steel hoop rolls, without sliding, down a plane inclined at an angle of 30° with the horizon. The mass of this hoop is 900 gm, and its radius is 8 cm. The moment of inertia of this hoop about an axis through its center of gravity perpendicular to the plane of the hoop is $I = MR^2$. Determine (a) its moment of inertia about its instantaneous axis, (b) its angular acceleration, and (c) the force of friction between the hoop and the plane.

14. A flywheel weighing 120 lb and having a radius of 18 in. rotates with a uniform angular speed of 9 radians/sec. The radius of gyration of the flywheel is 12 in. (a) Determine the angular momentum of the flywheel. (b) How big a force applied tangentially to its rim will be required to bring it to rest in 8 sec?

15. Starting with Equation 21 for the work done by a torque G acting through an angle θ, show that the power P supplied is given by $P = G\omega$, where ω is the angular velocity of the body supplying the torque.

16. A gasoline engine develops 210 hp when turning at 3,300 rpm. Determine the torque delivered by this engine to the drive shaft.

Part Two

HEAT

12

Temperature

12-1 CONCEPT OF TEMPERATURE

Temperature is one of the fundamental concepts of physics. We are all able to recognize that some bodies are hotter than others; that is, some bodies are at higher temperatures than other bodies. A piece of ice feels cold to the touch, while boiling water feels hot. The sense of touch can be used to distinguish between hotter and colder bodies, but it does not suffice for measurements of the temperature of a body. We are also familiar with the fact that when the temperature of a body is raised, some of its physical properties are changed. For example, when the temperature of a solid rod is increased, its length is increased; when the temperature of a gas is increased, its volume or its pressure or both may be increased. Some of the electric and magnetic properties of substances are affected by a change in temperature. The changes that take place in these physical properties can be used to measure the changes in the temperature which produced them.

In order to make a measurement of the temperature of a body, it is important to be able to decide when two bodies are at the same temperature. Suppose the length of a copper rod is measured in the laboratory and then put into a jar of cold water. The length of the copper rod will decrease until it reaches a new value. As long as the length of the rod is changing, its temperature is changing. When the length of the rod reaches its new value and no longer changes, we say that the water and the copper are at the same temperature. Our next task is to assign a definite number to this temperature.

In order to be able to assign a number to the temperature of a body, it is necessary to adopt a *scale of temperature*. As a guide in doing this, we can refer back to the methods used in assigning numbers to the fundamental quantities: length, mass, and time. The method is essentially to decide upon a *standard temperature interval* and upon a method of subdividing this standard temperature interval into smaller units known as *degrees*. In choosing a standard temperature interval, we need *two fixed points;* that is, we must find some physical processes which take place at constant temperature. The two processes chosen are the melting of ice at standard atmospheric pressure and the boiling of water at standard atmospheric

269

pressure. By using the length of the copper rod as an indicator, it can be shown that the temperature of a mixture of ice and water remains constant even though the ice is continually melting. Similarly, the temperature of the boiling water and of the steam above the water remains constant during the process of boiling, provided the pressure remains constant.

Having decided upon the method of determining the two fixed points of the standard temperature interval, we must now decide upon numbers to be assigned to these two points. There are two different sets of numbers in general use: one for the *Celsius* or *centigrade* scale of temperature, and the other for the *Fahrenheit* scale. On the centigrade scale of temperature, the temperature of melting ice at standard atmospheric pressure is assigned the value zero, while that of water boiling at standard atmospheric pressure is assigned the number 100. On this scale the standard temperature interval is 100 centigrade degrees, abbreviated 100°C; the temperature of melting ice is 0°C, and that of boiling water at 1 atm pressure is 100°C. We shall refer to the temperature of melting ice at standard atmospheric pressure as the *ice point* and the temperature of boiling water—that is, water changing to steam at standard atmospheric pressure—as the *steam point*.

On the Fahrenheit scale the ice point is assigned the value 32 degrees Fahrenheit, 32°F, and the steam point is assigned the value 212°F. The standard temperature interval on the Fahrenheit scale is 180°F.

12-2 THERMOMETERS

The expansion of a solid rod is rarely used as the thermometric property in the construction of practical thermometers. The expansion of mercury in a glass tube, however, is the basis for one of the commonest types of thermometer. The thermometric property in this case is the change in volume of liquid mercury relative to the glass container; the actual quantity measured, however, is the change in length of the column of mercury in a narrow capillary tube.

A typical mercury-in-glass thermometer, illustrated in Figure 12–1, consists of a long capillary tube with a glass bulb at one end. Mercury fills this bulb and extends into the capillary tube; the other end of the capillary tube is sealed. The positions of the end of the column of mercury in the capillary tube for the temperatures corresponding to the ice point and the steam point are determined by immersing the thermometer first in melting ice and then in the steam above the surface of boiling water. The graduations are usually etched on the glass or on attached scales. The intervals between the ice point and the steam point are divided either into 100 or 180 uniform divisions and marked appropriately. The temperature of any other body or system is determined by placing the thermometer in contact with it and waiting until the length of the mercury column no longer changes. The temperature is then read directly from the position of the mercury column on the scale. The bore of the capillary tube should be of uniform diameter; otherwise, corrections will have to be made to these readings.

Other important types of thermometers are (a) the constant-volume gas thermometer, in which the pressure changes with changes in temperature; (b) the constant-pressure gas thermometer, in which the volume changes with changes in temperature; (c) the platinum resistance thermometer, in which the change in electrical resistance of a platinum wire is measured as the temperature changes; and (d) the thermocouple thermometer, in which the electromotive force at the junction of two dissimilar metals changes as the temperature changes. These thermometers will be described at the appropriate places in the book.

The relationship between the temperature as read on the centigrade scale, which will be called t, and the same temperature as read on the Fahrenheit scale, which will be called t_F, can be readily derived by noting that the difference between two temperatures is directly proportional to the difference between the two lengths of the mercury columns at these temperatures. Now, a change in length of the mercury column from the ice point to the steam point corresponds to a change in temperature of $100 - 0$ degrees on the centigrade scale and also to $212 - 32$ degrees on the Fahrenheit scale. Similarly a change in length of the mercury column from the ice point to any other temperature corresponds to a change in temperature of $t - 0$ on the centigrade scale and a change in temperature of $t_F - 32$ on the Fahrenheit scale. Hence

Fig. 12–1 A mercury-in-glass thermometer with the ice point and the steam point marked in both the Fahrenheit and Celsius scales.

$$\frac{t}{t_F - 32°\mathrm{F}} = \frac{100°\mathrm{C}}{180°\mathrm{F}},$$

from which

$$t = \tfrac{5}{9}(t_F - 32)$$ (1)

or

$$t_F = \tfrac{9}{5}t + 32.$$ (2)

Illustrative Example. For a classroom to be comfortable, its temperature should be kept at 70°F. Determine the equivalent temperature on the centigrade scale.

Equation (1) can be used for converting the temperature from the Fahrenheit to the centigrade scale.

$$t = \tfrac{5}{9}(t_F - 32);$$

substituting for t_F, we get

$$t = \tfrac{5}{9}(70 - 32),$$

from which $t = 21.1°\text{C}.$

12-3 THERMAL EXPANSION OF SOLIDS

When the temperature of a solid rod is increased, its length is also increased. Rods made of different materials will increase in length by different amounts, even though their temperature changes and original lengths are the same. Figure 12–2 shows one method of measuring the

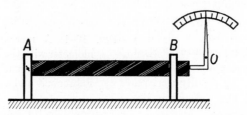

FIG. 12–2 Method of measuring the expansion of a metallic rod.

expansion of a metal rod. One end of the rod is fastened firmly to a support at A, while the other end slides freely through a guide at B. Since the change in length is usually very small, it can be magnified by attaching a lever to it pivoted at O and having a pointer at the other end which moves over a scale. The rod may be heated by a gas flame, or it may be surrounded by a jacket containing a liquid whose temperature can be varied. The term *coefficient of linear expansion* is used to designate the fractional change in length of a rod per degree change of temperature. If L_i is the length of the rod at the ice point, and L its length at any other temperature

t on the centigrade scale, then the average value of the coefficient of linear expansion α is given by

$$\alpha = \frac{L - L_i}{L_i t}, \tag{3}$$

from which

$$L = L_i(1 + \alpha t). \tag{4}$$

Average values of the coefficients of linear expansion of some common substances are listed in Table 12–1. These values are for temperature

Table 12-1   Coefficients of Linear Expansion

Substance	α
Aluminum	22×10^{-6} per °C
Brass	18 " "
Copper	16 " "
Glass (Pyrex)	3.2 " "
Invar	0.7 " "
Lead	28 " "
Platinum	9.0 " "
Steel	11 " "
Tungsten	4.4 " "

changes on the centigrade scale. If the temperature changes are measured on the Fahrenheit scale, each of these coefficients should be multiplied by $\frac{5}{9}$. It will be noticed that the coefficients of linear expansion are generally very small, but this does not mean that they can be neglected. In the building of railroads, bridges, and other structures which are subject to wide variations of temperature owing to seasonal changes, allowances must be made for the changes in length that are likely to occur.

Illustrative Example. The steel span of the George Washington Bridge over the Hudson River is about 1 mile long. The extremes of temperature in New York may be as great as 120°F. Determine the maximum change in length of the span between summer and winter.

Equation (4) will have to be modified slightly, since the length of the bridge at 32°F is not given in this example. If we call L_0 the length of the bridge at the temperature t_0, and L its length at any other temperature t, then Equation (4) may be rewritten as

$$L = L_0[1 + \alpha(t - t_0)] \tag{4a}$$

or

$$L - L_0 = \alpha L_0(t - t_0).$$

Now, letting $L_0 = 5{,}280$ ft, $t - t_0 = 120°\text{F}$,   and

$$\alpha = \tfrac{5}{9} \times 11 \times 10^{-6}/°\text{F},$$

we get $L - L_0 = \tfrac{5}{9} \times 11 \times 10^{-6} \times 5{,}280 \times 120$ ft

$$= 3.87 \text{ ft}.$$

If two metals, say brass and steel, are welded or riveted together so that they form a single straight piece at room temperature, then when the temperature is raised, this strip will bend in the form of an arc with the brass on the outside, as shown in Figure 12–3. This is due to the fact that

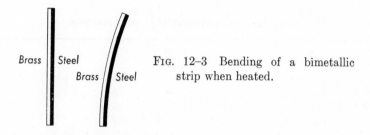

Brass │ Steel

Brass │ Steel

Fig. 12–3 Bending of a bimetallic strip when heated.

brass has a greater coefficient of expansion than steel. A bimetallic strip of this kind is used very frequently as an element in thermostats and other temperature-control devices. The bimetallic strip is adjusted so that when its temperature reaches a preassigned value, it will have bent over far enough to start the operation of a compressed-air pump which controls the opening and closing of steam valves; or it will operate a switch in an electric circuit.

When the temperature of a solid is raised, it expands in three dimensions. So far, we have confined our attention to the expansion in one direction only. Experiments can be performed to measure the coefficient of linear expansion of a solid for each of three directions at right angles to one another. It is found that certain crystals have different coefficients of expansion in different directions. But many solids commonly used have the same coefficient of linear expansion in every direction; such a substance is said to be *isotropic* with respect to this property. If we consider a cube of an isotropic solid of length L_i and volume V_i at the ice point, then

$$V_i = L_i^3. \tag{5}$$

If V is its volume at any other temperature t above the ice point, and L is the length of one of its edges, then

$$V = L^3,$$

but $$L^3 = L_i^3 (1 + \alpha t)^3,$$

so that $$V = V_i(1 + \alpha t)^3.$$

Now $$(1 + \alpha t)^3 = 1 + 3\alpha t + 3\alpha^2 t^2 + \alpha^3 t^3.$$

Since the value of α is very small, the value of α^2 and of α^3 will be much smaller than α, so that, in general, the last two terms of the above expansion may be neglected, which yields

$$(1 + \alpha t)^3 = 1 + 3\alpha t;$$

hence $$V = V_i(1 + 3\alpha t). \tag{6}$$

If we now introduce a new term called the *coefficient of volume expansion* β of a substance and defined as the fractional change in volume per degree change in temperature, then we can write

$$\beta = \frac{V - V_i}{V_i t}, \tag{7}$$

from which $$V = V_i(1 + \beta t). \tag{8}$$

A comparison of Equations (6) and (8) shows that, for isotropic solids,

$$\beta = 3\alpha, \tag{9}$$

or that the coefficient of volume expansion of an isotropic solid is three times its coefficient of linear expansion.

Illustrative Example. Determine the change in volume of a copper sphere of 4 cm radius when it is heated from 0°C to 400°C.

The volume of a sphere is given by

$$V = \tfrac{4}{3}\pi r^3,$$

in which r is the radius of the sphere.

Now $$V_i = \tfrac{4}{3}\pi \times (4 \text{ cm})^3 = 268 \text{ cm}^3.$$

From Equation (7),

$$V - V_i = \beta V_i t = 3\alpha V_i t;$$

therefore $$V - V_i = 3 \times 16 \times 10^{-6} \times 268 \times 400 \text{ cm}^3 = 5.15 \text{ cm}^3.$$

It may be interesting to note that the change in volume of the copper sphere is the same whether it is solid or hollow. We may think of a solid sphere as consisting of a solid central core and a hollow spherical shell whose inside diameter is the same as the diameter of the core. Before the sphere is hollowed out, the two fitted perfectly at all temperatures; hence the inside diameter of a hollow sphere should always be the same as that of the solid sphere at the same temperature. The same argument can be extended to a container of any other shape. Hence, when solid containers expand, the change in volume of the container may be calculated as though the inside were filled with a solid of the same substance.

12-4 THERMAL EXPANSION OF LIQUIDS

As a general rule a liquid expands when its temperature is raised; the notable exception to this rule is water, which, in the limited region of temperature from 0°C to 4°C, contracts when its temperature is raised. Above 4°C, water expands with an increase in temperature. In this discussion of changes in volume of a liquid, it is assumed that the pressure on the liquid remains constant while the temperature is changing. The most convenient way of determining the coefficient of volume expansion of a liquid is to put a known volume of liquid into a glass bulb with a narrow tube at one end and to note the level of liquid in the narrow tube, as sketched in Figure 12–4. When the temperature is raised, both the glass container and the

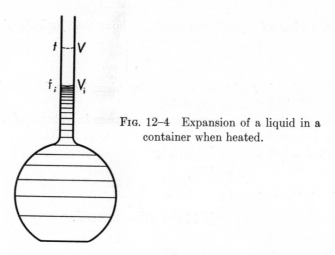

Fɪɢ. 12–4   Expansion of a liquid in a container when heated.

liquid expand. Since liquids generally have greater coefficients of expansion than glass, the level of the liquid will rise in the narrow tube. Hence only the *relative expansion* of the liquid with respect to the container can be measured directly by this method. Since the coefficient of volume expansion of the solid is known, the coefficient of volume expansion of the liquid can be calculated.

The behavior of water at atmospheric pressure in the range from −20°C to 100°C is shown in the graph in Figure 12–5, in which the volume of 1 gm of water is plotted as ordinate and the temperature as abscissa.

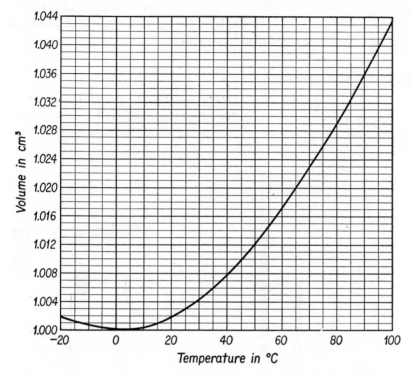

FIG. 12–5   Curve showing the volume of a gram of water as its temperature is raised from −20°C to 100°C with its minimum volume or maximum density at 4°C.

Table 12–2 gives the densities and the corresponding volumes of 1 gm of water for temperatures from −10°C to 100°C. It will be noted that the density of water is a maximum at 4°C.   An interesting result due to this

Table 12-2   Density and Volume of Water

Temperature, °C	Density in gm/cm^3	Volume in cm^3/gm
−10	0.99815	1.00186
0	0.99987	1.00013
4	1.00000	1.00000
10	0.99973	1.00027
20	0.99823	1.00177
40	0.99224	1.00782
60	0.98324	1.01705
80	0.97183	1.02899
100	0.95838	1.04343

property is that in the winter the temperature of the water at the bottom of a lake may be 4°C, while the temperature of the water at the surface may be 0°C, or the water may be frozen.

12-5 EXPANSION OF GASES

Suppose that a gas such as air is contained in a tube A, which is connected to a manometer consisting of a U-tube containing mercury, as in Figure 12–6. The pressure and volume of the air can be measured at room

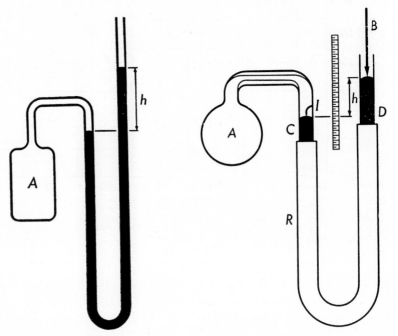

Fig. 12–6 A manometer for showing the expansion of a gas.

Fig. 12–7 A constant-volume gas thermometer.

temperature. If the temperature of the air is raised, both its volume and pressure will be changed, as indicated by the change in level of the mercury. Although it is possible to measure the simultaneous changes in pressure and volume with temperature, it is much more instructive to keep either the pressure or the volume constant and to study the change in the other one with changes in temperature. This can be done with only a slight change in this apparatus.

Figure 12–7 shows a modified form of the apparatus suitable for studying the change in pressure of the gas with change in temperature, the volume being kept constant. The gas under investigation is contained in tube A and in the narrow tube leading to the manometer. The mercury in tube C of the manometer is always kept at the same level by being raised to the index point I. The U-shaped part of the manometer is made of rubber hose; the level of the mercury in C is adjusted by the raising or lowering of the arm D. The pressure of the gas in the tube is the atmospheric pressure B and the pressure due to the difference in levels of the mercury columns in C and D.

Suppose that the gas in A is air. The tube A is surrounded with a mixture of ice and water, and the level of the mercury in C is adjusted so that the volume remains constant. When equilibrium is reached, the temperature of the air in A is 0°C, and its pressure P_i can be found by measuring the difference in levels between C and D and adding to it the atmospheric pressure. The mixture of ice and water can now be removed and the tube A surrounded by water at a known temperature t. The pressure P at this temperature can be measured. Let us define the *coefficient of pressure change at constant volume* β' as

$$\beta' = \frac{P - P_i}{P_i t}. \tag{10}$$

Substituting the measured values of P_i, P, and t will give the value of β' for air. This type of experiment can be performed with many different types of gases. The surprising result obtained from many careful experiments is that the value of β' is the same for all gases, providing the pressure of the gas is not too high. The measured value of β' is

$$\beta' = \frac{1}{273.2°C}. \tag{11}$$

One interpretation of this numerical value is that the pressure of any gas at constant volume will change by $1/273.2$ of its pressure at 0°C for each degree change in temperature.

A slight alteration of the apparatus can be made so that the volume of the gas will be read on tube C. The pressure can be kept constant by raising or lowering tube D so that the difference in levels of the mercury columns remains constant. Suppose that the gas in A is kept at atmospheric pressure throughout the experiment. If V_i is the volume of the gas when the temperature is 0°C, and V is its volume when its temperature is t, then the coefficient of volume expansion β at constant pressure is given by

$$\beta = \frac{V - V_i}{V_i t}. \tag{12}$$

This coefficient β has been measured for many gases under a variety of conditions. Among the earliest of such experiments were those of J. A. C. Charles, in 1787, and J. L. Gay-Lussac, in 1802. When the pressure of the gas is not too high, it is found that the numerical value of β is the same for all gases and is

$$\beta = \frac{1}{273.2°C} . \tag{13}$$

This is exactly the same as the value for β'.

This interesting behavior of gases suggests their use as thermometric substances.   Gas thermometers, of both the constant-pressure and the constant-volume type, have been widely used in scientific work.   Air, nitrogen, hydrogen, and helium are most commonly used in gas thermometers.   Each thermometer has to be calibrated in the usual manner by determining the pressure (or volume) at the ice point and then at the steam point.   The centigrade temperature t on the constant-volume thermometer, for example, would then be given by

$$t = \frac{P - P_i}{P_s - P_i} \times 100°C, \tag{14}$$

where P_i is the pressure of the gas at the ice point, P_s the pressure at the steam point, and P the pressure at the temperature t.

12-6   ABSOLUTE SCALE OF TEMPERATURE

The fact that all gases at low pressures have the same numerical values for the coefficients β and β' has led to the introduction of a scale of temperature known as the *absolute gas scale of temperature*.   To show how this scale is derived, let us rewrite Equation (10), putting in the numerical value for β' and obtaining

$$P = P_i \left(1 + \frac{t}{273.2} \right) \tag{15}$$

or

$$P = \frac{P_i}{273.2} (273.2 + t). \tag{16}$$

Equation (16) suggests the introduction of a new temperature scale, known as the absolute gas scale of temperature, in which the size of the degree is the same as the centigrade degree and the temperature T of the gas is given by the relationship

$$T = 273.2 + t. \tag{17}$$

Equation (16) now becomes

$$P = \frac{P_i}{273.2} \, T.$$ (18)

In this equation, P_i is the pressure of a fixed quantity of gas at constant volume, at the temperature of melting ice, and is therefore constant. We may replace the quantity $P_i/273.2$ by the letter K, so that Equation (18) may be written as

$$\boxed{P = KT}$$ at constant volume. (19)

Equation (19) shows that the pressure of a gas at constant volume is proportional to its absolute temperature.

The defining Equation (17) for the absolute temperature could also have been derived from Equation (12). This equation may be written as

$$V = \frac{V_i}{273.2} \, (273.2 + t),$$ (20)

and, introducing the absolute temperature T, we get

$$V = \frac{V_i}{273.2} \, T.$$ (21)

In this equation, V_i is the volume of a fixed quantity of gas at constant pressure at the temperature of melting ice; it is therefore constant. Writing

$$K' = \frac{V_i}{273.2},$$

we get $$\boxed{V = K'T}$$ at constant pressure. (22)

Equation (22) shows that the volume of a gas at constant pressure is proportional to its absolute temperature. This is sometimes called *Charles' law* or *Gay-Lussac's law*.

The temperature of melting ice T_i on the absolute scale is

$$T_i = 273.2° \text{ abs},$$

while the steam point is

$$T_s = 273.2 + 100 = 373.2° \text{ abs}.$$

A comparison of the centigrade scale and the absolute scale yields some interesting results. In the first place, both positive and negative numbers may be used to represent temperatures on the centigrade scale. A glance at Equations (19) and (22) shows, however, that negative numbers for the absolute temperature would lead to such absurd results as the existence of a negative pressure of a gas or a negative volume of a gas.   Hence the temperature of a body expressed on the absolute scale must always be a positive number.   It is not possible at this point to say whether there is an absolute zero of temperature.   All substances become liquids at temperatures above absolute zero.   The lowest temperature measured with a gas thermometer is about $-260°C$ or $13°$ abs using helium.   This temperature is close to the point at which helium becomes a liquid.   Furthermore, Equations (19) and (22) do not hold for gases which are close to the temperatures at which they become liquids.

It is apparent from the above discussion that what is needed is a temperature scale which is independent of the properties of particular substances.   There is such a scale known as the *absolute thermodynamic scale* or the *Kelvin scale of temperature*.   This scale will be discussed in Chapter 17.   Fortunately the temperatures on the thermodynamic scale are the same as the temperatures on the absolute gas scale.   For our purposes, these two scales will be treated as identical.

The temperature of the ice point T_i on the absolute scale has to be determined experimentally.   Although the value $273.2°$ abs is sufficiently accurate for our purposes, it should be noted that the average value of some of the best experimental determinations of the ice point is

$$T_i = 273.165° \text{ abs.} \tag{23}$$

The lowest temperature that has been obtained experimentally is about $0.001°$ abs.   This has been done by a process involving the magnetizing and demagnetizing of certain magnetic materials which had previously been cooled to a temperature of about $1°$ abs.

The absolute temperature can also be expressed in terms of the Fahrenheit degree by the equation

$$T_F = \tfrac{9}{5}T, \tag{24}$$

in which T_F is the absolute temperature in Fahrenheit degrees and T the absolute temperature in centigrade degrees.   The temperature of the ice point on the absolute Fahrenheit scale is

$$T_{iF} = \tfrac{9}{5} \times 273.2 = 491.8° \text{ abs F.}$$

To change from the temperature t_F on the Fahrenheit scale to the temperature T_F on the absolute Fahrenheit scale, we use the relationship

$$T_F = (t_F - 32) + 491.8 = t_F + 459.8, \tag{25}$$

since the temperature of the ice point on the Fahrenheit scale is $32°F$.

QUESTIONS

1. Suppose that three thermometers were used to measure the temperature of a room. One was a solid copper thermometer, the second a mercury-in-glass thermometer, and the third a constant-volume air thermometer. Would they give the same temperature readings? Explain your answer.

2. What are some of the objections to a water-in-glass thermometer?

3. Follow the procedure used in defining the coefficient of linear expansion and coefficient of volume expansion of a solid and define the coefficient of area expansion of the solid. Show that, to a good approximation, the coefficient of area expansion is twice the coefficient of linear expansion of the solid.

4. Account for the fact that the coefficients of linear expansion given in Table 12–1 must be multiplied by $\frac{5}{9}$ if used in connection with Fahrenheit temperature changes.

5. The inside diameter of a steel ring is slightly less than the diameter of a steel shaft. It is desired to put the steel ring on the shaft. Would you suggest heating or cooling the ring to get it on the shaft?

6. When a mercury-in-glass thermometer is put into a hot liquid, the column of mercury first descends and then rises. Try this experiment and explain the results.

7. The coefficients of linear expansion listed in Table 12–1 are all positive. Some substances, such as rubber, have negative coefficients of expansion. A simple experiment is to hang a weight at the end of a piece of thin-walled rubber tubing and then heat it. The length of the rubber will be observed to decrease.

8. Referring to the curve of Figure 12–5, compare the coefficient of volume expansion of water in the range of temperature below 4°C and above 4°C.

PROBLEMS

1. Normal body temperature is 98.6°F. What is this temperature on the centigrade scale?

2. The boiling point of sulphur is 444.6°C. Convert this to the Fahrenheit scale of temperature.

3. The melting point of mercury is -38.87°C. What is its melting point on the Fahrenheit scale?

4. The melting point of tungsten is 3,400°C. What is its melting point on the Fahrenheit scale?

5. The critical temperature of helium is -268°C. Convert this temperature to degrees Fahrenheit.

6. The critical temperature of hydrogen is -240°C. What is the critical temperature on the Fahrenheit scale?

7. At what temperature will the readings on the centigrade and the Fahrenheit scales be the same?

8. How long must a steel rod be in order that its length will increase by 0.04 in. as a result of a change in temperature of 10°C?

9. An iron steampipe laid underground between two buildings is 150 ft

long. How much room must be provided for expansion if its temperature will change from 30°F to 220°F?

10. The distance between two markers is measured with a steel tape at 25°C; the reading of the tape is 90 ft. If the calibration of the steel tape is correct at 0°C, determine the distance between the markers.

11. A copper ring has an inside diameter of 4.98 cm at 20°C. To what temperature must it be heated so that it will just fit on a shaft 5.00 cm in diameter?

12. A glass flask has a volume of 1 liter at 20°C. What will be its volume at 100°C?

13. The pressure of a volume of gas at 27°C is 546 mm of mercury. What will be its pressure if the temperature is increased to 28°C, the volume being kept constant?

14. The gauge pressure of the air in an automobile tire is 24 lb/in.^{2} at 0°C. Determine the new gauge pressure when the automobile is driven into a garage where the temperature is 20°C. Assume that the volume of air remains constant.

15. A constant-pressure air thermometer contains a mass of air whose volume is 300 cm^3 at 0°C. What will be its volume at 80°C?

16. A tungsten filament which is 12 cm long at 20°C is heated to 3,000°C. Determine its change in length.

17. The following data were taken in an experiment with a constant-volume air thermometer similar to that shown in Figure 12–7: barometric pressure 754.0 mm, height of column C 48.4 cm, height of column D 44.7 cm at the ice point; height of column C 48.4 cm, and height of column D 71.0 cm at the steam point; height of column C 48.4 cm, height of column D 62.3 cm when the air bulb is surrounded by warm water. Determine (a) the coefficient of the pressure change of the air and (b) the temperature of the warm water.

18. Water is poured into a calibrated glass flask until a level of 700 cm^3 is reached. The readings are correct at 20°C. If the system is heated from 20°C to 80°C, determine the new reading on the flask for the volume of the water.

19. A clock regulated by a seconds pendulum made of steel is correct when the temperature is 70°F. Determine the gain or loss, in seconds per day when the temperature rises to 97°F.

20. A steel rod 1 m long and 0.5 cm in diameter is clamped between two fixed supports at its ends. The temperature of the rod is raised 60°C. Determine (a) the stress in the rod and (b) the force exerted by each support.

21. A steel bomb is filled with water at 10°C. If the system is heated to 100°C, determine the increase in pressure of the water if the expansion of the steel is negligible.

13

Heat and
Work

13-1 THE NATURE OF HEAT

The concept of heat has undergone several changes during the develop, ment of physics. In the early days, heat and temperature were used inter-changeably. Joseph Black (1728–1799) was the first to show clearly that heat and temperature were entirely different concepts. Heat was believed to be some kind of matter which entered a body when the temper-ature rose and left the body when its temperature dropped. The term *caloric* came into use as the name for this matter. Attempts were made to determine the change in weight of a body as its temperature changed. Results generally were inconclusive; this is not surprising when one con-siders the inaccuracy of experiments in those days.

It was Benjamin Thompson (1753–1814), better known as Count Rumford, who first clearly demonstrated that heat could not be a form of matter, but must be a form of energy. Count Rumford was at one time engaged in the boring of brass cannon and noted that a great amount of heat was generated in this process; that is, by the friction between the boring tool and the brass gun. In one experiment he allowed the heat developed in the boring of the gun to raise the temperature of water. He found that more heat was developed with dull tools than with sharp boring tools. He surmised that the heat developed came from the work done against friction, and he traced this work back to the horse which supplied the energy to operate the boring tool. He also made a crude estimate of the relationship between the work done and the amount of heat developed; this quantity has come to be known as the *mechanical equivalent of heat* (see Section 13-6). However, about half a century was to elapse before it became definitely established and accepted that *heat is a form of energy.*

Since heat is a form of energy, it may be transformed into any of the other forms of energy, and, conversely, other forms of energy may be transformed into heat. To understand the meaning of the term *heat,* consider two bodies A and B made of any materials whatever and at tem-peratures T_1 and T_2, respectively (see Figure 13-1). Let us assume

that T_1 is greater than T_2.   If the two bodies are placed in contact, heat
will flow from A to B through their common surface, when A is at a higher
temperature than B.   For example, when a pot of water is placed on a hot

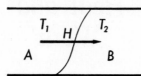

Fig. 13–1   When T_1 is greater than T_2,
heat flows from A to B.

stove, heat flows from the stove through the bottom of the pot into the
water.   In a so-called "steam-heated" room, heat flows from the steam
through the iron of the radiator into the air in the room.   The nature of the
changes that take place when heat enters or leaves a body forms the
subject of the rest of this section.

13-2   HEAT AND INTERNAL ENERGY

In our study of physics up to this point, we have investigated the
behavior of bodies and systems of bodies when acted upon by external
forces, when work was done upon them, and when heat was added to or
removed from them, without reference to the internal structure of matter.
This was done to bring out carefully and keep clear those ideas and physical
laws which have been established upon a firm experimental foundation
However, it is interesting, intellectually stimulating, and very fruitful to
try to determine what does happen to the internal structure of a substance when forces act on it, when work is done upon it, or when heat is
added to it.

We have already outlined briefly (Section 10–1) our present view
concerning the structure of matter with particular reference to the forces
existing between molecules.   Another approach to the subject of the
structure of matter is in terms of the energy of the constituent particles,
not only of the molecules of the substance but also of their atoms and of
the electrons, protons, and neutrons which constitute these atoms.   Each
of these constituent particles undoubtedly has energy, probably both
kinetic and potential.   A complete theory of the structure of matter would
enable us to evaluate the energy of each particle under all possible conditions, and from this we would then be able to evaluate the energy of the
substance under any given set of physical conditions.   This energy constitutes the *internal energy* of the substance under these conditions.   However, there is at present no satisfactory theory which will enable us to
evaluate the internal energy of a substance.   There is, however, another
approach by which we can evaluate *changes in the internal energy* of a

substance. For example, if a known quantity of heat is added to a substance and no external work is done on or by this substance, then this quantity of heat will be converted into additional internal energy of the substance. The complete theory of the structure of matter would be able to trace the changes in the energies of the individual particles of the substance corresponding to the quantity of heat added. However, the theory of the structure of matter in its present state is unable to provide us with a detailed analysis of how the internal energy of a substance is distributed among its constituent particles. But we can say that if $\mathcal{E}_i$ is the internal energy of the substance before a quantity of heat H is added to it, and if $\mathcal{E}_f$ is the internal energy of the substance after the addition of this amount of heat, then

$$H = \mathcal{E}_f - \mathcal{E}_i, \tag{1}$$

providing no external work was done on or by the substance.

One might inquire as to what evidence we have that the internal energy has been changed by the addition of heat to a substance. The evidence is of an indirect kind. We may note that the temperature of the substance has been changed, or that its physical state has been changed— say from a liquid to a gas—or that its pressure has been changed. A complete theory would relate the energies of the particles of the substance to its temperature, pressure, and physical state. To date, we have made only small progress in this direction. Probably the greatest progress has been made in the study of the behavior of substances which approximate closely the behavior of *perfect* or *ideal gases*. This will be studied in greater detail in the next chapter. We may anticipate this by stating that if the assumption is made that the absolute temperature of a perfect gas is proportional to the average kinetic energy of the gas molecules, the results are consistent with the known properties of a gas. While this direct proportionality between temperature and the kinetic energy of molecules holds for an ideal gas, it does not necessarily follow that it holds for a real substance in the solid, liquid, or gaseous phase. For real substances, the relationship between temperature and the kinetic energy of the molecules is a more complicated one.

13-3 HEAT UNITS

Since heat is a form of energy, any of the energy units such as the erg, joule, or foot pound may be used to measure a quantity of heat. However, it is usually more convenient to use some other unit of heat defined in terms of one of the effects produced by the addition of heat to a body, and then to determine the relationship between this heat unit and the more common energy units.

One of the effects that may be produced when heat flows into a body of mass M is that its temperature is changed. This effect can be used to define a unit of heat. The substance chosen is water at standard atmospheric pressure. The unit of heat in the cgs system is the *calorie; the calorie* is defined as *that quantity of heat which, when added to one gram of water, will raise its temperature one degree centigrade.* Careful experiments have shown that the quantity of heat required to change the temperature of 1 gm of water depends slightly upon the initial temperature of the water. For this reason a more precise definition of the calorie is used: *the calorie is that quantity of heat which will raise the temperature of one gram of water from* 14.5°C *to* 15.5°C. This unit of heat is usually referred to as the 15-degree calorie.

In engineering work the unit of heat is the *Btu*, an abbreviation of the words *British thermal unit; the Btu is that quantity of heat which will raise the temperature of one pound of water from* 63°F *to* 64°F. The pound is used here as a unit of mass. One Btu is equivalent to 252 cal.

Another unit of heat is the *large calorie* or the *kilogram calorie; the large calorie is the heat required to raise the temperature of one kilogram of water one degree centigrade.* The large calorie is equivalent to one thousand of the small calories. The large calorie is frequently used in biology, in dietetics, and in some engineering work. In this book, unless otherwise stated, the term *calorie* will always refer to the small calorie.

For the degree of accuracy required in the solution of most problems, it will be sufficient to assume that the quantity of heat required to raise the temperature of a unit mass of water has the same value over the whole range of temperatures from the freezing point to the boiling point of water. For example, to heat 1 gm of water from 20°C to 50°C requires the addition of 30 cal of heat; to heat 1 lb of water from 70°F to 150°F requires 80 Btu.

13-4 HEAT CAPACITY. SPECIFIC HEAT

The quantity of heat that is required to raise the temperature of a body by one degree is called the *heat capacity* of that body. This is also the same as the quantity of heat that is given out by the body when its temperature is lowered by one degree. The term *specific heat is* used to designate *the amount of heat that is required to raise the temperature of a unit of mass of the substance by one degree.* Thus, if an amount of heat H, when supplied to a body of mass M, raises its temperature from t_1 to t_2, then its specific heat s is, by definition,

$$s = \frac{H}{M(t_2 - t_1)}.$$

(2)

Solving Equation (2) for H yields

$$H = Ms(t_2 - t_1)$$ (3)

for the quantity of heat which must be added to the substance to raise its temperature from t_1 to t_2. Conversely, if the temperature of the substance is decreased from t_1 to t_2, then Equation (3) gives the quantity of heat H that is liberated or removed from the substance in this process.

The specific heat of water is one calorie per gram per degree centigrade and also one British thermal unit per pound per degree Fahrenheit. The specific heats of some of the common solids and liquids are listed in Table 13–1. The meaning of the term *specific heat* can be illustrated by com-

Table 13-1   Specific Heats

Substance	Specific Heat in $\dfrac{\text{cal}}{\text{gm °C}}$ or $\dfrac{\text{Btu}}{\text{lb °F}}$
Aluminum	0.21
Brass	0.09
Copper	0.093
Glass (crown)	0.16
Ice	0.50
Iron	0.11
Lead	0.031
Mercury	0.033
Silver	0.056
Tin	0.060
Zinc	0.095

paring the values of the specific heats of lead and water. One calorie is required to raise the temperature of one gram of water by one degree centigrade. If 1 cal of heat is added to 1 gm of lead whose specific heat is 0.031 cal/gm°C, its temperature will be raised by 32°C.

13-5   HEAT MEASUREMENTS

In making any heat measurements, it is important to analyze the experimental arrangement in order to be able to tell just what happens to each object that is used in the experiment. If a change in temperature takes place in any of the objects used in the experiment, Equation (3) can be used to determine the quantity of heat either added to the substance or given out by it. One of the methods most commonly used in heat measurements, or *calorimetry*, is that known as the *method of mixtures*. Essentially, this involves putting two or more substances, initially at different temperatures, into good thermal contact and allowing them to come to thermal equilibrium at some common final temperature. If the entire system is properly insulated so that no heat is exchanged with the surroundings, then the heat given out by the substances which are cooled is equal to the heat absorbed by those which are heated.

Suppose that there are 300 gm of water at 20°C in a copper container, usually called a *calorimeter*, of 100 gm mass. A piece of iron of 400 gm mass has been heated separately in a steam bath at atmospheric pressure, so that its temperature is 100°C. If this piece of iron is put into the water in the calorimeter, the temperature of the iron will drop, while that of the water and the copper calorimeter will rise. The water should be stirred until the temperature has reached its final equilibrium value, say t_f. The calorimeter should be placed in a well-insulated container to avoid heat exchanges with the outside. If this is properly done, then the heat that is given out by the iron in cooling from 100°C to temperature t_f will be equal to the heat added to the water and the copper calorimeter to raise their temperature from 20°C to t_f.

Now, the heat given out by the iron is, from Equation (3),

$$H = 400 \text{ gm} \times 0.11 \frac{\text{cal}}{\text{gm°C}} (100° - t_f).$$

The heat added to the water and the copper calorimeter is

$$H = 300 \text{ gm} \times 1 \frac{\text{cal}}{\text{gm°C}} (t_f - 20°) + 100 \text{ gm} \times 0.093 \frac{\text{cal}}{\text{gm°C}} (t_f - 20°).$$

We can find the final temperature t_f by equating these two quantities of heat, obtaining

$$400 \times 0.11(100° - t_f) = (300 + 100 \times 0.093)(t_f - 20°),$$

from which $$t_f = 30°C.$$

The method of mixtures can be used to determine any one of the quantities expressed in Equation (3) for any of the substances used in the particular experiment. It is frequently used for determining the specific heat of a substance. For example, in one experiment 250 gm of brass were heated to 100°C and then placed into a copper calorimeter of 60 gm mass containing 180 gm of water at 15°C. The measured final temperature was 24.2°C. Determine the specific heat of brass.

Let s be the specific heat of brass; the heat given out by the brass is

$$H = 250 \text{ gm} \times s(100° - 24.2°).$$

The heat added to the water and the calorimeter is

$$H = (180 + 60 \times 0.093)(24.2 - 15) \text{ cal.}$$

Equating the heat given out by the brass to that taken in by the water and calorimeter, we get

$$250 \text{ gm} \times s \times 75.8° = 185.6 \times 9.2 \text{ cal,}$$

from which
$$s = 0.091 \frac{\text{cal}}{\text{gm}°\text{C}}.$$

13-6   WORK AND HEAT

Some of the effects that are produced by adding heat to a body can also be produced in other ways without the addition of heat. For example, we know that the temperature of water can be raised by placing it on a hot stove; however, the temperature of water, which has been completely insulated from the outside, can also be raised by churning the water with a set of paddles. It is of the utmost importance to be able to determine whether the same amount of work is always required to produce the effect that would be produced by a given quantity of heat. This problem was investigated by James Prescott Joule, who undertook a series of careful experiments which extended over a long period of time, 1842–1870, to determine just how much mechanical work must be done on a system to produce the same change as that produced by a given quantity of heat when added to the same system. These experiments are usually referred to as the experiments on the *mechanical equivalent of heat.*

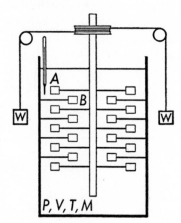

Fɪɢ. 13–2 Joule's apparatus for determining the mechanical equivalent of heat.

One form of the apparatus used by Joule is illustrated in Figure 13–2. The system on which work was done was a quantity of water of mass M

contained in a well-insulated glass jar. A set of paddles A was attached to a shaft which was set in rotation by the falling of a set of weights W attached to cords passing over pulleys. The motion of the paddles A past the stationary vanes B churned the water, thus increasing its temperature from some initial value t_i to a final value t_f. The work done by the paddles in churning the water was equal to the loss of potential energy of the weights which fell through a height h minus the kinetic energy that the weights had when they reached the bottom.

If m is the total mass of the falling weights, the loss in potential energy is mgh, and their final kinetic energy is $\frac{1}{2}mv^2$; hence

$$\mathcal{W} = mgh - \tfrac{1}{2}mv^2. \tag{4}$$

The amount of heat that would have had to be added to the water to produce the same change in temperature is

$$H = Ms(t_f - t_i). \tag{5}$$

Equation (4) gave the work done expressed in energy units, while Equation (5) gave the equivalent amount of heat in heat units, say calories. As the result of many careful experiments, it was found that

$$4.185 \times 10^7 \text{ ergs} = 1 \text{ cal}$$

or

$$4.185 \text{ joules} = 1 \text{ cal} \tag{6}$$

or

$$778 \text{ ft lb} = 1 \text{ Btu.}$$

If we desire to equate the values of $\mathcal{W}$ and H as given by Equations (4) and (5), it is necessary to introduce a conversion factor J, representing the mechanical equivalent of heat, so as to have the same units on both sides of the equation. Thus

$$\mathcal{W} = JH, \tag{7}$$

where

$$J = 4.185 \frac{\text{joules}}{\text{cal}}$$

or

$$J = 778 \frac{\text{ft lb}}{\text{Btu}};$$

that is, J must be given the appropriate value from the results tabulated in Equations (6). For example, suppose that the paddles, instead of being driven by falling weights, are driven by a small motor supplying 40 watts for 15 min and that the mass of water in the tank is 2,000 gm initially at a temperature of 20°C. It is desired to calculate the temperature of the water at the end of 15 min. The work done by the motor in churning the water is

$$40 \times 15 \times 60 \text{ joules} = 36,000 \text{ joules}.$$

Using Equation (7) and setting $J = 4.185 \dfrac{\text{joules}}{\text{cal}}$, we get

$$36,000 \text{ joules} = 4.185 \frac{\text{joules}}{\text{cal}} \times 2,000 \text{ gm} \times 1 \frac{\text{cal}}{\text{gm}°\text{C}} (t_f - 20°\text{C}),$$

from which $t_f = 24.3°\text{C}.$

13-7 THE FIRST LAW OF THERMODYNAMICS

We are now in a position to formulate the principle of conservation of energy to include heat energy and internal energy as well as mechanical energy. When so formulated it is called the *first law of thermodynamics.* Suppose that the substance or the system under investigation possesses initially an amount of internal energy $\mathcal{E}_i$ and that an amount of heat H is added to this system. In general, the result of adding this quantity of heat to the system will be to change its internal energy to some final value $\mathcal{E}_f$ and also to have the system do some work $\mathcal{W}$ on surrounding bodies. Stated in the form of an equation, the first law of thermodynamics becomes

$$\boxed{H = \mathcal{E}_f - \mathcal{E}_i + \mathcal{W}.}$$

(8)

The manner in which Equation (8) is written makes use of the convention that when heat is added to a system it is considered positive and that when the system does work on the neighboring objects the work $\mathcal{W}$ is considered positive. It must also be noted that all the quantities must be expressed in the same units; otherwise, the proper conversion factor F must be introduced.

An examination of Equation (8) shows that if no work is done on or by the system, then the change in its internal energy is equal to the quantity of heat added or removed from the system. Thus in adding 20 cal to 2 gm of water, its temperature will be changed by 10°C. Neglecting the work done as a result of the slight change in volume, we can say that the internal energy of this mass of water was increased by 20 cal, and the evidence for the change in its internal energy is the change in its temperature.

If no heat is added to or removed from the system, then Equation (8) becomes

$$H = 0 = \mathcal{E}_f - \mathcal{E}_i + \mathcal{W}.$$

(9)

A physical process which is so arranged that no heat is added to or removed from the system is called an *adiabatic process.* For example, in Joule's experiment on the mechanical equivalent of heat, the water in the cylinder was thoroughly insulated so that no heat entered or left the water. The churning process was an adiabatic process. The work done on the system was equal to the change in internal energy of the water. Another example of an adiabatic process is the compression of air in a cylinder with insulating walls. Work is done on the air by pushing down the piston and compressing the air. The change in internal energy of the air is equal to the work done on it and is shown by the changes in pressure, temperature, and volume of the air.

13-8 WORK DONE BY A GAS

Whenever a gas expands against some external force, it does work on the external agency; conversely, whenever a gas is compressed by the action of some outside force, work is done on the gas. To calculate the work done by a gas, consider a gas enclosed in a cylinder with a tight-fitting

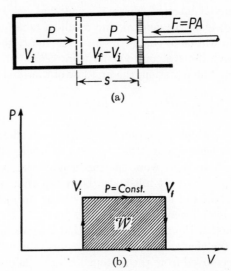

Fɪɢ. 13–3   (a) Expansion of a gas at constant pressure. (b) Graphical' representation of work done by a gas expanding at constant pressure.

piston. The piston may be connected by means of a piston rod to a crankshaft or other mechanical device on which it exerts some force. The force F acting on the piston due to the pressure P exerted by the gas is given by

$$F = PA, \tag{10}$$

in which A is the cross-sectional area of the piston and also of the cylinder [see Figure 13–3(a)]. Suppose that the piston is pushed out a small distance s and that the pressure of the gas remains constant. Then the work $\mathcal{W}$ done by the gas in moving the piston is

$$\mathcal{W} = Fs = PAs. \tag{11}$$

But As is the change in volume of the gas. Hence the work done by an expanding gas at constant pressure is

$$\boxed{\mathcal{W} = P(V_f - V_i),} \tag{12}$$

where V_i is the initial volume of the gas and V_f is its final volume.

The work done by the gas may be found from a graph in which the pressure is plotted as ordinate and the volume as abscissa, as shown in Figure 13–3(b). A constant pressure is represented by a horizontal line; the line extends from volume V_i to volume V_f. The work done by the gas is represented by the area under this line extending down to the V-axis. If the gas is compressed at constant pressure, the work done will still be represented by the area under this line but is considered negative since the volume is decreased.

If, during the expansion, the pressure of the gas changes, we can calculate the work done by taking small volume changes during which the pressure remains practically constant, multiplying each such volume change by the appropriate pressure, and then summing all of these products. This can easily be done graphically, as illustrated in Figure 13–4. In the

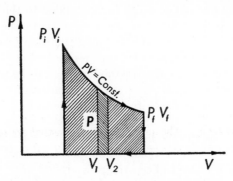

FIG. 13–4 Graphical representation of work done during an isothermal expansion of a gas.

case chosen, the temperature of the gas is maintained constant during the expansion. The relationship between pressure and volume is given by Boyle's law,

$$PV = \text{constant};$$

thus the pressure decreases as the volume increases. If we consider any small change in volume from V_1 to V_2, the work done is $P(V_2 - V_1)$ and is represented by the area of the small rectangle shown shaded in the figure. The work done by the gas in expanding from a volume V_i to a volume V_f is then the sum of such small areas and is equal to the area under the curve down to the V-axis and included between the vertical lines representing the values of V_i and V_f. A process which takes place at constant temperature is known as an *isothermal* process.

Illustrative Example. During one part of the operation of a Diesel engine, the gas expands at a constant pressure of 800 lb/in.², while the volume changes from 12 in.³ to 16 in.³. Calculate the work done by the gas during this process.

The work done during a constant-pressure expansion is

$$\mathcal{W} = P(V_f - V_i)$$

$$= 800\,\frac{\text{lb}}{\text{in.}^2}\,(16 - 12)\text{ in.}^3 = 3{,}200\text{ in. lb}$$

$$= 266.7\text{ ft lb.}$$

13-9 SPECIFIC HEATS OF A GAS

When the temperature of a gas is changed by the addition of heat to it, both its pressure and its volume can be changed. We may, however, choose the conditions under which heat is added to the gas. One simple method is to keep the volume of the gas constant; the quantity of heat added to unit mass of a gas at constant volume to produce a change in temperature of one degree is called the *specific heat at constant volume* and will be denoted by s_v. Another method is to keep the pressure of the gas constant while adding heat to it. The quantity of heat that must be added at constant pressure to raise the temperature of unit mass of gas by one degree is called the *specific heat at constant pressure* and will be denoted by s_p. The specific heat at constant pressure is greater than the specific heat at constant volume. This difference can be accounted for if we note that, in order to keep the pressure constant while the temperature is being raised, the volume of the gas must be allowed to expand. But when the volume increases at constant pressure, the gas does work on the surrounding atmosphere or mechanism connected to the movable part of the gas container equal to the pressure times the change in volume. Hence s_p is greater than s_v because, in addition to raising the temperature of the gas, some of the heat that is added to it is transformed into work by the expansion of the gas at constant pressure.

The values of s_p and s_v for some of the common gases are listed in Table 13-2.

Table 13-2   Specific Heats of Gases

Gas	s_p in $\dfrac{\text{cal}}{\text{gm °C}}$	s_v in $\dfrac{\text{cal}}{\text{gm °C}}$	Ratio s_p/s_v
Air	0.242	0.173	1.40
Ammonia	0.523	0.399	1.31
Carbon dioxide	0.200	0.154	1.30
Hydrogen	3.40	2.40	1.41
Nitrogen	0.248	0.176	1.41
Oxygen	0.218	0.156	1.40

Illustrative Example. A cylinder fitted with a movable piston which contains 4 gm of nitrogen at 0°C and 2 atm pressure occupies a volume of 3.2 liters. The nitrogen is heated at this constant pressure until its temperature is 127°C. Determine (a) the heat supplied to the nitrogen, (b) the work done by the nitrogen in expanding, and (c) the change in internal energy of the nitrogen.

(a) Since the heat H was supplied to the nitrogen at constant pressure, we can write Equation (3) in the form

$$H = ms_p(t_f - t_i).$$

Now $m = 4$ gm, $s_p = 0.248 \dfrac{\text{cal}}{\text{gm°C}}$, and $t_f - t_i = 127°C$;

therefore
$$H = 4 \text{ gm} \times 0.248 \frac{\text{cal}}{\text{gm°C}} \times 127°C,$$

so that
$$H = 126.0 \text{ cal.}$$

(b) The work done by the nitrogen in expanding at constant pressure is given by

$$\mathcal{W} = P(V_f - V_i). \tag{12}$$

$V_i = 3.2$ liters; V_f can be found with the aid of Equation (21) of Chapter 12, which can be written in the form

$$V_f = \frac{V_i}{273.2} \times T,$$

where T is the absolute temperature of the gas when its volume is V_f. In this case $T = 273.2° + 127° = 400.2°$;

hence
$$V_f = 3.2 \text{ liters} \times \frac{400.2}{273.2},$$

from which
$$V_f = 4.68 \text{ liters.}$$

The work done is therefore

$$\mathcal{W} = 2 \text{ atm} \times (4.68 - 3.20) \text{ liters}$$
$$= 2.96 \text{ atm-liters.}$$

Now $1 \text{ atm} = 1.013 \times 10^6 \text{ dynes/cm}^2,$

and $1 \text{ liter} = 10^3 \text{ cm}^3;$

hence $\mathcal{W} = 2.96 \times 1.013 \times 10^9 \text{ ergs}$
$$= 3.0 \times 10^9 \text{ ergs.}$$

(c) To determine the change in internal energy of the nitrogen, we make use of the first law of thermodynamics

$$H = \mathcal{E}_f - \mathcal{E}_i + \mathcal{W}. \tag{8}$$

Solving this equation for the change in internal energy, we get

$$\mathcal{E}_f - \mathcal{E}_i = H - \mathcal{W}.$$

In part (a) the value of H was determined in calories, while in part (b) the value of $\mathcal{W}$ was determined in ergs; we must thus use the mechanical equivalent $J = 4.185 \times 10^7$ ergs/cal in the above equation, so that

$$\mathcal{E}_f - \mathcal{E}_i = JH - \mathcal{W}$$

$$= 4.185 \times 10^7 \frac{\text{ergs}}{\text{cal}} \times 126.0 \text{ cal} - 3.0 \times 10^9 \text{ ergs,}$$

from which
$$\mathcal{E}_f - \mathcal{E}_i = (5.27 \times 10^9 - 3.0 \times 10^9) \text{ ergs}$$

$$= 2.27 \times 10^9 \text{ ergs.}$$

Thus the internal energy of the nitrogen was increased by 3.77×10^9 ergs in this process.

13-10 ADIABATIC PROCESSES

Whenever the expansion or compression of a gas takes place without the transfer of heat to or from the gas, the process is said to be *adiabatic*. In the ideal experiment, the gas should be placed in a cylinder or other container whose walls are perfectly insulated. In practical cases, expansions or contractions which take place so rapidly that practically no heat is transferred to or from the gas may be considered adiabatic. During an adiabatic process, the pressure and volume of a gas are related by the equation

$$PV^\gamma = \text{constant,} \tag{13}$$

where γ (Greek letter gamma) is a number between 1.0 and 1.67 and depends upon the gas used. For air, γ has the value 1.4; it also has this value for hydrogen, oxygen, and other diatomic gases. It has the value 1.67 for the inert gases such as helium, neon, and argon. Furthermore, it can be shown that

$$\gamma = \frac{s_p}{s_v} \qquad \text{(14)}$$

for each gas.

Let us apply the first law of thermodynamics to an adiabatic compression of a gas. During this process no heat is added to or removed from the gas, so that $H = 0$. Since work is done on the gas, then, according to our sign convention, it will be called $-\mathcal{W}$. Putting these values into the mathematical statement of the first law as given by Equation (8), we get

$$0 = \mathcal{E}_f - \mathcal{E}_i - \mathcal{W}$$

or $\mathcal{W} = \mathcal{E}_f - \mathcal{E}_i;$ **(15)**

that is, the work done on the gas results in an increase of the internal energy of the gas. This increase in internal energy shows itself by the increase in temperature of the gas. In a similar manner, the work done by the gas during an adiabatic expansion results in a decrease of the internal energy of the gas and shows itself by a decrease in temperature of the gas.

The increase in temperature which takes place during the adiabatic compression of a gas can be demonstrated by taking a thick-walled glass cylinder, closing one end, and fitting the tube with a

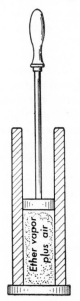

Fig. 13–5 During adiabatic compression the temperature will rise sufficiently to ignite the ether.

piston (see Figure 13–5). The piston should be moistened by dipping it into some ether and then inserted into the cylinder. If the piston is pushed down rapidly, the temperature of the air will rise sufficiently during the compression to ignite the ether. No heat is added during this process; the work done in compressing the air is converted into additional internal energy.

1. Show that the specific heat of a substance has the same numerical value in the cgs system and in the British engineering system.

2. Newspapers frequently carry extended reports about extremes of weather. Read one such report and see if the writer knows the difference between heat and temperature.

3. Can a substance have a specific heat greater than 1 cal/gm°C? Look up a more extensive set of tables and check your conclusions.

4. If heat is a form of energy, why are the additional units, calorie and Btu, introduced into the subject?

5. One pound of water will have its temperature raised by 1°F if it falls 778 ft and then has all of this energy converted into internal energy. What will be the rise in temperature of a million pounds of water which fall through 778 ft under similar conditions?

6. What fundamental principle is at the basis of the "method of mixtures" experiment?

7. State precisely the meaning of the term *mechanical equivalent of heat.*

8. In what respect does the first law of thermodynamics differ from the mechanical conservation of energy principle?

9. When a gas expands isothermally, it does work on some outside agency. Does the energy of the gas change during this process? If not, what is the source of the energy which enables the gas to do this work?

10. Does a gas do any work when it expands adiabatically? If so, what is the source of the energy which enables the gas to do this work?

PROBLEMS

1. One calorie of heat is added to one gram of iron. Determine the change in temperature of this piece of iron.

2. An aluminum calorimeter whose mass is 100 gm contains 200 gm of water at 24°C. A mass of 500 gm of tin at a temperature of 95°C is placed in the water. Determine the final temperature of the mixture.

3. In determining the specific heat of a metal, a 150-gm sample is heated to 99.5°C and then put into 225 gm of water at 18°C which is contained in a copper calorimeter whose mass is 160 gm. The final temperature of the mixture is 22.4°C. Determine the specific heat of the sample.

4. A metal calorimeter whose heat capacity is 20 cal/°C contains 300 gm of water at 10°C. One hundred grams of copper at 150°C and 250 gm of zinc at 115°C are placed in the water. What is the final temperature of the mixture?

5. A lead ball weighing 1 lb is dropped from a height of 240 ft to the pavement. Assuming that all of this energy is converted into internal energy in the lead ball, determine the rise in temperature of the lead.

6. The powder which is used to fire an 8-gm bullet produces 800 cal of heat when burning. In the firing of the bullet, only 25 per cent of this energy is converted into kinetic energy of the bullet. Determine the muzzle velocity of the bullet.

7. A lead ball strikes the pavement after having fallen through a height of 15,000 cm. Assuming that half of this energy is converted into internal energy in the lead, determine its rise in temperature.

8. A copper cylinder whose mass is 50 gm contains 200 gm of water. The cylinder is dragged along a rough horizontal floor by a force of 100,000 dynes, while the acceleration produced is observed to be 200 cm/sec². (a) Determine the force of friction between the cylinder and the floor. (b) If the cylinder is moved through a distance of 100 m, determine the rise in temperature of the water and the cylinder, assuming that all of the work done against friction is converted into heat in the cylinder.

9. The water at Niagara Falls drops 160 ft. Assuming that all of this energy is converted into internal energy in the water, what is the increase in temperature of the water after it strikes the bottom of the falls?

10. A large glass jar whose mass is 250 gm contains 2,000 gm of water at 18°C. An electric motor delivers $\frac{1}{8}$ hp to a stirrer in the water for 15 min. Determine the rise in temperature of the water if all this energy goes into the water.

11. How much work is done by the expansion of a gas in a cylinder if the pressure remains constant at 250 lb/sq in. and the volume of the gas changes from 10 cu in. to 16 cu in.?

12. A gas in a cylinder occupying a volume of 800 cu cm at a pressure of 1 atm is compressed adiabatically to a volume of 50 cu cm. If $\gamma = 1.5$, determine the final pressure of the gas.

13. A steel tank contains 500 gm of air at 23°C. The cylinder is heated to a temperature of 88°C. Neglecting the expansion of the cylinder, determine (a) the amount of heat added to the air and (b) the change in its internal energy.

14. A steel cylinder fitted with a movable piston contains 350 gm of air at 28°C, a pressure of 1 atm, and a volume of 3×10^5 cm³. The air is heated at constant pressure to a temperature of 88°C. Determine (a) the amount of heat supplied to the air, (b) the work done by the air, and (c) the change in its internal energy during this process.

15. A steel tank contains 25 gm of hydrogen at 15°C and at a pressure of 1 atm. The hydrogen is heated to a temperature of 80°C at constant volume. Determine (a) the heat supplied to the hydrogen and (b) the change in its internal energy.

16. A steel cylinder fitted with a movable piston contains 25 gm of hydrogen at 22°C at 1 atm pressure. The volume of the gas is 300 liters. The gas is heated to 70°C at constant pressure. Determine (a) the heat supplied to the hydrogen, (b) the work done by the gas, and (c) the change in its internal energy.

17. How much heat is required to raise the temperature of the air in a room 15 ft by 20 ft by 9 ft from 50°F to 70°F? Assume the volume of the air to remain constant.

14

Kinetic Theory of Matter

14-1 GENERAL GAS LAW

The behavior of a gas under various conditions of temperature and pressure has already been studied in some detail. The results of these investigations have been put in the form of three equations which hold under different conditions for a constant mass of gas. One of these conditions is that the pressure of the gas should not be very great, say less than about 2 atm. The other conditions are stated with the equations as follows:

$$\text{at constant temperature } PV = \text{constant}; \qquad (1)$$

$$\text{at constant volume} \quad P = KT; \qquad (2)$$

$$\text{at constant pressure} \quad V = K'T. \qquad (3)$$

These three equations are special cases of a single equation, known as the general gas law for ideal gases, which gives the relationship between the pressure, volume, and temperature of a constant mass of gas under all conditions. The general gas law can be derived on the basis of the experimental results as expressed by the three equations above. It can also be derived on the basis of suitable assumptions concerning the behavior of the molecules of a gas. Both methods will be used in this chapter.

Let us consider a gas contained in a cylinder with a closely fitting piston, as shown in Figure 14–1. Suppose that the cylinder is surrounded by a mixture of ice and water so that the temperature of the gas is that of the ice point T_i. Let V_i be the volume of this gas at temperature T_i and let P_i be its pressure. If the gas is allowed to expand by pushing the piston out until its volume is V_2 and its pressure is P_f while its temperature remains constant, then, according to Equation (1), we can write

$$P_iV_i = P_fV_2. \qquad (4)$$

Now suppose that the mixture of ice and water is removed and that the gas is heated to a higher temperature T_f, the volume being allowed to expand to a new value V_f, but the pressure on the piston being maintained at the same value P_f throughout this process. Then, from Equation (3), we can write

$$\frac{V_2}{T_i} = \frac{V_f}{T_f} = K'. \tag{5}$$

Solving this equation for V_2, we get

$$V_2 = V_f \frac{T_i}{T_f},$$

and, substituting this value into Equation (4), we get

$$P_i V_i = P_f V_f \frac{T_i}{T_f}$$

or

$$\boxed{\frac{P_f V_f}{T_f} = \frac{P_i V_i}{T_i}.} \tag{6}$$

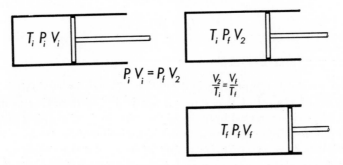

FIG. 14-1   Two steps in the derivation of the general gas law: an isothermal process followed by a constant-pressure process.

Equation (6) is one form of the general gas law. Each of the factors V_i, P_i, and T_i is a constant for a given mass of the gas. Hence Equation (6) may be written as

$$\boxed{\frac{P_f V_f}{T_f} = c = \text{constant.}} \tag{7}$$

Equation (7) is another form of the general gas law. This equation may be rewritten in more convenient form for use in numerical calculations as follows:

$$\boxed{\frac{PV}{T} = \frac{P_f V_f}{T_f},} \tag{8}$$

in which P and V are the pressure and volume of a constant mass of gas at temperature T, while P_f and V_f are the pressure and volume of the same mass of gas at the temperature T_f. Any convenient units may be used for pressure and volume; the temperature T, however, is always the absolute temperature.

Illustrative Example. A given mass of air occupies a volume of 2,000 cm³ at 27°C when its pressure is 75 cm of mercury. The air is compressed until its volume is 1,200 cm³ and its pressure is 225 cm of mercury. Determine its temperature.

Substituting in Equation (8), $P = 75$ cm, $V = 2,000$ cm³, $T = 273.2 + 27 = 300.2°$ abs; $P_f = 225$ cm, and $V_f = 1,200$ cm³, we have

$$\frac{75 \times 2,000}{300.2° \text{ abs}} = \frac{225 \times 1,200}{T_f},$$

from which $$T_f = 540.4° \text{ abs},$$

or $$t_f = 267.2°C.$$

14-2 THE UNIVERSAL GAS CONSTANT R

The constant c appearing in Equation (7) can be evaluated for any given mass of gas. But it assumes a particularly interesting form if the mass M of gas is expressed in terms of the *gram molecular weight* of the gas. The word *mole* is frequently used as an abbreviation of the term *gram molecular weight*. *A gram molecular weight of any substance is an amount of that substance whose mass, expressed in grams, is equal numerically to the molecular weight of the substance.* Furthermore, if the substance is a gas, then 1 gram molecular weight of the substance would occupy a volume of 22.4 liters at standard atmospheric pressure and at the temperature of 0°C or 273.2° abs. If we now set

$$V_i = 22,400 \text{ cm}^3/\text{mole},$$

$$P_i = 1 \text{ atm} = 1.013 \times 10^6 \frac{\text{dynes}}{\text{cm}^2},$$

and $$T_i = 273.2° \text{ abs},$$

the constant becomes

$$\frac{P_i V_i}{T_i} = 8.31 \times 10^7 \frac{\text{ergs}}{\text{mole deg}} = 8.31 \frac{\text{joules}}{\text{mole deg}} = R. \qquad (9)$$

This constant R is called the *universal gas constant* and is the same for all gases. The constant R may also be expressed in heat units and becomes

$$R = \frac{8.31}{4.185} = 1.986 \doteq 2 \,\frac{\text{cal}}{\text{mole deg}} \,.$$

In general, the mass M of a gas can be expressed in terms of its gram molecular weight M_w by the relationship

$$M = nM_w \tag{10}$$

where n is the number of moles of the substance. For this case the constant c becomes

$$c = nR, \tag{11}$$

and the general gas law may be written as

$$PV = nRT. \tag{12}$$

Illustrative Example.   Determine the pressure exerted by 8 gm of oxygen which occupy a volume of 4 liters at a temperature of 50°C.

The molecular weight of oxygen is 32; therefore $n = 8/32 = 1/4$ mole, $V = 4{,}000$ cm^3, and $T = 323.2°$ abs. Substituting these values in Equation (12), we get

$$P \times 4{,}000 \text{ cm}^3 = \tfrac{1}{4} \text{ mole} \times 8.31 \times 10^7 \,\frac{\text{ergs}}{\text{mole deg}} \times 323.2 \text{ deg,}$$

yielding

$$P = 1.68 \times 10^6 \,\frac{\text{dynes}}{\text{cm}^2} = \frac{1.68}{1.013} \text{ atm} = 1.66 \text{ atm.}$$

14-3 KINETIC THEORY OF GASES

The behavior of an ideal gas can be predicted on the basis of a few reasonable assumptions concerning the molecular structure of the gas and the action of these molecules. The first assumption is that a gas is composed of molecules which are so small that, to a first approximation, they may be considered as point masses. Suppose that a quantity of gas of mass M contains N molecules each of mass m; then we may write

$$M = Nm. \tag{13}$$

Another assumption is that these molecules do not exert forces of attraction or repulsion on each other except when they collide. A collision between two molecules should be thought of as an elastic collision in which the total kinetic energy after collision is equal to the total kinetic energy possessed by these molecules before collision. The gas will be assumed to be in a container which, for the sake of simplicity, will be taken as a cube of edge d and volume $V = d^3$.

On this theory, the pressure exerted by the gas on the walls of the container is due to the impact of the molecules on the walls, and when in equilibrium, this is the same as the pressure throughout the gas. To calculate this pressure, let us assume that the impact of a molecule with the wall is an elastic impact; that is, if a molecule is approaching the wall with a velocity v and momentum mv, then it will leave the wall with a velocity $-v$ and momentum $-mv$. The change in momentum of the molecule produced by this impact will thus be $-2mv$. To determine the pressure on the walls of the container, let us first calculate the force exerted by the molecules on one of the six faces of the cube, say the face $BCDE$ of Figure 14–2, and then divide by its area.

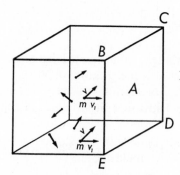

Fig. 14–2   Molecules with equal velocity components v_1 near face $BCDE$ of the cube.

Let us consider those molecules which at some instant are very close to this face. Only those molecules whose velocities have components perpendicular to this face, and directed toward it, will strike it and rebound. Suppose we consider a small number of molecules which have the same value v_1 for this velocity component. The number of these molecules which will strike this face during a small time interval t will be one half of the number contained in a small volume Al, where A is equal to the area of the face of the cube and $l = v_1t$; the other half having this velocity component v_1 are moving away from the wall. If n_1 represents the number of molecules per unit volume which have this velocity component v_1, then the number striking this face of the cube in time t will be

$$\frac{n_1}{2} Av_1t.$$

Since each such molecule will have its momentum changed by $-2mv_1$ as a result of this impact, the impulse imparted to the wall will be equal and opposite to it, or $+2mv_1$. The impulse F_1t on the wall produced by these collisions in time t will then be

$$F_1 t = \frac{n_1}{2} A v_1 t \times 2 m v_1,$$

from which $\qquad\qquad F_1 = A n_1 m v_1^2.$ (14)

The pressure on the wall produced by the impact of these molecules is

$$p_1 = \frac{F_1}{A} = n_1 m v_1^2.$$ (15)

We can now consider another group of molecules, n_2 per unit volume, which have a slightly different velocity component v_2 in this direction; they will produce an additional pressure p_2, given by

$$p_2 = n_2 m v_2^2.$$

In this way, we can break up the gas into different groups of molecules, each group contributing a similar term to the pressure on this face of the cube. The total pressure P due to all the different groups of molecules will therefore be of the form

$$P = n_1 m v_1^2 + n_2 m v_2^2 + n_3 m v_3^2 + \cdots.$$ (16)

The symbol $(+\cdots.)$ means that we have to add terms similar to those that precede it to include all the different groups of molecules that have velocity components in a direction perpendicular to this face of the cube.

Equation (16) can be simplified by introducing a new term called *the average of the squares of the components of the velocities of all the molecules moving perpendicular to face A* and defined by the equation

$$\overline{v_A^2} = \frac{n_1 v_1^2 + n_2 v_2^2 + n_3 v_3^2 + \cdots}{n},$$ (17)

in which n represents the total number of molecules per unit volume. Substituting this value of $\overline{v_A^2}$ in Equation (16), we get

$$P = n m \overline{v_A^2}.$$ (18)

There will be a similar expression for the pressure on each of the six faces of the cube, except that the factor $\overline{v_A^2}$ will be replaced by the appropriate average of the squares of the components of the velocities of the molecules for that particular face.

The velocity v of any one molecule may be in any direction; it can be resolved into three mutually perpendicular components v_x, v_y, v_z. The magnitude of v in terms of the magnitudes of these components is given by

$$v^2 = v_x^2 + v_y^2 + v_z^2.$$ (19)

There will be a similar equation for the square of the velocity of each molecule of the gas in terms of the squares of its three mutually perpendicular components. If we add the squares of the component velocities in the x-direction and divide this sum by the total number of molecules, we will get the average value of the square of this velocity component; it will be represented by $\overline{v_x^2}$. Similarly, $\overline{v_y^2}$ and $\overline{v_z^2}$ will represent the average squares of the velocities in the y- and z-directions, respectively. By adding these average squares of the three velocity components, we get

$$\overline{v^2} = \overline{v_x^2} + \overline{v_y^2} + \overline{v_z^2},$$

where $\overline{v^2}$ is the average of the squares of the velocities of all the molecules. Since the velocities of the molecules have all possible directions, the average value of the squares of the velocity in any one direction should be the same as in any other direction, or

$$\overline{v_x^2} = \overline{v_y^2} = \overline{v_z^2},$$

so that

$$\overline{v^2} = 3\overline{v_x^2}. \tag{19a}$$

If we take the x-direction as perpendicular to the face A, we can write

$$\overline{v^2} = 3\overline{v_A^2}, \tag{19b}$$

so that Equation (18) becomes

$$\boxed{P = \tfrac{1}{3}nm\overline{v^2}.} \tag{20}$$

The expression for the pressure of an ideal gas may be written in a more instructive way by noting that the kinetic energy of 1 molecule is $\tfrac{1}{2}mv^2$, and that $\tfrac{1}{2}nm\overline{v^2}$ can be considered as the total kinetic energy of translation of all the molecules in a unit volume under these conditions. Setting

$$\mathcal{E} = \tfrac{1}{2}nm\overline{v^2}, \tag{21}$$

the expression for the pressure can be written

$$P = \tfrac{2}{3}\mathcal{E}; \tag{22}$$

that is, the pressure of an ideal gas is equal to two thirds of the total value of the kinetic energy of the molecules in a unit volume of the gas.

If the volume of the gas is V and the total number of molecules is N, then the number of molecules per unit volume is

$$n = \frac{N}{V}, \tag{23}$$

so that the expression for the pressure of a gas can be written as

$$P = \tfrac{1}{3} \frac{N}{V} m\overline{v^2},$$ (24)

from which $$PV = \tfrac{2}{3} \cdot \tfrac{1}{2} N m\overline{v^2}.$$ (25)

From a comparison of Equation (25) with the general gas law as given by Equation (12), it follows that the average value of the kinetic energy of the molecules of an ideal gas is proportional to its absolute temperature T. If we set

$$\tfrac{1}{2} m\overline{v^2} = \tfrac{3}{2} kT,$$ (26)

where k is a constant of proportionality, then Equation (25) may be written as

$$PV = NkT = cT,$$ (27)

in which $c = Nk$. Thus, on the basis of the assumptions stated in this analysis, we have been able to derive the general equation of state for an ideal gas. As long as the substance behaves as an ideal gas we can have confidence in the correctness of these assumptions. But when the substance no longer behaves as an ideal gas, for example, when it is liquefied or solidified, it is no longer correct to state that its absolute temperature is proportional to the average value of the kinetic energy of its molecules.

14-4 AVOGADRO'S HYPOTHESIS

The success that we have had so far with the kinetic theory of gases suggests other extensions. Suppose that we consider two different ideal gases, each occupying the same volume V at the same temperature T and exerting the same pressure P. Let one of the gases contain N_1 molecules each of mass m_1, and let the other gas contain N_2 molecules each of mass m_2. We can then write Equation (24) for the first gas as

$$PV = \tfrac{1}{3} N_1 m_1 \overline{v_1^2},$$ (28)

and for the second gas

$$PV = \tfrac{1}{3} N_2 m_2 \overline{v_2^2}.$$ (29)

Since the product PV is the same for each gas, we may write

$$N_1 m_1 \overline{v_1^2} = N_2 m_2 \overline{v_2^2}.$$ (30)

Since the temperatures of the two gases are the same, we can write

$$\tfrac{3}{2} kT = \tfrac{1}{2} m_1 \overline{v_1^2} = \tfrac{1}{2} m_2 \overline{v_2^2}$$

or $$m_1 \overline{v_1^2} = m_2 \overline{v_2^2}.$$ (31)

Dividing Equation (30) by Equation (31) yields

$$N_1 = N_2; \qquad \text{(32)}$$

that is, two different gases which occupy equal volumes at the same temperature and pressure have equal numbers of molecules.

This result was first predicted by Avogadro in 1811 from the known properties of gases. *Avogadro's hypothesis stated that all gases occupying equal volumes at the same temperature and pressure contain equal numbers of molecules.* The molar volume, that is 22.4 liters at 0°C and 76 cm mercury pressure, is the volume occupied by a gram molecular weight of gas. Hence each gram molecular weight of a substance contains exactly the same number of molecules, which we shall denote by N_0. The accepted value of this number, determined experimentally, is

$$N_0 = 6.023 \times 10^{23} \text{ molecules per gram molecular weight.}$$

This number N_0 is called the *Avogadro number*.

If we are dealing with 1 mole of an ideal gas at temperature T and pressure P, then Equation (27) can be rewritten as

$$PV_1 = N_0 kT,$$

where V_1 is the volume of this mole of gas and $N = N_0$. Equation (12) can be rewritten as

$$PV_1 = RT,$$

since, for this case, $n = 1$. A comparison of these two equations shows that

$$N_0 k = R,$$

from which

$$k = \frac{R}{N_0} . \qquad \text{(33)}$$

Since R is the universal constant for a mole of a gas and N_0 is the number of molecules per mole, k then represents the universal constant per molecule. It is usually called the *Boltzmann constant;* its value can be obtained from the known values of R and N_0, and is

$$k = 1.38 \times 10^{-16} \text{ erg/deg.}$$

14-5 DIFFUSION OF GASES

Everyone is familiar with the fact that if a bottle of ammonia is opened in a room, the odor of the ammonia soon pervades the entire room. The ammonia is said to *diffuse* through the air in the room. The same is true of any other gas or vapor; that is, it will diffuse through the air and ultimately fill the entire volume. To illustrate this process, fill a flask with a gas which is lighter than air, such as fuel gas, and place it over a similar flask containing air, keeping the necks of the bottles open, as shown in Figure 14–3. Even though the gas is lighter than air, it will diffuse into the air in the lower bottle; at the same time, some of the air from the lower bottle will diffuse into the gas above it. This can be tested by separating the bottles and applying a lighted match to each one.

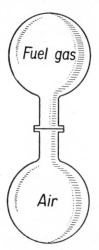

Gases can also diffuse through porous surfaces. Figure 14–4(a) shows a porous cup C with a glass tube T sealed to its open end and dipping into a jar of water. A glass jar G is inverted over the porous cup. If a stream of hydrogen, for example, is led into the space between the porous cup and the glass

FIG. 14–3   Diffusion of gases. After a short time, some fuel gas will be found in the lower flask and some air will be found in the upper flask.

jar, the hydrogen will diffuse into the porous cup faster than the air diffuses out of it. The pressure inside the cup is thus increased, and the

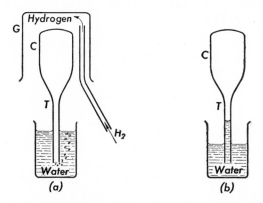

FIG. 14–4   Diffusion of gases through a porous cup.

gas is forced out of it through the tube T. The gas will bubble through the water and go out into the atmosphere. If the stream of hydrogen is shut off and the glass jar G is removed so that only air surrounds the porous cup *C*, the hydrogen will diffuse out of the porous cup faster than air will diffuse into it. The pressure inside the cup will decrease below atmospheric pressure, as evidenced by the rise of the water in the tube *T* [see Figure 14–4(b)].

When a mixture of gases of different densities is allowed to diffuse through a porous surface, the least dense gas will diffuse through at the greatest rate. This can be seen by an examination of Equation (31), which is

$$m_1\overline{v_1^2} = m_2\overline{v_2^2}. \tag{31}$$

If we take the square roots of the average squares of the velocities, we find that their ratio is

$$\frac{v_{1s}}{v_{2s}} = \sqrt{\frac{m_2}{m_1}}. \tag{34}$$

v_{1s} and v_{2s} are called the *root mean square* (rms) values of the velocities. These velocities vary inversely as the square roots of the masses of the molecules. This is one form of *Graham's law of diffusion.*

For example, if we have a mixture of hydrogen and helium diffusing through a porous surface, the ratio of the rms values of their velocities is

$$\frac{v_{\mathrm{H}}}{v_{\mathrm{He}}} = \sqrt{\frac{m_{\mathrm{He}}}{m_{\mathrm{H}}}}.$$

The molecular weight of hydrogen is about 2, and the molecular weight of helium is about 4. Since each mole of a substance contains the same number of molecules, the ratio of the molecular weights is equal to the ratio of the masses of the respective molecules. Hence

$$\sqrt{\frac{m_{\mathrm{He}}}{m_{\mathrm{H}}}} = \sqrt{\frac{4}{2}} = \sqrt{2},$$

so that
$$\frac{v_{\mathrm{H}}}{v_{\mathrm{He}}} = \sqrt{2} = 1.4.$$

The gaseous mixture coming through the porous surface will thus be richer in hydrogen than the original mixture. By passing this new mixture through a second porous surface, the mixture can be further enriched in hydrogen.

An important application of a process of diffusion through a porous surface or a "barrier," as it is sometimes called, is to the enrichment of uranium so that it will contain a larger percentage of the lighter *isotope* than is usually found in natural uranium (see Chapter 39). Natural uranium consists of 99.3 per cent of the isotope of mass 238, symbol U^{238}, and 0.7 per cent of the isotope of mass 235, U^{235}. A gaseous compound is formed of uranium and fluorine known as uranium hexafluoride; this is a combination of 6 fluorine atoms and 1 uranium atom, UF_6. Since the atomic weight of fluorine is 19.0, the mass m_1 of the compound formed with U^{235} is

$$m_1 = 235 + 6 \times 19 = 349.$$

The mass m_2 of the compound formed with U^{238} is

$$m_2 = 238 + 6 \times 19 = 352.$$

Applying Graham's law to this process, we get

$$\frac{v_1}{v_2} = \sqrt{\frac{352}{349}} = 1.0043$$

for the ratio of the respective rms velocities of the light and heavy molecules. This ratio is sometimes called the separation factor of the diffusion process. Since this separation factor is very small, it is necessary to use a great many such diffusion processes in succession, in order to get a final product which has a large percentage of uranium 235.

14-6 DALTON'S LAW OF PARTIAL PRESSURES

If a gas consists of a mixture of several different chemically inert gases all at the same temperature T and occupying the volume V, the pressure P of the gas can be shown to be equal to the sum of the pressures that the individual gases would exert if each occupied the same volume alone at the same temperature. The pressure that each gas exerts when in the mixture is called its *partial pressure*. If we use the form of the gas law given by

$$PV = nRT, \tag{12}$$

where n is the number of moles of gas occupying volume V at temperature T, then, in the case of a mixture of different gases, say n_1 moles of gas I, n_2 moles of gas II, and n_3 moles of gas III,

$$n = n_1 + n_2 + n_3.$$

Equation (12) then becomes

$$PV = n_1RT + n_2RT + n_3RT,$$

from which

$$P = \frac{n_1}{V} RT + \frac{n_2}{V} RT + \frac{n_3}{V} RT.$$

Now $\frac{n_1}{V} RT$ is the pressure P_1 which n_1 moles of gas I exerts when this gas occupies volume V at temperature T; similarly $\frac{n_2}{V} RT = P_2$ and

$\frac{n_3}{V} RT = P_3$, so that

$$P = P_1 + P_2 + P_3, \qquad (35)$$

where P_1, P_2, and P_3 are the *partial pressures* of the individual gases. Hence the *pressure exerted by a mixture of chemically inactive gases is the sum of the partial pressures of the individual gases.* This was first stated in 1802 by John Dalton, the founder of the atomic theory, and is called *Dalton's law of partial pressures.*

Illustrative Example. Assuming that 20 per cent of the air molecules are oxygen and 80 per cent are nitrogen, determine their partial pressures when the air occupies 1 liter at a pressure of 4 atm, and 0°C.

Let us call n_1 the number of moles of oxygen in this air and P_1 its partial pressure. Now

$$P_1 = \frac{n_1}{V} RT.$$

The total pressure P of the air is given by

$$P = \frac{n}{V} RT,$$

when n is the number of moles of air.

Hence $\dfrac{P_1}{P} = \dfrac{n_1}{n}.$

But n_1/n is simply the percentage of oxygen in the air, which in this case is 0.20.   Therefore

$$P_1 = 0.20P$$
$$= 0.20 \times 4 \text{ atm},$$

from which $P_1 = 0.8 \text{ atm}$

is the partial pressure of the oxygen; the partial pressure of the nitrogen is

$$P_2 = 4.0 - 0.8 = 3.2 \text{ atm}.$$

14-7 DIFFUSION OF LIQUIDS AND SOLIDS

Diffusion takes place in liquids and in solids, but at a much slower rate than in gases. If crystals of copper sulphate are placed at the bottom of a tall cylinder and water is then poured into it, a concentrated solution of copper sulphate will be formed at the bottom of the cylinder. If this cylinder is allowed to stand in a quiet place for several months, the progress of the diffusion process can be observed by the change in color of the liquid. As time progresses, the bluish copper sulphate solution can be seen to ascend through the column of the liquid showing the diffusion of the copper sulphate through the water.

The diffusion of the molecules of a solid through another solid takes place at a very slow rate. Nowadays the rate of diffusion can be determined by the use of radioactive atoms of an element as a *tracer* (see Chapter 39). For example, if a piece of copper is made with a certain percentage of radioactive copper atoms and if this piece of copper is placed in contact with another metal, the rate of diffusion of the copper into the other metal can be determined by measuring the radiations given out by the radioactive copper atoms which have diffused into the second metal.

14-8 OSMOSIS

There are many substances which, when in the form of thin membranes, will allow one type of molecule to pass through them readily, but prevent other types from going through. Such membranes are called *semipermeable membranes.* Some semipermeable membranes are made of organic substances such as the bladder of an animal, the skin of a fruit, or the inner skin of an egg, or are made by coating a paper with starch. One type is made by coating a porous porcelain cup with potassium ferrocyanide. The behavior of a semipermeable membrane can be illustrated by covering a glass thistle tube with a membrane such as pig's bladder, which is permeable to water but not to sugar; a small amount of sugar solution is poured into it and the tube is put into a beaker of pure water, as shown in Figure 14-5. The water will pass readily through the membrane into the solution,

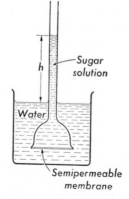

FIG. 14-5 Demonstration of osmotic pressure of a sugar solution.

decreasing its concentration. If a long glass tube is attached to the thistle tube, the solution will rise to a considerable height in it. When equilibrium is reached, that is, when just as much water goes through the membrane into the solution as goes into the water from the solution, the level of the solution in the tube will be at a height h above the level of the water. The pressure exerted by this column of height h is called the *osmotic pressure* of the solution. Osmotic pressures can reach very large values, of the order of 20 atm or greater.

Osmosis plays a very important role in many physiological phenomena. The passage of water through fruit skins and the passage of the products of digestion through the walls of the intestines are examples of osmosis. The passage of oxygen from the lungs to the blood takes place by osmosis.

An interesting thing about the osmotic pressure of a solution is its analogy with the pressure of a gas. The equation $PV = nRT$ can be applied to an osmotic pressure P, if V is interpreted as the volume of the solution and n is interpreted as the number of moles of the solute dissolved in the solution at temperature T. R is exactly the same as the universal gas constant. Thus, if 1 mole of sugar is dissolved in water so that the solution occupies a volume of 22.4 liters, the osmotic pressure is 1 atm at 0°C.

14-9 BROWNIAN MOTION

If very fine particles are put into a liquid and then examined with the aid of a microscope, it will be observed that the particles are executing haphazard motions. These random motions never cease. This phenomenon was first observed by the botanist Robert Brown in 1827. The motion of these particles has since become known as *Brownian motion*. The same type of motion can be observed if very fine particles are suspended in a gas. A simple way of observing Brownian motion is to blow some cigarette smoke into a glass cell which has flat sides and then examine it under a microscope, as shown in Figure 14–6.

The Brownian motion of a particle is produced by the bombardment of the particle by the molecules of the fluid in which it is suspended. Because of its small size, the particle is not bombarded equally from all sides, so that there is a resultant force on it. The particle is accelerated by this resultant force, and, as it moves through the fluid, it also experiences a force due to the viscosity of the fluid opposing the motion. The distance that a particle moves in any one direction is very small. The direction of its motion is continually changing, because the direction of the resultant force produced by the unequal bombardment by the molecules of the fluid is a matter of chance. Many observers noticed the similarity between the Brownian motion of the suspended particles and the motion that the molecules of an ideal gas are assumed to have.

Einstein, in 1905, developed a theory for the Brownian motion on the assumption that these particles behaved as though they were large-sized molecules of an ideal gas suspended in a fluid. From this theory, he developed two important results which could be checked experimentally. One of these is that the particles have a vertical distribution similar to the distribution of air in the atmosphere; that is, that the density of the particles, or the number of particles per cubic centimeter, should be greatest at the bottom and least at the top. Perrin, in 1908, performed a series of experiments using resinous particles of known sizes suspended in a variety of liquids, such as water and alcohol, and counted the number of

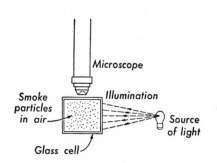

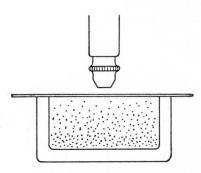

Fig. 14–6 Method of observing Brownian motion of smoke particles in air.

Fig. 14–7 Method of observing the vertical distribution of particles in a fluid.

particles at different heights in the solution (see Figure 14–7). If n_1 is the number of particles per cubic centimeter at any level in the liquid and n_2 is the number of particles per cubic centimeter at a height h above the first position, then Einstein's theory leads to the equation

$$\frac{n_2}{n_1} = 1 - \frac{N_0 mg}{RT}\left(1 - \frac{d_0}{d}\right)h, \qquad \textbf{(36)}$$

where N_0 is the Avogadro number, m is the mass and d is the density of the particle in the liquid, d_0 is the density of the liquid, T is the absolute temperature of the liquid, R is the universal gas constant, and g is the acceleration of gravity. Since all the quantities in Equation (36) except N_0 are known or measurable, Perrin was able to determine the Avogadro number from these experiments.

Another result of Einstein's theory concerned the displacement of a particle in Brownian motion in a given time interval t. Suppose the position of the particle is observed at any instant and plotted on x-y coordinates, and then, after the lapse of say 30 sec, its position is again observed and plotted; the line joining these two positions is the displacement of the particle in this time. Perrin performed a series of experiments in which he determined the displacements of a particle in known time intervals for as long as it remained in the field of view of the microscope. A typical graph of the displacements of such a particle is shown in Figure 14–8. Einstein developed the equation

$$\overline{x^2} = \frac{2RT}{N_0 K} t,$$

(37)

where x is the x-component of any displacement in time t, and $\overline{x^2}$ is the average of the squares of these displacements. R is the universal gas constant, T is the absolute temperature of the liquid containing the particles, K is a constant dependent upon the viscosity of the liquid, and N_0 is

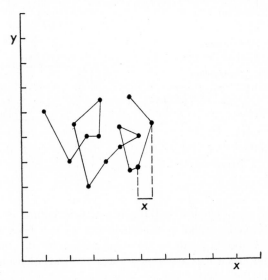

FIG. 14–8   Trajectory of a particle in Brownian motion. Each line connecting two dots represents the displacement of a particle in a fixed time interval.

Avogadro's number. Since all the quantities are known or measurable except N_0, the results of these experiments could then be used to determine the Avogadro number. In one set of experiments he measured 1,500 displacements of particles of 0.367×10^{-4} cm radius. His early results led to a value of 6.85×10^{23} for N_0, but, with improved technique, the values of N_0 determined from Brownian motion experiments are very close to the present accepted value of 6.023×10^{23} molecules per mole.

QUESTIONS

1. State the fundamental assumptions at the basis of the kinetic theory of gases.

2. Show that if two gases are at the same temperature, the average value of the kinetic energy of the molecules is the same for each gas.

3. Two different gases occupy equal volumes at the same pressure. What is the relationship between the kinetic energies of the molecules of the gases?

4. A semipermeable membrane in the center of a glass jar separates two sugar solutions of unequal concentrations. Explain what will happen to these solutions.

5. The molecular weight of helium is 4 and that of oxygen is 32. If these gases are at the same temperature, compare (a) the average kinetic energies of their molecules; and (b) the relative momenta of their molecules.

6. Can you suggest a simple device for increasing the percentage of oxygen in the air to be circulated in a room?

7. Two flasks have equal volumes; one contains neon, and the other contains argon. The temperatures are equal and the pressures are equal. The two flasks are connected by a short tube, and the stopcocks are opened. Describe the composition of each flask after equilibrium has been reached.

8. Look up the molecular weights of the gases listed in Table 13–2. The heat required to raise the temperature of 1 mole of a gas 1°C is called the *molar heat capacity* of the gas. Construct another table of values listing (a) the molar heat capacity at constant pressure, (b) the molar heat capacity at constant volume, and (c) the difference between the two values for each of the gases. It can be shown that the difference between the two heat capacities should be equal to the gas constant R. Compare these values with R.

PROBLEMS

1. A closed vessel contains dry air at 15°C and 76 cm of mercury pressure. Its temperature is raised to 100°C. Determine the pressure of the air, neglecting the change in volume of the container.

2. A mass of gas occupies a volume of 1.2 liter at a pressure of 76 cm of mercury when its temperature is 40°C. The gas is allowed to expand until its volume is 1.5 liters and its pressure is 80 cm of mercury. Determine its final temperature.

3. A certain gas has a density of 0.001 gm/cm^3 when its temperature is 50°C and its pressure is 4 atm. What pressure will be needed to change the density of the gas to 0.003 gm/cm^3 when its temperature is 100°C?

4. An automobile tire has a volume of 1,000 cu in. and contains air at a gauge pressure of 24 lb/in.^{2} when the temperature is 0°C. What will be the gauge pressure of the air in the tires when its temperature rises to 27°C and its volume increases to 1,020 cu in.?

5. A mass of gas occupies a volume of 400 cm^3 at a temperature of 17°C and a pressure of 76 cm of mercury. What will be the pressure of the gas when it occupies a volume of 600 cm^3 at a temperature of 80°C?

6. A mass of gas occupies a volume of 6 liters at a temperature of 27°C and 75 cm of mercury pressure. What will be its temperature when the gas is compressed to a volume of 4 liters at a pressure of 130 cm?

7. Determine the pressure of 4.032 gm of hydrogen which occupies a volume of 11.2 liters at a temperature of 0°C. The molecular weight of hydrogen is 2.016.

8. Determine the average value of the kinetic energy of the molecules of a gas at 0°C.

9. The mass of a hydrogen molecule is 3.25×10^{-24} gm. Determine the average velocity of a molecule of hydrogen at 0°C.

10. Assuming the mass of an oxygen molecule to be 16 times that of a hydrogen molecule, determine the average speed of an oxygen molecule when the temperature of oxygen is 0°C.

11. Calculate the work done in compressing a molecular weight of oxygen from a volume of 22.4 liters at 0°C and atmospheric pressure to 8.4 liters at the same pressure.

12. Determine the temperature of the oxygen at the end of the constant pressure process of Problem 11.

13. An analysis of a gas shows that it consists of 20 per cent nitrogen, 30 per cent neon, and 50 per cent argon. Determine the partial pressures of these gases when the total pressure is 3 atm.

14. A cylinder contains 2.016 gm of hydrogen at 0°C and 76 cm of mercury pressure. Calculate the amount of heat required to raise the temperature of this hydrogen to 80°C (a) keeping the pressure constant and (b) keeping the volume constant. (c) What is the volume of the hydrogen when at 0°C?

15. A cylinder contains 32 gm of oxygen at 0°C and 76 cm of mercury pressure. Calculate the amount of heat required to raise the temperature of this mass of oxygen to 60°C (a) keeping the pressure constant and (b) keeping the volume constant. (c) How much work is done by the oxygen in each case?

16. If d is the density of a gas, show, from Equation (24), that $v = \sqrt{\dfrac{3p}{d}}$.

15

Change of Phase

15-1 PHASES OF A SUBSTANCE

A substance which has a definite chemical composition can exist in one or more *phases* such as the vapor phase, the liquid phase, or the solid phase. When there are two or more phases of a substance in equilibrium at any given temperature and pressure, there will always be surfaces of separation between the phases. The change of phase of a substance from solid to liquid is called *melting* or *fusion;* heat must be added to the solid to melt it. The quantity of heat that must be added to melt a unit mass of the substance at a constant temperature is called the *heat of fusion.* Conversely, to freeze the substance, that is, to change its phase from liquid to solid, heat must be removed from it. The change of phase from liquid to vapor is called *vaporization* and involves the addition of heat to the substance. The quantity of heat which must be added to vaporize a unit mass of the substance at a constant temperature is called its *heat of vaporization.* Conversely, to *condense* the substance, that is, to change its phase from vapor to liquid, requires the removal of heat from the substance. A third type of phase change, that from solid to vapor, is called *sublimation.* Heat must be added to produce this change of phase; the quantity of heat required to change a unit mass of a substance from solid to vapor at a constant temperature is called the *heat of sublimation.* Conversely, when a substance is condensed directly from the vapor to the solid phase, heat must be removed from the substance.

Many substances are known to exist in several different solid phases; ice, for example, can exist in six different solid phases; sulphur is known to have four different solid phases. These solid phases are distinguished principally by the different groupings of the molecules to form different types of crystals. In rare cases, notably helium, two different liquid phases are known to exist. There can be only one vapor phase of a substance.

15-2 VAPORIZATION. VAPOR PRESSURE

One method for studying the process of vaporization and the properties of a vapor is illustrated in Figure 15–1. This is a modification of the simple

321

barometer. A tube A about 1 m long is first filled with mercury and then inverted and put into a long reservoir R containing mercury. The level of the mercury in A will be at the barometric height above the level in R.

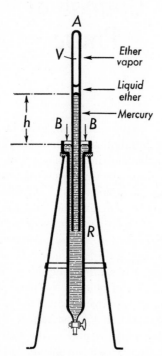

The space above the mercury in A contains mercury vapor at a very low pressure; this region is sometimes called a *Torricelli* vacuum. For the purpose of the present experiment, we shall neglect the effect of this mercury vapor. Suppose we take a small quantity of liquid ether in an eye dropper and put it into the open end of tube A, always keeping it under the top of the mercury in R. Since ether is less dense than mercury, the ether will rise to the top of the mercury column and vaporize into the space above it. We shall observe that the level of the mercury column in A is now much lower than before, and there probably is no trace of the liquid ether. If we now push the tube A slowly into the reservoir R, we shall find that at some stage in this process a small layer of liquid ether will appear on top of the column of mercury in A. As the tube is pushed down still further, the thickness of this layer of liquid increases, showing that more vapor is condensing. If we reverse this procedure and now move tube A up, the thickness of the layer of liquid ether will decrease and finally disappear completely.

FIG. 15–1   Method of measuring the saturated vapor pressure of ether.

An analysis of this experiment shows that the ether vapor exerts a pressure; this pressure is equal to the difference between the actual barometric pressure B and the height h of the mercury column in tube A. Let us designate the vapor, when there is no liquid present, as an *unsaturated vapor*. The unsaturated vapor behaves as a gas. When the tube A is pushed down into R, the volume of the unsaturated vapor is decreased and its pressure is increased. If we continue to move A down, the volume of the unsaturated vapor will decrease and its pressure will increase until a certain volume is reached, when some of the vapor condenses into the liquid phase. If the volume of this system is decreased still further, more vapor condenses into liquid, but the pressure remains constant as long as there is vapor present and the temperature remains unchanged. At these conditions of pressure and temperature, there is equilibrium between the liquid and its vapor, and the vapor is said to be a *saturated vapor*. The pressure of a saturated vapor does not depend upon its volume. If we modify this experiment so that we can vary the temperature of the liquid ether and its saturated vapor, it will be found that the pressure of the saturated vapor increases rapidly with increasing temperature.

15-3 BOILING

Our most common experience with the process of boiling is the boiling of water in a dish which is open to the atmosphere. The water is usually heated by means of a flame or an electric heater. A thermometer placed in the water will show an increase in temperature until the boiling point is reached; the temperature will then remain constant during the process of boiling. When water is boiling, the liquid is changing to vapor. If the dish is open to the atmosphere, the pressure of the water vapor just above the liquid surface must be equal to that of the atmosphere. The *boiling point* is that temperature at which the pressure of the vapor is equal to the pressure exerted on the liquid. When the pressure on the liquid is 76 cm of mercury, the boiling point of the water is, by definition, 100°C or 212°F. The boiling point of a liquid at a pressure of 76 cm of mercury is called the *normal boiling point*. The normal boiling points of some substances are given in Table 15–1.

Table 15-1   Normal Boiling Points

Substance	Temperature in °C
Sulphur	444.6
Mercury	356.7
Water	100.0
Alcohol (ethyl)	78.3
Ether	34.6
Oxygen	−183.0
Nitrogen	−195.8
Hydrogen	−252.8
Helium	−269

It has long been known that water will boil at a temperature lower than 100°C if the pressure of the atmosphere is less than 76 cm of mercury—for example, at the top of a mountain—and that its boiling point will be higher than 100°C if the atmospheric pressure is greater than 76 cm of mercury. For example, if we take a flask partly filled with water, heat it, and allow the water to boil vigorously for a few minutes, the air above it will be driven off by the steam. If the flask is now closed by means of a rubber stopper, there will be only water vapor or steam above the liquid surface. The pressure on the liquid will be due to the pressure of the water vapor. If this sealed flask is maintained at a constant temperature of 100°C by being placed in a steam bath, the pressure of the vapor in the sealed flask will remain at the value of 76 cm of mercury. This is its normal boiling point. There is a state of equilibrium between water and its saturated vapor (steam) at 100°C and a pressure of 76 cm of mercury. From the molecular point of view, we may think of this type of equilibrium as one in which there is a constant interchange of molecules between the liquid and the vapor phases: just as many molecules go from the liquid to the vapor phase as from the vapor back to the liquid phase.

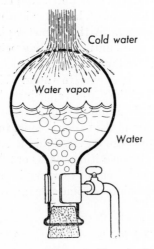

Fig. 15–2 Water boiling under reduced pressure.

If this sealed flask is turned over and clamped in the overturned position, as shown in Figure 15–2, and cold water is poured over it, the water in the flask will start boiling vigorously. If the flask is allowed to cool in the room for some time and cold water again is poured over it, the water in the flask will start boiling vigorously again. The effect of pouring cold water over the flask is to reduce the pressure of the vapor below the saturation pressure. There is no longer equilibrium between the liquid and the vapor, and the liquid starts vaporizing once more. Thus, when the pressure on the water is less than 76 cm of mercury, it boils at a temperature less than 100°C.

The relationship between the temperature of the water and the pressure of its saturated vapor can be investigated by placing the water in an iron boiler which has a thermometer and a pressure gauge fitted into it. The water is first boiled vigorously to drive off the air above it, and the boiler valve is then closed. For low temperatures, the boiler may be immersed in a cool bath and the pressure and temperature may be measured. It will be found that as the temperature of the water decreases, the vapor pressure also decreases. Some of the water vapor condenses, and equilibrium is established between the liquid and its vapor at this lower temperature and pressure.

To study the relationship between temperature and pressure at higher temperatures, the boiler can be surrounded by electric heater coils. The current through the coils can be adjusted to the value required to maintain the water at any desired temperature. It will be found that at temperatures above 100°C the pressure of the saturated vapor is greater than 76 cm of mercury. The curve OA in Figure 15–3 shows the relationship between

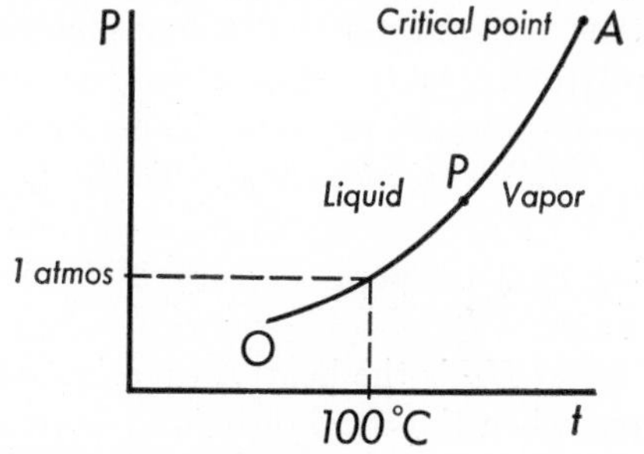

FIG. 15–3 Vaporization curve of water.

the pressure and temperature of water and its saturated vapor. Any point P on this curve represents a definite temperature and pressure at which water is in equilibrium with its saturated vapor (steam). This curve is called the *vaporization curve* of water. Similar vaporization curves can be obtained for other liquids.

15-4 HEAT OF VAPORIZATION

The process of vaporization requires the addition of heat to the liquid. *The quantity of heat required to vaporize a unit mass of a liquid at a constant temperature is known as its heat of vaporization.* Experiments show that the heat of vaporization of a liquid depends upon the temperature at which vaporization takes place; the higher the temperature, the smaller is the heat of vaporization. For example, in the case of water, the heat of vaporization at 100°C is 540 cal/gm or 972 Btu/lb. At 20°C, however, the heat of vaporization of water is 590 cal/gm, while at 300°C it is 331 cal/gm. The heat of vaporization is also the quantity of heat liberated when a unit mass of the substance condenses at a constant temperature from the vapor to the liquid phase. Thus, when steam at 100°C is condensed to water at the same temperature, 540 cal of heat are liberated for each gram of steam which is condensed.

In general, if m is the mass of a substance which is changed from the liquid to the vapor phase at constant temperature and if H_V is the heat of vaporization of the substance, then the quantity of heat H which must be added to produce this change of phase is

$$H = mH_V.$$

(1)

Equation (1) also holds when a mass m of the substance is changed from the vapor to the liquid phase.   In the latter case, H is the quantity of heat that must be removed from the vapor, or that is given out by the vapor, in this change of phase.   One of the methods for measuring the heat of vaporization of water is to take steam from a boiler and add it to a known quantity of water.   In this process the steam is first condensed to water and then cooled from the boiling point down to the final temperature of the mixture.   At the same time, the temperature of the cool water is raised from its initial value to the final temperature of the mixture.

Illustrative Example.   To 200 gm of water at 25°C in a copper calorimeter whose mass is 120 gm are added 5 gm of steam at 100°C.   The resulting final temperature is 39.2°C.   Determine the heat of vaporization of water.

If H_V is the heat of vaporization of water, the quantity of heat given out when the 5 gm of steam are condensed to water at 100°C is

$$H = 5 \text{ gm} \times H_V.$$

The additional heat given out by these 5 gm of condensed steam in cooling from 100°C to 39.2°C is

$$5 \times (100 - 39.2) \text{ cal} = 304 \text{ cal.}$$

Equating the heat thus liberated to the heat absorbed by the water and the copper calorimeter which raises their temperature from 25°C to 39.2°C, we get

$$5 \text{ gm} \times H_V + 304 \text{ cal} = 200 \times 14.2 \text{ cal} + 120 \times 0.093 \times 14.2 \text{ cal,}$$

from which $$H_V = 539 \, \frac{\text{cal}}{\text{gm}}.$$

15-5   THE CRITICAL POINT

The vaporization curve is not indefinite in extent; it has both a lower limit and an upper limit.   The upper limit is known as the *critical point;* the temperature and pressure of the critical point are known as the *critical temperature* and *critical pressure*.   At temperatures above the critical temperature the substance cannot exist as a liquid; that is, no matter how great the pressure, it cannot be put in the liquid phase.   At the critical temperature the densities of the liquid and the vapor are equal.   The heat of vaporization is zero at the critical temperature.   A distinction is sometimes made between the vapor states above and below the critical temperature: above the critical temperature it is usually called a *gas;* below the critical temperature it is called a *vapor*.   The critical temperature of water is 374°C and the critical pressure is 218 atm.   The critical point of carbon dioxide is 31.1°C and 73 atm pressure.   The critical points of some of the more common substances are given in Table 15–2.

The substances which are known as gases at ordinary temperatures have very low critical temperatures.   They must first be cooled to these low temperatures before they can be liquefied.   Helium has the lowest critical temperature, $-268°C$ or $5°$ abs.

Table 15-2   Critical Constants

Substance	Critical Temperature in °C	Critical Pressure in Atmospheres
Ammonia	132	112
Carbon dioxide	31.1	73
Ether	194	35.5
Helium	-268	2.3
Hydrogen	-240	13
Nitrogen	-147	34
Oxygen	-119	50
Water	374	218

15-6 EVAPORATION

A liquid such as water or alcohol, when left open to the atmosphere, will in time *evaporate;* that is, the liquid will change to a vapor and go into the atmosphere.   If the atmosphere above the liquid surface is set into motion by means of a fan, the rate of evaporation will be increased.   The heat that is required to vaporize a liquid must come either from the external surroundings or from the remaining liquid.   If the liquid is placed in a fairly well-insulated container or if the process of evaporation is so rapid that the liquid cannot get sufficient heat from the surrounding bodies, the temperature of the liquid will be lowered.

If a large jar is placed over the liquid container, some of the liquid will evaporate until equilibrium is established between the liquid and its vapor, that is, until the pressure of the vapor in the air is equal to the saturated vapor pressure at the temperature of the air.   The air is then said to be *saturated* with this vapor.   If the jar over the liquid container is removed and a fresh supply of unsaturated air is blown over the liquid, evaporation will start again.   Evaporation will continue as long as the vapor pressure in the air is less than the saturated vapor pressure.   The rate of evaporation will depend upon the difference between the saturated vapor pressure and the actual vapor pressure in the air.   Ether, for example, has a relatively large vapor pressure at room temperatures; it therefore evaporates very rapidly into a moving stream of air.   Some oils used in the operation of vacuum pumps have very low vapor pressures; octoil S, for example, has a vapor pressure of about 10^{-7} mm of mercury at room temperature; the evaporation of such oil is negligible.

There are some similarities and some differences between the processes of evaporation and boiling. In each case there is a change of phase from liquid to vapor. During the process of boiling, the pressure of the vapor is the *saturated vapor pressure* corresponding to the temperature of the liquid and vapor and is equal to or greater than the surrounding atmospheric pressure; whereas, during evaporation, the vapor pressure is less than the saturated vapor pressure. During evaporation, that part of the liquid which is near the surface changes to vapor; whereas, during boiling, bubbles of vapor can form in the body of the liquid, rise to the surface, and go out above the surface of the liquid. In both cases, the heat of vaporization at a given temperature of the liquid is the same.

As mentioned above, if, during evaporation, sufficient heat is not supplied from the outside to vaporize the liquid at a constant temperature, the temperature of the liquid will be lowered; that is, the energy necessary to vaporize the liquid will come from its internal energy. This can be demonstrated very readily by placing a small beaker of water under a bell jar, as shown in Figure 15–4, and pumping the air and water vapor from it very

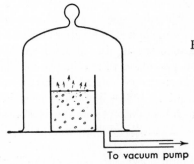

To vacuum pump

Fig. 15–4   Rapid evaporation of water when the pressure above it is reduced causes it to cool very rapidly. If the evaporation is sufficiently rapid, the remaining water may freeze.

rapidly. If the pressure in the bell jar is kept below the saturated vapor pressure of the liquid, the water will be converted to vapor very rapidly. Very little heat can be transferred to the water from the outside; hence the internal energy of the water will continue to decrease; it will be evidenced by the drop in its temperature. If the evaporation is sufficiently rapid, the temperature of the water may drop to the freezing point, and some of the water will begin to freeze.

A variation of the above experiment is provided by the laboratory method of making dry ice, that is, solid carbon dioxide. A glance at Table 15–2 shows that the critical temperature of carbon dioxide is 31.1°C and its critical pressure is 73 atm. A tank of carbon dioxide at room temperature, say 20°C, containing liquid and some vapor, is at a pressure somewhat less than 73 atm but still very high, about 55 atm. Liquid carbon dioxide cannot exist at room temperature at a pressure of 1 atm. Let us tie a heavy-walled canvas bag around the nozzle and invert the tank of carbon dioxide, as shown in Figure 15–5(a). When the valve is opened,

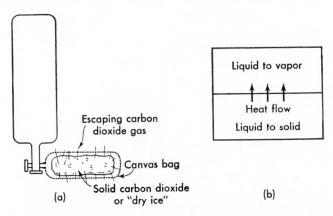

FIG. 15–5 The formation of "dry ice" or solid carbon dioxide when liquid carbon dioxide, which was in a tank at high pressure, is allowed to expand into an insulated bag at atmospheric pressure.

liquid carbon dioxide will flow out of the nozzle and begin to vaporize. The canvas bag is sufficiently porous so that the vapor can escape through its walls. In order to vaporize a liquid, however, it is necessary to supply heat to it. The only immediately available external source of heat is the atmosphere, but, since canvas is a poor heat conductor, heat does not come in rapidly enough from the surrounding air to supply the necessary heat of vaporization. As shown schematically in Figure 15–5(b), we can imagine a small portion of liquid divided into two parts: that part which evaporates getting the necessary heat from the remaining part, the latter cooling to a sufficiently low temperature to solidify. The vapor escapes through the walls of the canvas bag and the solid carbon dioxide accumulates inside it.

15-7 DIFFUSION PUMP

A diffusion pump is used to pump gas out of a tube and produce a region of very low pressure, or a high vacuum. Modern diffusion pumps, using some oil with a very low vapor pressure as the working substance, can reduce pressures inside closed containers to the order of 10^{-8} mm of mercury. The fundamentals of the operation of a diffusion pump can be described with the aid of the diagram sketched in Figure 15–6. The pump is connected through the exhaust tube *E* to a fore pump, such as a *rotary oil pump*, so that the pressure in the diffusion pump and in the system to be evacuated, which is connected to the intake tube *I*, is reduced to less than 0.01 mm of mercury. The oil in the reservoir *R* is heated to its boiling

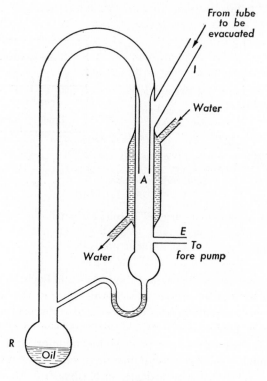

Fɪɢ. 15–6   Diffusion pump.

point by means of an electric heater, and the vapor travels down the tube *A*. Gas molecules from the tube to be evacuated diffuse into this region through the inlet tube *I*. These molecules move in the stream of oil molecules, are bombarded by them, and acquire a momentum in the direction of this stream of vapor and are forced toward the exit tube at a higher pressure. A cooling jacket through which water is flowing surrounds this stream of vapor and gas and causes the vapor to condense on the walls of the tube. The liquid then flows down the tube into the bent trap and then back into the reservoir. The gas is pumped out by the fore pump connected to the exhaust tube *E*.

15-8   MELTING.   FUSION

Heat must be added to a substance to change it from the solid to the liquid phase; conversely, when the substance freezes, that is, changes from the liquid to the solid phase, it will give out heat.   The temperature at which melting, or its converse freezing, takes place depends upon the pressure.   As long as the pressure on a substance remains constant, the temperature at which it melts remains constant.   We have already made use of this fact in choosing the melting point of ice at atmospheric pressure as one of the fixed points of the thermometer.   For convenience in calibrating thermometers at temperatures above 100°C, use is made of the melting points of other substances, such as zinc, sulphur, and gold, at atmospheric pressure.   Table 15–3 lists the melting points of some of the substances at atmospheric pressure.

Table 15-3   Melting Points at Atmospheric Pressure

Substance	Temperature in °C	Substance	Temperature in °C
Aluminum	660	Nickel	1,455
Copper	1,083	Platinum	1,773.5
Gold	1,063.0	Silver	960.5
Lead	327.4	Tungsten	3,410
Mercury	−38.87	Zinc	419.5

The volume changes which accompany the process of melting are rather small.   In most cases, the melting of a substance is accompanied by an increase in its volume.   In a few exceptional cases, such as ordinary ice and type metal, there is a decrease in volume on melting.   This unusual behavior of type metal is of practical value in the casting of type: the molten metal is poured into a mold, and, as it freezes, it expands and completely fills every part of the mold, yielding sharp, clear type.

The expansion which takes place when water freezes has many important consequences.   When water in a lake freezes, the ice floats on top; its specific gravity is 0.92.   In some lakes a solid layer of ice may be formed on the top during winter.   Thereafter, freezing takes place more slowly, since ice is a poor conductor of heat.   In lakes which are sufficiently deep, the water is never completely frozen, so that aquatic life can continue throughout the winter in the water below the frozen surface.   The temperature of this water may be as high as 4°C.

The quantity of heat that is required to melt a unit mass of a solid at constant temperature is called the heat of fusion of the substance.   If m is the mass of solid which is melted and H_F is its heat of fusion, then the heat H

that must be added to the solid to change its phase to that of a liquid is

$$H = mH_F. \qquad\qquad (2)$$

Conversely, if a liquid freezes at constant temperature, it will give out a quantity of heat H, as given by Equation (2).

The heat of fusion of water is about 80 cal/gm or 144 Btu/lb at 0°C. This means that about 80 cal must be supplied to melt 1 gm of ice or 144 Btu to melt 1 lb of ice. When water freezes, 80 cal are liberated for each gram of ice formed. The heat of fusion of ice may be determined very readily by putting a known mass of ice into a sufficiently large quantity of water so that all of the ice will melt. By measuring the original temperature of the ice and the original temperature of the water and the final temperature of the system, the heat of fusion may be calculated.

Illustrative Example. Twenty grams of ice originally at $-10°C$ are put into 250 gm of water originally at 80°C contained in a glass beaker. The final temperature of the system is 67.8°C. Calculate the heat of fusion of ice, neglecting the heat given out by the glass beaker.

The heat absorbed by the ice can be considered in three separate stages:

(a) The specific heat of ice is 0.5 cal/gm °C; hence the heat required to raise its temperature from $-10°C$ to 0°C is

$$20 \times 0.5 \times 10 \text{ cal} = 100 \text{ cal}.$$

(b) The heat required to melt it at 0°C is, from Equation (2),

$$H = 20 \text{ gm} \times H_F, \qquad \text{where } H_F \text{ is the heat of fusion of ice.}$$

(c) The heat required to raise the temperature of the 20 gm of water thus formed to 67.8°C is

$$20 \times 1 \times 67.8 \text{ cal} = 1,356 \text{ cal}.$$

All of this heat must come from the cooling of the 250 gm of water from 80°C to 67.8°C, which will liberate 3,050 cal. Equating these two quantities, we get

$$3,050 \text{ cal} = 1,456 \text{ cal} + 20 \text{ gm} \times H_F,$$

from which $\qquad\qquad H_F = 79.7 \dfrac{\text{cal}}{\text{gm}}.$

Sometimes so large an amount of ice is placed in the water that not all of it can be melted by the heat liberated by the water in cooling down to 0°C. If the final state of this system is a mixture of ice and water, its temperature is 0°C. In general, it is good practice to determine whether there is sufficient heat available to melt all of the ice.

Illustrative Example. A block of ice whose mass is 110 gm originally at −10°C is placed in a glass beaker containing 150 gm of water at 60°C. Determine the final state of the system; neglect the heat liberated by the beaker.

The maximum amount of heat that can be liberated by the water in cooling from 60°C to 0°C is

$$150 \times 60 \text{ cal} = 9{,}000 \text{ cal.}$$

To raise the temperature of 110 gm of ice from −10°C to 0°C

requires $$110 \times 0.5 \times 10 \text{ cal} = 550 \text{ cal.}$$

This leaves 8,450 cal to melt the ice. Since the heat of fusion is 80 cal/gm, enough heat is available to melt 105.6 gm of ice at 0°C. The final state of the system will be a mixture containing 4.4 gm of ice and 255.6 gm of water at 0°C.

15-9 DEPENDENCE OF MELTING POINT ON PRESSURE

The temperature at which a solid melts depends slightly upon the pressure. For most substances, the temperature of the melting point increases with increasing pressure. For the few substances which expand on freezing, the temperature of the melting point decreases with increasing pressure. Ice, for example, will melt at a temperature lower than 0°C if the pressure on it is greater than 1 atm. The curve *OB* in Figure 15–7

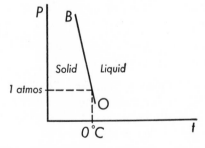

Fig. 15–7   Fusion curve of water.

shows the variation of temperature with pressure for the melting points of ice. Each point on the curve represents a definite temperature and pressure at which ice and water are in equilibrium.

The fact that an increase in pressure leads to a lowering of the melting point of ice gives rise to a series of interesting results. One of these is the common experience of making snowballs by pressing the loose snowflakes tightly. The increased pressure causes some of the snow to melt even though its temperature is lower than 0°C; when the pressure is released, the melted snow refreezes, forming the snowball.   This process of melting at a temperature lower than 0°C because of the increased pressure and then refreezing when the pressure is removed is known as *regelation*.

In ice skating and skiing, the ice and snow are melted even though the temperature is below 0°C, and a thin film of water is formed under the skate or the ski.   This water refreezes as soon as the pressure is removed, since its temperature is below 0°C.   Recent experiments show that at very low temperatures, friction between the blade of the skate and the ice plays an important part in melting the ice and forming the thin layer of water. Similarly, friction between the ski and snow aids in melting the snow.   The water formed in each case refreezes when the pressure is reduced to atmospheric pressure.

15-10 SUPERCOOLING OF A LIQUID

By cooling a liquid slowly, it is possible to lower its temperature below the freezing point without solidification taking place.   A substance in this state is called a *supercooled liquid*.   If the supercooled liquid is disturbed mechanically or if a small crystal of the substance is put into the liquid, it immediately starts to solidify, and its temperature rises to the normal freezing temperature.   The heat needed to raise the temperature comes from the heat of fusion liberated by that portion of the substance which solidifies.   Water has been cooled down to -40°C without changing to ice. A small crystal of ice put into this supercooled water causes solidification to start around it as a nucleus, and the temperature of the system rises to 0°C. This is of particular interest in meteorology, since the process of supercooling takes place in the formation of some of the clouds.

15-11 SUBLIMATION

The change from the solid directly into the vapor phase, although very common, is not usually observed directly, because the more common vapors are usually colorless.   A piece of solid carbon dioxide, which is white and usually called dry ice, goes directly into the vapor phase at atmospheric pressure.   It does not melt, because the liquid phase does not exist at ordinary temperatures and atmospheric pressure.   Another common example is the sublimation of tungsten in an ordinary tungsten lamp.   When the filament is hot, some of the tungsten goes directly into the vapor phase, and, when the vapor comes into contact with the cooler glass of the bulb, it condenses on it.   This is the explanation for the blackening of the inside of a tungsten lamp.

To focus our attention on the process of sublimation, let us consider a flask containing some ice, and let us suppose that the air has been completely removed from this flask. If we keep this flask at a temperature of about $-10°C$, the ice will sublime, forming water vapor in the tube. This process will continue until the vapor pressure reaches a value of 1.97 mm of mercury. Thereafter the vapor pressure will remain the same as long as the temperature of the system is $-10°C$. In this state, the ice and the water vapor are in equilibrium. If the temperature is lowered, the equilibrium vapor pressure will be lowered; if the temperature is raised, the equilibrium vapor pressure will be raised. The curve OC in Figure 15–8 shows the relationship between the vapor pressure and the temperature of sublimation for ice. The equilibrium vapor pressure drops rapidly with decreasing temperature.

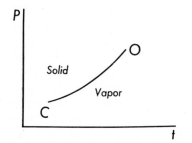

FIG. 15–8   Sublimation curve of water.

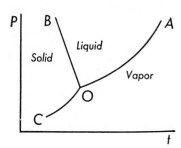

FIG. 15–9   Triple point of water.

15-12   TRIPLE POINT

The three curves for water—the vaporization curve, the fusion curve, and the sublimation curve—are plotted on a single graph in Figure 15–9. A point on a curve represents a state of equilibrium between two phases at a definite temperature and pressure. All three curves intersect at one point O, known as the *triple point*. At this point all three phases of water are in equilibrium. The temperature of the triple point is $+0.010°C$, and the pressure is 4.59 mm of mercury. As long as the temperature and pressure are maintained at these values, ice, water, and water vapor will coexist in the same flask and remain in equilibrium. If the temperature should be raised slightly, the ice will melt, and the state of the system will be represented by a point on the curve OA. If conditions are changed in any way, one of the phases will disappear. The three phases can exist in equilibrium only at the temperature and pressure of the triple point.

Substances which have more than one solid phase have several triple points. Ice is known to exist in several different solid phases. The known triple points of water are listed in Table 15–4. The common form of ice is called ice I. The other forms of ice exist only at very high pressures.

Table 15-4   Triple Points of Water

Phases in Equilibrium	Temperature in °C	Pressure
Ice I, liquid, vapor	+0.010	4.579 mm
Ice I, liquid, ice III	−22	2,115 kg/cm²
Ice III, liquid, ice V	−17	3,530 " "
Ice V, liquid, ice VI	+0.16	6,380 " "
Ice I, ice II, ice III	−34.7	2,170 " "
Ice II, ice III, ice V	−24.3	3,510 " "
Ice VI, liquid, ice VII	+81.6	22,400 " "

15-13   HUMIDITY OF THE ATMOSPHERE

One of the most important constituents of the atmosphere is water vapor. The amount of water vapor in the air is a variable quantity. As we have seen, a mass of air is saturated when the pressure of the water vapor in that mass of air is equal to the saturated vapor pressure at the temperature of the air. Figure 15–10 is a curve showing the saturated

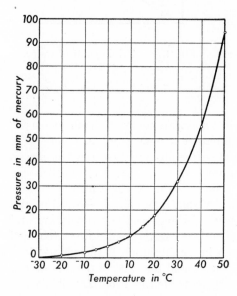

FIG. 15–10   Saturated vapor pressure curve

vapor pressure as a function of the temperature of the air, while Table 15–5 gives the saturated vapor pressure at various temperatures. Usually, however, the actual vapor pressure is less than the saturated vapor pressure. The term *relative humidity* is defined as the ratio of the actual vapor pressure to the saturated vapor pressure at the temperature of the air.

Table 15-5   Properties of Saturated Water Vapor

Temperature in °C	Temperature in °F	Pressure in Milli-meters of Mercury	Grams of Water Vapor in a Cubic Meter of Air
−10	14	2.15	2.16
−5	23	3.16	3.26
0	32	4.58	4.85
5	41	6.54	6.80
10	50	9.21	9.40
15	59	12.79	12.83
20	68	17.54	17.30
30	86	31.82	30.37
40	104	55.32	51.12
50	122	92.51	
60	140	149.41	
70	158	233.7	
80	176	355.1	
90	194	525.8	
100	212	760.0	
120	248	1,489.1	
140	284	2,710.9	
160	320	4,636	
180	356	7,520	
200	392	11,659	

Thus, if r is the relative humidity, p the actual vapor pressure, and P the saturated vapor pressure at the temperature of the air, then

$$r = \frac{p}{P} \tag{3}$$

and is usually expressed in percentages. For example, suppose that the actual vapor pressure is 3.0 mm of mercury when the temperature of the air is 50°F. Since the saturated vapor pressure at this temperature is 9.2 mm of mercury, the relative humidity is

$$r = \frac{3.0}{9.2} = 0.325 = 32.5 \text{ per cent.}$$

At any given temperature, the mass of water vapor in the air is proportional to the pressure of the water vapor. Hence the relative humidity can also be defined as the ratio of the mass of water vapor in a given volume of air to the mass of water vapor required to saturate it. Table 15–5 gives the mass of water vapor in a cubic meter of saturated air at various temperatures.

A simple instrument for measuring the relative humidity is the hair *hygrometer.* The length of the hair increases as its cells absorb moisture from the air. The hair hygrometer consists of a bundle of human hairs exposed to the atmosphere; one end of the bundle is attached to an adjustable screw and the other end to a lever which moves a pointer over a scale. The apparatus is sketched in Figure 15–11. The scale is calibrated in terms of the relative humidity.

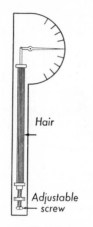

Hair

Adjustable screw

Fig. 15–11 Hair hygrometer.

Another type of hygrometer consists of a combination of a wet-bulb thermometer and a dry-bulb thermometer. The two thermometers are identical except that a piece of wet muslin is wrapped around the bulb of one thermometer and kept moist by a wick dipping into a trough of water. If the air is not saturated with water vapor, water will evaporate from the wet-bulb thermometer, producing a drop in temperature. The relative humidity is then determined from the difference in the readings obtained from the two thermometers and the tables or graphs of humidity.

15-14 DEW-POINT TEMPERATURE

It is a common experience to observe moisture condensing on the outside surface of vessels containing cold beverages. This moisture is produced by the condensation of the water vapor from the air onto the cold surface. When the relative humidity is less than 100 per cent, the vapor pressure is less than the saturation pressure. The temperature to which the air must be lowered in order to become saturated with the mass of water vapor in it remaining constant is called the *dew-point temperature.* When the dew-point temperature is known, its location on the saturation pressure curve of Figure 15–10 will also give the actual vapor pressure in the air. Since the saturation vapor pressure at the temperature of the air is also known from this curve, the relative humidity is easily determined. Human comfort depends on relative humidity as well as upon temperature, and this fact must be taken into account in air-conditioning equipment. Unless the temperature and relative humidity fall within certain limits, sometimes called the comfort zone, most of us experience discomfort.

A simple laboratory method for determining the dew-point temperature is to put some warm water into a polished tin can and then add a quantity of ice to it. Stir the mixture and observe the readings of a thermometer immersed in it. At some definite temperature, moisture will begin to condense on the outside of the can; note this temperature. Now warm it slowly and note the temperature at which the moisture on the outside disappears. The average value of these two temperatures is the dew-point temperature. This is the temperature of the thin layer of air very close to the walls of the can.

Illustrative Example. When the temperature of the air is 86°F, a dew-point determination shows that the dew-point temperature is 50°F. Determine the relative humidity of the atmosphere.

From Table 15–5 the saturated pressure P at 86°F is 31.8 mm. At the dew-point temperature, 50°F, the saturated vapor pressure p is 9.2 mm. The relative humidity r is therefore

$$r = \frac{p}{P} = \frac{9.2}{31.8} = 0.29 = 29 \text{ per cent.}$$

QUESTIONS

1. Suppose that heat is added to water at a pressure of 1 atm at a constant rate. Plot a curve of the temperature of water as ordinate and the time as abscissa starting with water at 0°C and ending with steam at 100°C.

2. Large tubs of water are sometimes put in cellars where vegetables are stored to prevent them from freezing during the cold winter months. Discuss the physics at the basis of this practice.

3. If a beaker containing ether is put under a bell jar and the vapor is pumped away rapidly enough, the ether may be solidified. Explain this process of freezing a liquid.

4. Does copper expand or contract when it solidifies?

5. Explain why water pipes sometimes burst in the wintertime.

6. When the pressure on ice is increased, will its melting point be higher or lower than 0°C?

7. When the pressure on a piece of copper is increased above atmospheric pressure, will its melting point be higher or lower than 1,083°C?

8. Draw a horizontal line on the triple point diagram; discuss the changes in the phases of the system as one proceeds along this line.

9. Draw a vertical line on the triple point diagram so that it intersects curves OC and OB. Discuss the changes that take place as one proceeds upward along this line.

10. Start with a piece of ice at −10°C and atmospheric pressure and suppose that heat is added to it at a constant rate. Plot a curve with temperature as ordinate and time as abscissa showing the changes that take place as the substance changes from ice at −10°C to steam at 110°C. Assume the specific heat of steam to be 0.5 cal/gm°C.

11. In hot climates, water kept in a porous earthen jar in the shade is much cooler than the surrounding atmosphere.   Account for the cooling process.

12. The temperature of a person with high fever may be brought down by a sponge bath using a mixture of alcohol and water.   Why is this mixture preferred to that of water at the same temperature?

13. Draw the triple point diagram of a substance, such as carbon dioxide, which contracts on freezing.   Compare this with the triple point diagram for water.

14. What are the essential differences between the processes of boiling and evaporation?

15. A pressure cooker is set at 15 lb.   What is the steam pressure inside the cooker?   Why is food cooked more rapidly in a pressure cooker?

16. A burn produced by live steam is usually more severe than one produced by boiling water at the same temperature.   Account for this in terms of the kinetic theory of matter.

17. On hot, humid summer days, this statement is frequently made: "it is not the heat, it is the humidity" which makes people uncomfortable.   (a) Are the technical terms in the statement used correctly?   (b) Is the statement correct?

18. What factors determine the pressure of the saturated water vapor in the air?

19. On cold winter mornings, the inside of the windows in some homes have a coating of frost while those in other homes do not.   Account for this difference, assuming that the temperatures in the rooms are approximately the same.

20. In a heating system which circulates heated air through the house, it is always necessary to add moisture to the air.   Explain why this is necessary.

21. Consider the processes which take place in the cycle which starts with 1 lb of water in the ocean, the evaporation of this water into the air, the formation of clouds, its precipitation in the form of rain or snow, and its descent in the form of water in streams or rivers back to the ocean.   State the energy change which takes place in each process.

22. In the water cycle described above, is there a net gain or loss of energy? Account for this net gain or loss of energy.

PROBLEMS

1. How much heat is required to vaporize 50 gm of water at 100°C?

2. How much heat will be given out by 6 lb of steam when it condenses to water at 212°F?

3. There are 400 gm of water at 20°C in a vessel whose heat capacity is very small.   How much steam at 100°C must be added to the water to raise the temperature to 60°C?

4. A wooden pail contains 40 lb of water at 70°F.   Some steam at 212°F is added to this water until the temperature is 150°F.   Determine the amount of steam added.

5. How much heat is required to melt 70 gm of ice at 0°C?

6. A tub contains 150 lb of water at 32°F. How much heat will be given out when this water freezes?

7. How much heat is required to melt 60 gm of ice originally at −10°C?

8. Find the equilibrium temperature when 15 gm of ice at 0°C are put into an aluminum calorimeter containing 200 gm of water at 40°C. The mass of the calorimeter is 120 gm.

9. An aluminum calorimeter of 100 gm mass contains 185 gm of water at 20°C. Thirty grams of ice at 0°C are placed in the water. Determine the final state of the system.

10. An aluminum calorimeter of 100 gm mass contains 185 gm of water at 20°C. A block of ice whose mass is 142.5 gm at 0°C is placed in the water. Determine the final state of the system.

11. Four hundred and fifty grams of lead shot at 100°C are dropped into a dry cavity in a block of ice and then covered with another piece of ice. How much ice will be melted?

12. A copper calorimeter whose mass is 50 gm contains 250 gm of water and 100 gm of ice in equilibrium. Sixty grams of steam at 100°C are added to this system. Determine the final equilibrium temperature.

13. An aluminum beaker of 120 gm mass contains 250 gm of water and 10 gm of ice at 0°C. A piece of zinc whose mass is 400 gm is heated to 130°C and dropped into this calorimeter. Determine the final temperature.

14. An iron pail whose mass is 1,600 gm contains 1,000 gm of snow at 0°C. The snow is melted by passing steam into it. The final temperature of the system is 15°C. Determine the amount of steam used.

15. When 1 gm of water boils at 1 atm pressure, its volume changes from 1 cm^3 in the liquid phase to 1,671 cm^3 in the vapor phase. Apply the first law of thermodynamics to this process and calculate (a) the work done by the fluid in expanding against the external pressure and (b) the change in internal energy of the fluid in this process. (c) Account for (b) in terms of the kinetic theory of matter.

16. Calculate the number of molecules in 1 cu cm of air at 0°C when the pressure is 10^{-8} mm of mercury.

17. What is the relative humidity of the air in a room if its temperature is 20°C and the vapor pressure is 9 mm of mercury?

18. What is the vapor pressure in the air if its temperature is 40°F and the relative humidity is 65 per cent?

19. The relative humidity of the air in a room is 50 per cent when the temperature is 72°F. What is the vapor pressure?

20. On a hot summer day, when the air temperature of the air is 90°F, the dew-point temperature is 70°F. Determine the relative humidity of the air.

21. When the air temperature was 10°C, the dew-point temperature was found to be 4°C. Determine the relative humidity of this air.

16

Transfer of Heat

16-1 METHODS OF TRANSMITTING HEAT

We have already observed that heat will flow whenever there is a difference
in temperature between two bodies or between two parts of the same body.
The methods by which heat is transmitted can be classified into three distinct types known as *conduction, convection,* and *radiation.* In any actual
case of heat transmission, a combination of any two of these methods, and
in some cases all three methods, may be operating simultaneously. The
principal problem in the transfer of heat is to determine the rate at which
heat flows from the source at the higher temperature to the source at the
lower temperature.

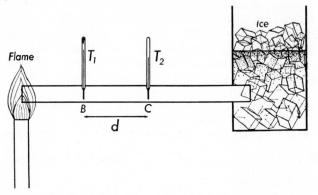

Fig. 16–1 Method of measuring the temperature gradient along a conductor
of heat to determine its conductivity.

16-2 CONDUCTION

The method of transferring heat by conduction can be illustrated by
means of a long cylindrical copper rod which has one end placed in a gas
flame, while the other end is placed in a mixture of ice and water, as shown
in Figure 16–1. Heat is conducted through the copper rod from the flame

to the ice-water mixture. The amount of heat which is conducted through
it in any time interval, assuming that the loss of heat to the surrounding
atmosphere may be neglected, can be measured by the amount of ice
which is melted in this time. Any two points along the rod such as B and
C a distance d apart are at different temperatures; let us call these temperatures T_1 and T_2, respectively. Heat flows from B to C through the
copper rod because of this difference in temperature. The ratio

$$\frac{T_1 - T_2}{d}$$

is called the *temperature gradient* in this region of the conductor. The
greater the temperature gradient, the greater is the amount of heat which
flows through this portion of the rod in any given time interval. The
process of conduction may be thought of as the transfer of heat from any
one point in the rod to a neighboring point because of the difference in
temperature existing between these two points.

The rate at which heat is transferred by conduction is found to depend
not only upon the temperature gradient but also upon the cross-sectional
area of the rod. Or, stated mathematically,

$$H \propto A \frac{T_1 - T_2}{d} t;$$

or, in the form of an equation,

$$H = KA \frac{T_1 - T_2}{d} t, \qquad (1)$$

in which H represents the quantity of heat which is transmitted in time t
through a rod of cross-sectional area A when the temperature gradient
along the length of the rod is $\dfrac{T_1 - T_2}{d}$. The factor K depends upon the
nature of the material of the rod and the units used in expressing the other
quantities; K is called the *thermal conductivity* of the substance.

The thermal conductivities of metals are generally greater than those
of other solids, and silver is the best conductor of all. It is interesting to
note that those substances which are good conductors of heat are also good
conductors of electricity. Although long rods are suitable for the measurement of the thermal conductivity of a metal, the measurement of the
thermal conductivity of a poor conductor is best made with a very thin slab
of material of large cross-sectional area. A knowledge of the thermal
conductivity of poor conductors is of great practical importance, since
such substances are widely used as heat insulators. The thermal con-

ductivities of the more common substances are given in Table 16–1. Two sets of units are in use for expressing these conductivities. In scientific work K is expressed in terms of the number of calories per second transmitted through an area of 1 cm^2 when the temperature gradient is 1°C per cm. In engineering work K is expressed in terms of the number of Btu/hr transmitted through an area of 1 ft^2 when the temperature gradient is 1°F/ft.

Table 16-1   Thermal Conductivities

Substance	K in $\dfrac{\text{cal}}{\text{cm sec °C}}$	K in $\dfrac{\text{Btu}}{\text{ft hr °F}}$
Metals		
Aluminum	0.49	118
Brass	0.26	63
Copper	0.91	225
Gold	0.71	169
Iron	0.16	39
Lead	0.084	20
Nickel	0.14	34
Platinum	0.17	41
Silver	0.99	242
Tin	0.15	37
Tungsten	0.38	92
Insulators		
Aluminum foil,	($\frac{3}{8}$ in. air spaces)	
crumpled	0.0001	0.025
Asbestos, sheets	0.0004	0.097
Insulating brick,		
kaolin	0.0006	0.15
Glass, window	0.0012-0.0024	0.3-0.6
Snow	0.0011	0.27
Fluids		
Air	0.000054	0.017
Water	0.0015	0.37

Although conduction does take place through liquids and gases, their conductivities are very small, gases being among the poorest conductors. Many insulating materials are constructed so that they trap small quantities of air in small closed spaces and thus make use of the poor conductivity of the air for insulation and at the same time avoid the transfer of heat through the air by convection (see Section 16–3).

Illustrative Example. A silver rod of circular cross section has one end immersed in a steam bath and the other end immersed in a mixture of ice and water. The distance between these ends is 6 cm, and the diameter of the rod is 0.3 cm. Calculate the amount of heat that is conducted through the rod in 2 min.

The thermal conductivity K is $0.99 \; \dfrac{\text{cal}}{\text{cm sec}°\text{C}}$. The cross-sectional area $A = \dfrac{\pi \times (0.3)^2}{4} \text{ cm}^2 = 0.071 \text{ cm}^2$;

$$t = 120 \text{ sec}, \qquad d = 6 \text{ cm}, \qquad \text{and} \qquad T_1 - T_2 = 100°\text{C}.$$

Using Equation (1), we get

$$H = 0.99 \times 0.071 \; \frac{100}{6} \times 120 \text{ cal},$$

$$H = 140 \text{ cal}.$$

Illustrative Example.   Calculate the rate at which heat flows through an insulating kaolin brick wall 6 in. thick and 16 ft^2 in area if the two faces are at temperatures of 450°F and 150°F.

Assuming the conductivity of kaolin brick to be $0.15 \; \dfrac{\text{Btu}}{\text{ft hr}°\text{F}}$ for this range of temperature, we get, from Equation (1),

$$\frac{H}{t} = 0.15 \times 16 \; \frac{300}{0.5} \; \frac{\text{Btu}}{\text{hr}}$$

$$= 1{,}440 \; \frac{\text{Btu}}{\text{hr}}.$$

16-3   CONVECTION

Convection is the transfer of heat from one part of a fluid to another by the mixing of the warmer particles of the fluid with the cooler parts. As an example, consider the case of a jar of water which is heated by applying a flame at one side A, as shown in Figure 16–2. Heat is conducted through the glass to the water. As the water in contact with the glass is heated by conduction, its density decreases, and it floats to the top. Colder water moves down to replace it. This colder water in turn is heated; once hot, it rises because of its smaller density, thus setting up a *circulation* of the liquid. During this circulation the warmer particles of the liquid mix with the cooler parts, and in a very short time a fairly uniform temperature is established throughout the liquid. This type of heat transfer is called *natural convection,* because the motion of the fluid is due to differences in the density of the fluid. The heat transfer can also be produced by *forced convection* by the use of a fan or pump or other mechanical device for stirring and mixing the warmer and cooler parts of the fluid.

In almost all cases of the transfer of heat by means of fluids, both convection and conduction must be considered. The heating of a room presents several interesting illustrations of convection and conduction and, to some extent, of radiation. If the room is heated by means of a radiator, heat is conducted through the walls of the radiator to the air in

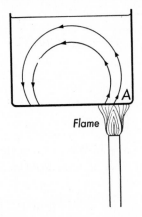

Fig. 16–2 Convection. A circulation is set up in the fluid by heating it near one end.

contact with it. This warmer air rises and displaces the cooler air, thus establishing a circulation of the air in the room. The warmer air, striking the cooler walls and windows, loses heat to the outside by conduction through the walls and windows. Fortunately, there is always a film of stagnant air close to the walls and windows so that the heat which is conducted to the outside must be *conducted* through this film of air as well as through the walls and windows. Since air is such a very poor conductor, a very thin layer of it is sufficient to form a good insulator.

16-4 RADIATION

The transfer of heat by conduction and convection involves the use of material media. The transfer of heat by the process of *radiation* need not involve the use of material media. An outstanding example is the radiation of energy from the sun to the earth; by far the greatest part of the space between these two bodies is a very good vacuum. This radiant energy consists of *electromagnetic waves* which travel with the speed of light, about 186,000 miles per second. We shall analyze these waves and study them in greater detail in the section on light. It can be shown experimentally that all bodies radiate energy and that the rate at which energy is radiated depends upon the temperature of the body and the nature of its surface.

Not only do bodies radiate energy, but whenever radiant energy falls on the surface of a body, some of this energy is absorbed and the remainder is either reflected or transmitted. A *black body* is defined as one which would absorb all the radiant energy which falls upon it. Although there is no actual body which satisfies this condition, a body whose surface is coated with lampblack is very nearly a perfect black body. For laboratory work, an insulated hollow box whose interior walls can be maintained at any desired temperature and which has a small hole in one of its sides forms a very close approximation to a black body. Any radiation which enters this hole will be almost completely absorbed. This is due to the fact that this radiation will be reflected many times by the walls until it is almost completely absorbed by them. Only a minute fraction of the radiation which enters the hole will come out again.

The *absorptivity* of a surface for radiant energy is defined as the fraction of the total incident radiation which is absorbed by the surface. The absorptivity of a black body is 1. The absorptivity of all other bodies is less than 1. Polished metallic surfaces reflect most of the radiation falling on them; their absorptivity is very small. Furthermore, bodies which are good absorbers of radiation are also good emitters of radiation, and those which are poor absorbers are poor emitters. Thus a black body is a good radiator while a polished surface is a poor radiator. A simple experiment to demonstrate this is shown in Figure 16–3. One side of a tin can is coated

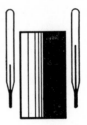

Fɪɢ. 16–3   Thermometer opposite blackened side of can records a higher temperature.

with lampblack and the other side is polished. The tin can is filled with hot water. Two thermometers with their bulbs blackened are then placed at equal distances from the surfaces of the tin can: one near the blackened surface, the other near the polished surface. The thermometer near the blackened surface will show a higher temperature reading. This is due to the fact that the blackened surface, even though it is at the same temperature as the polished surface, radiates more energy in a given time.

The rate R_B at which energy is radiated from a unit area of a black body at absolute temperature T in unit time has been measured and found to be given by the equation

$$R_B = \sigma T^4,$$

(2)

in which σ (Greek lower case sigma) is a constant which depends upon the units used. In the cgs system,

$$\sigma = 5.670 \times 10^{-5} \text{ erg/sec cm}^2 \text{ deg}^4.$$

Equation (2) is known as the *Stefan-Boltzmann law of radiation*. The rate at which any other body at temperature T radiates energy from a unit area in unit time is given by

$$R = e\sigma T^4, \tag{3}$$

in which e, known as the *emissivity* of the body, is a fraction always less than 1 and represents the ratio of the rate at which energy is emitted from the body to that emitted by a black body at the same temperature. Furthermore, it can be shown that the absorptivity and the emissivity of a body are the same at the same temperature. This is in agreement with the fact that good radiators are also good absorbers of radiation.

Illustrative Example. Calculate the rate at which energy is radiated from a ribbon tungsten filament 1 cm long and 0.2 cm wide which is maintained at a temperature of 2727°C; the emissivity of tungsten at this temperature is 0.35.

The absolute temperature $T = 2727° + 273° = 3000°$ abs; the surface area emitting radiation is $2 \times 1 \times 0.2 \text{ cm}^2 = 0.4 \text{ cm}^2$. The rate at which energy is emitted from a unit area is given by Equation (3). Hence the rate at which energy $\mathcal{E}$ is emitted from the filament is

$$\mathcal{E} = AR = Ae\sigma T^4.$$

Substituting numerical values, we get

$$\mathcal{E} = 0.4 \text{ cm}^2 \times 0.35 \times 5.670 \times 10^{-5} \frac{\text{ergs}}{\text{cm}^2 \text{ sec deg}^4} \times (3000°)^4,$$

from which

$$\mathcal{E} = 63.2 \times 10^7 \frac{\text{ergs}}{\text{sec}} = 63.2 \text{ watts}.$$

16-5 HEAT AND RADIANT ENERGY

Every object, no matter what its temperature is, radiates energy in the form of electromagnetic waves which travel with the speed of light. In addition, each object receives radiation from neighboring objects; some of the radiation incident upon it is absorbed by the object, the remainder is reflected. *The difference between the amount of radiant energy which the object absorbs and that which it radiates is the heat which is either added to or given out by the object.* If it absorbs more energy than it radiates, heat is added to the object; if it radiates more energy than it absorbs, heat is given out by the object.

Consider the case of an object at a high temperature T placed in a box or an enclosure whose walls are maintained at a constant temperature T_C. The rate at which energy is radiated from each unit area of the object is given by Equation (3),

$$R = e\sigma T^4.$$

At the same time, it receives energy from the walls, and, since the absorptivity of the object is the same as its emissivity, it absorbs energy at the rate of

$$R_C = e\sigma T_C^4.$$

The nature of the walls of the enclosure does not enter into the discussion since the radiation inside may be considered to be black-body radiation. The difference between R and R_C is the amount of heat given out by unit area of the body in unit time. If A is the surface area of the body, then the amount of heat H given out in time t is

$$H = Ae\sigma(T^4 - T_C^4)t. \tag{4}$$

This shows that the rate at which heat is emitted from a body is proportional to the difference in the fourth powers of the temperatures of the body and the surroundings.

16-6   HEAT INSULATION

A thorough understanding of the subject of the transmission of heat will enable one to solve the very important problem of heat insulation. This involves the use of proper materials for a given job as well as the development of new insulating materials. For example, gasoline storage tanks are frequently coated with aluminum or other reflecting material to reduce the absorption of radiation from the sun. Insulating materials are constructed so that they contain many small pockets of air to make use of the very low conductivity of the air; there is practically no convection since the air is trapped in these pockets. Crumpled aluminum containing small air pockets is a very good insulator: there is practically no transfer of heat by convection; the transfer by conduction is very slight, since the crumpling of the aluminum makes the conducting path very long while the cross-sectional area is very small; and very little heat is transferred by radiation.

The ordinary thermos bottle, sketched in Figure 16–4, is an excellent illustration of heat insulation. The Thermos bottle consists of two cylindrical glass flasks sealed together at the top. The inside surface of the outer cylinder and the outside surface of the inner cylinder are silvered. Then the air between the two walls is pumped out and the space is sealed off. If hot food is placed inside the bottle and the bottle is then corked, the food will remain hot for a long time. Very little heat will be conducted along the glass or through the cork to the outside; there is practically no convection, since there is a good vacuum between the walls; and radiation is reduced considerably by the silver coatings.

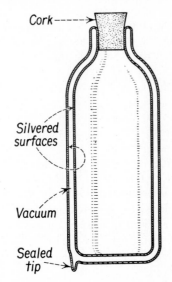

Cork

Silvered surfaces

Vacuum

Sealed tip

Fig. 16–4 Section of glass Thermos bottle.

QUESTIONS

1. Discuss the method used in heating the classroom in the wintertime.

2. A copper cylinder and a wooden cylinder are on a table in the room. If you pick up these cylinders, the copper cylinder will feel colder to the touch. Explain.

3. Why are stove-lid handles, coal tongs and other fireplace accessories made of iron rather than of copper?

4. A room is kept at a constant temperature of 70°F by means of a steam heating system. Trace what happens to the heat liberated by the condensation of the steam in the radiator of this room.

5. Gasoline storage tanks are frequently coated with aluminum foil or aluminum paint for insulation. Explain this process of insulation.

6. A parlor stove is used for heating a room. If the stove is covered with polished nickel ornaments, will its efficiency be impaired?

7. One method of getting very high temperatures is to use a concave mirror and reflect sunlight toward a point known as the focus of the mirror. Assume the temperature of the surface of the sun to be 6000°C. Will it be possible to melt a piece of tungsten placed at the focus of the mirror?

8. A searchlight uses a mirror for reflecting the radiation coming from a hot carbon arc placed at its focus. Will the mirror get hot?

9. If you wanted to keep a house cool in the summer, would it be more advisable to keep all the doors and windows closed during the daytime and opened during the night, or to keep them opened all the time?

10. Many homes in the northern part of this country have storm windows,

that is, additional windows which create an air space between them and the regular window. Show how this helps to insulate the house.

11. Suggest a method for heating a "spaceship" which is to travel in inter-stellar space without carrying along fuel for that purpose.

PROBLEMS

1. A metal rod 100 cm long and 4 cm^2 in cross-sectional area conducts 60 cal of heat per minute when the ends of the rod are maintained at a difference in temperature of 80°C. Determine the coefficient of thermal conductivity of the metal.

2. A copper rod 60 cm long and 8 mm in diameter has one end immersed in steam and the other end immersed in a mixture of ice and water. Determine the amount of heat which will be conducted through the rod in 8 min.

3. An aluminum pan has a diameter of 25 cm and is 0.5 cm thick. What is the rate of flow of heat through the bottom if the pan contains boiling water and is transmitting heat to it from a stove at a temperature of 120°C?

4. Water in a glass beaker is boiling away at the rate of 35 gm/min. The bottom of the beaker has an area of 300 cm^2 and is 0.2 cm thick. Calculate the temperature of the underside of the bottom of the beaker if $K = 0.002$ cal/cm sec deg.

5. An oven used for baking glass x-ray tubes is made of sheets of asbestos 0.75 in. thick. This oven is 4 ft high, 1 ft wide, and 1 ft deep. At what rate must heat be supplied to this oven to maintain the temperature inside at 400°C if the temperature of the air just outside the asbestos is 100°C?

6. Calculate the rate at which energy is radiated from a black body whose temperature is 1500° abs if its surface area is 1.5 cm^2.

7. Calculate the rate at which energy is radiated from a tungsten filament which is maintained at the temperature of 2500° abs if its surface area is 0.45 cm^2 and its emissivity at this temperature is 0.30.

17

Heat Engines

17-1 HEAT-ENGINE CYCLES

In this chapter we shall consider the physical principles underlying the operations of heat engines because of their intrinsic importance and because of the part they have played in the development of fundamental physical ideas. *Heat engines* are designed and built to *convert heat into work*. In most cases the heat is obtained from the combustion of a common fuel such as coal, oil, gasoline, or natural gas. An important new source of heat that is just beginning to be used, and will be used more extensively in the future, is the *mass which is converted into energy* by means of a process called *nuclear fission* (see Section 39–15). Several power plants are now in operation which get the heat for their engines from the nuclear fission of the element uranium.

There are many different types of heat engines; we shall present brief descriptions of the operations of a few of them. In general, a heat engine utilizes a *working substance*, usually steam, or a mixture of fuel and air, or fuel and oxygen, through a series of operations known as a *cycle*. The working substance goes through a series of changes of state in this cycle; as a result of these changes, some of the heat, which has been supplied to the substance from a source at a high temperature, is converted into work which is delivered to some external agency. Experience shows that not all of the heat supplied is converted into work; the heat which has not thus been utilized is delivered by the engine to some outside reservoir at a lower temperature.

The actual processes that occur in the operation of a heat engine are fairly complex. We can, however, simplify matters by replacing the actual heat engine cycle by an ideal cycle which can produce the same transformations of heat and work. In an ideal engine the working substance, such as steam, starts in some state designated by its pressure, volume, and temperature, is taken through a cycle in which its state continually changes, and then is brought back to its original state; the cycle then starts over again.

The operation of an ideal heat engine can be represented schematically by the diagram shown in Figure 17–1. A quantity of heat H_1 is delivered to the engine during one cycle by some source of heat, and the engine performs an amount of work $\mathcal{W}$ on some outside agency and rejects an amount of heat H_2 to another reservoir of heat. Since the substance in the

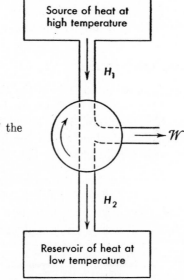

Fɪɢ. 17–1 Schematic diagram of the operation of a heat engine.

engine returns to its original state at the end of the cycle of operations, it contributes no energy to this cycle. There is therefore no change in the internal energy of the working substance; that is,

$$\mathcal{E}_f - \mathcal{E}_i = 0.$$

From the first law of thermodynamics applied to this cycle, we get

$$H_1 - H_2 = \mathcal{W}. \tag{1}$$

The *thermal efficiency* e of a heat engine is defined as

$$e = \frac{\text{work done during one cycle}}{\text{heat added during one cycle}}$$

or

$$e = \frac{\mathcal{W}}{H_1}. \tag{2}$$

Substituting the value for $\mathcal{W}$ from Equation (1), we get

$$e = \frac{H_1 - H_2}{H_1} = 1 - \frac{H_2}{H_1}. \tag{3}$$

Equation (3) shows that the thermal efficiency of an engine is less than 100 per cent because a quantity of heat H_2 is not transformed into work during the cycle. Experience shows that every heat engine rejects some heat during the exhaust stroke. One need merely recall the hot gases coming from the exhaust of an automobile engine or the steam exhausted by the engine of a steam locomotive. No engine has been built which takes in a quantity of heat H_1 from some source and converts it completely into work.

17-2 THE CARNOT CYCLE

An interesting cycle from the theoretical point of view is the *Carnot cycle*. This consists of two isothermal processes and two adiabatic processes. Although any material may be used as the working substance, we shall make use of an ideal gas as the working substance. Suppose that this gas is contained in a cylinder with a tight-fitting piston, as shown in Figure 17–2.

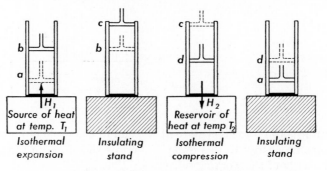

FIG. 17–2 Steps in the operation of a Carnot engine.

Let the walls of the cylinder and the top of the piston be covered with thick layers of asbestos or other insulating material. Suppose we place the cylinder on a stove or other source of heat; when equilibrium is reached, the temperature of the gas T_1 will be the same as that of the source, and its pressure and volume will be represented by the point a in the graph of Figure 17–3. Now let the gas expand slowly so that its temperature remains T_1 while its volume increases to the point b. During this isothermal expansion, a quantity of heat H_1 is delivered to the gas. The curve ab represents the isothermal expansion of the gas, and the area under it represents the work done by the gas during this expansion. Now imagine that the cylinder is placed on an insulated plate so that no heat can flow in or out of the cylinder. Let the gas now expand adiabatically from volume b to volume c. The amount of work done during this adiabatic expansion is the area under the curve bc. As a result of this expansion, the temperature of the gas will drop to some value T_2. Now place this cylinder on another reservoir at a temperature T_2; this reservoir may consist of a mixture of ice and water, for example. Now compress the gas isothermally to point d. During this process, work will be done *on* the gas equal to the area under the curve cd; at the same time, a quantity of heat H_2 will be delivered to this reservoir. Now place the cylinder on the insulating stand and compress the gas adiabatically until it is back to the state a. During this adiabatic compression, work will be done *on* the gas equal to the area under the curve da. The cycle has now been completed.

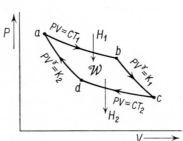

FIG. 17-3   Graphical representation of the steps in a Carnot cycle with an ideal gas as the working substance.

During this Carnot cycle, a quantity of heat H_1 was delivered to the gas at temperature T_1 and a quantity of heat H_2 was rejected by the gas to the lower reservoir at temperature T_2 and the net work $\mathcal{W}$ was delivered to the outside. This work is equal to the area enclosed by the curves $abcda$. Since the internal energy of the gas was restored to its original value, the work $\mathcal{W}$ is given by

$$\mathcal{W} = H_1 - H_2, \tag{1}$$

and the thermal efficiency is

$$e = 1 - \frac{H_2}{H_1}. \tag{3}$$

17-3   ABSOLUTE THERMODYNAMIC TEMPERATURE SCALE

The Carnot cycle is used to define the *absolute thermodynamic scale of temperature*. The properties of the working substance do not enter into the calculation of the efficiency. The only quantities which enter into this discussion are the temperatures of the two heat sources. Let us now arbitrarily define these two temperatures by the following relationship:

$$\boxed{\frac{H_1}{H_2} = \frac{T_1}{T_2};} \tag{4}$$

that is, the ratio of these two temperatures is the ratio of the quantities of heat extracted from and delivered to these sources by an engine operating in a Carnot cycle between these two temperatures. The efficiency of the Carnot engine now becomes

$$e = 1 - \frac{T_2}{T_1} . \tag{5}$$

We see that its efficiency can be 100 per cent only if the temperature of the lower heat source is 0° on this scale.

We can now choose the size of the degree to suit our convenience. In the scientific scale known as the Kelvin scale of temperature, the difference between the temperature of boiling water at atmospheric pressure and the temperature of melting ice at atmospheric pressure is set equal to 100°; thus

$$T_s - T_i = 100°. \tag{6}$$

This makes the size of the degree on the Kelvin scale the same as that on the centigrade scale. It can be shown that the temperatures on the Kelvin scale defined by Equations (4) and (5) are identical with the temperatures previously introduced for the absolute gas scale of temperature. But the Kelvin scale is independent of the properties of any particular substance. On this scale, the temperature of the ice point is $T_i = 273.2° K$. From now on, we shall make no distinction between the Kelvin scale and the absolute scale. Another scale used by engineers sets $T_s - T_i = 180°$. This scale is called the absolute Fahrenheit scale of temperature. On this scale, $T_i = 491.8°$ abs F.

17-4 THE GASOLINE ENGINE

Although the operation of the gasoline engine is fairly complex, it illustrates some applications of the principles discussed in this chapter. We shall make some simplifying assumptions in order to bring the discussion within the scope of this book. First we shall assume that we can treat the gases and vapors used in this cycle as though they behaved as ideal gases. The fuel commonly used is gasoline, and, since it is burned inside a closed cylinder, a sufficient amount of air must be mixed with the gasoline vapor before it is introduced into the cylinder. This mixing is done in a *carburetor*, shown in Figure 17-4, which consists essentially of two chambers A and B. The gasoline in chamber A is kept at a fixed level and is fed into chamber B through a narrow jet F. Air is taken into chamber B and made to pass through a narrow constriction near the jet, thus reducing the pressure at this point; gasoline therefore flows into this region of low pressure in the form of a fine spray and is thoroughly mixed with the air. By adjusting the position of the throttle T, the amount of this mixture fed to the gasoline engine may be increased or decreased.

The gasoline engine consists of several cylinders connected to a common crankshaft. Power is developed inside each cylinder by the burning of the mixture of gasoline and air. A typical cylinder is shown in Figure 17–5; it contains two valves I and E, a spark plug S, and a piston. A piston rod connects the piston to the crankshaft.

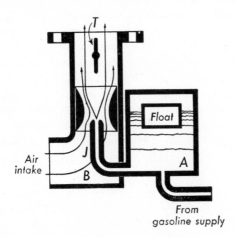

Fig. 17–4   Schematic diagram of a carburetor.

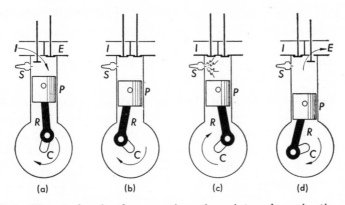

Fig. 17–5   The strokes in the operation of an internal combustion engine. (a) Intake stroke. (b) Compression stroke. (c) Ignition and power stroke. (d) Exhaust stroke.

Let us start with the piston at the top of its stroke, as shown in Figure 17–5(a). When the crankshaft is turned, either by hand or by means of a starting motor, the piston is moved down, increasing the volume and decreasing the pressure in the space above it. Valve I is opened automatically at the beginning of this downward stroke, allowing a mixture of gasoline vapor and air to enter the cylinder at atmospheric pressure. At the end of the downstroke of the piston, valve *I* is closed. The piston is now moved up, compressing the mixture approximately adiabatically into a small volume, thereby raising its temperature and increasing its pressure. At the end of the upstroke, an electric spark passes between the two terminals of the spark gap, igniting the mixture. We may think of this as a constant-volume process during which the energy liberated by the combustion of the gasoline produces an increase in the temperature and pressure of the gas. The temperature may go as high as 2,500°C and the pressure may reach a value of about 400 lb/sq in. This pressure now forces the piston down. We may think of this as an approximately adiabatic expansion of the gas during which work is done by the expanding gas and delivered to the crankshaft. This is usually referred to as the *power stroke*. At the end of the power stroke, the exhaust valve *E* is opened and some of the burnt gases leave the cylinder. On the succeeding upward motion of the piston, the remaining burnt gas is pushed through the exhaust valve. At the top of this upstroke, the valve *E* is closed, and the cycle of operations begins anew; that is, the piston moves down, the intake valve *I* is opened, and a fresh mixture is drawn into the cylinder.

There are four strokes of the piston in a complete cycle of operations. These may be summarized as follows:

(a) Downstroke: mixture taken into cylinder at atmospheric pressure

(b) Upstroke: compression of the gas, followed by ignition at the end of the stroke

(c) Downstroke: expansion of the gas; power stroke

(d) Upstroke: exhaust stroke—burnt gases forced out

Because there are four strokes to the cycle, this is called a four-cycle engine. Power is delivered to the crankshaft during only one of these four strokes, or only once in every two revolutions of the crankshaft. For smooth operation, a four-cycle gasoline engine should have at least two cylinders. The cylinders should be adjusted so that power is delivered at different times to the crankshaft. A flywheel of large moment of inertia is usually attached to the crankshaft to keep it running smoothly.

The thermal efficiency of a gasoline engine is about 25 per cent. This means that only 25 per cent of the energy liberated during the combustion of the fuel is converted into work; the remaining 75 per cent goes into the atmosphere during the exhaust stroke and through the cooling system. It can be shown that the thermal efficiency of the gasoline engine depends upon the *compression ratio*, that is, the ratio of the maximum volume of the gas in the cylinder to the minimum volume of the gas at the end of the compression stroke. In most modern gasoline engines, the compression ratio ranges from about 7:1 to 10:1.

17-5 THE DIESEL ENGINE

In the Diesel engine, only air is taken in during the intake stroke. The air is then compressed approximately adiabatically to about one sixteenth of its original volume, thus raising both its temperature and pressure. Oil in the form of a fine spray is now injected into this heated air. The air is hot enough to cause the oil to burn immediately; this raises the temperature and pressure in the cylinder still further. The pressure may reach a value of 800 lb/sq in. The piston moves down while the oil is being injected into the cylinder, keeping the pressure constant during the burning of the oil. After a predetermined quantity of oil has been injected and burned, the oil supply is shut off, and the gases continue to expand approximately adiabatically to the end of the stroke. The exhaust valve is then opened and some of the burnt gases are let out until the pressure drops to atmospheric pressure. The remaining gases are then forced out by the upward motion of the piston. The cycle is now completed, and the cylinder is now ready to receive a new charge of fresh air and begin the cycle all over again.

The strokes in the Diesel-engine cycle may be summarized as follows:

(a) Intake stroke: charge of air taken in at atmospheric pressure

(b) Compression stroke: air compressed approximately adiabatically

(c) Power stroke: oil injected and burned at constant pressure, followed by an approximately adiabatic expansion to the end of the stroke

(d) Exhaust stroke: burnt gases forced out through the exhaust

The efficiency of the Diesel engine may run as high as 38 per cent. The compression ratio of the Diesel engine may be as high as 16:1. Again, there is only one power stroke for every two revolutions of the crankshaft, so that two or more cylinders must be used for smooth engine operation. Because of the fact that only air is taken in on the intake stroke, it has been possible to design efficient Diesel engines which operate on a two-stroke-per-cycle basis. Such engines have been built in sizes up to 1,500 hp. In the two-stroke cycle, the intake and the exhaust take place at the same time. Fresh air is blown into the cylinder, and the hot exhaust gases from the previous cycle are blown out [see Figure 17–6(a)]. The piston then moves up, compressing the air practically adiabatically, thus raising its temperature and pressure [see Figure 17–6(b)]. Oil under high pressure is injected into the compressed air, as shown in Figure 17–6(c), and begins to burn, thus raising the temperature still higher. The piston moves down while oil is being injected so that the combustion of the oil takes place at constant pressure. The oil supply is shut off when the piston is down only part of the way, and for the remainder of its motion the heated gases expand approximately adiabatically. The temperature and pressure of the gases decrease during this part of the power stroke. At the end of this power stroke, the exhaust valve and the air intake valve are both opened,

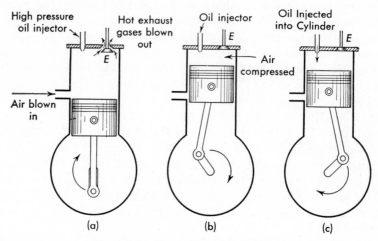

FIG. 17–6   Two-cycle Diesel engine.

fresh air is blown in, and the exhaust gases are blown out, thus starting the two-stroke cycle over again. In this two-stroke cycle or two-cycle engine, power is delivered once during each revolution.

17-6   THE SECOND LAW OF THERMODYNAMICS

In each of the cycles described in this chapter, we have seen that not all of the heat which is supplied to the engine is converted into work; some heat is always rejected to some outside reservoir. This is true not only for the cycles described here but for all other engines. These experiences form the basis for a far-reaching generalization known as the *second law of thermodynamics*. There are various ways of stating this law, and all these statements are equivalent to each other. One form of the second law of thermodynamics is as follows:

It is impossible to construct an engine which, operating in a cycle, will produce no effect other than the extraction of heat from a reservoir and the performance of an equivalent amount of work.

This statement implies that every cyclic engine which takes in heat from some source or reservoir must reject some of this heat to a reservoir at a lower temperature. Many inventors have thought of the idea of extracting heat from the ocean and using this heat to operate the engines of a ship. But the second law of thermodynamics states that this is impossible. An understanding of the first and second laws of thermodynamics by inventors would save them many hours of labor.

A very simple statement of the second law of thermodynamics is that *heat of its own accord will always flow from higher to lower temperature.* This statement is almost self-evident from our discussion of temperature and calorimetry. If it is ever desired to take heat from a source at low temperature to one at a higher temperature, it is necessary to do work on the system. This is essentially what takes place in a refrigerator (see Section 17–11).

17-7 THE STEAM ENGINE

In the operation of a steam engine, the combustion of the fuel does not take place in the cylinder of the steam engine but in a separate firebox or combustion chamber. The various components of a steam-engine power plant are shown schematically in Figure 17–7. Let us trace the changes in

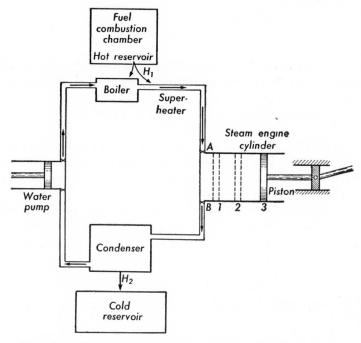

FIG. 17–7 Schematic diagram of a steam-engine power plant.

the state of a small quantity of water which goes through a complete cycle of operations in this power plant. A common method of showing these changes of state is with the aid of a graph such as that in Figure 17–8, in which the pressure and volume of this quantity of water are plotted for this cycle.

A small quantity of water at a low temperature and at a low pressure, represented by point *a* on the graph, is taken in by the water pump and compressed adiabatically to a very high pressure represented by point *b*. The temperature and volume of this water change only slightly during this

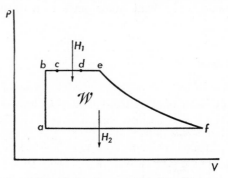

Fɪɢ. 17–8   Steam-engine cycle.

process. This water at high pressure is now led into the boiler where it is heated until its temperature reaches the boiling point at this pressure, point *c* on the graph. This quantity of water is then completely vaporized, its volume changing from *c* to *d* at constant pressure and temperature. It is common practice to take this saturated steam and lead it through a pipe which is heated by heat from the combustion chamber so that the temperature of the steam is raised above its boiling point but is still at the same pressure; this is represented by the line *de*. It is then said to be *superheated steam*. While the volume of the water is changing from *b* to *e* at constant pressure, an equal mass of superheated steam at this pressure is admitted into the cylinder of the steam engine by opening the intake valve *A* when the piston is at position 1 and allowing the steam to keep going into the cylinder while the piston is moving to position 2. Valve *A* is then closed, and the steam in the cylinder performs an adiabatic expansion in pushing the piston to position 3, the end of its stroke. During this process, the volume increases, the temperature and pressure drop, and some of the steam condenses to liquid. This adiabatic expansion is represented by the curve *ef*. The state of the system represented by point *f* is sometimes referred to as *wet steam*. On the return stroke of the piston, exhaust valve *B* is opened, and the wet steam is forced out of the cylinder into the condenser where the vapor is condensed to water by removing heat from it. This process is represented by the line *fa*. The small quantity of water has now completed the cycle and is back at state *a*, ready to repeat it.

The graph *abcdefa* is called the cycle of this steam engine and is usually referred to as the Rankine cycle. The area inside this cycle represents the work done during one cycle of operation. During this cycle, heat was added to the system during the constant-pressure processes *bcde*, and heat was removed from the system during the constant-pressure condensation process *fa*. If H_1 represents the heat added to the system, and H_2 the heat removed from it, then the work done $\mathcal{W}$ is given by

$$\mathcal{W} = H_1 - H_2,$$

and the thermal efficiency of this steam engine is

$$e = \frac{\mathcal{W}}{H_1} = 1 - \frac{H_2}{H_1}. \qquad (7)$$

17-8   THE TURBINE

Many modern steam power plants use steam-driven turbines rather than the reciprocating type of steam engine described above. A turbine consists essentially of a large wheel rigidly fastened to a shaft; a series of curved blades is mounted on the rim of the wheel, as shown in Figure 17–9.

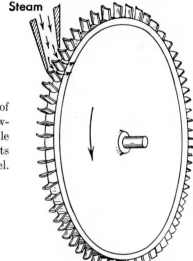

Steam

FIG. 17–9   Schematic representation of the action of a steam turbine showing steam coming from the nozzle and directed against the buckets mounted on the rim of the wheel.

A rapidly moving stream of fluid is directed against these blades, thus driving the wheel with great speed. In hydroelectric plants, the fluid is water, and the turbine is called a water turbine. In the *steam turbine*, steam at high pressure expands through a nozzle and is directed against the blades of the turbine wheel, causing it to rotate. The steam leaving the turbine blades at a lower pressure passes through another nozzle leading into a condenser. Here the steam is condensed to water, pumped back into the boiler, and changed to steam again, and the cycle is repeated. Other steam turbines use several turbine wheels separated from each other by stationary vanes which redirect the steam coming from the vanes of one wheel so that it will strike the vanes of the next wheel at the proper angle.

The power developed by the steam turbine is transmitted by coupling its shaft, either directly or through a gearbox, to the device which it is to operate, such as the propellers of a ship, or an electric generator.

The gas turbine differs from the water turbine and steam turbine in that the gases formed in the combustion of a fuel such as gasoline or oil are used to drive the turbine wheel. Gas turbines have recently been installed in airplanes, and will probably be used soon to operate locomotives. The practical development of a gas turbine depends to a great extent upon progress made in metallurgy in developing materials which can withstand the high temperatures necessary for the efficient operation of a gas turbine.

17-9   JET ENGINES

A jet engine is a modern adaptation of one of the oldest engines known, Hero's steam engine, sketched in Figure 17–10. Steam which is formed in

FIG. 17–10   Hero's steam engine.

the boiler comes out through the two nozzles. If a quantity of steam of mass m comes out of one nozzle with a velocity v, it has momentum mv. The nozzle acquires an equal and opposite momentum. Or if this mass of steam comes out in a time interval t, the force which acts on this steam to get it moving with a forward speed v is $F = mv/t$. From Newton's third law, this is also the force on the nozzle. The two nozzles of Hero's engine are so mounted that the forces which act on them produce torques in the same direction, causing a rotation about its axis.

The jet engine used in airplanes also makes use of the reaction produced when a stream of hot gases is ejected at high speed from a nozzle. Figure 17–11 is a schematic diagram showing the operation of a jet engine. Air

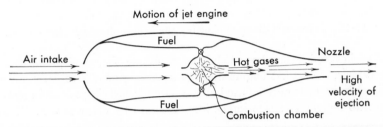

Fig. 17–11   Schematic diagram showing the operation of a jet engine.

is taken in through an opening at the front of the engine, with the aid of a pump or compressor, and led into the combustion chamber where it is used to burn the fuel. The hot gases formed in the process of combustion are directed to the nozzle at the rear of the engine and are ejected at high velocity. The force on the nozzle, and hence on the jet engine, depends upon the rate at which the heated gases leave the nozzle and upon the velocity of these gases.

If a jet engine is attached to an airplane, the force of reaction experienced by the jet engine is transmitted to the airplane. The latter will be accelerated and will acquire a speed which is limited only by the drag on the plane produced by resisting forces, such as air resistance. Planes equipped with jet engines have been flown at speeds in excess of the speed of sound. The speed of sound is about 760 mi/hr at sea level and decreases with increasing altitude; at 36,000 ft the speed of sound is about 660 mi/hr.

17-10   THE ROCKET ENGINE

The principle of the operation of a rocket engine, or rocket motor as it is sometimes called, is the same as that of the jet engine. A rocket engine differs from a jet engine in that it carries its supply of oxygen with it and is thus independent of the oxygen of the atmosphere. Figure 17–12 is a schematic diagram showing the essentials of a rocket engine. It consists of a cylinder containing a tank of liquid oxygen and a fuel tank containing gasoline, alcohol, or some other fuel. The hot gases formed in the combustion of the fuel are led through a nozzle. Again, if a quantity of gas of mass m leaves the nozzle in time t with a velocity v, the force exerted on this mass of gas, and hence also the force on the rocket, is $F = mv/t$.

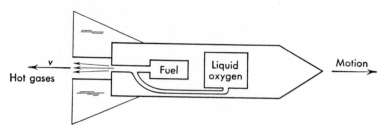

FIG. 17–12 Schematic diagram showing the operation of a rocket engine.

A rocket engine may be attached to an automobile, an airplane, or any other vehicle. A rocket engine may be used as a missile to carry an explosive charge; or it may be used as a device for carrying scientific instruments into regions of space impossible of access by other means. These

FIG. 17–13 (a) A V-2 rocket being placed in position for firing, May 10, 1946, at White Sands Proving Grounds, New Mexico. (b) V-2 rocket carrying instruments and cameras installed by USAF, takes off for flight into ionosphere. Note trail of gases from exhaust. (Courtesy of U.S. Air Force Photographs, Washington, D.C.)

instruments may be arranged so that they radio their information automatically to receiving instruments at the ground station, or an attempt may be made to recover them at a later time.

One of the rocket engines used for scientific experiments is an adaptation of a German V-2 rocket (see Figure 17–13). It is about 46 ft long, 6 ft in diameter at the base, and weighs about 28,000 lb. The propellent is liquid oxygen and alcohol, and the gases formed in the process of combustion escape from the nozzle with a speed of about 6,800 ft/sec. Some

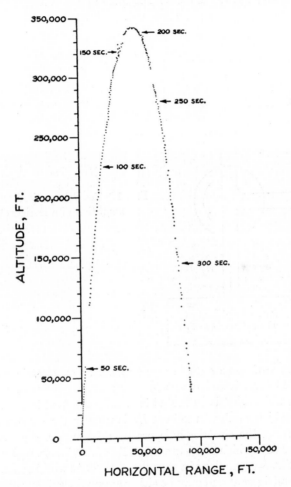

Fɪɢ. 17–14 Graph showing the trajectory of a V-2 rocket. Its positions at intervals of 50 sec are indicated by arrows on the graph. (Graph furnished by Evans Signal Laboratory and Ballistics Research Laboratory and reproduced through courtesy of *Journal of Applied Physics*.)

have attained altitudes of over 100 miles. Figure 17–14 is a graph of the trajectory of one rocket which attained an altitude of about 340,000 ft. The fuel burned for about 1 min, and the rocket continued its upward flight for an additional 2 min, with no additional power being delivered to it. Its total time of flight was about 6 min.

17-11   THE REFRIGERATOR

In principle, a refrigerator may be thought of as a heat engine operated in reverse. As shown schematically in Figure 17–15, heat H_2 is taken from some source or sources at a low temperature, work $\mathcal{W}$ is done on the en-

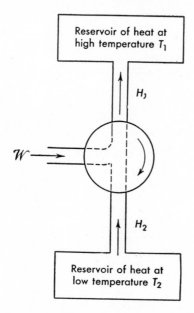

FIG. 17–15   Schematic diagram of the operation of a refrigerator.

gine by means of some outside agency such as an electric motor, and a quantity of heat H_1 is delivered to a source at a higher temperature. The source from which heat is extracted is usually the food in the refrigerator. The source which received the heat H_1 is usually the air surrounding the refrigerator. In the electrically operated refrigerator, the electric motor runs a compressor which consists essentially of a cylinder, a piston, and two valves just like the cylinder of a steam engine. The working substance used is called the refrigerant and may be either ammonia, sulphur dioxide, or any other substance whose boiling point is fairly low. The refrigerant is taken through a cycle of operations which is described below, and at the end of this cycle its internal energy remains unchanged. For the first law of thermodynamics as applied to the refrigerator, we can write

$$H_1 - H_2 = \mathcal{W}$$

or

$$H_1 = H_2 + \mathcal{W};$$ (8)

that is, the heat delivered to the air in the kitchen is greater than that taken from the food.

A typical cycle of operations for the refrigerant is as follows: suppose we start with the refrigerant, say ammonia as a liquid, at high pressure and at room temperature, and allow some of it to pass through a valve or throttle into a region of lower pressure (see Figure 17–16). This process is

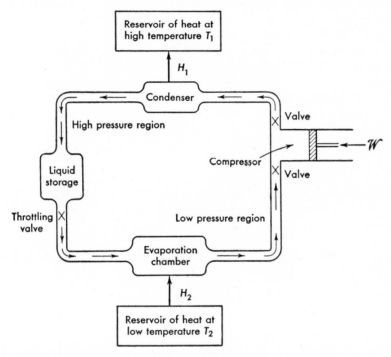

FIG. 17–16   Schematic diagram outlining the processes which occur in a refrigerator using ammonia as the refrigerant.

usually called a throttling process. During this process, the temperature also drops, and some of the ammonia is vaporized. This mixture is now led into the evaporation chamber in which the remaining liquid is vaporized at this low temperature and pressure. It is during this process of vaporization that heat is extracted from the food and water in the refrigerator and is used to vaporize the ammonia. The ammonia vapor is now taken into the compressor and is compressed adiabatically to a high pressure and a temperature slightly above room temperature. This compressed fluid is then sent through pipes which are cooled by the circulating air around them. It is during this process that the heat H_1 is given out by the refrigerant and the refrigerant is brought back to its initial state.

What is desired in a refrigerator is the extraction of an amount of heat

H_2 from the cold source with the performance of as little work $\mathcal{W}$ as possible. Instead of talking about the efficiency of a refrigerator, engineers use the term *coefficient of performance* of a refrigerator, defined as

$$K = \frac{H_2}{\mathcal{W}}, \tag{9}$$

where K is the coefficient of performance. In most practical refrigerators, K has the value of 5 or 6. The smaller the amount of work needed to extract a given amount of heat, the greater is the coefficient of performance. For example, if 1,000 cal of heat are extracted from the food in the refrigerator and the motor which operates the compressor performs an amount of work equivalent to 200 cal, then the coefficient of performance of this refrigerator is 5. The heat H_1 delivered to the air in the kitchen is 1,200 cal.

17-12 A HEAT PUMP

The analysis of the refrigeration cycle shows that, by the performance of a certain amount of work $\mathcal{W}$, a quantity of heat H_2 is taken from a reservoir at a low temperature T_2, and a larger quantity of heat H_1 is de-

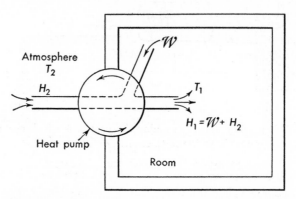

Fig. 17–17   Schematic diagram of the operation of a heat pump which takes a quantity of heat H_2 from the atmosphere at a low temperature T_2 and pumps a quantity of heat H_1 into the room at a higher temperature T_1 when an amount of work $\mathcal{W}$ is done on it.

livered to a reservoir at a higher temperature T_1. Lord Kelvin, in 1852, suggested that this is just what is desired in the operation of a *heat pump*. It took about 75 years for the first practical heat pump to be put in operation, and they are coming into more common use now for heating homes in the winter and cooling them in the summer. A schematic diagram showing the operation of a heat pump is sketched in Figure 17–17. This heat pump will take heat H_2 from the atmosphere and pump heat H_1 into the room at the higher temperature T_1 with the performance of work $\mathcal{W}$ on the compressor of the heat pump. The quantity of heat H_1 that is delivered to the room is given by

$$H_1 = \mathcal{W} + H_2, \tag{10}$$

although the energy that is paid for on the electric bill is represented by the work $\mathcal{W}$ which is done by the electric motor in operating the compressor.

By reversing the flow of the refrigerant in the heat pump, the temperature of the room can be kept below that of the atmosphere—a very desirable feature on hot summer days. In this case, a quantity of heat H_2 will be taken from the room at a low temperature T_2, a quantity of work $\mathcal{W}$ will be done on the compressor to accomplish this task, and a quantity of heat $H_1 = \mathcal{W} + H_2$ will be delivered to the outside.

Since the temperature of the atmosphere fluctuates widely in very short time intervals, most heat pumps utilize the more constant temperature of a nearby lake, river, or the ground as the external heat reservoir. Figure 17–18 is a schematic diagram of the operation of a heat pump.

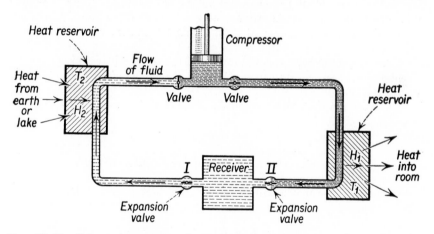

F<small>IG.</small> 17–18   Schematic diagram of a heat pump. When direction of fluid flow is as indicated, expansion valve II is kept open or bypassed; $T_1 > T_2$. When used to cool a room, fluid flow is reversed, expansion valve I is kept open or bypassed, and valve II is operative. Heat is taken from room and delivered to outside reservoir such as the ground or a lake; $T_2 > T_1$.

When the direction of flow of the refrigerant is that shown by the arrows in the pipes, a quantity of heat H_2 is taken from the earth in one cycle, the compressor does an amount of work $\mathcal{W}$ during this cycle, and a quantity of heat H_1 is delivered to the reservoir in the room. This reservoir may be connected to a radiator to deliver this heat to the air in the room. When used as a heat pump, the temperature T_1 is greater than T_2. If it is desired to operate the heat pump to cool the room, the direction of flow of the refrigerant is reversed and expansion valve II is used instead of expansion valve *I*. The direction of heat flow is reversed, so that a quantity of heat H_1 is taken from the room and a quantity of heat H_2 is delivered to the earth, where $H_2 = H_1 + \mathcal{W}$.

QUESTIONS

1. What is a heat engine?
2. Is it possible to convert a given quantity of mechanical energy completely into heat? If so, give an example of such conversion.
3. Is it possible to convert a given quantity of heat, say 1 cal, completely into mechanical work? If so, outline a method for doing so.
4. Is it possible to design a heat engine which will have a thermal efficiency of 100 per cent? Check your answer with the statements of the second law of thermodynamics.
5. How is the absolute thermodynamic scale of temperature defined?
6. Is it possible to have negative values for the temperature of a body on the absolute thermodynamic scale?
7. What is the fundamental physical principle at the basis of the operation (a) of a jet engine and (b) of a rocket engine?
8. A rocket is fired from the earth and releases a sphere which becomes a satellite moving around the earth. Compare the motion of such a satellite with that of the moon.
9. Why are heat engines rated in terms of their power output instead of their energy output?
10. What is the essential difference between a jet engine and a rocket engine?
11. Why do engineers prefer the term *coefficient of performance*, in rating refrigerators, to the term *efficiency*?
12. An electric motor is used to operate a heat pump. What fraction of the heat energy delivered to the room is paid for on the electric bill?

PROBLEMS

1. (a) Determine the thermal efficiency of a Carnot engine which operates between the temperatures of 100°C and 0°C. If 2,000 cal of heat are supplied to it, (b) how much work is done, and (c) how much heat is rejected to the low-temperature reservoir?
2. (a) Determine the thermal efficiency of a Carnot engine which operates between two reservoirs whose temperatures are 250°C and 0°C. If 1,000 cal of heat are supplied to it, (b) how much work is done, and (c) how much heat is rejected to the low-temperature reservoir?
3. Superheated steam at a temperature of 520°F is supplied to a steam

engine which exhausts the steam to a condenser kept at a temperature of 60°F. Determine the maximum thermal efficiency of this steam engine.

4. Steam at a temperature of 227°C is supplied to a steam turbine which exhausts it to a condenser kept at a temperature of 13°C. Determine the maximum thermal efficiency of this steam turbine.

5. The coefficient of performance of a refrigerator is 5. It takes 3,000 cal out of a quantity of food. (a) How much work is done by the electric motor which operates this refrigerator? (b) How much heat is supplied to the surrounding air?

6. A tray containing 2,500 gm of water at 20°C is placed in a refrigerator whose coefficient of performance is 6. The water is changed to ice at −10°C. Determine (a) how much heat is removed from the water in converting it to ice, (b) the work done by the electric motor which operates the refrigerator, and (c) the amount of heat supplied to the surrounding air.

Part Three

WAVE MOTION
AND SOUND

18-1 VIBRATING BODIES AND WAVE MOTION

We have previously considered the properties of some vibrating systems such as the simple pendulum and the vibrating spring (see Chapter 7) and discussed the general properties which characterize simple harmonic motion. Other vibratory motion will be described later, such as the vibrations of a permanent magnet when suspended in a magnetic field (Chapter 20) and the electrical oscillation in a circuit containing inductance and capacitance (Chapter 29). Vibratory motion is a fairly common and extremely important type of motion. Under proper conditions, vibratory motion leads to the production of *waves*. In this section, we shall consider the properties of wave motions set up in material media by vibrating systems. We shall leave to later sections the discussion of other types of wave motion such as radio waves, light, x-rays, and gamma rays. As we shall see in this and subsequent chapters, wave motion is an important method of transferring energy from one place to another without involving the actual transfer of matter.

A typical example of a vibrating body is a long stick with one end clamped in a vise and the other end displaced slightly from its equilibrium position; when released, this stick will vibrate with periodic motion (see Figure 18–1). The reason for the vibration is that the stick possesses inertia and is *elastic;* that is, when one end is displaced with respect to the other and then released, there is a force acting on it which brings it back to its original position. When it gets back to its original position, the end of the stick is still in motion; because of its inertia, it keeps on moving beyond its equilibrium position. This brings the elastic force into play again to bring the stick back to its original position. This oscillatory motion of the stick will continue until all its energy is lost. How-

Fig. 18–1   Vibrations of a stick fastened at one end.

ever, since the stick is vibrating in the air, some of its energy is transferred to the air; part of this energy is converted into heat, but another part of the energy may be transmitted by the air in the form of a *wave motion*. This wave motion in air is called a *sound wave*.

If a steel wire is stretched between two supports A and B, as in Figure 18–2, and then plucked at some point P, this point will vibrate with simple

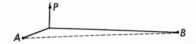

Fig. 18–2 Setting a stretched string into vibration by plucking it at some point P.

harmonic motion. When the wire is released, the plucked point is pulled down by forces exerted by the neighboring particles which are elastically connected to it. Some of the potential energy which was given to the wire when it was pulled aside is now converted into kinetic energy in that region, and, because of the elastic forces between the particles, some of this energy is transmitted to neighboring particles, setting them into vibration. These particles, in turn, transmit some of their energy to their neighboring particles. Thus the energy given to the wire when it was plucked reappears at different points along the wire after a lapse of time. This mode of transfer of energy along the wire is called a *wave motion* in the wire. This wave motion differs in some respects from a wave motion in air. We shall show that the wave motion in air is a *longitudinal wave;* that is, the direction of vibration of the particles is parallel to the direction of motion of the wave. The wave motion in the stretched wire is a *transverse wave;* that is, the particles in the wire vibrate at right angles to the direction of motion of the wave.

18-2 PRODUCTION OF LONGITUDINAL WAVES

Waves can be set up in any elastic body by producing some disturbance at a point in the body. For example, consider a helical spring stretched between two fixed points A and B, as in Figure 18–3, and suppose that we compress a small section of the spring near the bottom by taking one of its coils and pushing it down. When this coil is released, it will be pulled up by the coil above it and pushed up by the coil below it. Not only will this coil therefore move up to its equilibrium position, but, because of its inertia, it will continue beyond this point and move closer to the coil above it, thus producing a *compression* there. This upward displacement of the coil will, at the same time, leave a large space between it and the coil below it. Thus an *extension* will appear in the spring just below the compression. The coil at the top of the compressed portion of the wire will now be forced up to the next coil, producing a compression in the region above it. At the same time, the coil at the bottom of the compressed portion will be forced down into the stretched portion of the spring because of the increased pull exerted by the coil below it and the increased push exerted by the coil above it. Thus in the region where there formerly was a *compression* there is now an

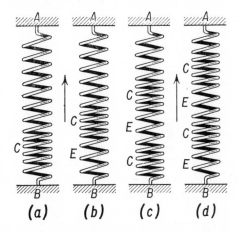

Fig. 18-3 Setting up a longitudinal wave in a coiled spring stretched between two points A and B. (a) Portion of spring C near the bottom is compressed. (b) Compression C has moved up the spring and is followed by an extension E below it. (c) and (d) Compressions C and extensions E moving up the spring.

(a)   *(b)*   *(c)*   *(d)*

extension, while the compression has moved farther up the spring. Each compression in any portion of the spring will be followed by an extension in the same region shortly afterward. This is illustrated in Figure 18–3,

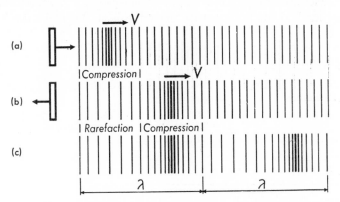

Fig. 18–4   (a) Compression in the air produced by the motion of the end of the rod to the right, followed by (b) a rarefaction produced by the motion of the end of the rod to the left. (c) Longitudinal wave in air consists of a series of compressions and rarefactions moving outward with velocity V.

which shows the compressions and extensions in the spring at different time intervals. This series of compressions and extensions moving up the spring constitutes the wave motion in the spring. While the compressions and extensions move up the spring, the individual coils vibrate up and down with simple harmonic motion.   Since the direction in which the wave motion travels is parallel to the direction of the vibrations of the particles, the wave is called a *longitudinal wave*.

The wave motion in air is also a longitudinal wave.   Let us consider the wave in air produced by the vibratory motion of a stick with one end fixed in a vise or by one prong of a tuning fork, as in Figure 18–4.   When the end of the stick or tuning fork moves to the right, the air next to it is compressed;   this in turn produces a compression in the next layer of air, which then compresses the layer to the right of it;   and in this way a *compression* travels out from the vibrating rod.   While the compression is moving out to the right, the end of the rod starts moving back toward the left, leaving a *rarefaction* or region of reduced pressure on its right.   Because of this reduced pressure, the layer of air nearest the stick starts moving back, leaving a rarefaction to its right;   the next layer of air starts moving back, producing a rarefaction to the right of it.   In this way a *rarefaction* travels out from the vibrating rod.   The succession of compressions and rarefactions traveling out from the rod constitutes the *longitudinal wave* in air.   The layers of air vibrate back and forth with the same frequency as the rod.   In the region of compression, the layers of air move in the direction of the wave, while, in the rarefaction, the layers of air move in the opposite direction.

A single wave consists of a compression followed by a rarefaction.   A graphical method for representing the wave is shown in Figure 18–5, in

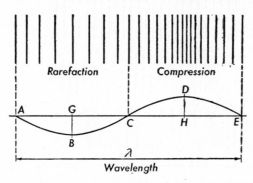

FIG. 18–5   Representation of a longitudinal wave.

which the change in pressure from normal atmospheric pressure is plotted along the vertical axis and the position where this pressure difference exists is plotted along the horizontal axis.   The section of the curve below the axis represents the rarefaction, while the section above the horizontal axis represents the compression.   The horizontal distance between two points in the same phase, such as the distance from A to E, is called *the length of the wave* and is denoted by the letter λ.

The changes in pressure which occur during the compressions and rarefactions are very small in comparison with the atmospheric pressure. The maximum depth *GB*, or the maximum height *HD*, is called the *amplitude* of the wave.

In the above discussion, we have considered only those layers of air very close to the source of the waves and on one side of it. At the same time, waves are also set up on the other side of the vibrating body. As these waves travel out, other layers of air all around the source are set in motion, and, at a comparatively large distance from the source, waves are traveling away from the source in all directions. If the source is small in comparison with the distance of the wave from it, we may consider the wave as a spherical wave; that is, all points in the air along a spherical surface having the source as a center will be at the same pressure. The circles of Figure 18–6 represent a plane section through these spherical surfaces

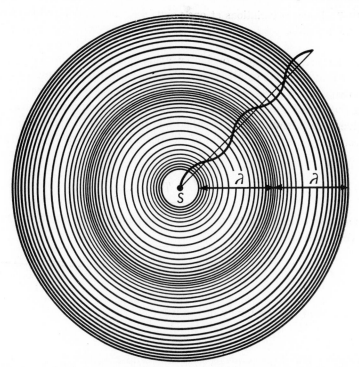

FIG. 18–6   Spherical waves traveling out from a small source of sound at *S*.

with the source *S* at the center. Points along any such surface are said to be in the *same phase;* the distance between two consecutive surfaces in which the pressure is a maximum is the wavelength of the wave. Similarly, the distance between two consecutive surfaces of minimum pressure is a wavelength. Any one of these spherical surfaces in which all points are in the same phase is called a *wave front*. The direction of motion of a wave is always at right angles to the wave front.

Suppose we focus our attention on some point in the medium and plot the variations in pressure which take place at this point of the medium as the wave progresses past it. Such a graph is shown in Figure 18–7, in

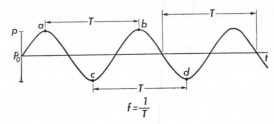

FIG. 18–7   Pressure variations at one point in a medium during the passage of a wave past it.

which the pressure above or below atmospheric pressure is plotted as ordinate and the time as abscissa. The time elapsed between the passage of two successive pressure maxima or two successive pressure minima is called the *period T* of the wave. The number of such maxima which pass the given point in unit time is called the *frequency f* of the wave. Hence the frequency f is the reciprocal of the period T; that is,

$$f = \frac{1}{T}. \tag{1}$$

Since a wave of length λ takes a time T to pass a given point, the velocity V of the wave is

$$V = \frac{\lambda}{T} \tag{2}$$

or, in terms of the frequency of the wave,

$$V = f\lambda. \tag{3}$$

Equation (2), or its equivalent Equation (3), is the fundamental equation for the velocity of a wave in any medium. The velocity of an elastic wave in a material medium depends upon its physical properties and is independent of the wavelength or frequency of the wave. For example, the speed of a wave in air at about 20°C is approximately 1,100 ft/sec. If a source vibrates at the rate of 550 times per second, for example, the frequency of the wave emitted by it is 550 per second and the wavelength of the wave emitted by it is, therefore, 2 ft.

18-3 PRODUCTION OF TRANSVERSE WAVES

Transverse waves can be produced in stretched strings, in rods, bars, disks, and other solids. For example, if a very long wire is stretched between two supports A and B, as shown in Figure 18–8, and if it is struck

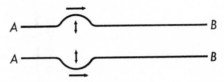

FIG. 18–8   A pulse traveling along a stretched wire.

with a hammer at some point to produce an elevation near one end, this elevation will travel along the wire to the other end. As this elevation moves along, the particles of the wire in front of it move up while those behind it move down toward their equilibrium positions. If it is given a blow which depresses a small section of the wire near one end, this depression will move along the wire to the other end. As this depression moves along the wire, the particles of the wire immediately in front of it will move down, and those behind it will move up toward their equilibrium positions. If the end of the wire A is moved up and down periodically, for example, by attaching it to one prong of a tuning fork, as shown in Figure 18–9,

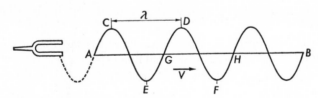

FIG. 18–9   Transverse wave in a long wire set up by a vibrating tuning fork.

a series of such elevations and depressions will travel along the wire. This series of elevations and depressions moving along the wire constitutes the *transverse wave* in the wire. The particles of the wire vibrate up and down at right angles to the length of the wire, while the wave set up in the wire moves along the length of the wire.

Just as in the case of longitudinal waves, so in the case of transverse waves, the wavelength λ is the distance between two consecutive points in the same phase. In Figure 18–9, the wavelength is the distance between two consecutive crests, such as C and D; or the distance between two consecutive troughs, such as E and F; or two consecutive points passing through their equilibrium positions in the same phase, such as G and H. The frequency f of the wave is the same as the frequency of vibration of any one of the particles of the wire and also the same as the frequency of vibration of the tuning fork to which the wire is attached. The frequency f of the wave is also equal to the number of crests which pass any one point in a unit time. Hence the velocity of a transverse wave is also given by Equation (3),

$$V = f\lambda. \tag{3}$$

The amplitude of the wave in the wire is the maximum displacement of any particle from its equilibrium position.

Equation (3) gives the relationship between the speed of a wave in a medium and the frequency and wavelength of the wave propagated through the medium. Since the existence of a wave in a medium is due to the properties of elasticity and inertia which are characteristic of the medium, the speed of the wave propagated through it should depend upon these factors. For example, in the case of a stretched wire, the speed of a transverse wave in the wire can be shown to be given by the equation

$$V = \sqrt{\frac{S}{M/L}}, \tag{4}$$

in which S is the tension in the wire, M is the mass of the wire, and L its length. The quantity M/L may be thought of as the linear density of the wire; it is the mass per unit length of the wire. Similar expressions can be given for the speeds of longitudinal and transverse waves in other media. Methods for measuring the speeds of such waves will be described in Section 18–9.

Equation (4) for the speed of a transverse wave in a wire of length L and mass M under tension S can be derived in an elementary way with the aid of a few simplifying assumptions. Let us consider a small transverse motion

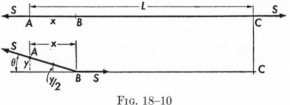

Fig. 18–10

imparted to one end A of the string, which, in a small time interval t, has advanced along the string to point B, a distance x along the original undisturbed position of AB (see Figure 18–10). In this time t, the end A has moved upward a very small distance y. Let us assume that AB can be considered a straight line which makes a small angle θ with the rest of the wire BC. Let us further assume that the tension S is the same throughout the wire.

We can apply Newton's second law to the motion of a portion of the wire AB by considering the resultant force to act at its center of gravity. The resultant force is in the y-direction and is simply the y-component of the force S at A; its value is $S \sin \theta$. If we call m the mass per unit length of the wire, then the mass of AB is mx. Newton's second law then yields

$$S \sin \theta = (mx)a, \tag{4a}$$

where a is the acceleration of the center of gravity of AB.

We can evaluate $\sin \theta$ by noting that, for very small angles,

$$\sin \theta = \tan \theta = \frac{y}{x}.$$

We can express a in terms of suitable variables by using the equation

$$s = \tfrac{1}{2}at^2 \qquad \text{[Equation (14$'$) in Chapter 3]}$$

for the distance traversed by a particle under constant acceleration for a time t, starting with zero velocity. In this case,

$$s = \frac{y}{2},$$

and the time t is, to a very good approximation, given by

$$t = \frac{x}{V},$$

where V is the velocity of the transverse wave along the wire. The approximation made is that the length of AB has been set equal to x, its original undisturbed length. Substituting these values of s and t into the equation for the acceleration yields

$$\frac{y}{2} = \tfrac{1}{2}a\,\frac{x^2}{V^2},$$

from which $\qquad\qquad a = y\,\dfrac{V^2}{x^2}.$

We can now substitute the values for $\sin \theta$ and a into Equation (4a) and obtain

$$S\frac{y}{x} = mx \cdot y\,\frac{V^2}{x^2},$$

so that
$$V^2 = \frac{S}{m}$$

or
$$V = \sqrt{\frac{S}{m}}.$$ (4b)

If M is the total mass of the wire and L is its length, then $m = M/L$; hence

$$V = \sqrt{\frac{S}{M/L}}.$$ (4)

Illustrative Example.   A long steel wire under a tension of 10^5 dynes has one end attached to a prong of a tuning fork which vibrates with a frequency of 128 vibrations/sec.   The linear density of the wire is 0.03 gm/cm.   Determine (a) the speed of the transverse wave in the wire and (b) the wavelength of this wave.

The speed of the wave in the wire can be obtained from Equation (4), which yields

$$V = \sqrt{\frac{10^5 \text{ dynes}}{0.03 \text{ gm/cm}}} = 1{,}830 \text{ cm/sec}.$$

Solving Equation (3) for λ, we get

$$\lambda = \frac{V}{f},$$

from which
$$\lambda = \frac{1{,}830}{128} \text{ cm} = 14.3 \text{ cm}.$$

18-4 HUYGENS' PRINCIPLE

The progress of a wave under a variety of conditions can be predicted with the aid of a principle first enunciated by the Dutch physicist Christian Huygens (1629–1695).   According to *Huygens' principle, each point in a wave front can be considered as a source of waves,* and the new position that the wave front will occupy after the lapse of a small time interval t can be found by drawing the envelope of all of the small waves which were sent out by all the individual points on the first wave front at the beginning of this time interval.   To illustrate the method of using Huygens' principle, let us consider the progress of a spherical wave front from a point source O, as shown in Figure 18–11.   The arc of the circle AB represents the position of a section of the wave front at a certain time.   The wave is progressing through the medium with a speed V.   To find the new position of the wave front at the end of a short time interval t, consider each point on the arc AB as a source of waves and draw circles of radii equal to Vt with each of these points as center.   The new wave front $A'B'$ is the envelope of all of these small circles; that is, $A'B'$ is tangent to each one of these circles.

The same type of construction can be used to find the subsequent position of any type of wave front. Figure 18–12 shows a plane wave

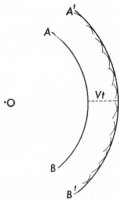

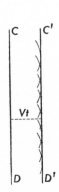

FIG. 18–11 Huygens' construction for determining the position of wave front AB after a time interval t. $A'B'$ is the new position of the wave front.

FIG. 18–12 Huygens' construction for determining $C'D'$, the new position of the plane wave front which started at CD at a time t earlier.

front CD progressing with speed V. Its new position in the same medium after a short time interval t is $C'D'$, the envelope of the small waves, each of radius Vt, sent out by each of the points on the wave front CD.

18-5 REFLECTION OF A WAVE

When a wave which is traveling in one medium reaches the surface of a second medium, part of the wave is *reflected* back into the first medium

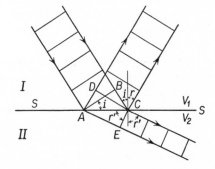

FIG. 18–13 Reflection and refraction of a plane wave at a surface separating two media.

and the rest penetrates the second medium; this latter part is said to be *refracted* into the second medium. Figure 18–13 shows a plane wave

striking a surface S separating media I and II. The incident wave fronts
are all parallel to AB and travel with speed V_1. The angle that each
incident wave front makes with the surface is called the angle of incidence i.
Experiments have shown that the angle r between the reflected wave fronts
and the surface is equal to the angle i; that is, *the angle of incidence is
equal to the angle of reflection.* A line drawn in the direction of motion of
the wave is called a *ray*; a ray is perpendicular to the wave front. The
angle of incidence i is then also the angle between the ray BC and a line
perpendicular to the surface at C; such a line is called a *normal.* Similarly,
the angle of reflection is the angle between the reflected ray and the normal.

The position of the reflected wave and the direction of its motion relative to that of the incident wave can be found with the aid of Huygens'
principle. Figure 18–14 shows the plane wave advancing toward the

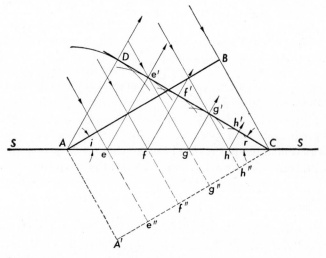

FIG. 18–14 Huygens' construction for determining the position and direction of
motion of the wave front reflected by surface SS. AB is the incident wave
front, and CD is the reflected wave front.

surface SS at an angle of incidence i. Let us consider the plane wave
front represented by the line AB such that point A has just reached the
surface while B is still moving toward it; the angle between AB and the
surface SS is the angle i. If the surface had not been there, the wave
front AB would have advanced to the position $A'C$ in a time t. But as the
different parts of the wave front reach the surface, each point on the
surface, such as $A, e, f, g, h, \ldots C$, is set into vibration and becomes a
source of waves. To locate the new position of the wave front, draw a
circle of radius AA' with A as a center in the region above SS, another

circle with e as a center and of radius ee'', and proceed in a similar manner for each point on the surface that is struck by the incident wave. Then draw the envelope $De'f'g'h'C$ tangent to these circles. This is the wave front reflected by the surface. The angle r between CD and SS is the angle of reflection of the wave and is equal to the angle of incidence. The direction of motion of the reflected wave is indicated by the arrows on the rays AD, ee', and so forth.

If a wave from some point source P strikes a flat surface and is reflected from it, the reflected ray will appear to come from a point P' behind the surface. This point P' is the *image* of P, and it can be located by applying the law of reflection to a series of rays coming from P, as in Figure 18–15.

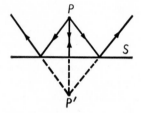

Fig. 18–15   Reflection from a plane surface gives rise to an image P' of a point source at P.

The walls of a room usually act as mirrors for the sounds produced in the room. In rooms of average size, these reflections add to the intensity of the sounds and in this sense the reflections are valuable. In a large auditorium, however, the reflected sound may reach the hearer a considerable time after he has received the directly transmitted sound. In the case of speech this may be very objectionable; in the case of music, the overlapping of different sounds is usually pleasing to the ear.

18-6   REFRACTION OF A WAVE

When a wave reaches a surface SS which separates two media, one in which its velocity is V_1 and the second in which its velocity is V_2, part of the wave enters the second medium and travels through it at an angle r' which differs from the angle of incidence i. If V_2 is greater than V_1, then the angle r', called the *angle of refraction,* is greater than the angle i, as shown in Figure 18–13. The method of determining the position and the direction of motion of the refracted wave with the aid of Huygens' principle is illustrated in Figure 18–16. Suppose that the incident wave is a plane wave; a portion of a wave front is represented by the line AB. A has just reached the surface SS while B is traveling toward it with the speed V_1. The position that the wave front would have occupied if it had continued in the same medium is shown by the dotted line $A'C$. But, since part of the wave front has entered the second medium, the new wave front is at a

different position and is traveling in a different direction.   To find this new
wave front, we note that while B was traveling in the first medium with
speed V_1 toward C, A was traveling in the second medium with speed V_2

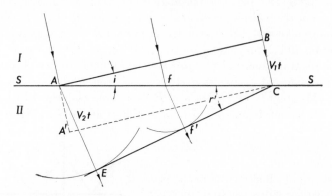

Fɪɢ. 18–16   Huygens' construction for determining the position and direction
of motion of a plane wave front after refraction from medium I into medium
II. AB is the incident wave front; EC is the refracted wave front.

for the same length of time t.   Hence, using A as a center, draw a circle of
radius V_2t for the wave which was emitted by point A.   If we take a point
at the center of the incident wave front AB, it will reach point f on the surface a time $t/2$ after the wave reached A.   For the remaining time $t/2$, the
wave will progress in the second medium with speed V_2.   Hence, with f
as a center and with a radius $V_2t/2$, draw an arc of a circle to determine the
position of the wave emitted by point f.   The waves emitted by all other
points on SS between A and C can be found in a similar manner.   The new
wave front EC is the envelope of all of the waves emitted by the points on
SS which were set into vibration by the incident wave AB.

If the speed of the wave V_2 in the second medium is greater than the
speed of the wave V_1 in the first medium, then the transmitted part of the
wave will be bent away from the normal.   In Figure 18–16, the wave front
AB is so chosen that point A travels to point E in medium II in the same
time that point B moves in medium I to the surface at C.   Thus

$$\frac{BC}{AE} = \frac{V_1}{V_2}.$$

Now
$$\sin i = \frac{BC}{AC},$$

and
$$\sin r' = \frac{AE}{AC};$$

therefore
$$\frac{\sin i}{\sin r'} = \frac{\dfrac{BC}{AC}}{\dfrac{AE}{AC}} = \frac{BC}{AE},$$

from which
$$\boxed{\frac{\sin i}{\sin r'} = \frac{V_1}{V_2}.}$$
(5)

Thus the ratio of the speeds of the waves in the two media is equal to the ratio of the sine of the angle of incidence to the sine of the angle of refraction. This ratio is called the *relative index of refraction* of the two media and will be designated by n_r. Thus

$$\boxed{n_r = \frac{\sin i}{\sin r'} = \frac{V_1}{V_2}.}$$
(6)

For example, the speed of sound in air is 331 m/sec and that in water is 1,447 m/sec. The relative index of refraction of water with respect to air for a longitudinal wave is

$$n_r = \frac{331}{1,447} = 0.228.$$

A longitudinal wave going from air to water and striking the surface at an angle of incidence of 10° will be refracted into the water and be transmitted at an angle r', which is given by

$$n_r = \frac{\sin i}{\sin r'},$$

so that
$$\sin r' = \frac{\sin 10°}{0.228} = \frac{0.1737}{0.228},$$

from which
$$\sin r' = 0.7619,$$

so that
$$r' = 49°38'.$$

18-7 DIFFRACTION OF WAVES

Many common phenomena such as the bending of a sound wave around obstacles, the spreading of a sound wave in different directions after passing through a small aperture, and the directional properties of megaphones are all examples of the *diffraction of waves*. Diffraction phenomena occur not only with sound waves but with all other types of waves. The ability to produce diffraction effects is one of the criteria used to decide whether we are dealing with a wave phenomenon. A simple method of demonstrating the diffraction of a wave through a small aperture is illustrated in Figure 18–17(a). *ABCD* is a shallow rectangular tank

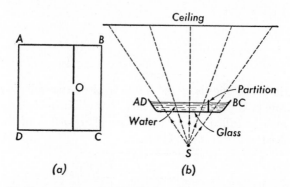

(a)   *(b)*

Fig. 18–17 Shallow rectangular tank for demonstrating wave phenomena.
(a) Top view showing partition in tank; narrow aperture *O* in partition.
(b) Side view showing source of light *S* under the glass bottom of the tank,
for projection of wave phenomena.

with a glass bottom. Water is poured into this tank to a depth of about 1 in. [see Figure 18–17(b)]. Light from a source *S* below the glass is transmitted through the water onto the ceiling. If a wave is started in the water by disturbing it with a stick, the form and progress of the wave can be followed by viewing its image on the ceiling. If a metal partition with a small aperture *O* is placed across the tank and if a plane wave is started near *AD* by dipping a stick into the water so that the length of the stick is parallel to *AD*, the plane wave will progress toward *BC*. When it comes to the partition, most of the wave will be reflected from it, but a small part will go through *O* (see Figure 18–18). The part that goes through *O* will not be plane however, but will spread out from *O* in a circular wave with *O* as the center. Thus points such as *P* and *Q* behind the partition will receive energy from the wave owing to its diffraction through the small aperture *O*.

In the production of diffraction effects, it is not the absolute size of the aperture that is significant but its size relative to the wavelength of the incident wave. A small aperture is one which is small in comparison with the incident wavelengths. If the aperture is somewhat larger than the wavelength incident upon it, diffraction effects are still present but not so marked. Figure 18–19 shows the diffraction of the same wave as in Figure 18–18, but through a larger aperture. The central part of the wave is practically plane, but the ends are curved, and the wave progresses to a slight extent beyond the edges of the aperture. A sound wave coming through an open window will bend around the frame of the window and be heard in various parts of the room. In the case of a megaphone, if the open end, that is, the end away from the mouth, is large in comparison with the

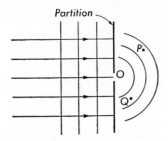

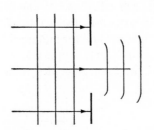

Fɪɢ. 18–18 Diffraction of a plane wave through a very small aperture *O*. Points *P* and *Q* behind partition will receive waves from *O*.

Fɪɢ. 18–19 Plane waves passing through large aperture show diffraction effect near edges.

wavelength of sound, the sound coming from it will be directed forward along the axis of the megaphone. If the open end of the megaphone is small in comparison with the wavelength of the sound, the waves will spread out in spherical waves as though the open end were the source of sound.

18-8 VIBRATIONS AND STATIONARY WAVES

When a wave strikes a reflecting surface normally, that is, at zero angle of incidence, the wave is reflected back at the same angle and consequently along the same line. If a continuous wave is propagated in this medium, the incident and reflected waves will *interfere* with each other. If the two waves traveling in *opposite directions* through the medium have the *same wavelength* and the *same amplitude*, their effect is to set up *steady vibrations* in the *medium;* these steady vibrations are called *stationary waves,* because in some special cases in which the vibrations are visible, as, for example, in a vibrating string, the appearance of the string is similar

Fɪɢ. 18–20 A string vibrating in segments shows a stationary wave pattern.

to that of our picture of a wave which remains stationary. A simple way of showing stationary waves is to attach one end *A* of a long string to a wall, as sketched in Figure 18–20, and move the other end up and down rapidly. Waves which travel out along the string are reflected back at the wall, and, if the timing of the impulses sent out by the motion of the end of the string B is adjusted properly, the string can be made to vibrate in segments, with the points marked N remaining stationary. These points are called *nodes;* the distance between two successive nodes can be shown to be half the length of the wave traveling along the wire.

The method for adding the effects produced by two waves of the same wavelength and amplitude but traveling in opposite directions is illustrated in Figure 18-21. The two waves traveling in opposite directions

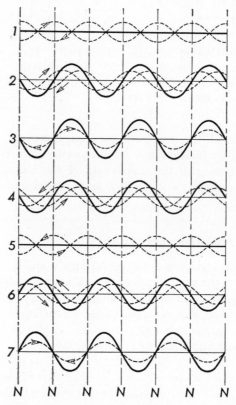

FIG. 18-21   Method of adding two waves of equal lengths and equal amplitudes traveling in opposite directions to produce a stationary wave.

are shown as dotted lines with arrows to indicate their direction of motion. Suppose that these two waves are traveling in a wire; the displacement of each point of the wire will be the sum of the displacements produced by the two waves; the resultant displacement is shown by the heavy line. In the uppermost figure, the two waves produce equal and opposite displacements, so that the resultant displacement of every particle is zero; this is indicated by the heavy horizontal line. In the second line, each wave is shown after it has advanced one eighth of a wavelength, that is, one eighth of a period later. The resultant displacements of the particles form the heavy curve shown. After another eighth of a period, the two traveling waves coincide, producing a resultant wave of twice the amplitude of either one. The other figures are each drawn to show the resultant wave after an additional eighth of a period has elapsed. In each figure, the points marked N remain on the horizontal axis; that is, they suffer no displacement at any time. These points are the *nodes*. The segment of the wire between the two nodes vibrates up and down, the displacements on either side of a node being in opposite directions. The segment between two nodes is called a *loop* and its midpoint is called an *antinode*.

Any one node is formed at a point where the crest of one wave meets a trough of the wave traveling in the opposite direction. The position where the next node is produced is one where the crest of one wave meets the next trough of the wave traveling in the opposite direction. Since they are both traveling with the same speed but in opposite directions, the two will meet halfway between their present positions. Since they were originally one wavelength apart, they will meet half a wavelength farther on. Hence the distance between two successive nodes is half a wavelength.

The vibrations of tuning forks, of strings in musical instruments, and of air columns such as those in organ pipes, trumpets, and other musical instruments, and the vibrations of bars and plates can all be analyzed into sets of stationary waves in the substance. For example, in the case of a vibrating bar, the waves are reflected at the ends. These ends are surfaces of separation between the solid bar and the air, and a portion of the energy is reflected back. Interference between the forward wave and this reflected wave produces the stationary waves. In most cases, the stationary waves are not visible, so that other methods for detecting them have to be used. For example, the stationary waves in a metal plate which is vibrating can be shown by sprinkling fine sand or powder on the plate; this method was

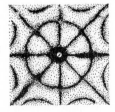

Fig. 18–22   Stationary wave pattern of a vibrating plate.

devised by E. Chladni (1756–1827). The sand or powder will pile up along the nodes. One way of setting a plate vibrating is to clamp it at the center in a horizontal position and to bow it at some point along the edge.

Different stationary wave patterns will be obtained by bowing at different places. One such pattern, or Chladni figure, is shown in Figure 18–22.

18-9 MEASUREMENT OF THE SPEED OF A WAVE

A simple direct method for measuring the speed of a wave in air is to fire a gun at one point A and to have an observer at a distant point B measure the time interval between the sighting of the flash produced when the gun is fired and the hearing of the sound produced when the wave reaches him. This method is not very precise, since the temperature and composition of the air are not always uniform over the whole distance. A better way is to make use of stationary waves produced in a column of dry air at a known temperature. A simple method for doing this is shown in Figure 18–23. A calibrated tuning fork of frequency f has a diaphragm

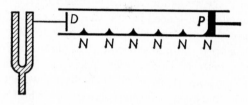

Fig. 18–23   Measurement of the speed of sound by producing a stationary wave in a column of air.

D attached to one prong. This diaphragm fits into one end of a long horizontal tube containing dry air; a movable piston P closes the other end of the tube. A small quantity of fine powder is sprinkled along the bottom of the tube. The tuning fork is set into vibration and the piston P is moved slowly until a steady vibration is produced in the air column; this means that there is a stationary wave in the air. The fine powder will be forced out of the region of the antinodes by the rapid motion of the air and will be piled up at the nodes. The distance between successive nodes can be measured; this distance is half a wavelength, $\lambda/2$, of the sound in air. Since the frequency of the sound is the same as that of the tuning fork, the speed of sound can then be calculated with the aid of the equation

$$V = f\lambda. \tag{3}$$

This method can easily be adapted to measure the speeds of waves in other gases. The tuning fork may be kept vibrating electrically. Or, instead of a tuning fork, a loud-speaker unit with a diaphragm attached to it and operated by an oscillating circuit may be used. This has the advantage that the frequency of oscillations, as well as the amplitude, can be varied over a wide range. The results of such experiments show that the speed of sound in air at 0°C and at a pressure of 1 standard atmosphere is 331.46 m/sec, or about 1,087 ft/sec, and is the same for all frequencies except at very high intensities. The speed of sound increases as the temperature of the air increases; the rate of increase is about 60 cm/sec, or 2 ft/sec, for each degree centigrade rise in temperature.

The speed of sound in a gas can be shown to be given by the following simple equation

$$V = \sqrt{\frac{\gamma P}{d}}, \tag{7}$$

in which P is the pressure of the gas, d its density, and γ a constant which is the ratio of the specific heat at constant pressure to the specific heat at constant volume of the gas. For air, $\gamma = 1.4$. Since the density of a given mass of gas varies inversely as its temperature if the pressure remains constant, the speed of sound increases as the temperature of the gas rises.

Table 18-1   Speed of Sound

(Longitudinal Waves)

Substance	Temperature in °C	Speed in meters per sec
Air	0	331.46
Hydrogen	0	1,262
Carbon dioxide	0	258.0
Water	15	1,447
Sea water	13	1,492
Glass	0	5,500
Steel		4,700–5,200

The speed of a transverse wave in a string or wire can be found by producing stationary waves in the wire with the aid of a tuning fork of known frequency. This experiment has already been described; the distance between nodes is $\lambda/2$, where λ is the length of the wave in the string. The speed of the wave can then be calculated with the aid of Equation (3).

The speed of sound in some typical substances is listed in Table 18–1.

18-10 SOUND RANGING

Some practical applications of a knowledge of the speed of sound in different media are the determination of the depth of water below a ship, the location of guns, and the detection of submarines. In determining the depth of water below a ship, an oscillator near the bottom of the ship sends out waves into the water; some of the energy of these waves is reflected from the bottom surface to a detector in the ship. The time elapsed between the transmission and reception of the signal is determined by the distance between the transmitter and receiver, the speed of the wave in water, and the depth of the water. The detector can be calibrated to yield the depth of the water directly, since all the factors except the time interval between transmission and reception are known.

The determination of the position of a gun G (see Figure 18–24) can be made by using three sound detectors at three separate points A, B, and C which transmit their signals to a single station where the time intervals

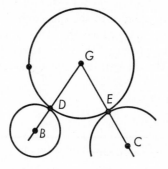

Fig. 18–24   Graphical construction for locating the position of a gun G from the sound waves proceeding from it.

between the reception of the signal at these points are measured. Suppose that B received the signal later than A by a time interval t_1, and that C received it later than A by a time interval t_2. If circles of radii Vt_1 and Vt_2 are drawn about B and C, respectively, the wave front of the sound sent out by the gun will be tangent to these circles and will also pass through A. The center of this wave front or the position of the gun G can then be determined. Since the speed of the sound wave depends upon the temperature of the air, the wind velocity, and the intensity of the sound, the calculations are a little more involved than indicated above. But, with the aid of tables in which the above factors have been properly evaluated, the calculations can be made in a few minutes with good precision.

QUESTIONS

1. What two properties must a body possess in order to be able to vibrate with harmonic motion?

2. What two properties must a medium possess in order that waves may be transmitted through it?

3. What properties determine the speed of a wave in a medium?

4. What is the essential difference between a longitudinal and a transverse wave?

5. What is the relationship between the vibrations of a body, such as a tuning fork or a violin string, and waves in the body?

6. What points are stationary in a stationary wave?

7. When a sound wave is refracted from air into water, does its frequency or its wavelength change and in what manner?

8. A bell is sounded for a short time in a closed room. After a while the sound becomes inaudible. Trace the sound waves and the energy they carry from the time that the waves are emitted by the bell until they become inaudible.

9. What conditions are essential for the production of standing waves in any medium?

10. Using Equation (7), calculate the speed of sound in air at 0°C and 76 cm of mercury pressure. Check the results of your calculations with the known speed of sound in air.

11. The speed of sound in air is being determined by firing a gun at A and noting the time it takes the sound to reach the observer at B. What will be the effect on this measurement if there is a wind blowing (a) from A to B and (b) from B to A?

PROBLEMS

1. What is the wavelength of a sound wave in air at 0°C produced by a tuning fork which vibrates with a frequency of 512 vibrations/sec?

2. A steel wire is stretched between two pegs 80 cm apart under a tension of 1 million dynes. The linear density of this wire is 0.15 gm/cm. When plucked, a wave is set up in this wire. Determine the speed of this wave.

3. A 1,000-cycle oscillator is used in determining the depth of a fresh-water channel. What is the length of the wave traveling through the water?

4. The oscillator and detector used in the determination of the depth of water are placed close together in the bottom of a ship. The time elapsed between the transmission and reception of a signal is 0.028 sec. Determine the depth of the salt-water channel at this point.

5. The depth-determination device used on a ship records a time interval of 0.50 sec between the emission and reception of a sound wave. How deep is the ocean at this point?

6. A long horizontal tube contains air at 20°C and some fine cork dust. One end of the tube contains a movable piston, while a diaphragm attached to a prong of a tuning fork fits into the other end of the tube. The tuning fork vibrates with a frequency of 1,000 cycles/sec. The piston is adjusted until resonance occurs. Determine (a) the distance between nodes and (b) the length of the wave in air.

7. The air in the tube of Problem 6 is replaced by carbon dioxide, and, when resonance is obtained, the distance between the nodes is found to be 13.5 cm. Determine (a) the wavelength of the sound in carbon dioxide and (b) the speed of sound in carbon dioxide.

8. The air in the tube of Problem 6 is replaced by hydrogen, and, when resonance is obtained, the distance between the nodes is found to be 66.0 cm. De-

termine (a) the wavelength of the sound in hydrogen and (b) the speed of sound in hydrogen.

9. One end of a horizontal string is attached to a prong of an electrically driven tuning fork which is vibrating with a frequency of 256 vibrations/sec, while the other end passes over a pulley and has a weight of 4 lb attached to it. The weight of a unit length of the string is 0.02 lb/ft. (a) Determine the speed of the transverse waves in the string. (b) Determine the distance between nodes when stationary waves are set up in the string.

10. A copper wire 2 m long and whose mass is 6 gm has one end attached to a fixed post and the other end attached to a prong of a tuning fork which vibrates with a frequency of 1,000 cycles/sec. A stationary wave is set up in the wire, and the distance between nodes is 8.0 cm. Determine (a) the wavelength of the transverse wave in the wire, (b) the speed of the wave, and (c) the tension in the wire.

11. (a) Determine the index of refraction of hydrogen with respect to air for a sound wave. (b) Determine the index of refraction of glass with respect to air for a sound wave. A glass partition 0.5 cm thick separates a volume of air from a volume of hydrogen, each at atmospheric pressure. A sound wave from the air strikes the glass surface at an angle of 3° with respect to the normal. Determine the angle at which the sound wave is refracted (c) into the glass and (d) into the hydrogen.

12. A vibrator is placed 6 ft below the surface of water in a lake. What is the apparent depth of the vibrator as determined from the sound waves refracted into the air?

13. A stone is dropped into a well, and the sound of the stone's splash in the water is heard 4.0 sec later. How deep is the well?

14. A steel pipe 200 ft long is struck at one end. A person at the other end hears the sound that traveled through the pipe and also the one that traveled through the air. Determine the time interval between the two sounds heard by this person.

15. (a) Beginning with Equation (7), show that the speed of sound in a gas at a temperature t measured in degrees centigrade is given by

$$V = V_0 \sqrt{1 + \beta t},$$

where V_0 is the speed of sound in the same gas at 0°C and β is the coefficient of volume expansion of a gas. (b) Calculate the speed of sound in air at 30°C.

Vibrations
and Sound

19-1 SOUND

There are two aspects of sound: one is the physical aspect which involves the physics of the production, propagation, reception, and detection of sound; the other, which is the sensation of sound as perceived by the individual, depends upon physiological and psychological effects. It is not desirable to separate the two aspects of sound completely, but the main emphasis in this book must necessarily be on the physical aspect. In this chapter we shall consider mostly musical sounds. A vocabulary has been developed to describe the sensation experienced when a musical sound is heard. Such terms as the *pitch* of a sound, its *loudness*, and its *tone quality* or *timbre* are used to describe the musical sound. The physicist, on the other hand, speaks of the *frequency* of the sound wave, its *intensity*, and the *number* and *intensities* of the *overtones* present in a musical sound. Unfortunately there is not a one-to-one correspondence between the terms used by the physicist and the terms used by the musician. A great deal of progress has been made in recent years as a result of tests involving thousands of persons which attempt to correlate the sensation of sound with the physical properties of sound. Some of these results will be mentioned at appropriate places in this chapter.

19-2 FREQUENCY OF A MUSICAL TONE

A musical tone is regarded as a pleasing sound, while a noise is usually thought of as disagreeable; there are some sounds which are difficult to classify. A musical sound, for example, can be produced by a series of regular blasts of air, while a noise results when these blasts occur at irregular intervals. This can be demonstrated by means of a disk containing five concentric rings of circular holes, as shown in Figure 19-1. In the innermost ring, these holes are irregularly spaced; the next four rings have circular holes which are regularly spaced. There are 40, 50, 60, and 80 holes in these rings, respectively. When this disk is rotated at uniform angular speed and a stream of air is directed at the innermost ring of holes, an unpleasant noise will be heard.   But when the stream of air is directed against any of the other rings, a pleasant musical tone will be heard.   When the stream of air is directed against the four outer rings from the second to

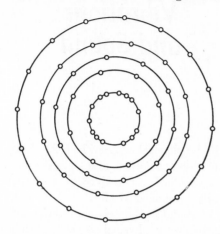

Fig. 19–1   Construction of the wheel for showing the difference between musical tones and a noise.

the fifth in sequence, the *pitch* of the sound coming from the third ring will be higher than that from the second ring of holes; the pitch of the sound from the fifth ring will be heard as an octave higher than that from the second ring.   The physicists' method of describing these tones is in terms of the *frequency* of the sound produced.   For example, if the disk is rotating at the rate of 10 rps, the frequency of the sound produced by the ring with 40 holes in it is 400 vibrations/sec;   the next ring produces 500 vibrations/sec;   the one after that, 600 vibrations/sec;   and the last one, 800 vibrations/sec.   To a first approximation we can say that the pitch of a tone depends upon its frequency, the tone with the higher pitch having the higher frequency.   Two tones an octave apart have a frequency ratio of 2:1, for example.   A musician will recognize the tones which have frequencies in the ratios 4:5:6:8 as the tones comprising a major chord.

19-3   RESONANCE

An interesting phenomenon occurs when a body which is capable of vibrating at a definite frequency receives small impulses of the same frequency.   These impulses set the body into vibration, with each succeeding impulse building up the amplitude of the vibration.   This phenomenon is known as *resonance*.   A simple way of demonstrating resonance is to take two tuning forks having the same natural frequency and place them a short distance apart.   One tuning fork is set vibrating by a hammer blow.   After a short time interval, it will be found that the other tuning fork is vibrating and emits sound. The compressions and rarefactions produced in the air by the first tuning fork set the second tuning fork vibrating. Since the sound wave and the tuning fork have the same frequency, the impulses on the tuning fork are properly timed to build up its amplitude of vibration. A steady state is reached when the energy radiated by the second tuning fork is equal to the energy it receives from the first one. Resonance of sound is sometimes called *sympathetic vibration.*

Resonance can occur between any two bodies which can vibrate with the same natural frequency. An interesting example is shown in Figure 19–2, which illustrates resonance between a tuning fork and an air column.

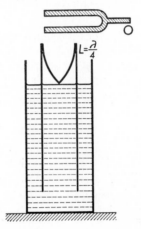

FIG. 19–2   Resonance between an air column and a tuning fork.

A hollow cylindrical glass tube is inserted in a jar of water. The vibrating system is the air in the hollow tube; the length of the air column can be varied by moving the tube up or down in the water. The air column ends at the surface of the water. If a tuning fork vibrating at a known frequency is held over the open end of the hollow tube, there probably will be no appreciable change in the loudness of the sound. But, if the hollow tube is raised, at some position there will be a marked increase in loudness of the sound. At this position, the air column in the tube is set into vibration with the same frequency as the tuning fork; the two are in resonance. We may think of the process of changing the length of the air column as "tuning" it to the frequency of the wave incident upon it. This may be compared to the tuning of a radio circuit to the same frequency as the incident electromagnetic wave.

A tuning fork which vibrates with a frequency f emits a wave of length λ, given by the usual equation

$$V = f\lambda,$$

where V is the speed of sound in air. When an air column which is closed at one end is set into vibration, standing waves are produced in the air with a node at the closed end and an antinode or point of great motion at the other end. Since the distance between two successive nodes is half a wavelength, the distance between a node and the adjacent antinode is a quarter of a wavelength. Thus the shortest length of tube L in which the air can be in resonance with a wavelength λ is

$$L = \frac{\lambda}{4}.$$ (1)

In the above experiment, if the tube is long enough, it will be found that resonance will occur again when the length of the tube is three quarters of a wavelength, for this length of air column will also have a node at the closed end and an antinode at the open end.

Tuning forks are often mounted on boxes whose air columns are in resonance with the sounds emitted by these forks. More energy is radiated per second from this system than from the tuning fork alone.

19-4 BEATS

When two bodies having slightly different natural frequencies are set into vibration, the two waves emitted by them will *interfere* with each other. At some instant the two waves will be in the same phase, and there will be a reinforcement of the waves resulting in a wave of increased ampli-

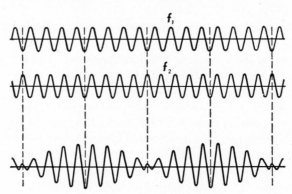

Fig. 19–3   Beats produced by the interference of two waves of slightly different frequencies.

tude. At some other instant the two waves will be completely out of phase; that is, a compression and a rarefaction will meet, resulting in a decreased amplitude producing a sound of very low intensity. At other times they will get in phase again. The addition of two waves of slightly different frequency is illustrated in Figure 19–3. If one wave has a frequency f_1 and the other a frequency f_2, the number of times that these waves will get out of phase in a unit time can be shown to be $f_1 - f_2$; this is called the number of *beats* per unit time. If the two frequencies differ slightly, a series of beats will be heard; that is, the loudness of the sound will decrease noticeably $f_1 - f_2$ times in 1 sec. For example, if one tuning fork is emitting 256 vibrations/sec and another is emitting 260 vibrations/sec, 4 beats will be heard each second.

The phenomenon of beats is frequently used in tuning two sources of sound to the same pitch. This is a very accurate method of tuning, since the ear can perceive beats which occur only once in about 10 sec. When there are only a few beats per second, the sound produces an unpleasant effect. When the difference in frequencies is large, no beats can be distinguished in the sound produced.

19-5 DOPPLER EFFECT

In the previous discussions, it was tacitly assumed that the source of sound and the observer were at rest with respect to each other. But when the source of sound is moving with respect to the observer, the pitch of the sound appears to be different from that when the two are stationary with respect to each other. There are two distinct cases to be considered: one in which the source is moving and the observer is at rest, and the other in which the observer is moving and the source is stationary.

FIG. 19–4   The sound waves which are emitted in unit time by the source as it moves from S to S' with speed v toward the observer at O are contained in the distance $S'O$.

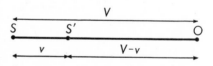

Suppose that an observer is stationary at O, as shown in Figure 19–4, and that the source of sound is stationary at S. If the source emits f vibrations/sec, the length of the wave λ emitted by it will be

$$\lambda = \frac{V}{f},$$

where V is the velocity of the sound. For simplicity, let us choose S to be at a distance from O equal to the distance traveled by sound in 1 sec; that is, $SO = V \times 1$ sec, where V is the speed of sound. Then, when the source and the observer are both stationary, there will be f waves in the distance SO, each of length λ. Let us now suppose that the source is moving with speed v toward O. At the end of 1 sec the source will have moved to S', where $SS' = v \times 1$ sec. During this time, the source has emitted f vibrations; the first one has already reached the observer at O, and the last one has just left the source at S'. These f vibrations are therefore located in the region $S'O$, whose length is

$$S'O = (V - v) \times 1 \text{ sec.}$$

Since f waves have been emitted in this second, the length of these waves is

$$\lambda' = \frac{V - v}{f}. \tag{2}$$

These waves travel with the velocity of sound V, and the frequency f' with which they reach the ear is therefore

$$f'\lambda' = V. \tag{3}$$

Eliminating λ' from Equations (2) and (3) yields

$$f' = f\,\frac{V}{V - v}. \tag{4}$$

In other words, more waves will now reach the ear per second than reach it when the source is stationary. This will be interpreted as a sound of higher pitch. The change in pitch produced by the relative motion of source and observer is known as the *Doppler effect*.

The same reasoning can be applied to show that when the source is moving away from the observer with a velocity v, the frequency f' of the sound reaching the observer is given by

$$f' = \frac{V}{V + v}\,f. \tag{5}$$

The pitch of the sound in this case is lower than the pitch of the sound when the source is stationary.

It is instructive to analyze the Doppler effect in terms of the waves emitted by the moving source. Let us assume that the source emits spherical waves which, in Figure 19–5, are drawn as circles with successive positions of the source as centers. These successive positions are shown at time intervals equal to T, the period of the vibrations emitted by the source. In the figure, S is the present position of the source, S_1 is the position of the source at a time T earlier than S, S_2 the position at a time $2T$ earlier, and S_3 the position at a time $3T$ earlier. The wave emitted when the source was at S_1 has traveled a distance VT, where V is the speed of sound; hence this wave is represented by a circle of radius VT. Similarly the wave emitted when the source was at S_2 is drawn as a circle of radius $2VT$; that emitted from S_3 is drawn as a circle of radius $3VT$. The source of sound is moving toward the right with a speed v less than V.

An observer in front of the moving source will receive more waves per second than if the source had been at rest. Conversely an observer behind the moving object will receive fewer waves per second than if the source

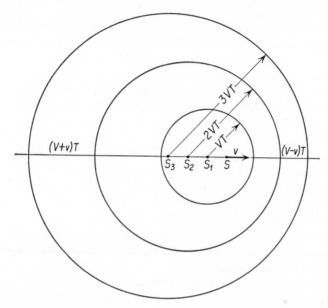

FIG. 19–5   Waves emitted by source moving to the right with speed v.

had been at rest. The observer in front of the moving source will hear a higher pitched sound than the observer behind the source. When the moving source passes the observer, he will always note a drop in the pitch of the sound.

The frequency of the sound f' received by the observer in front of the source is given by Equation (4) and can be derived very simply by referring to Figure 19–5. The distance between successive wave fronts which reach this observer is $(V - v)T$ and is therefore the length of the wave λ' perceived by the observer; that is,

$$\lambda' = (V - v)T,$$

but

$$T = \frac{1}{f};$$

$$\therefore \lambda' = \frac{V - v}{f},$$

and, since these waves travel with speed V in the air, the frequency f' of these waves is given by

$$f'\lambda' = V, \tag{3}$$

so that
$$f' = f\,\frac{V}{V - v} \tag{4}$$

follows immediately.

Equation (5) can be derived in a similar manner.

Figure 19–5 is instructive in that it can be used to determine the frequency of the sound heard by a stationary observer who is not in the line of motion of the source. It will be noted that the distance between wave fronts increases from the smallest value $(V - v)T$ for an observer in front of the source to its largest value $(V + v)T$ for an observer behind the source. To an observer at right angles to the line of motion, the distance between wave fronts is simply VT or λ; that is, it is exactly the same as if the source were stationary.

When the source is stationary and the *observer* is *moving* toward the source with a velocity v, the pitch is higher than that heard when the observer is stationary, but the actual value of the new frequency is slightly different from that given by Equation (4). The wavelength of the sound in air remains unchanged, but as the observer moves toward the source, he receives more waves per second than he receives when standing still. If he moves toward the source with a velocity v, he will receive v/λ additional waves per second or a total of

$$f' = \frac{V}{\lambda} + \frac{v}{\lambda}$$

or
$$f' = \frac{V + v}{\lambda},$$

Now, since
$$f\lambda = V,$$

we get
$$\boxed{f' = \frac{V + v}{V}\,f,} \tag{6}$$

which gives the new frequency of the sound heard by the observer.

In a similar manner, if the observer is moving away from the source of sound, it can be shown that the frequency f' of the sound heard by the observer is given by

$$\boxed{f' = \frac{V - v}{V}\,f,} \tag{7}$$

which is a sound of lower pitch than that heard by the observer when stationary.

It must be emphasized that in any one of these cases, the observer hears only one tone; he does not hear a change in pitch. Only when the motion is changed can he hear a change in pitch. Such a change in pitch can be noted when a train which is sounding its whistle passes an observer; the observer will hear a drop in pitch as the train passes him.

An interesting combination of the Doppler effect and the phenomenon of beats can be produced by moving a tuning fork rapidly toward a wall. The observer will receive two sounds: one directly from the tuning fork, and one reflected from the wall. The apparent source of sound of the reflected wave is the image of the tuning fork formed by the wall acting as a plane mirror. While the tuning fork is moving away from the observer, its image is moving toward him. The direct wave from the tuning fork will have a lower pitch than the wave coming from its image, and the observer will hear beats.

Illustrative Example. The siren of a fire truck is emitting a tone whose frequency is 1,200 vibrations/sec. The fire truck is traveling with a speed of 60 mi/hr. A man in the street notices a drop in pitch as the truck passes him. Determine the change in frequency of the tone heard by this observer.

While the fire truck was moving toward the observer at a speed of 88 ft/sec, he heard a tone whose frequency was higher than 1,200 vibrations/sec. This frequency f_1' can be determined from Equation (4)

$$f_1' = f \frac{V}{V - v},$$

yielding
$$f_1' = 1{,}200 \times \frac{1{,}100}{1{,}100 - 88} \frac{\text{vib}}{\text{sec}}$$

$$= 1{,}304 \frac{\text{vib}}{\text{sec}}.$$

As the fire truck passed the observer, it moved away from him with a speed of 88 ft/sec, and the tone he heard had a frequency lower than 1,200 vibrations/sec. This frequency can be determined from Equation (5)

$$f_2' = f \frac{V}{V + v},$$

yielding
$$f_2' = 1{,}200 \frac{1{,}100}{1{,}100 + 88} \frac{\text{vib}}{\text{sec}}$$

$$= 1{,}111 \frac{\text{vib}}{\text{sec}}.$$

Hence the drop in pitch of the tone heard by the observer was due to a change in frequency of

$$f_1' - f_2' = 193 \frac{\text{vib}}{\text{sec}}.$$

19-6 VELOCITY OF SOURCE GREATER THAN VELOCITY OF SOUND

When a body such as a projectile, a jet plane, or a rocket moves with a velocity v greater than the velocity of sound V in the medium, it sets up a compressional wave, as shown in Figure 19–6. The wave front, sometimes called a *shock wave*, is a cone, with the moving body at its apex S. The

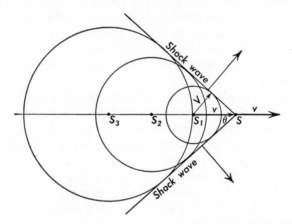

Fig. 19–6   Waves emitted by source moving with speed $v = 1.5\ V$.

cone inside which the sound waves travel can be constructed by drawing spherical waves which originated at various positions of the source during its motion. In Figure 19–6, S is the present position of the source, S_1 its position at a time t earlier, S_2 its position at a time $2t$ earlier, and S_3 its position at a time $3t$ earlier, where t is an arbitrary time interval. With S_1 as a center, we draw a circle of radius Vt; with S_2 as a center, we draw a circle of radius $2Vt$; and so forth. These circles represent the present positions of the compressions which started from S_1, S_2, and S_3. The wave front is the tangent to these circles. In a three-dimensional diagram, this wave front would be a cone whose elements are tangent to spheres of radii Vt, $2Vt$, and $3Vt$, respectively. In the unit of time that the wave progresses a distance V, the source moves a distance v, as shown in the figure. The angle θ that an element of the cone makes with the direction of motion of the source is

$$\sin \theta = \frac{V}{v},\qquad (8)$$

since V is at right angles to the element of the cone and v is the hypotenuse of the right triangle.

The cone of sound moves through the medium with the speed v of the source.   Outside the cone, no sound can be heard.

When an airplane wing moves through the air, it produces a change in the pressure, or a pressure pulse, which travels through the air with the speed of sound.   If the speed of the airplane is less than the speed of sound, the pressure pulse travels ahead of the wing and, in effect, sets up the flow pattern of the air ahead of it (see Figure 9–8).   When the speed of the airplane is greater than the speed of sound through the air, the wing meets the air head on, producing a shock wave which travels across the wing. This shock wave increases the drag on the wing and also sets up great stresses in it.   Because of these great stresses and our limited knowledge of the behavior of different materials under such stresses, very few piloted planes have been flown at supersonic speeds, that is, speeds above the speed of sound.   Pilotless planes and missiles have been flown at speeds almost twice the speed of sound.   In airplane engineering, the ratio of the speed v of a plane to the speed V of sound in air through which it is traveling is called the *Mach number*.   Thus the Mach number chosen for Figure 19–6 is 1.5.

19-7   INTENSITY AND LOUDNESS

The *intensity* of a wave at any point in space is defined as *the amount of energy passing perpendicularly through a unit area at this point in unit time.* The intensity can be expressed in ergs per cm^2 per sec, in watts/cm^2, or in any other appropriate units.   The intensity of the sound received from any source depends upon the rate at which the source emits energy, upon the distance of the observer from the source, and upon the reflections which the waves undergo from the walls, ceiling, floor, and objects in the room. If the size of the source is small in comparison with its distance from the observer and if no reflection or absorption takes place, the intensity of the sound at any place will vary inversely as the square of its distance from the source, but this is rarely the case with sound waves.   In terms of the sound wave which reaches the observer, it can be shown that *the intensity depends upon the square of the amplitude of vibration of the particles in the wave and upon the square of its frequency.*

The *loudness* of a sound is a sensation experienced by the observer, and, although loudness is related to the intensity of the sound, the relationship between the two is not a simple one.   Waves in air may be detected by the normal human ear if their frequencies lie between about 20 cycles/sec and 20,000 cycles/sec and if their intensities are within a certain range; the range of intensities audible to the ear also depends on the frequency of the wave.   Figure 19–7 shows the range of frequencies and their intensities which are perceived as sound by the normal human ear;   the intensity of the wave is plotted along the *y*-axis, while the frequency of the wave is plotted along the *x*-axis. Because of the wide range of intensities, these are plotted not on a uniform scale but on a logarithmic scale. One scale

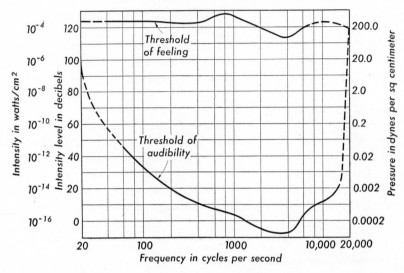

FIG. 19–7   Range of frequencies and their intensities which are perceived by the human ear. (After H. Fletcher, *Reviews of Modern Physics*, January, 1940.)

shows the intensities in watts/cm². Another scale shows the intensities in terms of the pressure changes in the wave which strikes the eardrum; since the pressure in a wave varies sinusoidally, the *effective* or *root mean square* values of the pressure changes are used. (Compare this with the effective value of an alternating current, Chapter 28). The lower curve represents the *threshold* of *audibility*. A point on this curve represents the smallest intensity of a sound of given frequency which is just audible to the average ear. The ear is most sensitive to sounds of about 3,000 cycles/sec. Points on the upper curve represent intensities which are so great as to be painful. The region between the two curves represents the range of hearing. Above a certain intensity, known as the *threshold of feeling*, the sound is not heard but is felt by the ear as a tickling or as a painful sensation. The range of intensities to which the ear is sensitive is about a millionfold. Because of this large range of intensities, a *logarithmic scale* has been adopted for expressing the *level of intensities of sound*, taking the zero level at about the limit of audibility of sound. The intensity level *B* of a sound is defined as

$$B = 10 \log \frac{I}{I_0},$$ (9)

where I is the intensity of the sound and I_0 is the zero level of intensity which is taken arbitrarily to be equal to 10^{-16} watt/cm^2 or 10^{-12} watt/m^2. The intensity level B is expressed in *decibels* (db). Thus, if a sound has an intensity $I = 10^{-14}$ watt/cm^2, its intensity level is

$$B = 10 \log \frac{10^{-14}}{10^{-16}} \text{ db}$$

or
$$B = 10 \log 100 \text{ db},$$

from which
$$B = 20 \text{ db}.$$

Sound levels have been measured at various places under a variety of conditions. For example, inside some noisy subway cars the sound level is about 100 db, while the threshold of feeling (or pain) is about 120 db; the sound level of a whisper in a quiet room is about 15 db

19-8 THE EAR

Figure 19–8 is a diagram showing the essentials of the structure of the human ear. Sound waves enter the ear through the auditory canal and

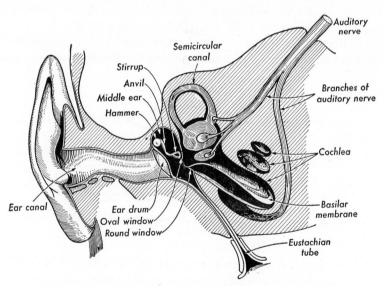

Fig. 19–8   Semidiagrammatic section of the right ear.

strike the eardrum. The pressure variations of the sound wave are transmitted from the eardrum by a system of three small bones, the hammer, anvil, and stirrup, to the oval window of the inner ear. The latter is filled with a liquid. The cochlea, a spiral-shaped part of the inner ear, contains the *basilar membrane* which runs along its entire length and divides it into two sections. The nerve endings of the auditory nerve are attached to one edge of the membrane. The entire length of the basilar membrane is about 30 mm (about 1.2 in.), and there are about 30,000 nerve endings attached to it. The vibrations which are transmitted to the liquid of the inner ear set the basilar membrane into vibrations, different tones affecting different sections of the membrane. These vibrations stimulate the nerve endings attached to it, and these transmit the signal along the auditory nerve to the brain.

19-9 QUALITY OF A MUSICAL SOUND

When two tones of the same pitch and same loudness are produced by two different musical instruments, such as a violin and a clarinet, the sensations produced by them are decidedly different. We recognize this difference because of the difference in *quality* or *timbre* between these two musical sounds. One of the main reasons for this difference in quality is that each sound produced by an instrument is not a tone of a single frequency but is a complex sound consisting of several different frequencies. Another reason for the difference in quality is the manner in which the human ear responds to tones of different frequency and different loudness. In this section we shall consider only the effect produced by the complexity of the sound on the quality of a tone emitted by vibrating bodies.

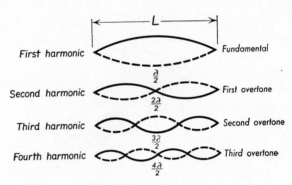

FIG. 19–9   Modes of vibration of a string which is fastened at both ends.

As shown previously, the vibrations in a body can be analyzed in terms of stationary waves which are set up in it by the interference of two waves traveling in opposite directions. The *fundamental* mode of vibration of a body corresponds to the longest wave, or wave of lowest frequency, which can be set up in the body. For example, in the case of a string which is fastened at both ends, the fundamental mode of vibration is one in which the string vibrates as a whole, as shown in Figure 19–9. Since the two ends are fastened, the standing wave must have nodes at these points, while the antinode is midway between them. The length L of the string is thus half the wavelength $\lambda/2$ of the transverse wave traveling in the string. The pitch of the sound emitted by the string when vibrating as a whole is called the *fundamental tone* of the string. The string can also vibrate in two parts, with a node in the center; the frequency of this sound is twice that of the fundamental tone. When vibrating in this manner, the pitch of the tone will be an octave higher than the fundamental. Other modes of vibration of the string are shown in the figure. When a string is set into vibration by plucking it or bowing it, several of these modes of vibration will be set up simultaneously; in addition to the fundamental tone, some of the higher-pitched tones or *overtones* will be emitted by the string. *The quality of the tone will depend upon the number of overtones produced and their relative intensities.*

The same thing is true of other vibrating bodies: the quality of the sound depends upon the number and relative intensities of the overtones produced. Although in the case of string instruments and wind instruments the frequencies of the overtones are whole multiples of the frequency of the fundamental tone, this is not generally true of other musical instruments such as bells, chimes, and drums.

19-10 VIBRATIONS OF STRINGS

The frequencies of the various modes of vibration of a string are in the ratios of whole numbers; such vibrations form a *harmonic series* with the fundamental vibration as the first harmonic, the overtone of twice this frequency as the second harmonic, and so forth. Any wavelength λ and its associated frequency f of a wave in a vibrating string are related] by the equation

$$V = f\lambda, \qquad \text{[Equation (3) in Chapter 18}$$

where V is the speed of the transverse wave in the string. This speed is given by

$$V = \sqrt{\frac{S}{m}}, \qquad \text{[Equation (4) in Chapter 18]}$$

where m is the linear density of the string, that is, its mass per unit length, and S is the tension in the string. Now the length of the wave in the fundamental mode of vibration is twice the length L of the string; that is,

$$\lambda = 2L; \qquad \qquad \text{(10)}$$

therefore the frequency f_1 of the fundamental or first harmonic is

$$f_1 = \frac{V}{2L},$$ (11)

from which

$$f_1 = \frac{1}{2L}\sqrt{\frac{S}{m}}.$$ (12)

The frequency of vibration and hence the pitch of a string can be varied by changing its length or by changing its tension.   Increasing the tension four times will double the frequency of vibration or produce a tone an octave higher.   Decreasing the length of the string—for example, by pressing the string against a board with the finger—will increase the frequency or pitch of the tone emitted.   Two strings of the same length and under the same tension, but of different linear densities, will have different frequencies for their fundamental tones.

The number of overtones set up in a string can be controlled to some extent by the method of bowing or plucking the string.   For example, if the string is plucked in the center, those modes of vibration will be most intense which have antinodes at this point; the overtones will consist of the odd harmonics.   If the string is plucked at a distance of about one seventh of its length from one end, the seventh harmonic will be absent, but most of the even harmonics will be present; the quality of this tone will be noticeably different from that heard when the string is plucked at the center, even though in each case the pitch heard is that of the fundamental tone.

The presence of overtones in a vibrating string can be shown very easily by plucking the string at one quarter of its length from one end and then placing a finger lightly on the center of the string; this will stop the fundamental mode of vibration, but the second harmonic can continue to vibrate since it has a node at the center.   When the finger is placed at the center, the fundamental tone will no longer be heard, but its octave will be heard, showing that the second harmonic is present.

Another method for demonstrating the presence of overtones in a vibrating string is illustrated in Figure 19–10.   A steel wire is stretched between two posts A and B on a board, and these two points are connected to the primary coil of a step-up transformer (see Chapter 28).   The secondary coil of this transformer is connected to an amplifier and a loud-speaker. Several U-shaped magnets are placed on the board so that the wire can vibrate freely between the poles of these magnets.   Suppose that these magnets are so placed that their north poles are all on one side of the wire and their south poles are on the opposite side, as shown in Figure 19–10(a). When the string is plucked near the center, an induced electromotive force will be set up in the wire. This will be amplified, and the fundamental tone will be heard coming from the speaker.

To show the presence of the second harmonic, we use only two magnets, each placed at a distance of about one quarter of the length of the string from the ends A and B, but with opposite poles on the same side, as

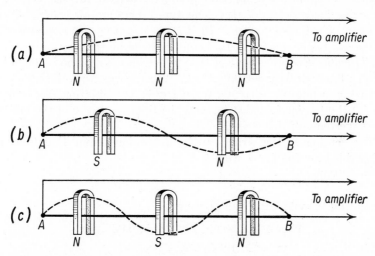

Fig. 19-10   Method for demonstrating the presence of overtones in a vibrating wire. The ends of the string AB are connected to the primary of a transformer whose secondary coil is connected to an amplifier and loud-speaker. N and S represent those poles of the magnets which are in front of the wire.

shown in Figure 19–10(b). The magnets are placed in this position because the string vibrates in two parts, with the portions of the string on either side of the central node moving in opposite directions. If the string is now plucked at a point near one of the magnets, a tone twice the frequency of the fundamental will be heard. If, while the string is still vibrating, one of the magnets is reversed so that like poles are on the same side, the fundamental tone will be heard. If the magnet is again reversed, the octave will be heard. This clearly demonstrates that both the fundamental tone and the first overtone are present at the same time.

To show the presence of the second overtone, or third harmonic, three magnets are used, as shown in Figure 19–10(c). If the string is plucked at a point near one of the end magnets, the third harmonic will be heard clearly. If, while the string is still vibrating, the center magnet is reversed, the fundamental tone will be heard, thus showing that the first and third harmonics are both present. This method can be extended to show the presence of several of the other harmonics.

The amount of energy transferred directly from the vibrating string to the air is very small. To permit a greater transfer of energy, the strings are mounted on various types of solid boards, called *sounding boards*, usually made of metal or wood. These sounding boards are set into *forced* vibration by the vibrating string; the vibrations of these boards set larger quantities of air into motion, thus producing a more intense sound. In some string instruments of the violin type, there are air columns in the instrument which also vibrate. All of these vibrating systems make their contribution to the quality of the sound emitted by the instrument.

Illustrative Example. One of the steel strings of a piano is 50 cm long and has a linear density of 0.02 gm/cm. When struck with the hammer, it emits a tone whose fundamental frequency is 520 vibrations/sec. Determine (a) the tension in the string and (b) the frequencies of the first and second overtones of this string.

The tension in the string can be determined from Equation (12). Solving this equation for S, we get

$$S = 4L^2f^2m.$$

Substituting the numerical values, we get

$$S = 4 \times 2{,}500 \times 270{,}000 \times 0.02 \text{ dyne}$$
$$= 5.4 \times 10^7 \text{ dynes.}$$

The first overtone of a string is its second harmonic, and the second overtone is its third harmonic; therefore their frequencies are

$$f_2 = 1{,}040 \text{ vibrations/sec}$$

and $$f_3 = 1{,}560 \text{ vibrations/sec.}$$

19-11 VIBRATING AIR COLUMNS

Wind instruments such as the clarinet, the trumpet, and the pipe organ all have vibrating air columns to reinforce some of the sounds produced by the source of sound. In this discussion we shall consider only cylindrical pipes such as those commonly used in pipe organs. There are two general classes of such pipes: the *open* pipe, that is, a pipe open at both ends, and a *closed* pipe, that is, a pipe closed at one end; the end containing the source of vibrations is always considered an open end. The vibrations can be produced in one of several ways, such as blowing air against a reed and setting it vibrating, or blowing a thin sheet of air against a thin lip at one end and setting the air into vibration. Whatever the method of setting up the vibrations, the column of air in the pipe will reinforce those modes of vibration corresponding to the standing waves which can be set up in this column.

Figure 19–11 (a) shows several modes of vibration which can be set up in a closed organ pipe. The method for determining these modes of vibration depends upon the fact that only those vibrations can exist in the air column which have a node at the closed end and an antinode at the open end. It can be seen that the fundamental mode of vibration corresponds

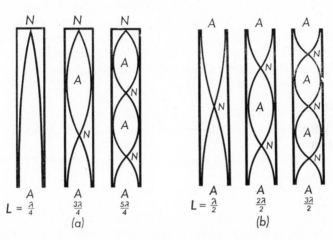

Fig. 19-11   (a) Modes of vibration of an air column closed at one end.   (b) Modes of vibration of an air column open at both ends.   The nodes are at the positions marked N, and the antinodes are at the positions marked A.

to a wavelength λ which is four times the length L of the air column. The first overtone possible in this case is one whose wavelength λ is four thirds of the length L of the air column. The frequency of the first overtone is therefore three times the frequency of the fundamental tone. The frequency and the wavelength are related by the usual equation

$$V = f\lambda,$$

where V is the speed of sound in air.

An examination of all other possible modes of vibration of an air column in a closed pipe shows that all the overtones are odd harmonics; their frequencies are in the ratios of $1:3:5:7: \ldots$ and so on.

A pipe open at both ends must have antinodes at these ends. The fundamental mode of vibration of the air in an open pipe is shown in Figure 19-11(b); its wavelength λ is twice the length of the pipe. The first overtone has a wavelength λ which is equal to the length L of the pipe; its frequency is therefore twice that of the fundamental. An examination of the other possible modes of vibration shows that all the harmonics may be set up in this air column.

A simple comparison of the open and closed pipes will show that if two such pipes of the same length are emitting their fundamental tones, the open pipe will emit a tone an octave higher than the closed pipe.

The pitch of a sound produced by an air column can be varied without varying the length of the air column. For example, when the air is blown harder against the reed, one of the overtones produced in the air column may have a greater intensity than the fundamental, and the pitch of the sound will correspond to this overtone. A bugle, for example, has a fixed length, but different tones can be obtained from it by changing the tension of the lips and the manner of blowing the air through them.

QUESTIONS

1. What is the ratio of the frequencies of two musical tones which are an octave apart?

2. State the condition necessary for resonance between two mechanical systems.

3. Devise an experiment for producing resonance between two pendulums. Describe how the energy is transferred from one pendulum to the other.

4. An air column open at both ends is in resonance with the sound from a tuning fork. What is the relationship between the length of the air column and the wavelength of the sound emitted by the tuning fork?

5. State the conditions necessary for the production of beats.

6. What are the three characteristics of a musical tone?

7. Explain what is meant by the statement, "The sound level in the room is 25 db."

8. What is the relationship between the higher overtones of a vibrating string and its harmonics?

9. In Figure 19-10(b), why is the second harmonic heard when the two magnets are aligned in opposite directions? Would the second harmonic have been heard if the string were plucked in the center instead of one quarter of the way from one end?

10. In Figure 19-10, how should the magnets be arranged and where should the string be plucked to show the presence of the fourth harmonic?

11. How can you account for the fact that two wires made of the same substance can have different linear densities?

12. How is a violin string tuned?

13. An open organ pipe and a closed organ pipe are tuned to the same pitch. What is the relationship between the lengths of these air columns?

14. How do the overtones of an open organ pipe differ from those of a closed organ pipe having the same fundamental frequency?

15. A bugle consists of an open air column of fixed length. How are the different tones produced? What is the relationship between the frequency of any tone and that of its fundamental?

16. Explain why there is always a drop in the pitch of the sound from an automobile horn when it passes you.

17. An airplane is to be designed to fly at supersonic speeds. Can it be

driven (a) by a propeller operated by a gasoline engine; (b) by a jet engine? Explain your answers.

PROBLEMS

(Note: The speed of sound in air at room temperature may be taken as 1,100 ft/sec.)

1. A siren wheel has 20 uniformly spaced holes near its rim and is rotated by means of a stream of air. (a) What is the frequency of the sound emitted when its speed is 44 rps? (b) What is the wavelength of the sound wave in air?

2. An air column closed at one end is in resonance with a sound wave whose frequency is 128 vibrations/sec. Determine the length of this air column.

3. What is the lowest frequency note that can be produced by an organ pipe 8 ft long which is closed at one end?

4. A metal tube 4 ft long has a piston placed in it near one end; the position of this piston is adjustable. A vibrating tuning fork whose frequency of vibration is 440 vibrations/sec is held near the open end of the tube. At what distances from the open end must the piston be placed to produce resonance?

5. A siren on a fire-engine truck emits a sound whose frequency is 1,000 vibrations/sec. What will be the frequency of the tone heard by a spectator (a) when the truck is moving toward him with a speed of 45 mi/hr and (b) when it is moving away from him with a speed of 45 mi/hr?

6. A fire siren in a village is emitting a sound whose frequency is 880 vibrations/sec. What is the frequency of the tone heard by the firemen approaching this source at a speed of 60 mi/hr?

7. A loud-speaker is hung from a cord attached to the ceiling of a lecture room and is connected by flexible wire to a 1,000-cycle oscillator. While emitting this note, the loud-speaker is swung toward the front wall with a speed of 4 ft/sec. (a) What is the frequency of the tone coming from the loud-speaker as heard by a student sitting in the rear of the room? (b) What is the frequency of the tone coming from the image of this loud-speaker as heard by this student? (c) How many beats per second will this student hear?

8. A string 100 cm long has a linear density of 0.04 gm/cm. When vibrating transversely with a node at each end, it has a frequency of 180 vibrations/sec. Determine (a) the speed of the wave in the string and (b) the tension in the string.

9. Two tuning forks are vibrating simultaneously: one with a frequency of 512 vibrations/sec, and the other with a frequency of 516 vibrations/sec. How many beats are produced?

10. Two tuning forks A and B are observed to produce beats at the rate of 5 per second. Fork A has a frequency of 440 vibrations/sec. If fork B is loaded with a bit of putty, the number of beats increases to 8 per second. What is the frequency of vibration of fork B when it is not loaded?

11. An open organ pipe sounds the note A whose frequency is 440 vibrations/sec. (a) What is the length of the air column? (b) What are the frequencies of the first and second overtones produced by this air column?

12. A closed organ pipe sounds the note A whose frequency is 440 vibra-

tions/sec.   (a) What is the length of the air column?   (b) What are the frequencies of the first and second overtones produced by this air column?

13. A steel wire 80 cm long is fastened at the ends.   The mass of the wire is 1.2 gm.   When plucked, it emits a tone whose fundamental frequency is 520 vibrations/sec.   (a) Determine the tension in the wire.   (b) What are the frequencies of the first and second overtones of this string?

14. A steel wire 3 ft long is rigidly fastened to two posts.   The wire weighs 0.02 lb.   When bowed, it emits a tone whose fundamental frequency is 110 vibrations/sec.   (a) Determine the tension in the wire.   (b) What are the frequencies of the first and second overtones produced by this string?

15. A bullet is fired with a velocity of 2,700 ft/sec.   Determine (a) its Mach number and (b) the angle that the shock wave makes with the line of motion of the bullet.

16. A siren mounted on a car emits a note whose frequency is 500 vibrations/sec.   (a) Determine the frequency of the sound heard by a stationary observer when the car approaches him with a speed of 80 ft/sec.   (b) Determine the frequency heard by an observer moving toward the car with a speed of 80 ft/sec while the car remains stationary.

17. Assuming that the ear can detect sounds whose frequencies range from 20 vibrations/sec to 20,000 vibrations/sec, determine the range of wavelengths that the ear can detect.

Part Four

ELECTRICITY AND MAGNETISM

20

Magnetism

Natural magnets, called lodestones, have been known since ancient times. Lodestone is an iron ore which has the property of attracting pieces of iron and steel and, to a lesser extent, nickel and cobalt. A *permanent magnet* can be made by putting a piece of steel close to a lodestone; when removed from it, the piece of steel will be found to be *magnetized;* that is, it will now be able to attract other pieces of iron, steel, nickel, and so on. If a magnetized bar is dipped into iron filings and then removed, iron filings will be found to cling mostly to the ends of the bar, as shown in Figure 20–1. These ends are called the *poles* of the magnet.

FIG. 20–1   Iron filings cling to the poles of a bar magnet.

The earliest practical use of permanent magnets, dating back to the twelfth century, was for compasses. This use depends upon the fact that if a permanent magnet in the form of a needle or a bar is suspended so that it can swing freely in a horizontal plane, the magnet will set itself in an approximately north-south direction. The end which points approximately north is called the north-seeking pole or, more simply, the *north pole* of the magnet, while the other end is called the *south pole*. A line joining the south to the north pole is called the *axis* of the magnet.

FIG. 20–2   A simple magnetic compass needle.

A simple magnetic compass is shown in Figure 20–2. A ship's compass is a somewhat more elaborate instrument (see Figure 20–3). It consists of a compass card fastened to a set of parallel magnets with their north poles facing in the same direction and mounted so that the whole assembly rotates freely in a horizontal plane. The case housing the compass is mounted in a set of bearings so that it can remain horizontal even though the ship rolls or pitches. A marker on the case housing the compass shows the direction in which the ship is headed. The angle between this direction and that of the magnetic north pole can then be read directly from the compass card.

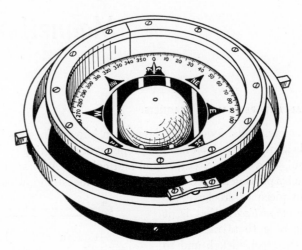

Fig. 20–3 A ship's compass. The compass card is mounted on four parallel magnets.

20-2 COULOMB'S LAW OF FORCE

Suppose that a bar magnet is suspended from a string so that it can swing freely in a horizontal plane. If the north pole of a second bar magnet is brought near the north pole of the first one, there will be a force of repulsion between these poles. This will be shown by the fact that the suspended magnet will move so that its north pole goes away from the north pole of the approaching magnet. On the other hand, there will be a force of attraction when the north pole of one magnet approaches the south pole of the other one.

An early attempt to account for the properties of magnets is ascribed to the philosopher and scientist Thales of Miletus (c. 580 B.C.). But it was not until William Gilbert's (1540–1603) work in the sixteenth century that the first scientific study of magnets was made. In his book, *De Magnete,* Gilbert showed that the earth could be considered as a huge spherical magnet with two poles and that the compass needle was oriented by the forces exerted by the earth's magnetism. About two centuries later the French scientist Charles Augustin de Coulomb (1736–1806) determined the law of force between magnetic poles. The next important development was the discovery by Hans Christian Oersted, in 1820, of the magnetic effect of an electric current. After that, the two subjects of magnetism and electricity developed together to their present state.

Coulomb, in 1785, made the first careful measurements on the law of force between magnetic poles. A long thin magnet was suspended from a fine wire, and the pole of another thin magnet was brought near a like pole of the suspended magnet (see Figure 20–4). Because of the force

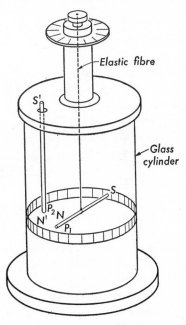

Fig. 20–4   Coulomb type torsion balance. NS, magnet of pole strength p_1, is suspended from elastic fiber. $N'S'$ is another magnet of pole strength p_2.

between these two poles, the suspended magnet experienced a torque which caused it to rotate about the wire as an axis, at the same time twisting the wire. The amount of twist of the wire was measured when the magnet came to rest. From the amount of this twist, the force exerted on the pole of the magnet could be measured. By using one magnet as a standard and bringing to it different magnets, keeping all other things constant, it was observed that different forces acted on the standard magnet. This showed that the test magnets had different pole strengths; the relative pole strengths of the magnets were defined to be proportional to the forces that they exerted on the standard magnet. By varying the distance between the pole of the standard magnet and any one of the test magnets, it was found that the force between them varied inversely as the square of the distance between the poles. The results of Coulomb's experiments could be summed up by stating that *the force between two magnetic poles is proportional to the product of the strengths of the poles and inversely proportional to the square of the distance between them,* or

$$F \propto \frac{p_1 p_2}{r^2},$$

in which p_1 is the strength of the pole of one magnet, p_2 is the strength of the pole of the second magnet, r is the distance between the poles, and F is the force between them.

The proportionality can be changed into an equation by introducing a factor of proportionality μ (Greek letter mu), so that *Coulomb's law* becomes

$$F = \frac{p_1 p_2}{\mu r^2}. \qquad (1)$$

The constant μ depends upon the units used for the various quantities in Equation (1) and upon the nature of the medium between the poles. μ is called the *permeability* of the medium.

If the cgs mechanical system of units is used, F is measured in dynes and r in centimeters. The permeability μ will be arbitrarily set equal to 1 when the space between the two magnets is a vacuum, or as experiment shows, without serious error, if there is air between them. Since the units of F and r are already decided, Equation (1) defines the unit of pole strength. *A unit pole is one which, when placed in a vacuum one centimeter from a like equal pole, will repel it with a force of one dyne.* The pole strengths p_1 and p_2 of any other magnets are expressed in terms of this unit of pole strength.

The unit pole, as defined above, forms the basis of the electromagnetic system of units, usually abbreviated as emu. For the sake of simplicity, this will be the only system of units used in this chapter.

Each bar magnet has at least two poles, so that, in most actual experiments, it is necessary to take into consideration the force exerted by each of these poles on the poles of the other magnet. In a Coulomb type of experiment, however, it is possible to use magnets long enough so that when two poles are placed near each other, the other poles are far enough removed so that they do not affect the result appreciably.

In the above discussion it was assumed that the poles of a bar magnet are situated at its ends. This is not generally true. When a permanent magnet is dipped into iron filings, it will be found that these filings cling not only to the ends but to large regions around the ends. We can, however, imagine an ideal type of magnet in the shape of a thin rod, or a needle, magnetized so that the poles are at its extreme ends. This ideal magnet will be used in the mathematical treatment. We shall show later how to treat real magnets in which the poles are distributed over large areas (see Section 20–6).

20-3   MAGNETIZING BY INDUCTION

When a piece of soft iron is brought near a permanent magnet, the iron becomes a magnet temporarily; that is, it will attract other magnetic materials and will possess poles. If the piece of iron is brought near the north pole of a permanent magnet, the face nearest the north pole will become a south pole and the opposite face will become a north pole (see Figure 20–5). This polarity can easily be verified by bringing a compass

Fig. 20–5   Magnetizing a piece of soft iron by induction.

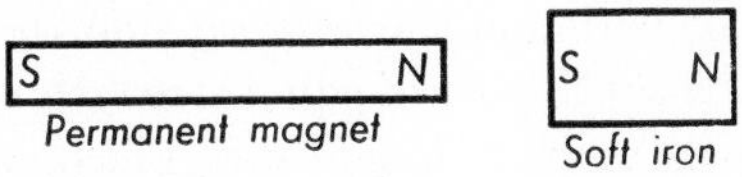

needle near one of these faces. When the permanent magnet is removed, it will be found that the soft iron has lost most of its magnetism. When any magnetic material is brought near a permanent magnet, it becomes a magnet temporarily; we say that it is *magnetized by induction.*

It is now easier to understand why magnetic substances are attracted to magnets. When such substances are brought near permanent magnets, these substances are magnetized by induction in such a way that opposite poles face each other, and the bodies attract each other in accordance with Coulomb's law.

Some magnetic materials, particularly various types of steel, when magnetized by being brought close to a permanent magnet, will retain a large part of the magnetic properties after the original magnet has been removed; that is, they are permanently magnetized. These are the materials which are used in making permanent magnets.

20-4   INTENSITY OF MAGNETIC FIELD

Because of the effect that a magnet produces on magnetic materials placed anywhere in its neighborhood, we say that a *magnetic field* exists in the neighborhood of a magnet. We can give a quantitative statement of the intensity of the magnetic field at any point in the neighborhood of this magnet by placing the north pole of a long thin magnet at this point. If the pole strength of this long thin magnet is p, its north pole will experience a force F. Assuming that the presence of this magnetic pole has not disturbed the original source of the magnetic field in which it was placed, we can use the ratio of F to p to define the *intensity of the magnetic field at a point;* we shall denote it by the letter H; thus

$$H = \frac{F}{p}.$$

(2)

H at any point remains constant for different values of p. If F is measured in dynes and p in unit poles, H is expressed in *oersteds*. If the intensity of the magnetic field H is known for every point in the space around a magnet, the force that would be experienced by each pole of a magnet placed in this field can be calculated from Equation (2). For example, if the north pole of a long thin magnet having a pole strength of two unit poles is placed

at a point in a magnetic field where the intensity is 45 oersteds, the force
on it is
$$F = 2 \times 45 = 90 \text{ dynes.}$$

The intensity of the magnetic field is a vector quantity, and its direction is that of the force on a north pole placed at the point under discussion.
If a south pole of equal strength is placed at this point, it will experience a
force equal in magnitude, but opposite in direction, to that experienced by
the north pole.

20-5 MAPPING THE MAGNETIC FIELD

The fact that magnetic materials become magnetized when brought
near a magnet is the basis for one simple method for exploring the magnetic
field around a magnet. In this method, the magnet is placed under a
board or a piece of glass, and small iron filings are sprinkled on the board
or glass plate. Each little iron filing becomes a small bar magnet by induction, and each pole of this magnet experiences a force which is the resultant

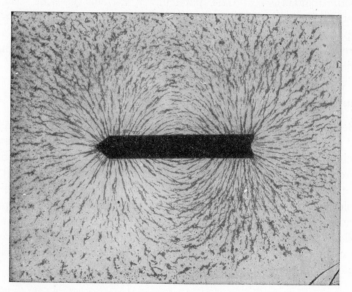

FIG. 20–6 Pattern formed by iron filings in the neighborhood of a bar magnet.

of the forces due to the poles of the permanent magnet. If the iron filing
is small enough, the force on its north pole will be equal in magnitude to
that on its south pole but opposite in direction. The torque produced by
these two forces will rotate the iron filing until the lines of action of the two
forces coincide and act along the length of the iron filing. There usually
is some friction between the iron filings and the board which may prevent
the filings from rotating. If the board is tapped gently, the iron filings will

orient themselves under the action of the forces due to the poles of the bar magnet.   Figure 20–6 shows a typical arrangement of iron filings in the neighborhood of a bar magnet as seen in one plane.   It will be the same in all planes which contain the axis of the bar magnet.   This figure also shows that the poles are distributed over large areas near the ends of the magnet.

These iron filings are not simply oriented in the magnetic field but appear to lie along definite lines which extend from one end of the magnet to the other.   This alignment of the iron filings can be explained by the fact that they behave as small magnets which, after they have been oriented in the magnetic field, are arranged so that the north pole of one small magnet is adjacent to the south pole of another small magnet.   The forces of attraction between these opposite poles pull these small magnets into line, and they line up just as though they were small links in a chain.

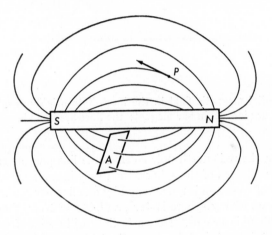

FIG. 20–7   Lines of force drawn to represent the intensity of the magnetic field
in the neighborhood of a bar magnet.

The pattern formed by these oriented iron filings suggests the possibility of *mapping* the magnetic field of a magnet by means of lines going from the north pole, say, to the south pole of the permanent magnet. These lines generally are curved.   We may draw these lines in such a manner that they would tell us at a glance how a very small magnet would behave when placed at any point in the neighborhood of the bar magnet. Lines so drawn are termed *magnetic lines of force*.   The shape of each line is such that a line drawn tangent to any point on it would show the direction a small magnet would take if placed there;   an arrowhead can be placed on this tangent line to indicate the direction in which the north pole of this little magnet would point, as illustrated in Figure 20–7.

To complete this mapping, we must establish some kind of scale which will tell us at a glance the intensity of the magnetic field at all points in the

neighborhood of a magnet.   To do this, we must be able to draw a definite
number of lines of force extending from one pole of the magnet to the other.
Just how many lines are to be assigned to a particular magnet can be determined from a consideration of the intensity of the magnetic field around the
north pole of a long thin magnet of unit pole strength.   The force that it will
exert on the north pole of another magnet of unit pole strength placed 1 cm
away will be 1 dyne.   Hence the intensity of the magnetic field at a distance
of 1 cm from a unit north pole is 1 oersted and is directed away from the
north pole.   If we imagine a sphere of 1 cm radius drawn around this unit
north pole, the magnetic intensity everywhere on the surface of this sphere
will be 1 oersted and will be directed radially, that is, perpendicular to the
surface of the sphere, as shown in Figure 20–8.   Now if we imagine lines

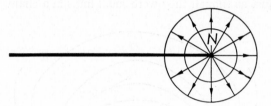

Fig. 20–8   Radial magnetic field in the immediate neighborhood of the north
    pole of a very long, thin bar magnet; the lines are in a plane containing the
    magnet.

radiating from the unit north pole so that one line passes perpendicularly
through each unit area of the sphere, then we will have a scale in which a
field intensity of 1 oersted is represented by one line per square centimeter.
The surface area of any sphere is $4\pi r^2$, and, if $r = 1$ cm, then the surface
area of this sphere is 4π cm^2.   Hence 4π lines will radiate from a unit pole
to represent the intensity of the magnetic field around it.   If the long thin
magnet has a pole strength p instead of 1, there will be $4\pi p$ lines radiating
from this magnetic pole.   The intensity of the magnetic field at any one
point in the neighborhood of this magnet will then be represented by the
number of lines of force passing through a unit area perpendicular to the
direction of the field at this point.

  If, instead of a long thin magnet, we have any other type of magnet,
such as that shown in Figure 20–7, the same method of representing the
magnetic field intensity can be used.   If p is the pole strength of the magnet,
we draw $4\pi p$ lines coming from its north pole and going to its south pole.
With the aid of iron filings or a small compass needle, we can determine the
direction of the magnetic field at any point in space.   The magnetic field
intensity at any point can be determined either by calculation or by experiment.   For example, if, at some point such as A in the figure, the intensity
has been found to be 3 oersteds, we draw a unit area at A perpendicular to
the direction of the magnetic field and then draw three lines passing

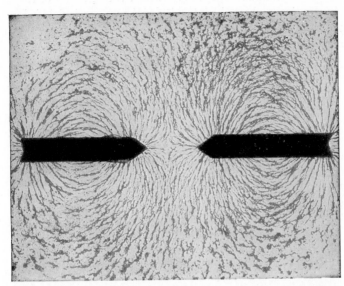

FIG. 20–9   Pattern formed by iron filings in the neighborhood of two bar magnets with their north poles facing each other and with their axes in the same straight line.

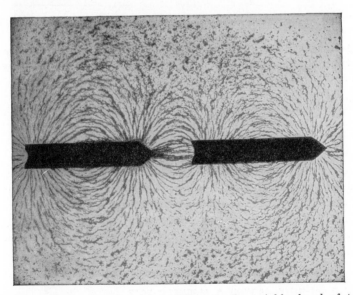

FIG. 20–10   Pattern formed by iron filings in the neighborhood of two bar magnets with opposite poles facing each other and with their axes in the same straight line.

perpendicularly through this area to represent the intensity of the magnetic field at A.   In places where the intensity of the magnetic field is large, there will be a large number of lines of force per unit area, and, where the intensity of the magnetic field is small, there will be few lines per unit area.   In this way we can map the magnetic field around a magnet of any shape or around any combination of magnets.

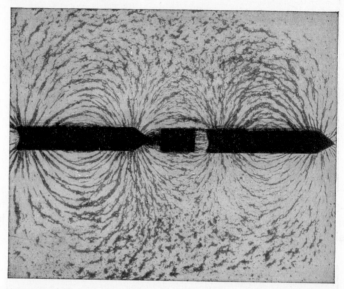

Fig. 20–11   Pattern formed by iron filings when a piece of soft iron is placed between the opposite poles of two bar magnets which have their axes in the same straight line.

Figure 20–9 shows the magnetic fields in the neighborhood of two bar magnets in line, with their north poles facing each other, while Figure 20–10 shows the magnetic fields of two bar magnets in line with opposite poles facing each other.   In the latter case, it will be noticed that some of the lines from the north pole of one magnet go to the south pole of the other magnet.   Figure 20–11 shows the effect of placing a piece of soft iron between the opposite poles of two magnets, thereby changing the nature of the medium between them.   It will be observed that the iron filings tend to crowd into the soft iron, thus showing that the intensity of the magnetic field has been increased in this region.

20-6 FIELD INTENSITY AROUND A MAGNETIC POLE

We have shown in a qualitative and pictorial manner several types of magnetic fields produced by magnets.   To determine the field intensity quantitatively is a rather complicated matter. In general, it is necessary to determine the intensity of the magnetic field at a given point in space produced by each of the magnetic poles of the magnet or magnets and then to add these contributions vectorially. We have already shown that there is a radial magnetic field around a single pole, that is, a magnetic pole far removed from other poles. In general, if such a pole has a strength p, then the force F it will exert on another pole of strength p' at a distance r from it is, from Equation (1),

$$F = \frac{pp'}{\mu r^2}.$$

The intensity of the magnetic field H at a distance r from p is, from Equation (2),

$$H = \frac{F}{p'};$$

hence

$$H = \frac{p}{\mu r^2}. \tag{3}$$

Equation (3) gives the intensity of the magnetic field at a distance r from a pole of strength p. In air, or a vacuum where $\mu = 1$, this equation becomes

$$H = \frac{p}{r^2}. \tag{4}$$

Illustrative Example. A bar magnet 24 cm long has a pole strength of 800 unit poles. Calculate the intensity of the magnetic field at point A 16 cm from the magnet measured along the line which is the perpendicular bisector of the bar.

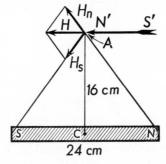

Fig. 20–12

Referring to Figure 20–12, we note that the point A is 16 cm from the center C of the bar and 20 cm from each end, N and S. Using Equation (4), we find that the intensity of the magnetic field at A produced by the north pole is

$$H_N = \frac{800}{400} \text{ oersteds} = 2 \text{ oersteds}$$

directed away from N along NA. Similarly the magnetic field intensity at A produced by the south pole is

$$H_S = 2 \text{ oersteds}$$

directed toward S along AS. Since the angle between H_N and H_S is equal to the angle SAN, it is simple to add these two vectors by the parallelogram method. The resultant magnetic field intensity is

$$H = 2.4 \text{ oersteds}$$

and is parallel to the axis of the magnet NS. If a small magnet of pole strength p' is placed at A, the force on its north pole will be Hp' in the direction of H, and the force on its south pole will be equal to Hp', but in the opposite direction. These two forces will act to rotate the small magnet at A so that it will line up parallel to the magnet SN.

20-7   MAGNETIC MOMENT OF A MAGNET

If a bar magnet of length L and pole strength p is placed in any magnetic field, its north pole will experience a force H_1p, while its south pole will experience a different force H_2p, owing to the fact that the intensity of a magnetic field generally varies from point to point throughout space. But, if it is placed in a region of the field which is uniform, that is, in which the intensity H has the same value throughout this region, then each pole of the

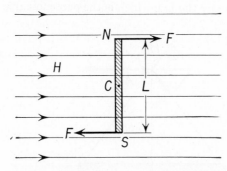

Fig. 20–13   Torque on a bar magnet placed in a uniform magnetic field.

magnet will experience a force equal to Hp in magnitude. The force on the north pole will be in the direction of the field, while that on the south pole will be in the opposite direction, as shown in Figure 20–13. The resultant force on the magnet will therefore be zero. But, if the magnet is not parallel to the lines of force, the forces on the poles will not have the same line of action, and they will therefore produce a torque which will rotate the magnet so that it lines up with the field. Let us calculate the magnitude of this torque for the special case in which the magnet is perpendicular to the lines of force. Taking moments about an axis through the center C perpendicular to the axis of the magnet and to the lines of force, we get for the moment of the force on the north pole

$$Hp\,\frac{L}{2}$$

in a clockwise direction, and for the moment of the force on the south pole also

$$Hp\,\frac{L}{2}$$

in a clockwise direction, so that the total moment or torque is

$$G = HpL. \tag{5}$$

Now the product pL is seen to be a property of the magnet only and is called its *magnetic moment* and denoted by the letter M, so that

$$\boxed{M = pL.} \tag{6}$$

The torque G on the magnet, when placed perpendicular to the magnetic field, can therefore be written as

$$\boxed{G = HM.} \tag{7}$$

Different magnets may have different values for p and L, but, if their product is the same, then the magnets all have the *same magnetic moment* and will experience the same torque when similarly placed in a magnetic field. However, since the poles of a magnet are usually distributed over a large area, it is not generally possible to evaluate p and L. For most purposes it is sufficient to know the magnetic moment M of a magnet; this quantity can be determined experimentally with the aid of Equation (7).

One method of determining the magnetic moment of a bar magnet is to suspend it so that it can rotate freely about an axis through C perpendicular to the length of the magnet. When it is placed in a uniform magnetic field of intensity H, at some angle θ with the field, as shown in Figure 20–14, it will experience a torque given by

$$G = MH \sin \theta$$

tending to line it up parallel to the field. The effect of this torque will be to cause the magnet to oscillate like a pendulum. If the angle θ is not too great, the period T of this oscillation will be given by

$$T = 2\pi \sqrt{\frac{I}{MH}},$$

(8)

in which I is the moment of inertia of the magnet about its axis through C, M is its magnetic moment, and H is the strength of the magnetic field.

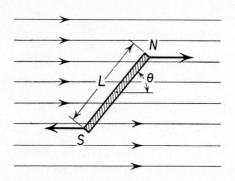

Fig. 20–14

Illustrative Example. A thin bar magnet 8 cm long has a mass of 20 gm. It is mounted so that it can oscillate about its center and placed in a uniform magnetic field of 100 oersteds. Its period of oscillation in this field is found to be 0.30 sec. (a) Determine the magnetic moment of the magnet. (b) Assuming the poles to be at the ends of the thin bar, determine its pole strength.

(a) The magnetic moment M is, from Equation (8),

$$M = 4\pi^2 \frac{I}{T^2 H}.$$

(8a)

Now the moment of inertia of a thin bar of length L and mass m about an axis through C is given by

$$I = \frac{1}{12} mL^2;$$

therefore $I = \dfrac{1}{12} \times 20 \text{ gm} \times 64 \text{ cm}^2 = 106.7 \text{ gm cm}^2.$

Substituting numerical values for I, T, and H in Equation (8a) yields

$$M = \frac{4\pi^2}{0.09} \cdot \frac{106.7}{100} \text{ pole cm} = 475 \text{ pole cm.}$$

(b) The pole strength p of this magnet can be found with the aid of

Equation (6)

$$p = \frac{M}{L} = \frac{475}{8} \text{ poles} = 59.4 \text{ poles.}$$

20-8 A THEORY OF MAGNETISM

An insight into the origin of the magnetic properties of magnetic substances can be obtained from the following simple experiment.   First magnetize a long steel needle or steel strip; then break the magnet in half. By dipping these parts in iron filings, it will be found, as sketched in Figure 20–15, that each half is itself a magnet.   By testing the polarity of each

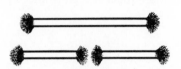

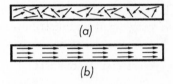

(a)

(b)

FIG. 20–15 A bar magnet broken in half forms two bar magnets.

FIG. 20–16   (a) Molecular magnets in an unmagnetized steel bar have random orientations.   (b) When the steel bar is magnetized, the molecular magnets line up parallel to the external field, producing poles at the ends of the bar.

part, it will be found that opposite poles appear on the faces where the break was made.   If one of these parts is again broken in half, we will again have two magnets.   This process can be repeated until the magnets become too small to handle.   Each part broken from the original magnet will always be found to be magnetized.   This suggests that a magnet is made up of very tiny magnets, perhaps of molecular size.

On this theory of magnetism, magnetic substances are assumed to contain little magnets of approximately molecular size.   When the bar of steel is unmagnetized, these molecular magnets are oriented at random, as sketched in Figure 20–16(a), so that the bar shows no polarity and has no magnetic moment.   But, when the bar of steel is brought into a magnetic field, its molecular magnets rotate until they line up with the field, as shown in Figure 20–16(b);   the bar thus acquires magnetic poles and a magnetic moment.   When the steel bar is removed from the magnetic field, most of these little magnets retain their orientation so that the steel bar remains permanently magnetized, although its magnetic moment may not be as big as it was when in the magnetic field.   Other substances, such as soft iron, lose most of their magnetism when taken out of the magnetic field.

Other evidence in support of this molecular theory of magnetism may be cited. If a magnetized steel bar is dropped, hammered, or otherwise jarred, it loses some of its magnetism. If it is heated to a temperature beyond about 800°C, it loses its magnetic properties, probably because of the fact that the increased vibratory motion of the molecules destroys the orientation of the molecular magnets. This molecular theory is not, of course, the complete explanation. One would like to know the origin of these elementary magnets, why some substances are magnetic while others apparently are not magnetic. We shall consider this topic again after we have shown some of the relationships between electricity and magnetism and the structure of the atom. We shall show that the magnetic properties of matter are determined by the arrangement and distribution of electrons in the atoms and by the effects of neighboring atoms of a substance upon this arrangement and distribution.

20-9 TERRESTRIAL MAGNETISM

We have already shown that a bar magnet, when suspended so that it can swing freely about a vertical axis, will ultimately come to rest in an approximately north-south position. The use of a compass is based upon this observation. It is important, however, to know how much the magnetic north-south direction differs from the geographic or true north-south direction. Various surveys have been made to determine this difference for various points of the earth's surface. This difference is termed the *declination* of the magnetic from the geographic north-south direction. It differs from point to point on the earth's surface and also is found to vary in a complex manner with time. Charts are plotted for any region of the earth's surface with lines showing equal declinations, or *isogonic* lines, marked on them. One such chart is shown in Figure 20–17. In New York, the declination is about 11° W; in Detroit, it is 3° W; while in San Francisco, it is about 18° E.

The declination gives the direction of the horizontal component only of the earth's magnetic field at any one point. The fact that there is a vertical component to the earth's magnetic field can be shown by the following simple experiment. A long unmagnetized steel needle is mounted so that it can pivot about a horizontal axis through its center of gravity. It is balanced in the horizontal position and pointed in the direction in which a compass needle would point. The needle is now magnetized by means of a strong magnet and then allowed to swing freely. It will be found that the magnetized needle no longer balances in the horizontal position but dips with its north pole downward. The angle of dip varies from place to place over the earth. At New York, the angle of dip is 72° with the horizontal; near the equator, it is almost 0° ; and at the magnetic pole in the Northern

Hemisphere, it is 90°. In this manner, the earth's magnetic poles are located.

When the dip needle is properly used, as described above, its direction is that of the earth's magnetic field at the given place. The horizontal com-

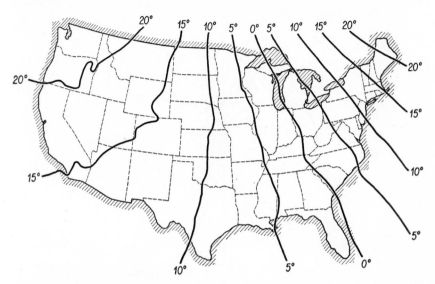

FIG. 20–17 Chart showing isogonic lines for the United States, 1955. From the 1955 edition of chart 3077, of the U.S. Coast and Geodetic Survey, showing distribution of magnetic declination throughout the United States. (Courtesy of Coast and Geodetic Survey.)

ponent H_H of the intensity of the earth's magnetic field can easily be determined by means of an oscillating horizontal magnet, as described above. By means of a simple vector diagram, illustrated in Figure 20–18, the total magnetic field intensity H and its vertical component H_V can be computed.

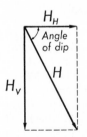

FIG. 20–18 Angle of dip.

The earth behaves, as far as the magnetic field is concerned, as though it contained a large magnet passing through the center, with its axis inclined to the axis of the earth (see Figure 20–19). Although this magnet is large, it is small in comparison with the diameter of the earth. The south pole of this magnet gives rise to what we call the north magnetic pole in the Northern Hemisphere located at and below Boothia Peninsula in northern Canada, and the other pole in the Southern Hemisphere near Ross Sea in Antarctica. The origin of the earth's magnetic field is at present unknown. The hypothesis that seems most reasonable is that the earth's magnetic field is produced by electric currents within the earth, probably

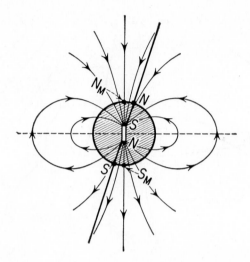

Fig. 20–19   The earth as a magnet.

within its core; the core is assumed to be composed of molten iron. If the above hypothesis is accepted, one must explain the source of these electric currents. One possible explanation is that' the earth acts as a dynamo (see Chapter 26) and generates these currents. The details of this theory are still to be worked out.

QUESTIONS

1. Does a piece of steel which is magnetized have more energy than it had before it was magnetized? If so, explain the source of this energy.

2. Account for the fact that if one end of a long iron rod is hammered while it is held parallel to the earth's magnetic field, it becomes magnetized. Which end becomes the north pole?

3. What type of magnetic pole exists in northern Canada? in Antarctica?

4. Two identical steel rods are found to attract each other no matter which ends face each other. Can you tell which one is the magnet?

5. The positions of the earth's magnetic poles change with time. Describe an experiment for locating the new positions of the earth's magnetic poles.

6. Nickel is a magnetic substance. Explain what will happen when a nickel rod is brought near the north pole of a strong magnet.

7. A small compass needle is suspended by means of a string. What will be

the difference in behavior of this needle when it is placed (a) in a nonuniform magnetic field and then (b) in a uniform magnetic field?

8. Why is it better to describe a magnet in terms of its magnetic moment instead of its length and the strength of its poles?

9. Suppose you were given two cylindrical rods, one of soft iron and one of hard steel. What magnetic experiment would tell you which was soft iron and which was hard steel?

PROBLEMS

1. The north pole of a bar magnet having a pole strength of 400 unit poles is placed 12 cm from the north pole of another bar magnet whose pole strength is 600 unit poles. Determine the force of repulsion between them.

2. The north pole of one magnet with a pole strength of 48 unit poles is placed 6 cm from the south pole of another magnet with a pole strength of 72 unit poles. Determine the force of attraction between them.

3. What is the intensity of the magnetic field at a point 20 cm from the north pole of a bar magnet, measured along the axis of the magnet, if the magnet is 30 cm long and has a pole strength of 1,600 unit poles for each pole?

4. Determine the intensity of the magnetic field at a point 20 cm from each of the poles of a bar magnet 20 cm long with poles of strength 2,400 unit poles.

5. Determine the intensity of the magnetic field at a point 30 cm from the north pole and 50 cm from the south pole of a bar magnet 40 cm long with poles of strength 1,500 units.

6. What is the magnetic moment of a bar magnet 25 cm long having a pole strength of 80 unit poles?

7. A bar magnet 4 cm long, having a pole strength of 12 unit poles, is placed in a uniform magnetic field with the axis of the magnet perpendicular to the direction of the magnetic field. The intensity of the magnetic field is 60 oersteds. Determine the torque acting on this magnet.

8. A bar magnet 6 cm long is suspended, by means of a wire passing through its center, in a uniform magnetic field with the axis of the magnet perpendicular to the direction of the magnetic field. The torque, as measured by the twist in the wire, is 1,500 dynes cm. Determine (a) the magnetic moment of the magnet and (b) its pole strength, if the intensity of the field is 50 oersteds.

9. A small compass needle, when placed at a point where the horizontal component of the intensity of the earth's magnetic field is 0.2 oersted, oscillates with a period of 2.5 sec. Determine the magnetic moment of the compass needle if its moment of inertia about its vertical axis is 24 gm cm^2.

10. A small compass needle vibrates with a frequency of 4 vibrations/sec when placed in a uniform horizontal magnetic field of 25 oersteds. What will be its frequency of vibration when placed in the earth's magnetic field where the horizontal component of its intensity is 0.25 oersted?

11. A small bar magnet has a period of oscillation of 2 sec when pivoted in a uniform magnetic field of 36 oersteds. When it is used to measure the intensity of a second magnetic field, its period is found to be 0.40 sec. Determine the intensity of this second magnetic field.

12. Determine the intensity of the earth's magnetic field at a point where its horizontal component is 0.20 oersted and its vertical component is 0.70 oersted downward.

13. A bar magnet 12 cm long and with pole strength of 80 unit poles is placed in a uniform magnetic field of 120 oersteds, with the axis of the magnet at an angle of 30° to the lines of force of the field. Determine the torque acting on this magnet.

14. A bar magnet has a magnetic moment of 600 pole cm. Find the torque necessary to keep it perpendicular to the direction of the lines of force of a uniform magnetic field of 75 oersteds.

Electrostatics

21-1 INTRODUCTION

One simple phenomenon of electricity was known to the ancients: that when a piece of amber was rubbed, it acquired the property of attracting small pieces of paper and other light particles. Records show that Thales of Miletus knew of this property of amber; the Greek word for amber is *elektron*, hence the name *electricity* for this subject. There was practically no further development of this subject until about the seventeenth century. Otto von Guericke (1602–1686) of Madgeburg built a large sulphur sphere, which, when rotated about an axis and rubbed with his hand, gave off electric sparks. It was not until the eighteenth century that real progress was made in this subject. It was then found that there were two kinds of electricity: one similar to the kind acquired by amber when rubbed with wool, and the other similar to that acquired by glass when rubbed with silk. They were called *resinous* and *vitreous* electricity, respectively. They are now known as *negative* and *positive* electricity, names first introduced by Benjamin Franklin (1706–1790). Franklin made many important contributions to the subject, experimentally and philosophically. He showed the electrical character of lightning and designed lightning rods for the protection of buildings. The subject of electricity was put on a firm mathematical foundation as a result of the experiments of Coulomb, in 1785, on the law of force between electrically charged bodies. After that, progress was very rapid.

21-2 ELECTRIFIED OR CHARGED BODIES

Any substance, when rubbed with another one, becomes *electrified* or *charged electrically*. If a glass rod is rubbed with a piece of silk, both the rod and the silk become electrified or charged. It is now known that the purpose of rubbing two substances together is to bring parts of their surfaces into sufficiently close contact so that electrically charged particles, called *electrons*, can be transferred from one body to the other. The process of charging bodies by rubbing them together used to be called frictional electrification; it is now more properly called *electrification by contact* or *charging by contact*.

445

In order to study the behavior of electrically charged bodies, let us suspend a glass rod *A* by means of a string and then charge the rod electrically by rubbing it with a piece of silk. Suppose we take another glass rod *B*, which has been rubbed with a piece of silk, and bring it near the first rod *A*, as shown in Figure 21–1. We shall find that there is a force of

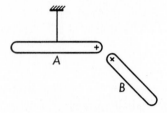

Fig. 21–1   Two glass rods, charged in the same manner, repel each other.

repulsion between them. If we perform a similar experiment with two rubber rods, each of which has been rubbed with a piece of fur or wool, we shall find that there is a force of repulsion between the two charged rubber rods. If we now take one of the charged rubber rods and bring it near the charged glass rod *A*, we shall find that there is a force of *attraction* between them. From this set of simple experiments we can conclude, first, that *there are two kinds of electric charges;* and, second, that *like charges repel each other and unlike charges attract each other.*

We can use the charged glass rod and the charged rubber rod as our standards and compare all other charged bodies with them. We shall find that there are only two kinds of charges: those which are similar to the charge on the glass rod and are repelled by it, and those which are similar to the charge on the rubber rod and are repelled by it. To distinguish between these two kinds of charges, the charge carried by the glass rod which has been rubbed with silk is arbitrarily called a *positive charge*, and the charge on the rubber rod which has been rubbed with wool or fur, a *negative charge*. The ultimate test of the nature of the charge on any body is to bring this charge near a properly charged glass rod or rubber rod. If the charged body is repelled by the positively charged glass rod, its charge is positive. If it is not repelled by the charged glass rod, bring it near the negatively charged rubber rod; if it is repelled by the charged rubber rod, the body carries a negative charge.

21-3   COULOMB'S LAW OF FORCE BETWEEN CHARGES

With the same type of torsion balance which he used for determining the law of force between magnetic poles, Coulomb determined the law of force between electrically charged bodies. A rod with a small charged sphere at one end was suspended in a horizontal position from an elastic fiber, and another small charged sphere was brought near it. The force between the two charged bodies was measured by noting the amount of twist in the fiber supporting the rod. Coulomb found that the force F between two small charges q_1 and q_2 was proportional to the product of the charges and inversely proportional to the square of the distance r between them. This result can be put in the form of an equation.

$$F = \frac{q_1 q_2}{kr^2},$$

(1)

in which k is a constant which depends upon the units used in expressing the charges and the force and also upon the nature of the medium between the charges. In Equation (1), the distance r is assumed to be large in comparison with the sizes of the bodies which carry the charges q_1 and q_2.

In the cgs system of units, F is measured in dynes and r in centimeters. The constant k is set equal to 1 when the two charges are in a vacuum; experiment shows that, without appreciable error, k may also be set equal to 1 when the two charges are in air. k is now called the *dielectric coefficient* of the medium. (It was previously called the dielectric constant of the medium.) By experiment, it is possible to find two bodies which have equal charges; for example, two charged bodies have equal charges if they exert equal forces on a third charged body which is equidistant from them. We can use an appropriate pair of such equally charged bodies for defining a unit charge. *A unit charge is one which, when placed in a vacuum one centimeter from an equal charge of the same kind, will repel it with a force of one dyne.* This charge is sometimes referred to as the *electrostatic unit of charge,* abbreviated as the *esu of charge;* it is also called the *statcoulomb,* abbreviated as *stcoul.* The statcoulomb is a very small unit of charge for most practical purposes; a much larger unit of charge called the *coulomb,* abbreviated as *coul,* is used in practical work. The relationship between these units is

$$1 \text{ coul} = 3 \times 10^9 \text{ stcoul.}$$

In using Coulomb's law, the constant k has the value 1 for a vacuum only when the charges are expressed in statcoulombs, the distance in centimeters, and the force in dynes. If other units are used for any of these quantities, one has the choice of determining the value of k appropriate to these units or of converting all quantities to the cgs system and letting $k = 1$. The latter method will be found less confusing.

Illustrative Example. A small body carrying a charge of $+20$ stcoul is placed 6 cm from another small body carrying a charge of $+30$ stcoul, both of them in air. Determine the force between them.

Since the charges are given in stcoul, the value of k for air is 1, and Equation (1) yields

$$F = \frac{20 \times 30}{36} \text{ dynes} = 16.7 \text{ dynes}$$

for the force of repulsion.

Illustrative Example. A small sphere carries a charge of $+4.5$ micro-coulombs (abbreviated μcoul). Determine the force on it produced by a charge of -8.0 μcoul at a distance of 0.75 m from it, both charges being in air.

(Note: A μcoul $= 10^{-6}$ coul.)

Let us first convert all quantities to cgs units. Thus

$$4.5 \ \mu\text{coul} = 4.5 \times 10^{-6} \times 3 \times 10^9 \text{ stcoul}$$
$$= 13.5 \times 10^3 \text{ stcoul};$$
$$-8.0 \ \mu\text{coul} = -24 \times 10^3 \text{ stcoul};$$
$$0.75 \text{ m} = 75 \text{ cm}.$$

Using Equation (1), we obtain

$$F = -\frac{13.5 \times 10^3 \times 24 \times 10^3}{(75)^2} \text{ dynes},$$

from which $\qquad F = -58 \times 10^3$ dynes.

The minus sign indicates that the force is one of attraction.

21-4 INSULATORS AND CONDUCTORS

It was previously stated that all bodies can be charged electrically by being rubbed. But if a metal sphere is held in the hand and rubbed with a piece of fur and then tested, it will be found not to be charged. However, if the metal sphere is mounted on a hard-rubber stand or a glass stand and then rubbed with a piece of fur, it will be found to be charged. The reason for this behavior is that metals are *good conductors* of electricity, while rubber and glass are *nonconductors* or *insulators*. The human body is also a conductor of electricity, and so is the ground. When the metal sphere was held in the hand, the charge produced on it by rubbing was conducted away by the hand through the body to the ground. But when the sphere was placed on an insulator, the charge produced by rubbing remained on the sphere.

Materials can generally be classified as either conductors or insulators with some degree of accuracy, although there are borderline cases. The quantitative measurement of the conductivity of substances will be considered in Chapter 23. For the present, it will be sufficient to give a qualitative discussion of conductivity. All metals in the solid state have been found to be good conductors of electricity and are also fairly good conductors in the liquid state. Some nonmetals, such as carbon and selenium, are also good conductors. Solids such as glass, rubber, amber, and most plastic materials are very good insulators. All gases are poor conductors of electricity. Certain liquid solutions of materials, which in chemistry are known as acids, bases, and salts, are conductors of electricity; while oils, liquid solutions of organic substances such as sugar, and pure water are nonconductors.

21-5 THE ELECTRICAL THEORY OF MATTER

During the past half century, a great deal of information has been obtained concerning the structure of matter and its behavior under the action of various external forces. Some of the important ideas have already been discussed, and others will be developed as we progress. It will be worth while at this point to outline briefly the electrical theory of matter to aid us in understanding the phenomena to be discussed later. The fact that all bodies can be charged electrically suggests that electric charges are common to all matter. Since, under normal conditions, a body is electrically neutral, such a body must contain equal amounts of positive and negative electricity so arranged that no electrical effects can be observed outside the body. From investigations of the structure of the atom, it is now known that each atom consists of a *small positively charged massive nucleus* surrounded by groups of small negatively charged particles called *electrons*. The mass of an electron is very small in comparison with that of the nucleus, but its charge is not very small in comparison to the charge of the nucleus. The force of attraction between the nucleus and any electron in the atom depends upon the position of the electron with respect to the nucleus; the force on an electron in an outer group is much smaller than that on an electron in an inner group. The charges which can be removed from the atom most readily are the negative electrons. We may think of the process of rubbing two bodies together as bringing electrical forces into play during the time of contact between the two surfaces. These forces produce a displacement of the negative electrons from one body to the other. The body from which electrons have been removed becomes positively charged, while the one to which electrons have been added becomes negatively charged.

When atoms are brought close together, as they are in liquids and solids, the electric charges exert forces on each other, causing some rearrangement among the charges, particularly among the outermost electrons. In the case of metals, this rearrangement is such that some of the outermost electrons in each atom can move freely from atom to atom. These are sometimes referred to as the *free electrons* of the metal. In the case of insulators, the electrons are tightly bound to the atoms and can be moved from atom to atom only by the application of a comparatively large force.

21-6 CHARGING BY INDUCTION

If a negatively charged rubber rod is brought near an insulated metal sphere *A*, as shown in Figure 21–2, the electrons in the metal will be repelled; the farther side of the sphere will become negatively charged,

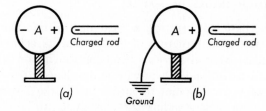

Fig. 21–2   Method of charging a metal sphere by induction.

and the side near the rubber rod will become positively charged. If the experimenter touches the sphere with his hand for a short time, while the charged rubber rod is still near the sphere, some electrons will be repelled through him into the ground, thus leaving the sphere positively charged. This method of charging a body by bringing it close to a charged body is called *charging by induction*. The fact that the sphere is positively charged can be verified by bringing it near a positively charged glass rod and noting the force of repulsion between them. The sphere can also be grounded by connecting a wire directly from the ground to the sphere. If the insulated positively charged sphere is removed from the neighborhood of other charged bodies and then again connected to ground, electrons will be attracted up from the ground until the sphere is neutral.

To charge a metal sphere negatively by induction, we can bring a positively charged body near the sphere. Some of the electrons will be attracted toward the positively charged body and will go to the surface nearest it, leaving the rest of the surface positively charged. If the sphere is momentarily connected to ground, electrons will be attracted up from the ground during the time of contact; the sphere is now negatively charged. If the original positively charged body is now removed, the excess electrons will redistribute themselves uniformly over the surface of the sphere because of the forces of repulsion between them.

An interesting variation of this experiment which does not involve the use of a ground connection is illustrated in Figure 21–3. Two metal spheres A and B, each on an insulated stand, are brought together so that their surfaces touch each other. If a negatively charged body is now

Fig. 21–3   Charging two metal spheres by induction.

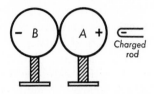

brought near A, electrons will be repelled from it to B. If the spheres are now separated, A will be positively charged and B will be negatively charged.

21-7   THE ELECTROSCOPE

The electroscope is a simple and sensitive electrical instrument which can be put to a variety of uses. It consists essentially of a metal rod AB to which two pieces of very thin, light, gold or aluminum foil are attached. The two pieces of foil, or leaves as they are usually called, are enclosed in a container made either of glass, or of metal with glass windows, as shown in Figure 21–4. Part of the metal rod projects outside the case so that

Fig. 21–4   A gold-leaf electroscope.

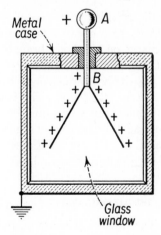

contact can be made with it. If the case is made of metal, the rod passes through an insulating plug made of amber or some other good insulator. The metal case is connected to the ground by means of a wire going from it either directly or, more commonly, to a water pipe or other piece of metal which goes into the ground.   A metal sphere or flat plate is usually mounted on the rod at A.

The electroscope can be charged by contact between the rod AB and a charged body.   If a positively charged body is brought into contact with A, electrons from the leaves and the rod will be attracted to it, so that the leaves and the rod become positively charged.   If, instead, a negatively charged body is placed in contact with A, electrons leave the charged body and distribute themselves over the top, the rod, and the leaves.   In either case, the charge on the leaves has the same sign as that of the charge brought in contact with the rod.   Since the leaves acquire like charges, the force of repulsion between them causes the leaves to diverge.   The angle of divergence depends upon the quantity of charge on each leaf and the weight of each leaf.

The electroscope can also be charged by induction.   If a positively charged body is brought near an uncharged electroscope, the electrons are attracted up from the leaves to the top of the electroscope; the leaves will diverge.   The electroscope is now grounded momentarily, while the positively charged body is held in place.   Electrons from the ground will be attracted up to the leaves, which will now no longer diverge.   The ground connection should first be broken, and then the positively charged body be removed.   The electrons which were held near the top of the electroscope now redistribute themselves over the leaves and the rod as well.   The leaves will diverge.   The electroscope is now negatively charged.   The electroscope can be charged positively by induction by repeating the above operations except that a negatively charged body should be brought near it.

A charged electroscope is very convenient for determining the sign of the charge on any body brought near it.   Suppose that the electroscope is positively charged, so that the leaves diverge through a definite angle. If a positively charged body is brought near the electroscope, the leaves will diverge still more.   The reason for this is that negative electrons will be attracted up from the leaves by the positively charged body, thus increasing the positive charge on the leaves.   Of course if a negatively charged body is brought near the positively charged electroscope, the angle of divergence of its leaves will be decreased.

21-8   THE ELECTROPHORUS

The process of charging by induction is the basis for the design and construction of many electrostatic machines used for supplying electricity for certain special needs.   The *electrophorus*, invented by A. Volta in 1775, is a simple type of electrostatic machine.   It consists of a flat disk made of some insulating material, such as hard rubber, sealing wax, or resin, and a metal disk with an insulating handle.   The disk A, made of insulating material, is first charged by rubbing it with wool or fur; this gives the disk a negative charge. The metal disk B is now brought very close to the charged disk A. (In actual practice, B is placed on A, but because of the roughness of its surface, contact is made at very few points; the charge transferred at these points is negligibly small.) The electrons in the metal disk are repelled to its upper surface, leaving the lower surface positively charged (see Figure 21–5). The plate B is now grounded

Fig. 21–5   The electrophorus.

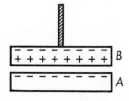

momentarily by touching it with the hand or with a grounded wire; the electrons will go to ground, leaving the plate B positively charged. As long as this plate is close to the charged disk A, the positive charge will remain on the lower surface of B. But if this metal disk is removed far enough from the plate A, the charges in the metal disk will redistribute themselves so that both upper and lower surfaces are positively charged. This positive charge is now available for use in any manner we please. For example, the plate can be discharged through a tube containing neon so that it causes the emission of light characteristic of neon.

If we examine the operation of the electrophorus once again, we note first that no charge has been removed from the original charged disk A; hence this plate can be used over and over again. Second, in removing the disk B from the vicinity of disk A, we had to work against the forces of attraction between the charges on the two disks. It was because of this work that there was energy available to operate the neon lamp or any other appropriate device. This process can be repeated indefinitely and as often as desired, the work being supplied by the person who separates the charges.

21-9 THE ELECTRIC FIELD

Just as in the case of magnetism, so in the case of electricity, we may think of the region around a charged body as containing an *electric field*. If any charges are placed in this electric field, these charges will experience forces. If a small positive charge q is placed at some point P in an electric field, it experiences a force F; the ratio F/q is called the *intensity of the electric field* and is denoted by the letter E; thus

$$E = \frac{F}{q} \cdot$$

(2)

The electric field intensity may vary from point to point in the electric field; its direction at any point is the same as the direction of the force on a positive charge placed at that point. If a negative charge is placed in an electric field, the force on it will be in a direction opposite to the direction of the electric field. For example, if a small sphere containing a charge of $+15$ stcoul, placed at a point in an electric field, experiences a force of 240 dynes, then the electric field at this point is, from Equation (2),

$$E = \frac{240 \text{ dynes}}{15 \text{ stcoul}},$$

from which $\qquad\qquad E = 16 \text{ dynes/stcoul}.$

The force F experienced by a charge q, at a point where the electric field is E, is, from Equation (2),

$$\boxed{F = Eq.} \tag{3}$$

For example, if an electron which has a charge of -4.8×10^{-10} stcoul is placed in an electric field which has an intensity of 500 dynes/stcoul, it will experience a force

$$F = -500 \times 4.8 \times 10^{-10} \text{ dyne}$$

or $\qquad\qquad F = -24 \times 10^{-8} \text{ dyne}.$

The minus sign indicates that the direction of the force on the electron is opposite to that of the electric field.

We can again make use of the concept of *lines of force*, this time to map the *electric field* in the neighborhood of a charge or set of charges. The *electric lines of force* are to be drawn so that a tangent to a line at any

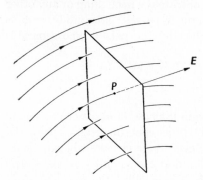

Fig. 21–6   Representation of the electric intensity at P by the number of electric lines of force passing perpendicularly through a unit area at P.

point will give the direction of the electric field intensity at that point, and the magnitude of the electric field intensity will be given by the number of lines passing through a unit area at that point perpendicular to the direction of the lines of force. Frequently the scale of the drawing is so chosen that the number of lines of force passing perpendicularly through a square centimeter at any point represents the electric field intensity at that point. For example, suppose that the electric field intensity at point P is 4 dynes/stcoul; we can draw 4 lines/cm^2 through a unit area at P perpendicular to the direction of the lines of force, as shown in Figure 21–6. If the lines of force are curved, a tangent to the line of force at the point in question represents the direction of E.

The origin of an electric field can always be traced to one or more charges situated at some points in space. Each line of force starts from a positive charge and ends on a negative charge. If the choice of scale is that outlined above, then it can readily be shown that a charge $+Q$ gives rise to $4\pi Q$ lines of force. Let us take, for example, a charge $+Q$ on a very

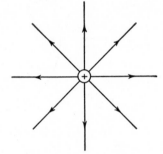

FIG. 21–7 The electric field around a small positive charge is radial and directed away from the charge.

small sphere. The electric field around it is radial, as shown in Figure 21–7. The intensity of the field at a distance r from this charge can be found with the aid of Coulomb's law. If we assume that the charge Q is in a vacuum, then $k = 1$; if we imagine a small charge q at a distance r from it, the force on it is

$$F = \frac{Qq}{r^2},$$

and the electric field intensity E at this point is

$$E = \frac{F}{q} = \frac{Q}{r^2}. \tag{4}$$

Equation (4) gives the electric field intensity at a distance r from the charge Q; there will therefore be Q/r^2 lines of force per unit area at a distance r from Q. If we surround Q with a sphere of radius r, Q/r^2 lines of force will pass through each unit area of this sphere (see Figure 21–8). Since the surface area of a sphere is $4\pi r^2$, the total number N of lines of force coming from the charge Q and passing through this sphere is then

$$N = \frac{Q}{r^2} \times 4\pi r^2$$

or

$$\boxed{N = 4\pi Q.}$$ (5)

Similarly a charge $-Q$ will have $4\pi Q$ lines of electric force ending on it.

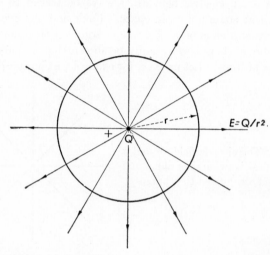

FIG. 21-8 $4\pi Q$ lines of force pass through a sphere of radius r enclosing a charge $+Q$ at its center.

The electric field due to different charge distributions can be calculated in many cases and then drawn to scale.   Figure 21-9 shows the electric field due to two equal charges of opposite sign.   Other electric fields will be discussed later.

Since the electric field intensity represents the force per unit charge at any point in the field, it will be found convenient in making calculations

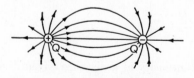

FIG. 21-9   Electric field around two equal and opposite charges.

to assume that a unit positive charge is placed at the point in question and to calculate the force on this charge, taking proper account of the direction of the force.

Illustrative Example. Two small charges, one of +800 stcoul and the other of −1,600 stcoul, are spaced 20 cm apart in air. Determine the electric field intensity at point P, 20 cm from each charge.

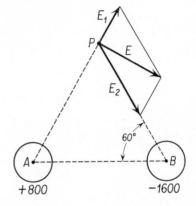

FIG. 21–10 Calculating the electric field intensity at a point.

Referring to Figure 21–10, we find that the point P, at which the electric intensity is to be determined, is at the vertex of an equilateral triangle with the +800-stcoul charge at vertex A and the −1,600-stcoul charge at vertex B.

The electric field intensity E_1 at P due to the charge at A is, from Equation (4),

$$E_1 = \frac{800}{400} \frac{\text{dynes}}{\text{stcoul}} = 2 \text{ dynes/stcoul}$$

directed along the line AP. Similarly the electric field intensity E_2 at P due to the charge at B is

$$E_2 = \frac{1600}{400} \frac{\text{dynes}}{\text{stcoul}} = 4 \text{ dynes/stcoul},$$

directed from P to B.

The vector sum of E_1 and E_2 is the electric field intensity E. Its value can be found by any of the

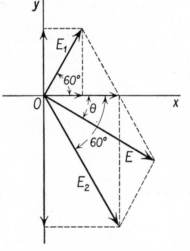

FIG. 21–11

well-known methods for adding vectors such as the parallelogram method or by the analytic method. Using the latter and choosing the x-direction parallel to AB, as shown in Figure 21–11, we get, for the x-component, E_x of the electric field,

$$E_x = E_1 \cos 60° + E_2 \cos 60°$$

or $$E_x = 2 \times \tfrac{1}{2} + 4 \times \tfrac{1}{2} = 3 \text{ dynes/stcoul.}$$

Similarly for E_y, the y-component of the electric field, we get

$$E_y = E_1 \sin 60° - E_2 \sin 60°,$$

from which $$E_y = -\sqrt{3} \text{ dynes/stcoul.}$$

Since $$E = \sqrt{E_x^2 + E_y^2},$$

$$E = \sqrt{12} \text{ dynes/stcoul,}$$

or $$E = 3.46 \text{ dynes/stcoul.}$$

The angle θ that the electric field intensity E makes with the x-axis is given by

$$\tan \theta = \frac{E_y}{E_x} = -\frac{\sqrt{3}}{3},$$

so that $$\theta = -30°.$$

21-10 POTENTIAL DIFFERENCE

A small positive charge q placed at some point A in an electric field will experience a force F. In general, to move this charge to some other point B in the electric field, an amount of work $\mathcal{W}$ will have to be performed. With the aid of the principle of conservation of energy, it can be shown that no matter what path is followed in moving the charge from A to B, the work $\mathcal{W}$ is always the same. The ratio of the work done to the charge that is moved from A to B is defined as the *difference of potential* between A and B; or, in symbols,

$$V = P_B - P_A = \frac{\mathcal{W}}{q}, \tag{6}$$

in which P_A is the potential at point A, P_B is the potential at point B, and V is the difference of potential between A and B. If the work is done by *some outside agency on the positive charge* in moving it from A to B, then point B is said to be at the higher potential; if the work is done by the electric field in moving the charge from A to B, then point A is at the higher potential.

The units for measuring difference of potential depend upon the units used for expressing work and electric charge. If the work is expressed in ergs and the charge in stcoul, the difference of potential is expressed in esu of potential difference, called *statvolts*. In the practical system, the work is expressed in joules and the charge in coul; the difference of potential is expressed in *volts*. For example, if 25 joules of work are required to move 0.1 coul from point A to point B, the difference of potential V between these two points is

$$V = \frac{25 \text{ joules}}{0.1 \text{ coul}} = 250 \text{ volts}.$$

The relationship between the practical unit, the volt, and the electrostatic unit, the statvolt, can readily be derived by noting that 1 joule $= 10^7$ ergs and 1 coul $= 3 \times 10^9$ stcoul. Now

$$1 \text{ volt} = \frac{1 \text{ joule}}{1 \text{ coul}}$$

$$= \frac{10^7 \text{ ergs}}{3 \times 10^9 \text{ stcoul}},$$

so that $1 \text{ volt} = \frac{1}{300} \text{ statvolt}$

or $300 \text{ volts} = 1 \text{ statvolt}.$

Although measurements are always made of differences of potential between points, it is frequently desirable to talk about the *potential at a point*. The potential at a point can have a definite value only if there is some reference point or region which can be considered as at zero potential. In engineering practice, the potential of any point on the surface of the earth is assigned the value zero, and the potential of any other point can be measured with reference to it.

Even if the electric intensity is known completely, it is generally a difficult mathematical problem to calculate the difference of potential between two points in an electric field. However, the calculations can be carried out in a few simple cases. We shall consider two such cases: that

FIG. 21–12   Work done in moving a charge from A to B in an electrostatic field is independent of the path.

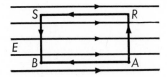

of a uniform electric field, illustrated in Figure 21–12; and later, in Section 21–11, that produced by a point charge. If we consider a small charge $+q$ at some point A in this field, it will experience a force F given by

$$F = Eq.$$

There are many ways of moving this charge from A to B; let us first move it parallel to the lines of force. Since we are moving it opposite to the field, we have to exert a force F opposite to the direction of the field. If s is the distance from A to B, then the work done in moving the charge is

$$\mathcal{W} = Fs = Eqs,$$

and the difference of potential V between A and B is

$$V = \frac{\mathcal{W}}{q} = Es, \tag{7}$$

with point B at the higher potential.

Let us choose some other path such as $ARSB$. In moving the charge along AR, the displacement will be at right angles to the force F, and no work will be done. In going from R to S, the displacement is again s, and the work done is

$$\mathcal{W} = Fs = Eqs.$$

In going from S to B, the displacement is at right angles to the force F, and again no work is done. Hence the total work done in taking the charge q from A to B along the path $ARSB$ is the same as along the straight line AB. Although this calculation was made for only two different paths, it can be shown that, in general, there can be only one difference of potential between two points in an electric field.

21-11 POTENTIAL DUE TO A POINT CHARGE

In evaluating the potential in the neighborhood of a small positive charge $+Q$, we can make use of the fact that the electric field produced by a point charge is radial and that the intensity of this electric field at a distance r from it is Q/r^2. Since the difference of potential between two points is independent of the path, let us choose a convenient path such as

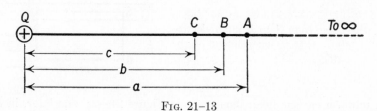

FIG. 21–13

a straight line from the charge out to infinity and first calculate the difference of potential between two points A and B along this path, distant a and b, respectively, from the charge Q (see Figure 21–13).

Since the electric field intensity varies inversely as the square of the distance from the charge, let us choose points A and B very close together and determine the average value $\bar{E}$ of the electric field in this region. The difference of potential V_{AB} between these two points will then be given by Equation (7); thus

$$V_{AB} = \bar{E}(a - b).$$

Now the value of E at A is Q/a^2, and the value of E at B is Q/b^2. To a good approximation the average value of E between A and B can be set equal to Q/m^2, where m is the geometric mean between a and b. Thus

$$a:m = m:b,$$

from which

$$m^2 = ab;$$

hence

$$\bar{E} = \frac{Q}{ab},$$

so that

$$V_{AB} = \frac{Q}{ab}(a - b)$$

or

$$V_{AB} = \frac{Q}{b} - \frac{Q}{a}.$$

We can continue this procedure and evaluate the difference of potential between B and a neighboring point C and obtain

$$V_{BC} = \frac{Q}{c} - \frac{Q}{b}.$$

The difference of potential between A and C will be the sum of V_{AB} and V_{BC}, yielding

$$V_{AC} = \frac{Q}{c} - \frac{Q}{a}.$$

By continuing this process, we can show that the difference of potential between any two points, distant r and r_1 from Q, is

$$V = \frac{Q}{r} - \frac{Q}{r_1}.$$

The potential at a point is defined as the work done in bringing a unit charge from infinity to the point in question. Hence, if we set $r_1 = \infty$, then the potential at a point distant r from Q is

$$\boxed{V = \frac{Q}{r}.}\qquad(8)$$

Illustrative Example. The proton has a charge equal to that of the electron.   (a) Determine the electric field intensity at a point distant 5.3×10^{-9} cm from it, and (b) determine the electric potential at this point.

(a) The charge of the proton is 4.80×10^{-10} stcoul. Hence the electric field intensity at the point in question is, from Equation (4),

$$E = \frac{4.80 \times 10^{-10}}{(5.3 \times 10^{-9})^2} \frac{\text{dynes}}{\text{stcoul}},$$

from which $E = 1.71 \times 10^7$ dynes/stcoul.

(b) The potential at the same point is, from Equation (8),

$$V = \frac{4.80 \times 10^{-10}}{5.3 \times 10^{-9}} \text{statvolt},$$

from which $V = 9.06 \times 10^{-2}$ statvolt

or $V = 27.2$ volts.

21-12 EQUIPOTENTIAL SURFACES. CONDUCTORS

We have shown that a charge placed on a conductor will distribute itself over the surface of the conductor. When equilibrium is established, there can be no resultant force acting on the charges along the surface of the conductor; otherwise the charges would move. The electric field due to these charges must therefore be at right angles to the conducting surface. The potential must be the same everywhere on the surface of the conductor, since no work would be done in moving a very small charge along the surface at right angles to the electric field. Such a surface is called an *equipotential surface.* Any surface in space so drawn that the electric field is everywhere at right angles to the surface must be an equipotential surface. The equipotential surfaces around a point charge are concentric spherical surfaces with the point charge at the center [see Figure 21–14(a)]. The potential at any point is Q/r, where Q is the charge and r is the distance from it. If these electric charges are on the surface of a sphere and are uniformly distributed on this surface, the equipotential surfaces are concentric spherical surfaces outside the sphere [see Figure 21–14(b)], and have the same values as for a point charge. The potential of the sphere can be obtained by setting $r = R$, where R is the radius of the sphere. The potential of a sphere with charge Q is Q/R. The electric field around a charged sphere is exactly the same as that of an equal charge placed at the center of the sphere, because the total number of lines of force radiating from the sphere will be the same in each case.

FIG. 21–14   (a) The equipotential surfaces around
a point charge are con-
centric spherical surfaces
with the point charge at
the center.

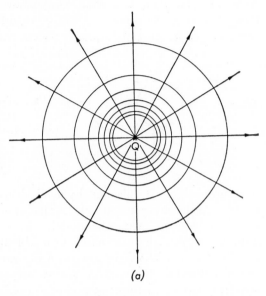

(a)

FIG. 21–14 (b) The equi-
potential surfaces out-
side a charged metallic
sphere are spherical
surfaces concentric
with the charged
sphere.

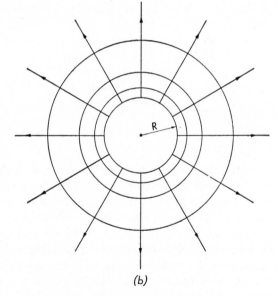

(b)

The fact that in the case of a charged conductor the charges are always on the surface of the conductor can be demonstrated by the following experiment.   Let us charge a metal sphere which is mounted on an insulating stand. Using two metal hemispheres which fit snugly over the sphere and are provided with insulating handles, as shown in Figure 21–15, place them over the charged sphere. Now remove the hemispheres and bring them near an electroscope. It will be found that these hemispheres are charged. Now bring the original sphere near the electroscope; it will

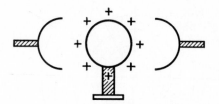

FIG. 21–15 Experiment for showing that the charge resides on the sur- face of a conductor.

show no charge. By placing the hemispheres over the metal sphere we made a single larger sphere out of this system. Owing to the force of repulsion between them, the charges move as far from each other as possible, in this case to the outer surface of the new sphere.

An examination of the electric field near the surface of a conductor shows that although the field is always perpendicular to the conductor, it is not necessarily uniform; it depends upon the geometrical shape of the conductor. Figure 21–16 shows the electric field of a pear-shaped con-

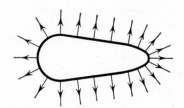

FIG. 21–16 Electric field near the sur- face of a pear-shaped conductor.

ductor. The electric field is most intense at the narrow end of the con- ductor. If the conductor has sharp points, the electric field near these points may be so great that they will ionize the air near it. This means that the field acts on the charges within the molecules of the air strongly enough to break them up into positively and negatively charged particles or *ions*. If a pointed conductor is negatively charged, for example, it will attract positively charged ions to it and repel the negatively charged ions. Under these conditions a sharply pointed conductor quickly loses its charge. If its charge is continually replenished by means of an electro- static machine, the process of ionization of the air in the neighborhood of the charged point can be continued indefinitely. The motion of the ions through the air undoubtedly results in collisions with neutral molecules.

Some of these collisions may result in ionization of more molecules, giving rise to what is known as an *electric discharge* in the air. One of the results accompanying this electric discharge is the emission of light characteristic of the substance in which the discharge occurs. Under favorable conditions, in a darkened room, for example, the electric discharge in the neighborhood of a pointed conductor maintained at a high potential becomes visible. The light emitted is characteristic of the nitrogen of the air. Because of its appearance it is sometimes called a *brush* discharge. The study of the electric discharge in gases has played a very important role in the investigation of the structure of the atom; we shall consider it in greater detail later.

21-13 EQUALITY OF INDUCED AND INDUCING CHARGES

A very important experiment, sometimes referred to as the *ice-pail experiment* because of the shape of the hollow conductor employed, was performed by Faraday to show that a charged body always induces equal and opposite charges on conductors which completely surround it. Suppose we connect such a hollow uncharged conductor to an electroscope, as shown in Figure 21-17. If we now suspend a small metal body carrying

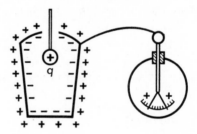

Fig. 21-17   The ice-pail experiment.

charge q inside the hollow conductor, the leaves of the electroscope will diverge; the angle of divergence may be measured by means of a scale attached to the glass face of the electroscope. Moving the charge around inside the conductor has no effect on the angle of divergence of the leaves of the electroscope. This shows that the charges induced on the conductor are always the same no matter where the inducing charge q is inside the conductor which completely encloses it.

If the inducing charge q is removed, the leaves of the electroscope collapse. If now the inducing charge is again placed anywhere inside the hollow conductor, the leaves will again diverge, and the angle of divergence will be the same as before. Let the charged body now touch the inside surface of the hollow conductor; the angle of divergence of the leaves will still remain the same. Now remove the metal body which had the charge on it; it will be found that the angle of divergence of the leaves does not change. Furthermore, if we test the small metal body which previously carried the charge q, we shall find it is no longer charged. Its total charge was transferred to the hollow conductor.

Let us examine this experiment in greater detail. Suppose that the charge q is a positive charge. When it is placed inside the hollow conductor, negative charges are attracted to the inner surface, leaving its outer surface positively charged. The angle of divergence of the leaves of the electroscope can be used as a measure of the amount of charge on this outer surface. The fact that the leaves collapse when the positive charge is removed from the interior of the hollow conductor shows that the positive and negative charges induced on the conductor are equal in magnitude. When the positive charge is reintroduced inside the hollow conductor, the charges induced in it are exactly the same as before. When the small charged body is allowed to touch the inside of the hollow conductor, the charge on the outside remains the same, but the negative charge on the interior of the conductor combines with the positive charge on the small charged body, completely neutralizing it. The positive charge on the small body and the *induced negative charge must therefore be equal in magnitude;* and of course, since the angle of divergence of the leaves remains the same, the positive charge on the outside must have remained the same, and therefore it must be equal to the positive charge originally on the small body.

In general, a charge on any body gives rise to induced charges on the surfaces of neighboring conductors. The *total* charge induced on all of these surfaces is equal to the charge which induces them.

QUESTIONS

1. Why is a force of repulsion the only conclusive test as to the nature of a charge on a body brought near another body?

2. Compare Coulomb's experiments on magnetism and on electricity, pointing out similarities and differences.

3. Describe how you would charge a metal sphere positively by induction.

4. Determine the forces which act on the leaves of a charged electroscope when equilibrium is reached.

5. Why are gold and aluminum foil generally used for the leaves of electroscopes?

6. What are the units of electric field intensity in the practical system?

7. Show how the results of Faraday's ice-pail experiment can now be deduced from our present knowledge of the structure of matter.

8. How would you use a negatively charged rubber rod to charge an electroscope (a) negatively and (b) positively?

PROBLEMS

1. Two small spheres have charges of +600 stcoul and +300 stcoul and are 8 cm apart. Determine the force between them.

2. Two small spheres have charges of +200 stcoul and −50 stcoul and are 6 cm apart. Determine the force between them.

3. What is the intensity of the electric field at a distance of 20 cm from a small sphere containing a charge of +2,400 stcoul?

4. What is the intensity of the electric field at a distance of 30 cm from a small body charged with −7,200 stcoul?

5. An electric charge of +50 stcoul is placed 25 cm from one of −400 stcoul. Determine the magnitude and direction of the electric field intensity at the mid-point of the line joining them.

6. Determine the intensity of the electric field at a point midway between two charges, each of +600 stcoul, placed 10 cm apart.

7. Determine the electric field intensity at a point midway between two charges, one of +400 stcoul and the other of −400 stcoul, placed 12 cm apart.

8. Two equal charges, each of +2,500 stcoul, are placed 24 cm apart. Determine the electric field intensity at a point 15 cm from each charge.

9. The field intensity at a point P near a charge of +144 stcoul is 9 dynes per stcoul. Where must a charge of +324 stcoul be placed to reduce the field intensity to zero? Give the position of point P relative to each charge.

10. Two small charged bodies are placed 25 cm apart. One has a charge of +600 μcoul and the other a charge of −3,000 μcoul (1 μcoul = 10^{-6} coul). Determine the magnitude and direction of the intensity of the electric field at a point 60 cm from the positive charge and 65 cm from the negative charge.

11. A small charge of +12 stcoul is placed in a uniform electric field of intensity 600 dynes per stcoul. Determine the force on this charge.

12. A small charge of +8 stcoul is placed in a uniform electric field whose intensity is 5,000 dynes per stcoul. (a) What is the force acting on this charge? (b) How much work will be done by the electric field in moving this charge a distance of 4 cm in the direction of the field? (c) What is the difference of potential between its initial and final positions?

13. A small body carrying a charge of 72 μcoul is placed 60 cm from another small body carrying a similar charge of 180 μcoul. Determine the force of repulsion between them.

14. How many lines of force emanate from a charge of +40 stcoul?

15. Determine the electric field intensity at a point 250 cm from a small body carrying a positive charge of 0.008 coul.

16. Determine the force between the proton and the electron of a hydrogen atom when the distance between them is 0.53×10^{-8} cm if each has a charge of 1.60×10^{-19} coul.

22

Capacitors

22-1 CAPACITANCE OF A CAPACITOR

One of the most important electrical devices used in electrostatic experiments and used even more widely in alternating current circuits and radio and television circuits is the *capacitor*. The essential parts of a capacitor are two metallic surfaces separated by a dielectric. To understand the action of a capacitor, let us first take a metal plate S and connect it to an electroscope by means of a conducting wire, as shown in Figure 22–1. Let

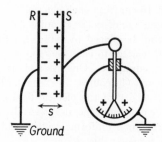

Fig. 22–1 A parallel-plate capacitor connected to an electroscope.

us now put a positive charge Q on the plate S. A very small part of this charge will go to the electroscope causing its leaves to diverge through a definite angle. The metal plate S, the connecting wire, and the rod and leaves of the electroscope form a single conducting system with all parts at the same potential. In previous experiments, the electroscope was used as a charge measuring device. The electroscope may also be used as a potential measuring device, since work is required to charge it. Thus the angle of divergence of the leaves of the electroscope will indicate its potential and also that of the plate S.

Suppose we now bring a grounded metal surface R of the same area as S close to it but separated from it by a distance s. A negative charge will be induced on the plate R. It will be noted that the angle of divergence of the leaves of the electroscope will decrease just because R was brought close to S. We would now have to add more positive charge to S to bring the angle of divergence of the leaves back to its original value, that is, to bring the conductor S back to its original potential.

The electrical system consisting of the metal plates S and R, separated by an insulator such as air, is called a *capacitor* (formerly known as a *condenser*). The *capacitance* C of the system is defined as the charge Q on either plate divided by the difference of potential V between the plates, or

$$C = \frac{Q}{V},$$

(1)

The plates of a capacitor have equal charges but of opposite sign. The ratio Q/V is a constant for a given system. When Q is expressed in stcoul and V in statvolts, C is expressed in *statfarads*, abbreviated as *stfd*. In the practical system, when Q is expressed in coulombs and V in volts, C is expressed in *farads;* thus

$$1 \text{ farad} = \frac{1 \text{ coul}}{1 \text{ volt}}.$$

The farad is such a large unit of capacitance that for most work a *microfarad*, that is, a millionth of a farad (abbreviated μfd), is used to designate the capacitance of capacitors. The relationship between the farad and the stfd is

$$1 \text{ farad} = 9 \times 10^{11} \text{ stfd.}$$

22-2 FACTORS AFFECTING CAPACITANCE

There are three factors which influence the capacitance of a capacitor. They are (a) the distance s between the metal plates, (b) the nature of the insulating or *dielectric* material between the metal plates, and (c) the area of the plates. Suppose that there is air in the space between the plates. Referring back to Figure 22–1, we find that if the distance s between the plates is decreased, the angle of divergence of the leaves will also be found to decrease. This means that more positive charge can be added to the plate S to bring it back to its original potential. Thus, decreasing the separation of the plates increases the capacitance of the system, and, of course, increasing the separation decreases the capacitance. Or more generally, the capacitance varies inversely as the distance s between the plates of a capacitor, other things remaining unchanged.

The effect that the insulating material which fills the space between the metal plates has on the capacitance of the system can be demonstrated by taking a plate of glass of thickness s and of an area approximately equal to that of the metal plates and inserting it between them. It will be found that the angle of divergence of the leaves decreases considerably. Again additional charges must be added to the plate S to bring its potential up to its original value. Quantitative measurements show that the capacitance varies directly with the dielectric coefficient k of the insulating material between the plates of the capacitor.

The effect of a dielectric on the capacitance can also be described in terms of the changes produced in the electric field in the space between the plates. Suppose that there is a vacuum between the two plates R and S of a parallel-plate capacitor, and that one has a charge $+Q$ and the other a charge $-Q$ (see Figure 22–2). Since each metal plate is necessarily an

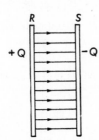

Fɪɢ. 22–2 Uniform electric field between the plates of a capacitor.

equipotential surface and the electric field is perpendicular to the equipotential surface, the lines of electric force will be parallel and uniformly spaced; the electric field is uniform throughout the space between the plates, except at the edges. We shall neglect the edge effect in this discussion. There are $4\pi Q$ lines of force going from the positively charged plate to the negatively charged plate. If the area of each plate is A, the number of lines of force per unit area is $4\pi Q/A$, and this is equal to the electric field intensity E in the space between the plates.

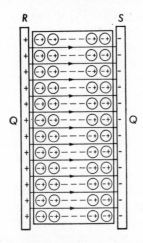

Fɪɢ. 22–3 Charges within molecules of a dielectric are displaced by the action of the electric field between the capacitor plates R and S.

If we now place a dielectric, that is, a nonconductor, in the space between the plates, the electric field E will produce a reorientation of the charges within the molecules of the dielectric, as shown in Figure 22–3.

The negative charges of the molecules will be attracted toward the posi- tively charged plate R, and the positive charges toward the negatively charged plate S. Since the dielectric is an insulator, these charges will move only through short distances, of the order of the molecular diameters. Some of the electric lines of force of the original electric field will end on the charges on the surface of the dielectric, so that the field inside the dielectric will be smaller than the original electric field by an amount which **is** designated by k, the dielectric coefficient of the material. Thus the field in the medium will now be

$$E = \frac{4\pi Q}{kA}.$$
(2)

This result might have been inferred from Coulomb's law

$$F = \frac{Qq}{kr^2},$$

which shows that the force between two charges, when they are in a medium whose dielectric coefficient $k > 1$, is smaller than it would have been if the space between them had been a vacuum.

The capacitance C of a parallel-plate capacitor can be readily deter- mined. We have already shown that the difference of potential V between two points a distance s apart in a uniform electric field E is

$$V = Es;\qquad \text{[Equation (7) in Chapter 21]}$$

hence the difference of potential between the two capacitor plates is

$$V = Es = \frac{4\pi Q}{kA}s,$$
(3)

where s is the distance between the plates. Now, from Equation (1), we have

$$C = \frac{Q}{V};$$
(1)

therefore, by substituting the value of V from Equation (3), we get

$$\boxed{C = \frac{kA}{4\pi s}}$$
(4)

for the capacitance of a parallel-plate capacitor with an insulator of di electric coefficient k between the plates.

In the electrostatic system of units, k is a pure number, A is expressed in square centimeters and s in centimeters, so that the unit of capacitance, the statfarad, has the dimensions of length and is sometimes expressed in centimeters. A few typical values of the dielectric coefficients are listed in Table 22–1. Two substances, both titanium compounds, which have uncommon electrical and optical properties, are also listed in this table.

Table 22-1

Substance	Dielectric Coefficient k
Vacuum	1
Glass	5–10
Mica	3–6
Rubber	2.5–35
Water	81
Rutile (titanium dioxide)	86 along one axis
	170 along perpendicular axis
Barium titanate	$\approx 10,000$

Illustrative Example. The plates of a parallel-plate capacitor have dimensions of 30 cm by 50 cm and are separated by a glass plate of the same area and 2 mm thick; its dielectric coefficient is 8. (a) Determine the capacitance of the capacitor. (b) What will be the charge on either plate when the difference of potential between the plates is 2,000 volts?

(a) The capacitance of the parallel-plate capacitor is given by

$$C = \frac{kA}{4\pi s} = \frac{8 \times 30 \times 50}{4\pi \times 0.2} = 4{,}770 \text{ cm};$$

or, since $1 \ \mu\text{fd} = 9 \times 10^5 \text{ cm},$

$$C = \frac{4{,}770}{9 \times 10^5} \ \mu\text{fd} = 530 \times 10^{-5} \ \mu\text{fd} = 0.0053 \ \mu\text{fd}.$$

(b) Using Equation (1) written as

$$Q = VC,$$

we get $Q = 2{,}000 \text{ volts} \times 0.0053 \ \mu\text{fd}.$

Now $1 \ \mu\text{fd} = 10^{-6} \text{ farad};$

therefore $Q = 2{,}000 \times 0.0053 \times 10^{-6} \text{ coul}$

$$= 10.6 \times 10^{-6} \text{ coul};$$

or, since $1 \text{ coul} = 3 \times 10^9 \text{ stcoul},$

$$Q = 10.6 \times 10^{-6} \times 3 \times 10^9 \text{ stcoul}$$

$$Q = 31.8 \times 10^3 \text{ stcoul}.$$

22-3   ENERGY OF A CHARGED CAPACITOR

Work has to be performed in charging a capacitor with a charge $+Q$ on one plate and a charge $-Q$ on the other plate. This work $\mathcal{W}$ can be calculated by considering the process as consisting of the transfer of very small quantities of charge from one plate to the other, starting initially with uncharged plates. As more and more charge is transferred from one plate to the other, the difference of potential between the plates increases from its value zero initially to its final value V after a charge Q has been transferred. Since V increases as Q increases according to Equation (1),

$$Q = VC, \tag{1}$$

we can say that the average value of the potential difference between the plates during the charging process is $\frac{1}{2}V$. From the definition of difference of potential, the work done in transferring Q units of charge under a difference of potential $\frac{1}{2}V$ is

$$\boxed{\mathcal{W} = \tfrac{1}{2}QV.} \tag{5}$$

Equation (5) represents the work done in charging a capacitor to a difference of potential V with a charge $+Q$ on one plate and $-Q$ on the other plate.

By combining Equations (1) and (5), the work done in charging a capacitor may also be written as

$$\mathcal{W} = \tfrac{1}{2}\frac{Q^2}{C} \tag{6}$$

and

$$\mathcal{W} = \tfrac{1}{2}CV^2. \tag{7}$$

Equation (5) represents the energy of a charged capacitor because of the work done in charging it. If the capacitor is discharged by connecting the two plates by means of a conductor, charge Q will flow through the conductor until the plates are neutral once more. While these charges are moving, the energy originally stored in the capacitor is transformed into heat and possibly other forms of energy.

Illustrative Example. A capacitor having a capacitance of 4 microfarads is charged until the difference of potential between the plates is 150 volts. Determine (a) the charge on the capacitor and (b) the energy of this charged capacitor.

Using Equation (1) for determining the charge Q, we get

$$Q = 150 \times 4 \times 10^{-6} \, \text{coul} = 6 \times 10^{-4} \, \text{coul};$$

and, from Equation (5), the work done in charging this capacitor is

$$\mathcal{W} = \tfrac{1}{2} \times 6 \times 10^{-4} \times 150 \, \text{joule}$$
$$= 450 \times 10^{-4} \, \text{joule.}$$

22-4 CAPACITORS IN PARALLEL

If it is desired to increase the capacitance of a system which contains only one capacitor, additional capacitors may be connected to it in parallel, as shown in Figure 22–4. C_1 represents the original capacitor, and C_2 and C_3 additional capacitors connected to it; all three capacitors are

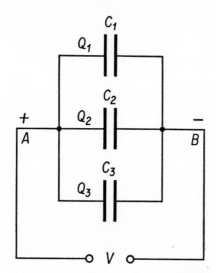

Fig. 22–4   Three capacitors connected in parallel.

connected in *parallel*. It can be seen from the figure that the effect of connecting capacitors in parallel is equivalent to making one large capacitor with a very large area. If a battery or some other source of electrical energy is connected to the common terminals AB, a charge $+Q$ will be put on one set of plates, and an equal charge $-Q$ will be put on the other set of plates. The difference of potential across the plates of each of the capacitors is exactly the same and is equal to the difference of potential V between A and B. This system of capacitors acts as a single capacitor of equivalent capacitance C, given by Equation (1)

$$C = \frac{Q}{V}.$$

The quantity of charge Q, however, is distributed over the three capacitors. If Q_1 is the charge on the capacitor whose capacitance is C_1, then, from Equation (1),

$$C_1 = \frac{Q_1}{V}.$$

Similarly, if Q_2 is the charge on the second capacitor of capacitance C_2, then

$$C_2 = \frac{Q_2}{V};$$

and, if Q_3 is the charge on the third capacitor of capacitance C_3, then

$$C_3 = \frac{Q_3}{V}.$$

Now the total charge Q is equal to the sum of the charges on the capacitors; hence

$$Q = Q_1 + Q_2 + Q_3,$$

so that the equivalent capacitance C becomes

$$C = \frac{Q}{V} = \frac{Q_1 + Q_2 + Q_3}{V};$$

hence

$$C = \frac{Q_1}{V} + \frac{Q_2}{V} + \frac{Q_3}{V};$$

therefore

$$\boxed{C = C_1 + C_2 + C_3.} \tag{8}$$

This result may readily be extended to any number of capacitances in parallel. Hence, *if a group of capacitors is connected in parallel, the equivalent capacitance of the system is the sum of the individual capacitances of the system.*

Illustrative Example. Two capacitors, one of 4 μfd capacitance and the other of 1 μfd capacitance, are connected in parallel and charged until the difference of potential is 120 volts. Determine (a) the charge on each capacitor, (b) the capacitance of the system, and (c) the energy of the system.

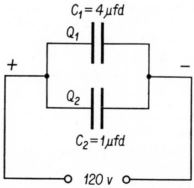

Fig. 22–5

(a) The difference of potential across each capacitor is 120 volts. Referring to Figure 22–5, the charge Q_1 on C_1 is, from Equation (1),

$$Q_1 = 4 \times 10^{-6} \text{ farad} \times 120 \text{ volts}$$
$$= 4.80 \times 10^{-4} \text{ coul.}$$

The charge Q_2 on C_2 is

$$Q_2 = 1 \times 10^{-6} \text{ farad} \times 120 \text{ volts}$$
$$= 1.20 \times 10^{-4} \text{ coul.}$$

The total charge on the two capacitors is

$$Q = Q_1 + Q_2 = 6.0 \times 10^{-4} \text{ coul.}$$

(b) The equivalent capacitance of the system is

$$C = C_1 + C_2 = 4 \,\mu\text{fd} + 1 \,\mu\text{fd} = 5 \,\mu\text{fd.}$$

(c) The energy of the system is

$$\mathcal{W} = \tfrac{1}{2}QV$$
$$= \tfrac{1}{2} \times 6 \times 10^{-4} \text{ coul} \times 120 \text{ volts}$$
$$= 360 \times 10^{-4} \text{ joule.}$$

Illustrative Example. A 2-μfd capacitor is charged to a difference of potential of 300 volts. The terminals of this capacitor are then connected to those of an uncharged capacitor of 2 μfd capacitance. Determine (a) the original energy of the first capacitor, (b) the difference of potential across the two capacitors after they have been connected, and (c) the energy of the two capacitors. (d) Compare the total energy of the two capacitors with the original energy of the first charged capacitor.

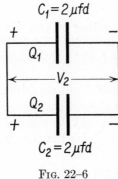

Fig. 22-6

(a) The energy $\mathcal{W}_1$ of the first capacitor is, from Equation (7),

$$\mathcal{W}_1 = \tfrac{1}{2}C_1V_1^2$$
$$= \tfrac{1}{2} \times 2 \times 10^{-6} \text{ farad} \times (300 \text{ volts})^2$$
$$= 0.090 \text{ joule.}$$

(b) Referring to Figure 22-6, when the terminals of C_1 are connected to those of C_2, the two capacitors form a parallel combination. The total charge Q of the system remains unchanged, but is now distributed between the two capacitors. The charge Q was originally on the capacitance C_1 at a difference of potential V_1 and is

$$Q = V_1C_1$$
$$= 300 \text{ volts} \times 2 \times 10^{-6} \text{ farad}$$
$$= 600 \times 10^{-6} \text{ coul.}$$

After the two capacitors have been connected in parallel, the difference of potential V_2 of the system of capacitance $C = C_1 + C_2$ is

$$V_2 = \frac{Q}{C_1 + C_2},$$

so that
$$V_2 = \frac{600 \times 10^{-6} \text{ coul}}{4 \times 10^{-6} \text{ farad}},$$

from which $\quad\quad\quad\quad V_2 = 150 \text{ volts.}$

(c) The energy of the two capacitors $\mathcal{W}_2$ is

$$\begin{aligned}
\mathcal{W}_2 &= \tfrac{1}{2}QV_2 \\
&= \tfrac{1}{2} \times 600 \times 10^{-6} \text{ coul} \times 150 \text{ volts} \\
&= 0.045 \text{ joule.}
\end{aligned}$$

(d) The final energy of the system $\mathcal{W}_2$ is obviously less than the initial energy $\mathcal{W}_1$. The difference $\mathcal{W}_2 - \mathcal{W}_1$ has been converted into some other forms of energy. Unless more information is given about the nature of the connecting wires, it is impossible to give a detailed account of the different types of energy transformations which took place. For example, it will be shown in the next chapter that if charge flows through a metallic wire, some energy is converted into heat, the actual amount depending upon a property of the wire known as its resistance. It is also possible, as we shall see in Chapter 29, that some of the energy left the system in the form of electromagnetic waves similar to radio waves.

22-5   CAPACITORS IN SERIES

Another method of connecting capacitors for use in a circuit is shown in Figure 22-7; the capacitors are said to be *connected in series*. One

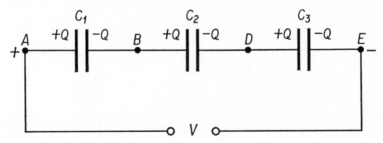

Fɪɢ. 22–7   Three capacitors connected in series.

terminal A of one capacitor, say C_1, is connected to the positive terminal of a source of electrical energy, while its other terminal is connected to one terminal of capacitor C_2; the second terminal of C_2 is connected to one terminal of C_3; and the second terminal of C_3, called E in the figure, is connected to the negative terminal of the source of electrical energy. The action of the source of electrical energy, such as a battery, is to transfer a quantity Q of negative charge from plate A to plate E; this, in turn, produces a shift of an equal negative charge from the other plate of C_3 past point D to C_2, and from the other plate of C_2 past point B to C_1. Thus there is the same quantity of charge Q on each plate of each capacitor— positive on one plate and negative on the other.

The equivalent capacitance C of the system is given by Equation (1)

$$C = \frac{Q}{V},$$

where V is the difference of potential between A and E. Let us call P_A, P_B, P_D, and P_E the potentials at points A, B, D, and E, respectively, and set

$$V_1 = P_A - P_B,$$

$$V_2 = P_B - P_D,$$

$$V_3 = P_D - P_E,$$

where V_1, V_2, and V_3 are the differences of potential across capacitors C_1, C_2, and C_3, respectively. By adding the above equation, we get

$$V_1 + V_2 + V_3 = P_A - P_E = V.$$

Thus the potential difference across capacitors connected in series is the sum of the potential differences across each of the capacitors.

But $\qquad V_1 = \dfrac{Q}{C_1}, \qquad V_2 = \dfrac{Q}{C_2}, \qquad$ and $\qquad V_3 = \dfrac{Q}{C_3};$

and, since $\qquad\qquad V = \dfrac{Q}{C},$

we can write $\qquad\qquad \dfrac{Q}{C} = \dfrac{Q}{C_1} + \dfrac{Q}{C_2} + \dfrac{Q}{C_3},$

so that $\qquad\qquad \boxed{\dfrac{1}{C} = \dfrac{1}{C_1} + \dfrac{1}{C_2} + \dfrac{1}{C_3}.} \qquad\qquad$ (9)

This analysis may be extended to any number of capacitors in series. Equation (9) states that *the reciprocal of the equivalent capacitance of a set of capacitors in series is the sum of the reciprocals of the individual capacitances.* The equivalent capacitance of a series combination is less than the smallest capacitance in the combination.

Illustrative Example. Two capacitors are connected in series across a 240-volt line, as shown in Figure 22–8. The capacitance $C_1 = 4$ µfd, and $C_2 = 2$ µfd. Determine (a) the equivalent capacitance of the system, (b) the charge of each capacitance, and (c) the difference of potential across each capacitance.

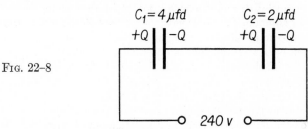

FIG. 22–8

(a) The equivalent capacitance C of the two capacitors in series is, from Equation (9),

$$\frac{1}{C} = \frac{1}{C_1} + \frac{1}{C_2},$$

which becomes

$$\frac{1}{C} = \frac{1}{4} + \frac{1}{2} = \frac{3}{4},$$

so that

$$C = \frac{4}{3} \text{ µfd.}$$

(b) The charge Q is the same for each capacitor and is given by Equation (1)

$$Q = CV,$$

so that

$$Q = \frac{4}{3} \times 10^{-6} \text{ farad} \times 240 \text{ volts}$$

$$= 3.20 \times 10^{-4} \text{ coul.}$$

(c) The difference of potential across the first capacitor C_1 is, from Equation (1),

$$V_1 = \frac{Q}{C_1} = \frac{3.20 \times 10^{-4}}{4 \times 10^{-6}} \text{ volts,}$$

from which

$$V_1 = 80 \text{ volts.}$$

Similarly

$$V_2 = \frac{3.20 \times 10^{-4}}{2 \times 10^{-6}} \text{ volts,}$$

from which

$$V_2 = 160 \text{ volts.}$$

The potential difference across the smaller capacitance is greater than that across the larger capacitance.

1. What is the relationship between a microfarad and the electrostatic unit of capacitance?

2. Account for the work done in charging a capacitor.

3. A parallel-plate capacitor with air between the plates has a charge Q at a difference of potential V. Oil is now poured into the space between the plates, filling the space completely. Discuss the changes that take place in the values of the capacitance and the difference of potential of the capacitor.

4. A parallel-plate capacitor with air between the plates is arranged so that the distance between the plates can be varied. The distance between the plates is increased while the plates are connected to a battery so that the difference of potential between the plates remains constant. (a) Discuss what happens to the charge on the capacitor during the separation of the plates. (b) What would happen if the separation between the plates was decreased?

5. Two identical capacitors connected in parallel are charged to a difference of potential V. They are then connected in series; determine the difference of potential across this combination.

PROBLEMS

1. The plates of a parallel-plate capacitor have dimensions of 30 cm $\times$ 80 cm each and are spaced 1 mm apart with air between them. Determine its capacitance (a) in cgs units and (b) in farads.

2. The two plates of a horizontal parallel-plate capacitor are 1.5 cm apart with air between them. A small oil drop containing a charge of 32×10^{-19} coul moves with uniform motion between the plates. The plates are then charged to a difference of potential of 6,000 volts. (a) Determine the electric field intensity between the plates. (b) Determine the force exerted by the electric field on the oil drop.

3. Each of the two plates of a parallel-plate capacitor has an area of 12,000 cm^2; the plates are separated by a solid dielectric 2 mm thick and of dielectric coefficient 6. (a) Determine the capacitance. (b) If a difference of potential of 125 statvolts is maintained between the plates, determine the charge on either plate. (c) Determine the energy of this charged capacitor.

4. A capacitor of 3 μfd capacitance is charged until the difference of potential between its plates is 120 volts. (a) Determine the charge of the capacitor. (b) Determine the amount of work done in charging it.

5. Two parallel-plate capacitors of identical dimensions differ only in that one has air between the plates and the other has oil of dielectric coefficient 2 between the plates. The capacitance of the air capacitor is 175 stfd. (a) What is the capacitance of the oil capacitor? (b) Each capacitor is charged from the same electric generator to a difference of potential of 50 statvolts. Determine the charge of each capacitor. (c) Determine the energy of each capacitor.

6. (a) Express the energy of a charged parallel-plate capacitor in terms of the electric field E, the area of each plate A, the distance between the plates s,

and the dielectric coefficient k. [Hint: use Equations (1) and (6) and also Equation (7) in Chapter 21.] (b) Show that, if the energy of the capacitor is assumed to be in the electric field between the plates, the amount of energy per unit volume of space is $kE^2/8\pi$.

7. The plates of a parallel-plate capacitor are arranged so that the distance between them can be varied. When the distance between them is s, the capacitor is charged until the difference of potential is V. The plates are then separated until the distance between them is $2s$. Assuming that the charge Q on the plates is unchanged, determine (a) the difference of potential between the plates of this capacitor, (b) the change in the energy of the capacitor due to an increase in the distance between the plates, and (c) the work done in separating the plates.

8. Two capacitors, one of 3 μfd capacitance and the other of 5 μfd capacitance, are connected in parallel and charged until the difference of potential is 110 volts. Determine (a) the charge on each capacitor, (b) the capacitance of this system, and (c) the energy of this system.

9. Two capacitors, one of 4 μfd capacitance and the other of 6 μfd capacitance, are connected in series and charged to a difference of potential of 120 volts. Determine (a) the equivalent capacitance of this combination, (b) the charge on each capacitor, (c) the potential difference across each capacitor, and (d) the energy of this system.

10. A capacitor of 4 μfd capacitance has a charge of 60 μcoul; a capacitor of 3 μfd capacitance has a charge of 40 μcoul. The negative plate of each one is connected to the positive plate of the other. Determine (a) the charge on each capacitor, and (b) the potential difference across each one.

23

The Electric
Circuit

23-1 SOURCES OF ELECTRIC ENERGY

Electricity is at the basis of our present highly technical civilization. It is the means whereby energy from various sources is delivered to the consumer in a form suitable for its conversion into the many forms of energy demanded by him. It is through the intermediary of the electric circuit that energy is transmitted electrically from the primary source, no matter where it is situated, to the ultimate consumer wherever he desires it. A complete electric circuit contains some form of electric generator, which is essentially a device for separating positive and negative charges, a set of conductors for transmitting the electric energy, and some device for converting this electric energy into the desired form of energy. The fundamental principle governing all of these changes is the principle of the conservation and transformation of energy.

There are various types of electric generators. We have already mentioned one type: the electrostatic induction machine, of which the electrophorus is a crude example; it has only limited application. A more common type is the chemical generator, of which there are two general types: (a) the primary chemical cell in which a potential difference is developed by means of chemical action between some of the substances composing the cell—the so-called "dry cell" is a common form of primary chemical cell; and (b) the secondary chemical cell or *storage cell* which must first be charged by sending electricity through it from some other generator, after which it acts just like a primary cell. The storage battery used in cars and on farms consists of several storage cells connected together. As a result of the chemical action which takes place in each of these cells, positive and negative charges are separated.

For the generation of large amounts of electric energy, the *dynamo* is used. The principle on which the operation of the dynamo is based is that an electromotive force is induced in a conductor whenever the conductor cuts across magnetic lines of force. The dynamo is driven by some kind of engine such as a steam engine, gasoline engine, or water

482

turbine. Essentially, the dynamo converts mechanical energy into electric energy.

The chemical cell, the dynamo, and other forms of electric generators will be discussed in greater detail in later chapters. In the present chapter, we shall make use of electric generators, particularly *direct-current* generators, to study the properties of the electric circuit, but we will reserve for a later chapter the discussion of how the generator operates. A d-c generator has two terminals, one of which is at a higher potential than the other. The terminal at the higher potential is called the *positive terminal,* and the other is called the *negative terminal.*

23-2 ELECTRIC CURRENT

If the two terminals of a d-c generator are connected by means of some conducting material, we have a *complete electric circuit.* The action of the electric generator produces a *current* in this circuit. A current in a circuit is a flow of electric charges through the materials composing the circuit. If at any place in the conductor, as in Figure 23–1, we imagine a complete

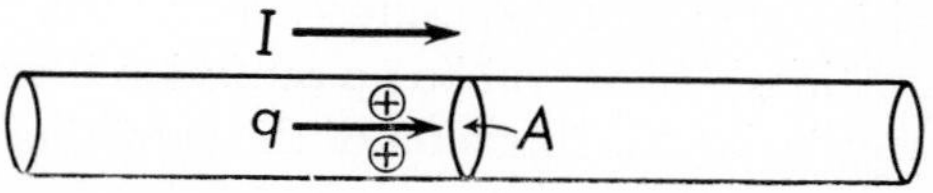

FIG. 23–1   A current in a conductor consists of the flow of charges through any cross-sectional area *A*.

cross-sectional area *A*, the total charge passing through this area in unit time is the *electric current* in the conductor at this place. If a total charge *q* flows through this area in a time *t*, then the current *I* is given by

$$I = \frac{q}{t} .$$

(1)

If *q* is expressed in statcoulombs and *t* in seconds, the current *I* is in es units of current, sometimes called *statamperes.* If *q* is expressed in coulombs and *t* in seconds, then the current *I* is expressed in *amperes;* thus

$$1 \text{ ampere} = \frac{1 \text{ coulomb}}{1 \text{ second}},$$

and $1 \text{ ampere} = 3 \times 10^9 \text{ statamperes.}$

The *direction* of the current is defined as the direction in which the *positive charges* would move. The nature of the charges which are set in motion depends upon the nature of the conducting substance. If the conductor is a *solid,* the current consists of the motion of the *free electrons* in the solid.   If the conductor consists of a gas, the charges which are set in motion are *positive* and *negative ions,* and, under conditions of low pressure, there may be electrons as well as positive and negative ions.   In nonmetallic liquid conductors, the current consists of the motion of positive and negative ions.   The positive charges move in the direction of the current, while the negative charges move in the opposite direction (see Figure 23–2).   If

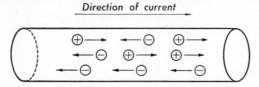

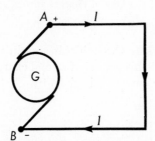

FIG. 23–2   The direction of the current is the direction of motion of the positive charges.   Negative charges move in a direction opposite to that of the current.

both positive and negative charges are set in motion in the conducting medium, the current in it is the sum of the currents produced by the motion of the positive charges in one direction and the negative charges in the opposite direction.   There will be no confusion if we specify in each case whether we are stating the direction of the *current* or the direction of *motion* of the *charges.*

FIG. 23–3   Direction of the current in a circuit.

We have previously shown that when a positive charge moves under the influence of an electric field, its direction of motion is from a point of higher potential to a point of lower potential.   If two such points, say the terminals *A* and *B* of a generator, are connected by a conductor, the direction of the current in the conductor will be from *A,* the point at the higher potential, to *B,* the point at the lower potential (see Figure 23–3).

23-3 ELECTRICAL WORK AND ENERGY

Whenever a charge *q* flows through a conductor under a constant difference of potential *V,* an amount of work $\mathcal{W}$ is done, given by the equation

$$\mathcal{W} = Vq. \tag{2}$$

Like other forms of work and energy, this electrical energy is usually transformed into other types of energy, depending upon the nature of the device through which the current is flowing. In almost all cases, some heat is developed. In electric toasters, heaters, and irons, practically all of the electrical energy is transformed into heat. In the process of charging a storage battery, some of the energy is transformed into chemical energy. An electric motor is used to transform electrical energy into mechanical energy. A tungsten filament lamp and a mercury vapor lamp are some of the devices for transforming electrical energy into light. These and other transformations will be considered in detail at appropriate sections. Of particular interest in this section is the transformation of electrical energy into heat.

Current-measuring instruments, known as *ammeters*, are more readily available and easier to use than charge-measuring instruments. Equation (2) for the electrical work done can be put in a more useful form by replacing the charge q by its value in terms of the current I which is maintained in the conductor for a time t. From Equation (1),

$$q = It;$$

therefore
$$\mathcal{W} = VIt. \tag{3}$$

Another useful term in the discussion of electric circuits is the power delivered to a circuit or to any portion of a circuit. The general definition of power is

$$P = \frac{\mathcal{W}}{t},$$

where P is the power supplied and t is the time taken for the performance of the work $\mathcal{W}$. Using the value of $\mathcal{W}$ given by Equation (3), we get, for the electrical power delivered,

$$P = VI, \tag{4}$$

where V is the difference of potential across the circuit and I is the current in it.

No new units need be introduced for any of the quantities in Equations (2), (3), or (4); it is essential, however, that a set of consistent units be used in each case. For example, in the practical system of units, if I is expressed in amperes, V in volts, and t in seconds, then $\mathcal{W}$ will give the number of joules of work done. Similarly, the power P will be in watts when the current I is expressed in amperes and the potential difference V in volts. For example, if a current of 5 amp is supplied to a conductor under a difference of potential of 110 volts, the power supplied is 550 watts.

23-4 HEATING EFFECT OF AN ELECTRIC CURRENT

Among the many experiments which Joule performed to determine the mechanical equivalent of heat, there were some which involved the transformation of electrical energy into heat. The heating element was simply a coil of wire. The coil of wire was immersed in water of known mass contained in a calorimeter, as shown in Figure 23–4. A current I

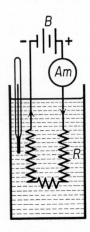

Fig. 23–4   Transformation of electrical energy into heat; heating a quantity of water by means of an electric current in a wire of resistance R immersed in it. Am is an ammeter for measuring the current supplied by the battery B.

was maintained in the coil under a known difference of potential V for a time t. In this way, the electrical energy VIt was measured, while the heat developed was measured by noting the change in temperature of the known mass of water. The mechanical equivalent of heat could be determined from these measurements, and its value was found to be the same as that determined by the conversion of mechanical energy into heat.

Joule also investigated the relationship between the heat developed and the current in the coil; he found that the rate at which electrical energy was converted into heat in any conductor was proportional to the square of the current flowing through the conductor, or

$$P = I^2R, \tag{5}$$

in which P is the electric power delivered to the conductor, I the current in it, and R a constant depending upon the nature and size of the conductor. R is called the *resistance* of the conductor.

Comparing Equations (4) and (5) for the power supplied to a conductor, we get

$$VI = I^2R,$$

from which

$$\boxed{V = IR.} \tag{6}$$

Equation (6) shows that the current in a particular conductor is proportional to the difference of potential across that conductor. This result was first arrived at by Ohm, in 1827, in his investigation of the relationship of the current in a conductor and the potential difference across it, and is known as *Ohm's law.* In the practical system of units, the resistance R is expressed in ohms when the current is expressed in amperes and the potential difference is expressed in volts. Thus

$$1 \text{ ohm} = \frac{1 \text{ volt}}{1 \text{ ampere}}.$$

Illustrative Example. The heating coil of an electric iron operating on a 110-volt line has a current of 5 amp in it. Determine (a) the resistance of the coil, (b) the power supplied to it, and (c) the amount of heat which flows out of it in 4 min.

(a) The resistance of the coil is, from Equation (6),

$$R = \frac{V}{I} = \frac{110}{5} = 22 \text{ ohms.}$$

(b) The power supplied to it is, from Equation (4),

$$P = VI = 110 \times 5 = 550 \text{ watts,}$$

or, from Equation (5),

$$P = I^2R = 25 \times 22 = 550 \text{ watts.}$$

(c) Since all of the electrical work done is converted into heat H, we can write

$$H = Pt = 550 \text{ watts} \times 240 \text{ sec}$$

or

$$H = 132{,}000 \text{ joules;}$$

or, using the mechanical equivalent of heat,

$$J = 4.2 \frac{\text{joules}}{\text{cal}},$$

we get

$$H = \frac{132{,}000}{4.2} \text{ cal} = 31{,}400 \text{ cal.}$$

23-5   RESISTIVITY OF A CONDUCTING SUBSTANCE

A simple way of measuring the resistance of a wire is illustrated in Figure 23–5. The wire CD whose resistance R is to be measured is connected to a storage battery B and an ammeter A. A *voltmeter* V, an instrument for measuring potential difference, is connected across the terminals

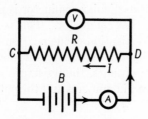

Fig. 23–5 Voltmeter-ammeter method for measuring the resistance of a conductor.

of the wire CD. (The various elements of the electrical circuit are drawn in a conventional manner. The larger of the two strokes representing each of the cells of the storage battery represents the positive terminal. A conductor having appreciable resistance is represented by a zigzag line, while a conductor having negligible resistance is represented by a straight line.) The reading of the ammeter gives the current I in the wire CD, and the voltmeter reading gives the difference of potential V between C and D. This is also sometimes referred to as the *voltage* across the wire CD. The resistance R of the wire is then calculated from Ohm's law

$$R = \frac{V}{I}$$

The factors upon which the resistance of a wire depends can easily be investigated. For example, by using wires of the same material and the same cross-sectional area but of different lengths, it will be observed that the resistance of the wire is directly proportional to its length, providing the temperature is constant. Similarly, by using wires of different cross-sectional areas but of the same material and the same length, and keeping the temperature constant, it will be observed that the resistance varies inversely as the cross-sectional area. By using wires of different materials but of the same length and the same cross-sectional area, again keeping the temperature constant, it will be found that the resistance depends upon material of which the wire is composed.

We can write all of this in the form of a simple equation

$$R = \rho \frac{L}{A},$$ (7)

in which R is the resistance of the wire, L its length, A its cross-sectional area, and ρ (Greek letter rho), a constant depending upon the nature of the material of the wire; ρ is called the *resistivity* of the material. From Equation (7), it can be seen that ρ can be considered as representing the resistance of a small cube of the substance of unit cross-sectional area and unit length on the assumption that the current flows through two opposite faces of the cube. Silver and copper are among the best conductors of electricity. Table 23–1 gives the resistivity, in ohm centimeters, at 0°C, of some of the common conductors.

Table 23-1   Resistivity of Conducting Materials

Substance	Resistivity in ohm cm at 0°C	Temperature Coefficient per °C
Aluminum	2.83×10^{-6}	0.0045
Carbon	4×10^{-3}	-0.00025
Copper	1.70×10^{-6}	0.0039
Iron	10×10^{-6}	0.0062
Manganin	48×10^{-6}	0.00001
Nichrome	108×10^{-6}	0.00017
Platinum	11×10^{-6}	0.0038
Silver	1.63×10^{-6}	0.0038
Tungsten	5.5×10^{-6}	0.0045

23-6 TEMPERATURE AND RESISTANCE

The resistance of a conductor generally depends upon its temperature. To a close approximation, the resistance R at any temperature t is given by the equation

$$R = R_0(1 + \alpha t), \qquad (8)$$

in which R_0 is its resistance at 0°C and t is its temperature in centigrade degrees. The quantity α is called the *temperature coefficient of resistance*. Values of α for some of the common conducting materials are listed in Table 23–1. For metallic conductors, α is always positive, which means that the resistance of a metallic conductor increases with an increase in temperature. Many nonmetallic conductors, such as carbon, have negative temperature coefficients; that is, the resistance of such a conductor decreases as its temperature increases. Other substances, known as semiconductors, such as germanium and silicon, exhibit positive temperature coefficients at low temperatures and negative coefficients at high temperatures. This behavior is related to their impurity content. Some alloys, such as manganin (copper, manganese, and nickel), have been developed which have negligible temperature coefficients of resistance. These are very valuable for making coils whose resistance does not vary with temperature to any appreciable extent.

Some substances which are very good insulators at ordinary temperatures may become good conductors at high temperatures. Glass, for example, is a very good insulator at ordinary temperatures; its resistivity is of the order of 10^{14} ohm cm. But, if a glass rod is raised to a temperature of about 400°C, it becomes a good conductor. A simple demonstration of this is to connect a glass rod to the terminals of a 110-volt source with an ammeter in the circuit and then to heat the rod with a flame. Initially the ammeter will read zero, but, when the temperature of the glass rod reaches about 400°C, an appreciable current will start flowing through the glass. If the flame is now removed, the current will continue to flow and even increase in value until the glass melts. The reason for this is that the glass has a negative temperature coefficient of resistance; once the current rises to an appreciable value, its heating effect, I^2R, raises the temperature of the glass, again lowering its resistance and permitting more current to flow through it. This keeps up until the glass melts and breaks the circuit.

The fact that the resistance of a wire varies with its temperature provides us with an important thermometric property which can be used in the design of thermometers. The dependence of the resistance of platinum wire upon its temperature has been very carefully studied in a range of temperatures from about −200°C to about 1200°C. All that is needed is a very convenient device for measuring the resistance of a coil of platinum wire. One such device, known as a Wheatstone bridge, will be described in Section 23-8. The temperature-measuring element consists of a small coil of fine platinum wire wound on an insulating quartz rod and surrounded by a quartz cylinder with a protecting shield. Long wires then lead from this coil to the resistance-measuring device. The platinum coil with its protecting shield is inserted into the medium whose temperature is to be determined, and the resistance of the coil is then measured. The temperature is then determined from this resistance. A specially designed platinum resistance thermometer is used as a standard in the range from −190°C to 660°C on the international centigrade scale of temperature.

23-7 SERIES AND PARALLEL CONNECTIONS

An electric circuit may be very simple and consist of one or two electrical devices connected to a source of power, or it may be very complex and consist of many different elements connected in a variety of ways. In practical applications, it is important to be able to determine the *equivalent resistance* of any circuit or any section of the circuit in terms of the resistances of the individual elements of a circuit. We shall use the term *resistor* when referring to a coil of wire having appreciable resistance. Suppose we have a circuit consisting of a battery, three resistors, and four ammeters, connected as shown in Figure 23–6. This is called a *series* circuit, and the

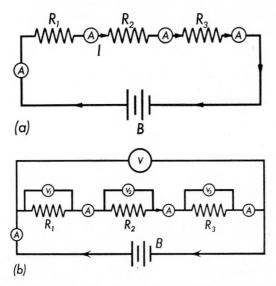

Fɪɢ. 23–6   Resistors connected in series. (a) The current is the same in each resistor. (b) The difference of potential across all the resistors in series is equal to the sum of the differences of potential across each of the resistors.

various elements are said to be connected in *series*. The most important fact to note about a series circuit is that *the current is the same in all parts of the circuit.* The same current flows in each of the resistors, each of the ammeters, and the battery.

Another type of connection is shown in Figure 23–7, in which the three resistors are connected in *parallel*. Since the difference of potential between two points, such as C and D, can have only one value, the difference of potential across each resistor is the same. A voltmeter connected across C and D will give the difference of potential across each resistor and, in this case, will give also the difference of potential across the terminals of the battery. It will be noted that the voltmeter is always connected in parallel with that portion of the circuit whose voltage is to be measured, while the ammeter is always connected in series in that portion of the circuit in which the current is to be measured.

In Figure 23–6(b), if three voltmeters are connected across the three resistors in series, R_1, R_2, and R_3, and a fourth voltmeter is connected across all three resistors, it will be observed that the difference of potential V

across all three resistors in series is equal to the sum of the differences of potential across each of the resistors, or

$$V = V_1 + V_2 + V_3. \qquad (9)$$

Applying Ohm's law to each resistor and remembering that the current I is the same in each one, we get

$$V_1 = IR_1, \qquad V_2 = IR_2, \qquad \text{and} \qquad V_3 = IR_3,$$

which yields, upon substitution in Equation (9),

$$V = IR_1 + IR_2 + IR_3. \qquad (10)$$

The equivalent resistance R of this circuit is one which would have the same current I flowing in it when the same potential difference V is applied to it; that is,

$$V = IR. \qquad (11)$$

Equating these two values of V, we get

$$R = R_1 + R_2 + R_3. \qquad (12)$$

The equivalent resistance of a group of resistors connected in series is the sum of their individual resistances.

If ammeters are inserted into the circuit containing three resistors in parallel, as shown in Figure 23–7, it will be observed that the current I,

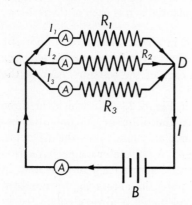

Fig. 23–7   Resistors in parallel. The difference of potential is the same across each resistor.

which leaves the battery, divides at C in such a way that it is equal to the sum of the currents in the individual resistors, or

$$I = I_1 + I_2 + I_3, \qquad (13)$$

where I_1 is the current in R_1, I_2 the current in R_2, and I_3 the current in R_3.

These currents recombine at D and flow back to the battery. Applying Ohm's law to each resistor and remembering that the potential difference V is the same across each one, we get

$$V = I_1R_1, \qquad V = I_2R_2, \qquad \text{and} \qquad V = I_3R_3.$$

We may therefore write Equation (13) as

$$I = \frac{V}{R_1} + \frac{V}{R_2} + \frac{V}{R_3} \, ;$$

and, if R is the equivalent resistance of these three parallel resistors, then

$$I = \frac{V}{R} = \frac{V}{R_1} + \frac{V}{R_2} + \frac{V}{R_3} \, ,$$

from which
$$\boxed{\frac{1}{R} = \frac{1}{R_1} + \frac{1}{R_2} + \frac{1}{R_3} \, ;} \qquad (14)$$

this is the relationship between the equivalent resistance R and the individual resistances of three resistors in parallel. The reciprocal of the resistance is sometimes called the *conductance* of the resistor. Equation (14) may be read as follows: *the equivalent conductance of a parallel circuit is the sum of the conductances of the individual resistors connected in parallel.* Equation (14) also shows that the equivalent resistance of a parallel combination is less than the resistance of any one of the resistors.

In many practical applications, only two resistors are connected in parallel. In this case, the equivalent resistance may be calculated readily as follows: from Equation (14),

$$\frac{1}{R} = \frac{1}{R_1} + \frac{1}{R_2} = \frac{R_1 + R_2}{R_1R_2} \, ;$$

therefore
$$R = \frac{R_1R_2}{R_1 + R_2} \, . \qquad (15)$$

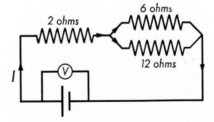

Fig. 23–8

Illustrative Example. In the circuit sketched in Figure 23–8, the voltmeter reads 36 volts. Determine the current in each of the three resistors.

Let us first determine the equivalent resistance of the three resistors. The equivalent resistance R of the two parallel resistors of 6 ohms and 12 ohms is, from Equation (15),

$$R = \frac{6 \times 12}{6 + 12} = 4 \text{ ohms.}$$

We can consider this equivalent resistance to be in series with the 2-ohm resistance so that the equivalent resistance of all three resistors is 6 ohms. Since the potential difference across these resistors is 36 volts, the current I supplied by the battery is

$$I = \frac{36}{6} = 6 \text{ amp.}$$

This is also the current in the 2-ohm resistor. To determine the currents in the two resistors in parallel, we make use of the fact that the potential difference is the same across each one, so that

$$V = I_1 R_1 = I_2 R_2,$$

from which
$$\frac{I_1}{I_2} = \frac{R_2}{R_1} ;$$

that is, the currents in the resistors are in the inverse ratio of the resistances. Letting $R_1 = 6$ ohms, and $R_2 = 12$ ohms, we get

$$\frac{I_1}{I_2} = \frac{12}{6} = 2$$

or
$$I_1 = 2I_2;$$

and, since
$$I = I_1 + I_2 = 6 \text{ amp,}$$

we get
$$3I_2 = 6 \text{ amp,}$$

$$I_2 = 2 \text{ amp,}$$

$$I_1 = 4 \text{ amp.}$$

23-8   RESISTANCE MEASUREMENTS: WHEATSTONE BRIDGE

We have already discussed one method for measuring a resistance which involves the use of an ammeter and voltmeter. A much more accurate method for determining the resistance of a resistor, known as the *Wheatstone bridge method*, involves the use of three other resistors and a very sensitive current-measuring instrument known as a *galvanometer*. The circuit used is shown in Figure 23–9(a), in which X is the resistance to be measured, R_1, R_2, and S are three other resistors, G is the galvanometer, and B is a battery. Let us suppose that the values of the three resistances R_1, R_2, and S have been so chosen that the galvanometer reads zero; that is, no current flows through it, which means that the difference

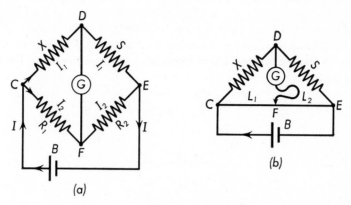

Fɪɢ. 23–9   (a) The Wheatstone bridge.   (b) The slide-wire form of Wheatstone bridge.

of potential between D and F is zero, or that D and F are at the same potential.   Hence the potential difference between C and D is equal to the potential difference between C and F, or

$$V_{CD} = V_{CF},$$

and similarly

$$V_{DE} = V_{FE}.$$

Since there is no current from D to F, the current in DE is the same as that in CD.   For the same reason, the current in FE is the same as that in CF.

Applying Ohm's law to each of the resistors and substituting in the above equations, we get

$$I_1X = I_2R_1$$

and

$$I_1S = I_2R_2,$$

in which I_1 is the current in X and S, and I_2 is the current in R_1 and R_2.

From the above equations, we get

$$\boxed{X = \frac{R_1}{R_2} S.} \tag{16}$$

Thus, if S is a known resistance and the ratio of the two resistances R_1 and R_2 is known, the resistance X can be easily determined.

In laboratory work, S is either a single standard resistance whose value is known accurately, or else it consists of a series of coils of known resistances permitting a choice of a variety of values for S. R_1 and R_2 usually consist of a single wire of known length and a slider making contact at some point F, Figure 23–9(b). Usually when contact is first made at some point on this wire, a current will be started in the galvanometer. The slider is then moved along the wire until a point F is reached which is at the same potential as D, so that there is no current through the galvanometer. If the length of the wire from C to F is L_1, and from F to E is L_2, then, since the resistance of a uniform wire is proportional to its length, we can write

$$\frac{R_1}{R_2} = \frac{L_1}{L_2},$$

and Equation (16) becomes

$$X = \frac{L_1}{L_2} S. \tag{17}$$

Thus the measurement of a resistance is reduced to the measurement of the ratio of two lengths. This form of the Wheatstone bridge is usually called a *slide-wire* bridge.

QUESTIONS

1. Determine the types of electric energy sources available in your home and in your school.

2. Discuss the electric heater from the standpoint of the transformation of energy, beginning with the original source of supply.

3. In what units will the electrical energy be expressed when V and I are both in the cgs electrostatic system of units and t is in seconds?

4. What conditions determine how hot a resistor will become when electricity flows through it?

5. Two 110-volt, 40-watt lamps, one having a tungsten filament and the other having a carbon filament, are switched on simultaneously. Which will reach its incandescent temperature first? Explain your answer.

6. Show that Equation (13) follows from the principle: "the total electric charge in a closed system remains constant."

7. A man decides to do his own wiring at home. After wiring two lamps, he finds that they will light only when both are turned on. If one is turned off, they both go out. What mistake did he make in the wiring?

8. What difference would it make in the measurement of a resistance if an ammeter were used in place of a sensitive galvanometer in a Wheatstone bridge?

9. Will the values of the currents in a Wheatstone bridge affect the measurement of a resistance?

10. Account for the fact that when an electric heater is turned on, the lights in the room get dimmer; when the heater is turned off, the lights get brighter again.

PROBLEMS

1. What is the current when a charge of 8 coul passes through a wire in 2 sec?

2. How many electrons pass through the cross-sectional area of a wire in 1 sec if the wire is carrying a current of 1 amp?

3. How much work is required to transfer a charge of 6 coul against a difference of potential of 110 volts?

4. How much work is done in moving 1 electron through a difference of potential of 1 volt?

5. Calculate the work done in transferring a charge of 500 stcoul between two points in an electric field if the difference of potential is 300 statvolts.

6. A resistor carries a current of 5 amp when the voltage across it is 120 volts. (a) Determine its resistance. (b) How much power is supplied to the resistor?

7. A 120-volt, 60-watt lamp is connected to a 120-volt line. (a) How much current does it take under normal operating conditions? (b) What is the resistance of the lamp filament?

8. (a) Calculate the resistance of a copper wire 1 m long and 2 mm in diameter at 0°C. (b) What is the resistance of a piece of nichrome wire of the same size?

9. The resistance of a platinum wire used in a resistance type of thermometer is 4.25 ohms at 0°C. What is its resistance at 100°C?

10. The resistance of a platinum wire used in a resistance type of thermometer is 4.85 ohms at 0°C. When used to measure the temperature of a liquid, the coil is found to have a resistance of 5.97 ohms. Determine the temperature of the liquid.

11. Two resistors of 60 and 90 ohms resistance, respectively, are connected in parallel, and the combination is connected to a 120-volt source. Determine (a) the effective resistance of this combination and (b) the current through each resistor.

12. Three coils of 20, 30, and 40 ohms resistance, respectively, made of uniform wire, are connected in parallel, and the group is then connected to a 110-volt source. Find (a) the resistance of the combination and (b) the current through each resistance.

13. Three resistors having resistances of 15, 25, and 40 ohms, respectively, are connected in series, and a difference of potential of 120 volts is maintained across the combination. (a) What is the current in each resistor? (b) What is the voltage across each resistor? (c) How much power is supplied to this combination?

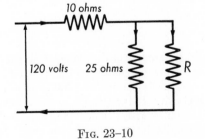

Fɪɢ. 23–10

14. In the circuit sketched in Figure 23–10, the current in the 10-ohm coil is 4.5 amp. (a) Calculate the value of the resistance R. (b) Determine the amount of heat developed in 1 min in the 10-ohm coil.

15. Three resistors having resistances of 5, 8, and 12 ohms, respectively, are connected in series. A storage battery maintains a difference of potential of 12 volts across the combination. How much power is delivered to each resistor?

16. A lamp, an electric heater, and an electric iron are connected in parallel, as shown in Figure 23–11. Their resistances, when hot, are 100, 50, and 20 ohms,

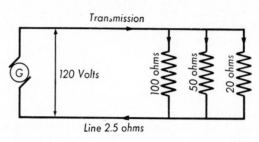

Transmission

G   120 Volts   100 ohms   50 ohms   20 ohms

Line 2.5 ohms

FIG. 23–11

respectively. If the generator produces a potential difference across its terminals of 120 volts and if the transmission line has a resistance of 2.5 ohms, find (a) the current supplied by the generator, (b) the voltage across the terminals of the lamp, (c) the current in the heater, and (d) the power consumed by the heater.

17. A generator which maintains a constant terminal voltage of 120 volts supplies a current of 16 amp to a group of 10 identical lamps in parallel. The line connecting the generator to the lamps has a resistance of 0.5 ohm   (a) What is the voltage at the lamps?   (b) What is the resistance of each lamp?

18. Figure 23–12 is a diagram of a part of an electric circuit. If the current in the 6-ohm resistor is 3 amp, find the following quantities: (a) the reading of the voltmeter connected between C and D; (b) the current in the 8-ohm resistor;

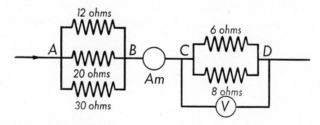

12 ohms

A   B   6 ohms   D

20 ohms   Am   C

30 ohms   8 ohms   V

FIG. 23–12

(c) the reading of the ammeter placed between B and C; (d) the potential difference between points A and B; and (e) the current in the 20-ohm resistor.

19. Two lamps, each rated at 40 watts and 120 volts, are used as resistors in a circuit. If the two lamps are connected in series, (a) what is their combined resistance and (b) how much power is dissipated by these lamps when the potential difference across the two is 120 volts?

20. Derive an equation for the effective resistance R of three resistors connected in parallel if their resistances are R_1, R_2, and R_3, respectively.

21. An electric immersion heater takes 0.32 amp at 120 volts when immersed in 800 gm of water in an aluminum container whose mass is 150 gm. What will be the rise in temperature of the water after 15 minutes of heating?

22. Water flows through a tube at the rate of 180 gm/sec. A heating element inside the tube has a resistance of 8.0 ohms and is connected to a 120-volt line. Determine the rise in temperature of the water flowing through the tube.

24

Electrochemical Effects

24-1 CONDUCTIVITY OF LIQUIDS. ELECTROLYTES

Liquids as well as solids can be classified either as conductors or as non-conductors. Metals in the liquid phase are conductors, and the process of conduction is essentially the same as in the solid phase. There is another class of liquid conductors known as *electrolytes*, which consist of water solutions of acids, bases, and salts. The passage of a current through an electrolyte is generally accompanied by some chemical action; hence the process of conduction in an electrolyte must be different from that in a metal. In order to send a current through an electrolyte, it is necessary to place two solid conductors in the solution to make contact with the rest of the circuit. The solid conductors are usually called *electrodes;* the one through which the current enters the solution is called the *anode,* and the one through which the current leaves the solution is called the *cathode.* The electrodes, electrolyte, and container constitute a chemical cell.

Figure 24–1 shows an electric circuit in which there is a glass jar C containing pure water with two lead electrodes in it; these are connected in series with a resistor R, an ammeter A, and some source of electric power B.

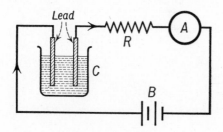

Fig. 24–1 Circuit for studying electrolysis.

Since water is practically a nonconductor, no current will flow through this circuit, and the ammeter reading will be zero. If we now dissolve a small amount of salt, sodium chloride, in the water, a current will flow through the circuit, as shown by the reading on the ammeter, and in addition some chemical action will go on in the chemical cell. This chemical action is known as *electrolysis*. We are at present primarily interested in the nature of the charges which move through the electrolyte. The present theory is that the salt solution consists of *positive ions of sodium* and *negative ions of chlorine*. An *ion* is an atom or group of atoms charged electrically. It was stated previously that, on the modern theory of the structure of the atom, each atom consists of a positively charged nucleus surrounded by a sufficient number of negatively charged electrons so that under normal conditions the atom is neutral. If one electron is removed from the atom, it becomes an ion with a positive charge equal in magnitude to the charge of an electron. If an electron is added to an atom, it becomes a negative ion with a charge equal to that of an electron. When an ion has a charge equivalent to that of one electron, it is said to be singly charged. Some ions may have an excess or a deficiency of two, three, or more electrons. Also, groups of atoms which are closely associated may have an excess or a deficiency of one or more electrons; these are also ions. We shall have many occasions to discuss various types of ions.

To return to the case of the salt solution, chemists have shown that the sodium ion carries a single positive charge (the symbol for the singly charged sodium ion is Na^+), while the chlorine ion carries a single negative charge (it is written as Cl^-). Under the action of the difference of potential between the electrodes, these ions are set in motion, the positive sodium ions moving toward the cathode and the negative chlorine ions moving toward the anode. It is the motion of these ions which constitutes the current in the solution; the motion of the positive ions is in the direction of the current, while the motion of the negative ions is opposite to the direction of the current. The current in the solution consists of the motion of both positive and negative ions.

From the study of the structure of crystals, it is known that salt in the solid phase is a cubic crystal consisting of sodium ions and chlorine ions, and the distance between the centers of two neighboring ions is 2.814×10^{-8} cm. When salt is dissolved in water, the salt is *dissociated;* that is, the separation of these ions is increased. In the solution a small electric field is sufficient to set these ions in motion. Some rather strong, although indirect, evidence that salt consists of sodium ions and chlorine ions is provided by the fact that when salt is melted in a crucible and two electrodes are placed in the molten salt, the sodium ions move toward the cathode, acquire additional electrons from it, and form metallic sodium; while the chlorine ions move toward the anode, give up their extra electrons, and form neutral chlorine which leaves the region of the anode as chlorine gas. The metallic sodium which collects at the cathode is easily removed. As a matter of fact, this is the modern industrial method for preparing metallic sodium.

24-2 ELECTROLYSIS. ELECTROPLATING

As an example of the action which takes place when a current is sent through a chemical cell, let us consider the circuit, shown in Figure 24–2, which contains an electric generator B in series with a variable resistor R,

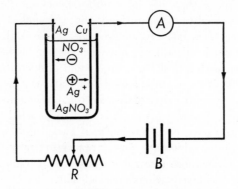

Fɪɢ. 24–2   Circuit for electroplating silver.

an ammeter A, and a chemical cell containing a solution of silver nitrate $AgNO_3$, a silver anode, and a copper cathode. Some of the silver nitrate in solution is dissociated into singly charged positive silver ions Ag^+ and singly charged negative nitrate ions NO_3^-. Under the action of the electric field between the electrodes, the silver ions move toward the cathode, and the nitrate ions move toward the anode. Each silver ion which reaches the cathode acquires an electron from it, forming a neutral silver atom which adheres to the cathode; that is, there is a *plating* of silver on the cathode. The action which takes place at the anode is somewhat different; silver atoms from the anode go into solution as silver ions forming silver nitrate, thus replacing those ions which have left the solution at the cathode. For each silver ion which goes into solution, one electron is left on the anode and moves through the external metallic portion of the circuit. The net effect of the action in this circuit is that silver atoms are taken from the anode and deposited on the cathode, with the silver ions moving through the solution, while the electrons move through the external metallic conductors. The concentration of the solution remains unchanged: just as much silver is deposited on the cathode as is removed from the anode. This can easily be verified by measuring the increase or decrease in mass of each electrode. In the industrial process of electroplating, silver solutions of more complex silver salts are used to get a fine, smooth, silver coating.

In electroplating copper, the material to be plated is made the cathode of the chemical cell, the anode is made of copper, and the solution consists

of copper sulphate $CuSO_4$ dissolved in water (Figure 24–3). Some of the
copper sulphate is dissociated into doubly charged positive copper ions
Cu^{++} and doubly charged negative sulphate ions $SO_4^{=}$. The action which
takes place in the chemical cell is essentially similar to that which takes
place in the plating of silver from a silver nitrate solution, except that the

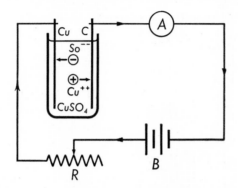

FIG. 24–3   Circuit for electroplating copper.

copper ion acquires two electrons at the cathode and is there deposited as
a copper atom, while at the anode the copper which goes into the solution
is a doubly charged positive ion. For each copper ion which goes into
solution, two electrons are left on the anode, and these travel through the
metallic conductors. Again, as much copper is deposited on the cathode
as is removed from the anode, the solution remaining unchanged.

24-3   ELECTROLYSIS OF WATER

Pure water ionizes to such a small extent that it is practically non-
conducting. A small amount of acid, say sulphuric acid H_2SO_4, is usually
added to it to make it conducting. A water molecule H_2O dissociates into
a hydrogen ion H^+ (the proton) and an hydroxyl ion $(OH)^-$. It is believed
that the hydrogen ion attaches itself to a neutral water molecule forming a
hydronium ion $(H_3O)^+$. Figure 24–4 is a schematic diagram of an apparatus for the electrolysis of water. Platinum electrodes are built into the two
tubes A and B; water, containing a little sulphuric acid, fills these tubes
from a reservoir C. Platinum is used for the electrodes because it is
chemically inactive.

When a small current is sent through the solution, the positive
hydronium ions migrate toward the negative terminal, and the negative
hydroxyl ions and sulphate ions migrate toward the positive terminal.
The exact nature of the reactions at these terminals is not known. Probably a hydronium ion acquires an electron forming a neutral hydrogen

atom and a water molecule.   Two neutral hydrogen atoms combine to form a hydrogen molecule; the hydrogen molecules form a gas in tube B. At the positive electrode, the hydroxyl ions give up their electrons, forming

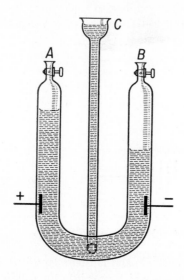

Fig. 24–4   Apparatus for the electrolysis of water.

oxygen and water molecules; the oxygen molecules form the gas in tube A. The net result of this action is that the water molecules dissociate into hydrogen and oxygen according to the chemical equation

$$2H_2O \rightarrow 2H_2 + O_2;$$

that is, the number of hydrogen molecules liberated is twice that of oxygen. This will be observed in the apparatus of Figure 24–4: the volume of gas in B will be twice that in A.

24-4   FARADAY'S LAWS OF ELECTROLYSIS

The results of experiments with electrolytic cells can be summarized in terms of two laws first formulated by Faraday.   The first law states that *the mass of any substance liberated from the solution is proportional to the total quantity of charge Q passing through the circuit,* or

$$M = KQ, \tag{1}$$

in which M is the mass of material liberated at one electrode and K is a factor of proportionality called the *electrochemical equivalent* of the substance.   If Q is expressed in coulombs and M in grams, K will be expressed in grams per coulomb.   For example, the electrochemical

equivalent of silver, which has been determined very accurately, is
$K = 0.0011180$ gm/coul. If the current through the electrolytic cell is I
and flows steadily for a time t, then we may write

$$Q = It,$$

and Faraday's first law can be put in the form

$$M = KIt. \tag{2}$$

It will be recalled that each silver ion is singly charged; we can express
this by saying that silver has a *valence* of 1. The copper ion in the copper
sulphate solutions is doubly charged; we say that it has a valence of 2.
The ratio of the atomic weight A of an element to its valence v is called the
chemical equivalent of the element. Suppose we connect two electrolytic
cells in series, say the two discussed above, as shown in Figure 24–5, so

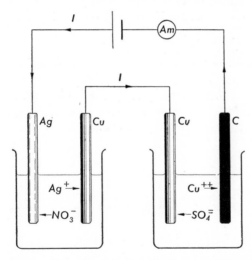

FIG. 24–5   Two electrolytic cells connected in series.

that the same current is maintained in each cell for the same length of
time, and then measure the masses of silver and copper plated out of their
respective solutions. The results of such measurements can be put in
the form

$$\frac{M_1}{M_2} = \frac{A_1/v_1}{A_2/v_2}, \tag{3}$$

where M_1 is the mass of silver deposited and A_1/v_1 is its chemical equivalent; M_2 is the mass of copper deposited and A_2/v_2 is its chemical equivalent. Equation (3) is one method of expressing Faraday's second law of

electrolysis. In words, Faraday's second law states that *if the same quantity of electrical charge passes through a series of cells, the masses of the elements deposited or liberated are in the ratio of their respective chemical equivalents.*

Faraday's two laws of electrolysis can be combined into the following single equation:

$$M = Q \frac{A}{v} \frac{1}{\mathcal{F}},$$ (4)

where M is the mass of an element deposited or liberated by the transfer of a quantity of electricity Q through the electrolytic cell, A is the atomic weight of the element, v its valence, and $\mathcal{F}$ is a constant known as the *Faraday constant.* This constant is equal to the quantity of electricity that is transferred through the cell in depositing or liberating a gram chemical equivalent of an element, where the gram chemical equivalent is the number of grams of the element equal numerically to its chemical equivalent. This can be seen if we set $M = A/v$ in Equation (4); then

$$\mathcal{F} = Q.$$

The Faraday constant $\mathcal{F}$ can be evaluated from known experimental data, say that from the plating of silver. If we substitute the value of M from Equation (1) into Equation (4), we get

$$\mathcal{F} = \frac{A}{Kv}.$$ (5)

For silver, $A = 107.88$ gm/gm-atomic wt, $v = 1$, and $K = 0.0011180$ gm/coul; hence

$$\mathcal{F} = \frac{107.88}{0.0011180} = 96{,}500 \; \frac{\text{coul}}{\text{gm-atomic wt}}.$$

This means that the transfer of 96,500 coul through an electrolytic cell containing a silver solution will deposit 107.88 gm of silver on the cathode; or, this charge will liberate half an atomic weight of copper from a copper solution, since the valence of copper is 2. In general, a charge equal to the Faraday constant will liberate a mass of an element equal to its atomic weight in grams divided by the valence of the element.

24-5   THE CHARGE OF AN ELECTRON

From the results of the experiments on electrolysis, we should be able to determine the charge carried by the ions. The Faraday constant represents the total charge transferred by the ions when a gram-atomic weight of an element of unit valence is liberated from the solution; this means that N_0 ions, each carrying a charge e equivalent to the charge of an electron, were transferred during the process, where N_0 is the Avogadro number. We can thus write

$$\mathcal{F} = N_0 e. \tag{6}$$

The Avogadro number N_0 has been determined by means of other experiments, and its present accepted value is

$$N_0 = 6.023 \times 10^{23}.$$

Equation (6) therefore yields for the electronic charge

$$e = \frac{\mathcal{F}}{N_0} = \frac{96{,}500 \text{ coul}}{6.023 \times 10^{23}} = 1.60 \times 10^{-19} \text{ coul,}$$

or, in electrostatic units,

$$e = 4.80 \times 10^{-10} \text{ stcoul.}$$

An independent method for determining the electronic charge, known as the *oil-drop* method, was first developed by Robert A. Millikan. Millikan's apparatus consisted essentially of two brass plates A and B about 22 cm in diameter and about 1.5 cm apart, as shown in Figure 24–6. These

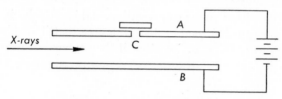

Fig. 24–6   Essentials of Millikan's apparatus for determining the charge of an electron.

plates were placed in a large metal box to avoid air currents. Small drops of oil were sprayed into this box by means of an atomizer. These oil drops became charged in their passage through the fine nozzle of the atomizer. After a while one of these drops drifted through the pinhole C in the top of plate A and could be observed with the aid of a telescope. As the drop is falling between the plates, it experiences a resisting force owing to the viscosity of the air. This resisting force is proportional to the velocity of the oil drop. When there is no electric field between the plates, the oil drop quickly reaches a limiting uniform velocity; it is then in equilibrium under the action of two forces: its effective weight mg, and the resisting force Kv, where v is its velocity and K is a factor of proportionality; that is,

$$mg = Kv. \tag{7}$$

Its effective weight is its weight less the buoyant force of the air.

The two plates A and B separated a distance s may be considered to be the plates of a capacitor. If these plates are connected to the terminals of an electric generator so that a difference of potential V is maintained across them, then the electric field between the plates will be V/s, and the force F on a charge q will be given by

$$F = \frac{V}{s} q. \tag{8}$$

Let us assume that the plate A is always positive. If the charge on the oil drop is negative, the force due to the electric field will be upward. Because of this additional force, the oil drop will now move with a new limiting velocity v_1 which we shall assume to be positive upward. Equating the upward force to the downward forces, since the oil drop is in equilibrium, we get

$$\frac{V}{s} q = mg + Kv_1. \tag{9}$$

In Millikan's experiment, the air between the capacitor plates was ionized by various methods, such as sending x-rays or radiations from radioactive substances through the air. The oil drop occasionally acquired an additional ion, either positive or negative, and its velocity in the electric field was observed to change abruptly. Suppose that it acquired an additional ion carrying a charge q_n, and that it then moved with a new velocity v_2; then equating the upward force to the downward forces, we get

$$\frac{V}{s} (q + q_n) = mg + Kv_2. \tag{10}$$

The mass m in Equations (9) and (10) can be assumed to be the same, since the mass of the oil drop does not change measurably by the loss or addition of an ion. Subtracting Equation (9) from Equation (10), we get

$$\frac{V}{s} q_n = K(v_2 - v_1)$$

or

$$\boxed{q_n = \frac{s}{V} K(v_2 - v_1).} \tag{11}$$

The experiment consists in determining q_n, the charges on the ions captured by the oil drop during the time of observation; in some cases, the same oil drop was observed for several hours. Each time it captured or lost a charge, its velocity would change. Owing to the viscosity of the air, equilibrium was quickly established, and the new velocity of the oil drop was then measured. The velocity was measured by timing the passage of the oil drop between two cross hairs in the telescope a known distance apart. The difference of potential between the plates was of the order of several thousand volts. The quantity K had to be determined by a series of separate experiments on the limiting velocity of fall of drops of various sizes. From this information, q_n could be determined.

As a result of a great many determinations of q_n, it was found that q_n could always be represented by the relationship

$$q_n = ne, \qquad (12)$$

where n is an integer and e represents a small constant charge presumed to be that of an electron. The accepted value of e today is

$$e = 4.80 \times 10^{-10} \text{ stcoul}$$

or $$e = 1.60 \times 10^{-19} \text{ coul.}$$

It must be emphasized that the value of e is the same for both positive and negative charges, since q_n, the ionic charge captured by the oil drop, could be either positive or negative, depending on chance.

24-6 PRIMARY OR VOLTAIC CELLS

Primary or voltaic cells are devices for transforming chemical energy into electric energy. A primary cell usually consists of two different solid conductors as electrodes immersed in an electrolyte. These cells have their origin in two discoveries made at the end of the eighteenth century. In 1786, Luigi Galvani attached a wire to the muscle of a frog's leg and another wire of a different metal to the frog's nerves. When he connected the two free ends of the wires together, he observed that the muscle contracted. He ascribed this phenomenon to the action of animal electricity present in the tissues. Alessandro Volta thought that this phenomenon was due to the contact between two dissimilar metals. He was the first to show the existence of a *contact potential*, or *Volta potential*, by placing a piece of zinc in contact with a piece of copper, then separating them, and showing that the zinc was charged positively and the copper negatively. Volta's next step, in 1800, was the construction of a battery of electrolytic cells with electrodes of copper and zinc immersed in a solution of brine or other electrolyte. He also constructed the forerunner of the modern dry cells by making a "pile" consisting of disks of copper and zinc and some blotting paper soaked in some solution. The order of piling these up was copper, zinc, blotting paper, copper, zinc, blotting paper, and so forth. By connecting the top disk and the bottom disk of the pile with a wire, he was able to get a large continuous current.

As a typical primary cell, let us consider one containing a dilute solution of sulphuric acid, a zinc electrode, and a carbon electrode, as shown in Figure 24–7. When the zinc electrode is put into the solution, some of the

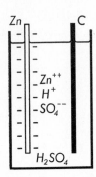

FIG. 24–7 A primary or voltaic cell.

zinc is dissolved, the positive zinc ions Zn^{++} going into the solution and the negative electrons remaining on the electrode. The zinc thus becomes negatively charged, while the solution becomes positively charged. The solution is therefore at a higher potential than the zinc (see Figure 24–8).

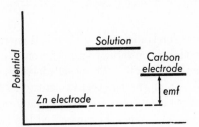

FIG. 24–8 Diagram of the potentials of a primary cell when there is no current through it.

Carbon does not react with sulphuric acid; hence, when carbon is put into the solution, it remains uncharged; its potential will be lower than that of the solution, but higher than that of the zinc. Since the carbon electrode is at the higher potential, it is called the positive electrode, while the zinc is called the negative electrode. The difference of potential between the carbon and the zinc is called the *electromotive force* (emf) of this primary cell. Its value can be measured with an electrostatic type of voltmeter, which is a modification of the gold-leaf electroscope. The conditions diagramed in Figure 24–8 exist as long as no charge flows through the cell.

If a wire is connected across the terminals of the primary cell, electric charges will be set in motion throughout the entire circuit by the emf of the cell. The direction of the current in the conductors outside the cell is from the positive terminal to the negative terminal; inside the cell, the direction of the current is from the negative electrode to the positive electrode (see Figure 24–9). If E is the emf of the cell and I is the current in the circuit, then the energy $\mathcal{W}$ supplied by the cell in time t is

$$\mathcal{W} = EIt. \quad \text{[Equation (3) in Chapter 23]} \tag{13}$$

If the wire connected across the terminals of the cell has a resistance R, and if the conducting substances within the cell have a resistance R_i, and

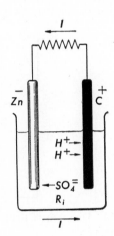

FIG. 24–9 Direction of the current outside a primary cell is from the positive to the negative terminal; inside primary cell, direction of current is from the negative electrode to the positive electrode. Positive charges move in the direction of the current; negative charges move in the opposite direction.

if there are no other devices connected to it, then all of the energy supplied by the cell is converted into heat. We have already shown that the rate at which energy is converted into heat is

$$P = I^2(R + R_i); \quad \text{[Equation (5) in Chapter 23]} \tag{14}$$

hence the energy converted into heat in time t is

$$\mathcal{W} = Pt = I^2Rt + I^2R_it. \tag{15}$$

Substituting the value of $\mathcal{W}$ from Equation (13) yields

$$EIt = I^2Rt + I^2R_it. \tag{16}$$

Solving this equation for E, we get

$$E = IR + IR_i. \tag{17}$$

Now, applying Ohm's law to the wire outside the cell, we get

$$V = IR, \tag{18}$$

where V is the potential difference across the wire outside the cell. Substituting this value in Equation (18), we get

$$\boxed{E = V + IR_i.} \tag{19}$$

This equation states that when a primary cell is supplying current to an external circuit, the electromotive force of the cell is greater than the voltage across the external circuit. The difference between the two, IR_i, is sometimes referred to as the voltage drop inside the cell.

It is instructive to follow the change in potential around the simple circuit of Figure 24–9: starting with the high potential at the positive electrode, we note that the potential drops steadily as we proceed along the resistor to the negative terminal, as shown in Figure 24–10; this drop

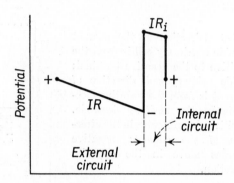

FIG. 24–10   Diagram of the potentials of a primary cell when there is a current through it.

in potential is equal to IR. In going through the surface of the negative electrode into the solution, the potential increases sharply; it then decreases by an amount IR_i as we proceed through the solution, because of the internal resistance. In going from the solution into the positive electrode, there is again an abrupt change to the value of the potential of this electrode.

The flow of charges which takes place in the circuit when a wire is connected across the terminals of this primary cell may be analyzed in the following way. The electrons from the zinc plate flow through the wire to the carbon electrode, where they combine with some of the hydrogen ions from the solution, forming neutral hydrogen atoms. These atoms combine in pairs to form molecular hydrogen, which is then liberated in the form of a gas in the neighborhood of the carbon electrode. Some of this hydrogen forms bubbles, rises to the top of the solution, and goes into the atmosphere. The rest of the hydrogen collects around the carbon electrode and produces an increase in the internal resistance of the cell. The collection of hydrogen gas around the positive electrode is called the *polarization* of the cell. The hydrogen may be removed either mechanically or by putting some oxidizing agent such as manganese dioxide into the cell. Whenever hydrogen ions are neutralized, the positive charge of the solution is decreased so that more zinc can be dissolved. For each zinc ion which goes into solution, two electrons are added to the metallic portion of the circuit and two hydrogen ions H^+ are neutralized and removed from the solution. This action will continue as long as there are zinc and sulphuric acid in the cell.

The so-called *dry* cell is an adaptation of the cell described above. It has a zinc electrode in the form of a cylinder and a carbon electrode in the form of a rod inside but not touching this cylinder (see Figure 24–11).

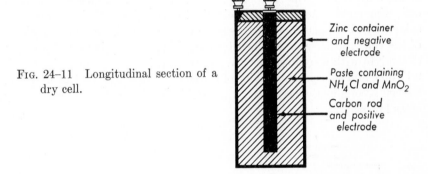

Fig. 24–11   Longitudinal section of a dry cell.

Zinc container and negative electrode

Paste containing NH_4Cl and MnO_2

Carbon rod and positive electrode

The solution, however, is usually a solution of ammonium chloride contained in some blotting paper placed next to the zinc. The rest of the space is filled with a mixture of carbon powder and manganese dioxide—the latter to act as a depolarizer—and some of the solution. The cell is then sealed either with sealing wax or cement so that it will be "dry." The emf of this cell is about 1.55 volts. The dry cell is used for small steady currents; it is also suitable for intermittent use with larger currents.

There are many different types of primary cells designed for different purposes. The emf of a primary cell depends only upon the materials of the cell and to a slight extent upon its temperature. Specially designed cells are used as practical standards for measuring emf's and potential differences. For example, the Weston standard cell has a paste of mercurous sulphate for the positive electrode, an amalgam of cadmium and mercury for the negative electrode, and a saturated solution of cadmium sulphate as the electrolyte. Its emf is 1.01830 volts at 20°C.

Illustrative Example. When a 5-ohm resistor is connected across the terminals of a dry cell which has an emf of 1.55 volts, a current of 0.30 amp flows through it. Determine the internal resistance of the cell.

Using Equation (17)

$$E = IR + IR_i,$$

we get $1.55 = 0.30 \times 5 + 0.30 \times R_i,$

from which $R_i = 0.17$ ohm.

24-7 SECONDARY OR STORAGE CELL

Storage cells differ from primary cells in that the chemical actions can be reversed by charging the cell and thus restoring the cell to its original condition. The fully charged lead storage cell has a positive electrode made of lead dioxide and a negative electrode of lead with a dilute solution of sulphuric acid as the electrolyte. When the cell is discharging, that is, delivering current to an external circuit, the chemical reaction forms lead sulphate on both plates and makes the solution more dilute. The condition of the cell is usually determined by measuring the specific gravity of the electrolyte with a hydrometer. When the cell is fully charged, its emf is 2.1 volts, and the specific gravity of the electrolyte should be 1.285. When the cell is completely discharged, the specific gravity of the electrolyte may be as low as 1.15.

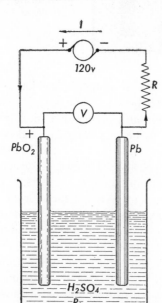

Fig. 24–12   Charging a storage cell.

When the cell is being charged, electric energy is supplied to the cell by some outside electric generator; current enters the cell at the positive electrode and leaves at the negative electrode (see figure 24–12). The chemical action which takes place during charging changes the positive plate back to lead dioxide and the negative plate back to lead, at the same time forming more sulphuric acid. The cell is then ready to be used as a source of electric energy.

In order to charge the storage cell, the difference of potential V across the terminals of the cell must be greater than its electromotive force E. This can be seen from a consideration of the energy transformations which occur. The energy supplied to the cell when a current I is maintained in it for a time t is VIt. Part of this is converted into chemical energy inside the cell; the amount so converted is EIt. Another part is converted into heat because of the internal resistance R_i of the cell; the amount converted into heat is I^2R_it. Using the principle of conservation of energy, we get

$$VIt = EIt + I^2R_it, \tag{20}$$

from which

$$\boxed{V = E + IR_i.} \tag{21}$$

V is called the *terminal voltage* of the cell. Equation (2) states that the terminal voltage across a cell that is being charged exceeds its electromotive force by the voltage drop inside the cell.

The current in the cell can be obtained by solving Equation (21), obtaining

$$\boxed{I = \frac{V - E}{R_i}.} \tag{22}$$

The internal resistance of a storage cell is usually very small—less than 0.1 ohm. If it is to be charged by current from a source which has a much higher terminal voltage than E, the current supplied may be too large for proper charging. In such a case, it is common to insert an additional resistor R to limit the current to an appropriate value.

Illustrative Example. A lead storage cell whose emf is 2.1 volts and whose internal resistance is 0.05 ohm is to be charged from a 120-volt line (see Figure 24–12). The desired charging current is 10 amp. Determine (a) the resistance that must be put in series with the cell, and (b) the terminal voltage of the cell.

(a) Equation (20) must now be modified to include the heat developed in the external resistor R. If V_S is the difference of potential across the source of current, then the energy it supplies to the cell and the resistor is

$$V_SIt = EIt + I^2R_it + I^2Rt. \tag{23}$$

Solving this equation for V_S yields

$$V_S = E + IR_i + IR. \tag{24}$$

In this problem, $V_S = 120$ volts, $E = 2.1$ volts, $I = 10$ amp, and

$R = 0.05$ ohm.   Substituting these values in Equation (24) yields

$$120 = 2.1 + 10 \times 0.05 + 10R,$$

so that $R = 11.74$ ohms.

(b) The terminal voltage V of the cell is, from Equation (21),

$$V = 2.1 + 10 \times 0.05,$$

so that $V = 2.6$ volts.

24-8 COMBINATIONS OF CELLS. BATTERIES

Cells, either primary or storage, may be connected in any manner desired, depending upon the use to which they are to be put.   When cells are connected in *series*, the negative electrode of one cell should be connected to the positive of the second, the negative of the second to the positive of the third, and so on, until the last cell is reached; the negative terminal of that cell is left free (see Figure 24–13).   The positive terminal of

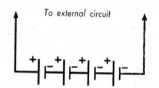

To external circuit

FIG. 24–13   Cells connected in series.

the first cell and the negative terminal of the last cell are then available for connection to the external part of the circuit.   The emf of a battery of cells in series is the sum of the emf's of the individual cells, and the internal resistance of the battery is the sum of the internal resistances of the individual cells.

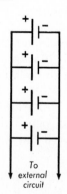

To external circuit

FIG. 24–14   Cells connected in parallel.

When cells of similar construction are connected in *parallel*, all the negative terminals of the cells should be connected together and all the positive terminals should be connected together (see Figure 24–14).   The external load is connected to the terminals of any one of the cells. The emf of this parallel combination is the same as the emf of one cell. If each cell has exactly the same internal resistance R_i, the internal resistance of a battery of n parallel cells is R_i/n.

Illustrative Example. Two batteries of lead storage cells, each consisting of six cells in series, are connected in parallel. Each cell has an emf of 2 volts and an internal resistance of 0.01 ohm. How much current will each cell supply when an external resistor of 4 ohms resistance is connected to this combination of cells?

When considering a circuit containing sources of emf, each with an internal resistance, it will be found very useful to replace each source, in this case each cell, by one having no internal resistance and, connected in series with it, an external resistor whose resistance is equal to that of the cell.

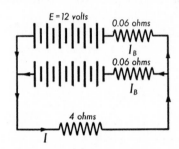

FIG. 24–15

Figure 24–15 is a diagram of the circuit with the internal resistance of each battery, 0.06 ohm, indicated next to it and shown as an external resistance in series with it. The emf of this combination is the same as the emf of each battery, so that $E = 12$ volts. The effective resistance of this circuit is 4.03 ohms, since the two parallel resistances of 0.06 ohm are in series with the 4-ohm resistor. The current I supplied by the batteries is therefore

$$I = \frac{E}{R} = \frac{12}{4.03} = 2.98 \text{ amp.}$$

This is the current in the 4-ohm resistor. Since each of the batteries in parallel has the same emf and the same internal resistance, the current in each one is half the total current; therefore

$$I_B = 1.49 \text{ amp.}$$

Since the six cells of each battery are connected in series, $I_B = 1.49$ amp is also the current in each cell.

24-9   THERMOELECTRIC EFFECT

It is possible to join two dissimilar metals and obtain an electromotive force without any chemical action. If two wires made of dissimilar metals, say copper and iron, have their ends joined together and if the temperatures of the two junctions are different, an electromotive force will be developed in this circuit. The two metals joined in this way constitute a *thermocouple*. Figure 24–16 shows one method of observing this

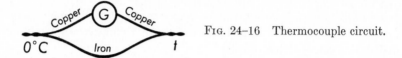

Fig. 24–16   Thermocouple circuit.

effect. One junction is kept at a low temperature, say that of melting ice, and the other junction is heated to a higher temperature. The electromotive force developed by this temperature difference of the two junctions produces a current in the circuit which is registered by the galvanometer. This effect was first discovered by Seebeck, in 1826. Figure 24–17 shows

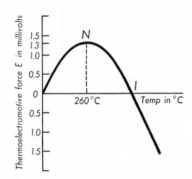

Fig. 24–17   Thermoelectromotive force of a copper-iron thermocouple as a function of the temperature of the hot junction.

the thermoelectromotive force as a function of the temperature of the hot junction when the cold junction is kept at 0°C. The thermoelectromotive force at first increases with increasing temperature until the point N, known as the neutral point, is reached, and then decreases as the temperature of the hot junction is increased still further until the point I, known as the inversion point, is reached, when the emf reverses direction as the temperature is increased still further. The neutral point for a copper-iron thermocouple is about 260°C; it varies with the purity of the metals.

In 1834, Peltier discovered that when there is a current in a thermocouple circuit because of a difference in temperatures at the two junctions, heat is absorbed at the higher temperature junction, and a smaller quantity of heat is emitted at the cooler junction. If a battery is connected in the thermocouple circuit in such a way as to send a current through it in the reverse direction, heat will be given out at the hot junction and absorbed at the cooler junction. The quantity of heat given out or absorbed at a junction depends upon the temperature of the junction, the nature of the materials, and the current in the circuit. This is entirely different from the heating effect due to the resistance of the wire, since the latter depends upon the square of the current while the former depends simply upon the current. For the very small currents in thermocouple circuits, the RI^2 term may be neglected.

Thermocouples can be made of any combination of metals. The electromotive force E of a thermocouple depends upon the nature of the two metals used and the temperatures of the junctions. It is not affected by the presence of any other metal in the circuit if the latter is at the same temperature throughout its length. If one junction is kept at a fixed temperature and the other at any other temperature t, the emf of the thermocouple will be given, to a very close approximation, by the equation

$$E = a + bt + ct^2, \qquad (25)$$

where a, b, and c are constants for the particular thermocouple and have to be determined experimentally from measurements at known temperatures. Once these constants have been determined, the thermocouple may be used as a thermometer. A thermocouple thermometer, one wire of which is made of platinum and the other of an alloy, 90 per cent platinum and 10 per cent rhodium, is used for measuring temperatures on the international scale in the range from 660°C to 1063°C. Special alloys have been developed for use in thermocouples. One of the advantages of a thermocouple thermometer is that only one junction need be heated; and, since this can be made very small, only very small quantities of heat are needed to produce a measurable effect. Because of its small size and mass, the thermocouple junction will follow very rapid changes in temperature.

The thermoelectromotive force has its origin in the difference in the densities of free or conduction electrons of the two metals forming the thermocouple. The free electron density is also a function of the temperature of the metal. When two different metals are placed in contact, electrons diffuse from one into the other, the rate of diffusion depending upon the temperature. When the two junctions of a thermocouple circuit are at different temperatures, the rates of diffusion at these junctions are different, thus producing a current. The idea of electron density suggests that even a homogeneous wire should develop a thermoelectromotive force if the temperature of the wire is nonuniform. This effect was first suggested by William Thomson (Lord Kelvin) and has been observed experimentally. Hence the electrical energy developed in a thermocouple has its origin in two distinct sources: (a) the heat transferred through the junctions, and (b) the heat transferred through the metal wires because of the temperature gradients.

24-10   THE POTENTIOMETER

The potentiometer is an extremely useful and essentially simple instrument for measuring emf and for the calibration of instruments such as voltmeters and ammeters.   Figure 24–18 is a diagram of a potentiometer to be used for measuring the emf of a cell.   It consists of a battery B, a

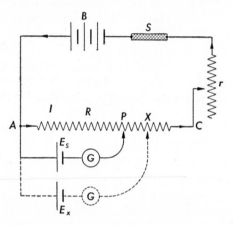

Fig. 24–18   Potentiometer circuit.   Dotted connections represent substitution of cell E_x for standard cell E_s.

switch S, a variable resistor r, and a long wire AC of uniform cross-sectional area, represented in the figure as a resistor.   A suitable current I is maintained in the wire AC; its value can be adjusted by means of the rheostat r.   The value of the current I should be such that the difference of potential between A and C is greater than the emf of the cell to be measured.

The normal method of using a potentiometer is first to calibrate it with the aid of a standard cell, such as a Weston normal cell, whose emf E_S is known.   The standard cell is connected so that its positive terminal is connected to the same point A as the positive terminal of the battery B. One terminal of a sensitive galvanometer G is connected to the negative terminal of the cell, and the other terminal of the galvanometer is connected to a sliding contact key which can be moved along the wire AC. Let us assume that the switch S is closed and that there is a steady current I in the wire AC.   If the movable contact key is made to touch a point on the wire, there will be a deflection of the galvanometer needle, indicating that there is a current in the standard cell.   A glance at Equation (19) shows, however, that the terminal voltage V differs from the emf of the cell if there is any current in it because of the voltage drop inside the cell.

Now $$V = E_S$$

only when there is no current in that branch of the circuit containing the standard cell. The contact key must therefore be moved along the wire until it reaches some point P, so that the galvanometer reads zero, indicating no current in the cell. At this setting, the difference of potential between A and P is equal to the electromotive force E_S of the standard cell. If I is the current in the wire and R_P is the resistance of that length of wire from A to P, then the difference of potential between A and P is IR_P. Hence

$$E_S = IR_P. \tag{26}$$

To measure the electromotive force E_X of any other cell, it is merely necessary to substitute this cell in place of the standard cell and repeat the above procedure. The movable contact key is now moved along the wire until, when it is at some point X, the galvanometer again reads zero. Calling R_X the resistance of that length of wire between A and X, the difference of potential between A and X is IR_X, so that

$$E_X = IR_X. \tag{27}$$

Hence

$$\boxed{\frac{E_X}{E_S} = \frac{R_X}{R_P}.} \tag{28}$$

Since the resistance of a wire of uniform cross-sectional area is proportional to its length, we can write

$$\frac{R_X}{R_P} = \frac{l_X}{l_P}, \tag{29}$$

where l_X is the length of wire from A to X, and l_P is the length of wire from A to P. From Equations (27) and (28), we get

$$\frac{E_X}{E_S} = \frac{l_X}{l_P}$$

or

$$\boxed{E_X = E_S \frac{l_X}{l_P}.} \tag{30}$$

The measurement of the electromotive force of a cell is thus reduced to the measurement of two lengths l_X and l_P.

QUESTIONS

1. Analyze the types of particles whose motion constitutes the current in a silver nitrate solution.

2. Suppose that a carbon electrode replaces the silver anode in the experiment on the electroplating of silver. What would happen to the concentration of the solution?

3. Distinguish between the electrochemical equivalent of an element and the chemical equivalent of the element.

4. Distinguish clearly between the electromotive force of a cell and its terminal voltage. Which of these is greater when the cell is (a) delivering energy and (b) receiving energy?

5. Referring to Equation (19), state under what special conditions the terminal voltage would be equal to the electromotive force of the cell.

6. Discuss what would happen if two cells of different emf's were connected in parallel.

7. Lead storage batteries consisting of three cells in series are sometimes rated as "100 ampere hours" capacity or "120 ampere hours" capacity. Interpret these terms from the standpoint of the electrical energy which is converted into chemical energy in the cells.

PROBLEMS

1. Determine the mass of silver which is deposited on a cathode from a silver nitrate solution by a current of 2 amp in the circuit flowing for 30 min.

2. Determine the mass of copper which is deposited from a copper sulphate solution on the cathode if a steady current of 10 amp flows for 20 min.

3. How long will it take to deposit 1 gm of silver from a silver nitrate solution by a steady current of 4 amp?

4. How long will it take to deposit 4 gm of copper from a copper sulphate solution by a current of 5 amp in the circuit?

5. When a current is passed through water containing a small amount of sulphuric acid to make it conducting, the water is decomposed into hydrogen and oxygen. Hydrogen is liberated at the negative terminal, and oxygen at the positive terminal. (a) How large an electric charge must pass through the solution to liberate 1 gm-atomic weight of hydrogen? (b) How much oxygen will be liberated at the same time? The chemical formula for water is H_2O.

6. A dry cell having an emf of 1.55 volts and an internal resistance of 0.08 ohm supplies current to a 3-ohm resistor. (a) Determine the current in the circuit. (b) Calculate the terminal voltage of the cell.

7. Three lead storage cells are connected in series to form a battery to supply current to automobile head lamps. If the emf of each cell fully charged is 2.1 volts and its internal resistance is 0.02 ohm, what is the terminal voltage of the battery when supplying 15 amp to the lamps?

8. A battery of cells has a total emf of 24 volts and an internal resistance of 2.0 ohms. It is connected in series with a resistor of 16 ohms resistance, and a parallel combination of two resistors of 4 and 8 ohms resistance, respectively. (a) Draw a diagram of this circuit. (b) What is the current supplied by the battery? (c) What is the terminal voltage of the battery? (d) How much energy does the battery supply to the external circuit in 30 min?

9. An automobile battery whose emf is 6.3 volts, when being charged with a current of 12 amp, has a terminal voltage of 7.2 volts. (a) Determine the internal resistance of the battery. (b) Determine how much energy is supplied to the

battery in 5 hr. (c) How much of this energy is converted into heat? (d) What becomes of the rest of this energy?

10. A lead storage battery whose emf is 12 volts and internal resistance is 0.8 ohm is to be charged by connecting it to a 120-volt source. (a) What resistance must be put in series with the battery to limit the current to 5 amp? (b) What is the terminal voltage of the battery under these conditions? (c) What fraction of the energy supplied by the source is converted into heat?

11. A circuit is composed of three resistors and a battery, as shown in Figure 24–19. The internal resistance of the battery is 0.3 ohm, and the potential difference across the 1.5 ohm resistor is 6 volts. (a) Find the current through

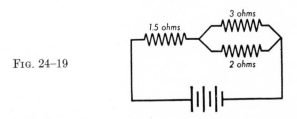

Fig. 24–19

the battery. (b) What is the potential difference between the battery terminals? (c) What is the emf of the battery? (d) What energy is dissipated in the 3-ohm resistor per minute?

12. How many cells, each having an emf of 1.55 volts and an internal resistance of 0.2 ohm, must be connected in series to supply a current of 1.2 amp to operate an instrument having a resistance of 18 ohms?

13. Two identical cells, when connected in series, supply a current of 0.40 amp to a 10-ohm resistor. When these cells are connected in parallel, they supply 0.25 amp to the same resistor. Determine (a) the emf of each cell and (b) the internal resistance of each cell.

14. The slide wire of a potentiometer is 200 cm long. When it is balanced with a standard cell whose emf is 1.0183 volts, the length of wire needed is 121.5 cm. When a dry cell is substituted for the standard cell, the contact point is at 185. cm. Determine the emf of the dry cell.

25

Electromagnetic Effects

25-1 MAGNETIC FIELD AROUND AN ELECTRIC CURRENT

The first evidence for the existence of a magnetic field around an electric current was observed in 1820 by Hans Christian Oersted (1777–1851). He found that when a wire was placed over and parallel to a freely pivoted compass needle (see Figure 25–1), the needle was deflected toward a position at right angles to the wire CD. If the north pole of the magnet is

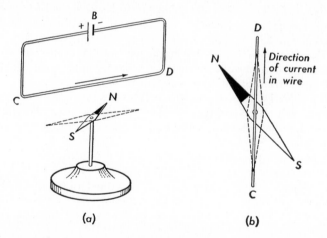

(a)   (b)

Fig. 25–1 Oersted's experiment. Compass needle is deflected toward the west when the wire CD, carrying current, is placed above it and the direction of the current is toward the north, from C to D.

directed from C toward D and if current is now sent through the wire from C to D, then, viewed from above, the north pole will be deflected toward the left. If the current were to be reversed and directed from D to C, then the north pole would be deflected to the right as seen from above.

The magnetic field in the neighborhood of a wire carrying a current can be investigated either by exploring the region with a small compass or by using iron filings (see Chapter 20). Figure 25–2 shows a wire passing perpendicularly through a plane board. A battery maintains current in the wire, and iron filings are then sprinkled on the board. The pattern

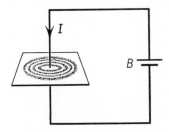

FIG. 25–2 Pattern formed by iron filings showing the circular magnetic field around a wire carrying current.

formed by the iron filings shows that the magnetic field is circular in a plane at right angles to the current, with the wire carrying the current at the center of all of these circles. The direction of the magnetic field can be determined with the aid of a small compass. If we look along the wire so that the current is coming toward us, the magnetic field is counterclockwise. Figure 25–3(a) shows the directions of the circular magnetic

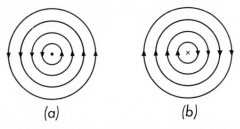

(a)   (b)

FIG. 25–3 Direction of the magnetic field around a wire (a) when the current is out of the paper, (b) when the current is into the paper.

lines of force when the current in the wire is perpendicular to the paper and coming toward the reader, while Figure 25–3(b) shows the magnetic lines of force around a wire perpendicular to the plane of the paper when the current is away from the reader. A small compass placed anywhere in the field will set itself tangent to one of these circles with its north pole in the direction of the arrow.

When the wire carrying current is bent in the form of a circular loop, as shown in Figure 25–4, the direction of the magnetic field around each small portion of the wire can be determined from the rule given above. If the current in the loop is counterclockwise when viewed along the x-axis, the direction of the magnetic field inside the loop will be perpendicular to its plane and directed parallel to the x-axis toward the viewer.

A simple way of determining the direction of the magnetic field relative to the direction of the current is to use the *right-hand rule*. If the current is in a straight portion of wire, then if we imagine the thumb of the right hand placed along the wire and pointing in the direction of the cur-

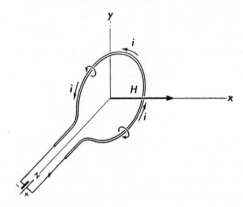

FIG. 25–4   Magnetic field produced by a current in a circular loop of wire. The magnetic field at the center is at right angles to the plane of the loop.

rent, the fingers of the right hand will curve in the direction of the magnetic field. If the current flows in a circular path, then if we imagine the fingers of the right hand curving in the direction of the current, the thumb will point in the direction of the magnetic field inside the coil (see Figure 25–4).

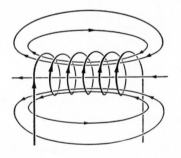

FIG. 25–5   Magnetic field due to a current in a long cylindrical coil or helix.

When, as in Figure 25–5, the wire is wound in the form of a helix which is very long in comparison with its diameter, the magnetic field outside the coil is very similar to that of a bar magnet, while the field inside the coil is uniform and parallel to the axis of the coil.

25-2 EQUIVALENCE OF A MOVING CHARGE AND A CURRENT

Our original definition of current was based on the flow of charges through a surface in a given time interval. It remains to be shown that a set of moving charges will produce the same magnetic effect as a current in a wire. This was first shown experimentally by H. A. Rowland in 1876. In one experiment, he used an ebonite disk having metallic sectors distributed near its rim. The metallic sectors were charged electrically, and the disk was set into rapid rotation. A magnetic needle suspended near the disk was deflected by the magnetic field set up by the moving charges. The direction of the deflection was the same as that which would have been produced by a current in a circular loop of wire coinciding with the rim of the disk. When the direction of rotation of the disk was reversed, the deflection of the magnetic needle was also reversed. More recently (1929), R. C. Tolman set a charged cylinder oscillating about its axis. This produced an alternating magnetic field, the same as that produced in the neighborhood of alternating current. These experiments show that as far as the magnetic effect is concerned, a moving charge and a current in a wire are equivalent.

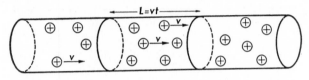

Fig. 25–6

Figure 25–6 shows a tube in which a current I consists of the motion of positive charges with uniform velocity v. From the definition of current,

$$I = \frac{q}{t}, \qquad \text{[Equation (1) in Chapter 23]} \tag{1}$$

where q is the quantity of charge which passes through a complete cross-sectional area of the tube in a time t. The charge q will traverse a length L of the tube where

$$L = vt. \tag{2}$$

Eliminating t from these two equations yields

$$\boxed{IL = qv.} \tag{3}$$

In other words, a charge q moving with velocity v may be considered to be a current element of length L carrying current I, where L and v are related by Equation (2).

25-3 INTENSITY OF THE MAGNETIC FIELD OF A CURRENT ELEMENT

As soon as Oersted's discovery was announced, scientists in Europe began repeating and extending these experiments. Biot and Savart, in 1820, determined the magnetic field produced by a current in long straight wire, and Ampère, 1820, studied the forces due to the magnetic fields between wires carrying currents. The experiments of Biot and Savart showed that the intensity of the magnetic field ΔH, at a point P, a distance r from a small section Δs of wire carrying current I, varies inversely

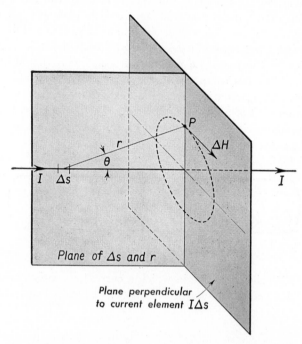

FIG. 25-7   The magnetic field ΔH at any point P a distance r from a small
section Δs of wire carrying current I. The magnetic field is circular in a
plane at right angles to the straight wire; ΔH is perpendicular to r and the
plane containing Δs and r.

as the square of this distance and is directly proportional to the current,
to the length Δs of this section of wire, and to the sine of the angle θ between Δs and r (see Figure 25-7).   Or, in symbols,

$$\Delta H \propto \frac{I \Delta s \sin \theta}{r^2}.$$

The above relationship can be written as an equation,

$$\Delta H = K \frac{I \Delta s \sin \theta}{r^2},$$ (4)

where K is a factor of proportionality whose value depends upon the
system of units used.

The direction of the magnetic field ΔH at the point P produced by
the current element $I \Delta s$ at a distance r from P can be found with the aid

of the right-hand rule; ΔH is perpendicular to the plane containing $I \Delta s$ and r. This is illustrated in Figure 25–7 in which two mutually perpendicular planes are drawn, one containing the current element $I \Delta s$ and the line r, and the other plane through P perpendicular to $I \Delta s$. The vector ΔH is in the latter plane. Since the magnetic field around a straight wire carrying current is circular in a plane perpendicular to the wire, the vector ΔH is tangent to a circle through P having the wire as center.

To determine the intensity of the magnetic field due to the current in a long conductor, it is necessary to add, by vectorial methods, the contribution of each small portion of the conductor to the magnetic field intensity at any given point. The mathematics required for this is generally beyond the scope of this book, but one special case can be easily evaluated: it is the magnetic field produced at the center of a circular coil carrying current. We shall use the result thus obtained for the evaluation of the constant K.

25-4   MAGNETIC FIELD OF A CIRCULAR CURRENT

Suppose that a current I is flowing in a circular loop of radius r, as shown in Figure 25–8. The length of wire in this circle is $2\pi r$; we can imagine the wire to consist of small contiguous elements, each of length

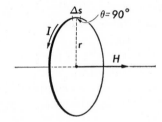

Fig. 25–8   Intensity of the magnetic field at the center of a circular coil is at right angles to the plane of the circle.

Δs, producing a magnetic field of intensity ΔH at the center, a distance r from each such element. The direction of ΔH at the center will be perpendicular to the plane of the circle; that is, the contribution ΔH from each current element $I \Delta s$ will have the same direction; hence they can be added algebraically. Since Δs is at right angles to the radius r, the angle θ is the same for each element and is 90°, so that $\sin \theta = 1$. Putting this value into Equation (4), we get

$$\Delta H = K \frac{I \Delta s}{r^2}$$

as the contribution from each current element to the intensity of the magnetic field H at the center. Summing up these contributions yields

$$H = K \frac{2\pi r I}{r^2},$$

from which

$$H = K \frac{2\pi I}{r}.$$ (5)

The constant K can be evaluated with the end of Equation (5) by sending a known current through a coil of known radius and measuring the intensity of the magnetic field at the center. If I is measured in amperes, r in centimeters, and H in oersteds, then the constant $K = 1/10$. Equation (5) thus becomes

$$H = \frac{2\pi I}{10r}.$$ (6)

In many theoretical discussions it is desirable to set $K = 1$. This can be done by adopting a new unit of current, known as the *electromagnetic unit* and called an *abampere*, where

1 abampere = 10 amperes.

For the above case, Equation (5) becomes

$$H = \frac{2\pi I_m}{r},$$ (7)

where I_m designates the electromagnetic unit of current.

Illustrative Example. A circular coil of wire, consisting of 30 closely wound turns of 15 cm average radius, carries a current of 20 amp. Determine the intensity of the magnetic field at the center of this coil.

Assuming that the turns are so closely wound in this coil that the current in each one contributes the same amount to the intensity of the magnetic field at the center of the coil, Equation (6) can be modified to read

$$H = \frac{2\pi n I}{10r},$$ (8)

in which n is the number of closely wound turns in the coil. Substituting the appropriate numerical values, $n = 30$ turns, $I = 20$ amp, and $r = 15$ cm, we get

$$H = \frac{2\pi \times 30 \times 20}{10 \times 15} = 25.1 \text{ oersteds}$$

as the intensity of the magnetic field at the center of the coil.

25-5 THE TANGENT GALVANOMETER

If a small magnet with poles of strength p were to be placed at the center of a circular coil, each pole would experience a force Hp. The direction of this force is at right angles to the plane of the circle, the force on the north pole being in one direction and that on the south pole in the opposite direction. It will be recalled that the direction of H is the same as the direction of the force on the north pole. If the direction of the current in the coil is counterclockwise, as seen by the reader, then experiment shows that the direction of H is at right angles to the plane of the coil and directed toward the reader (see Figure 25–9). The right-hand rule can be

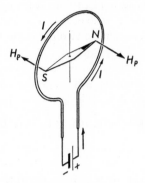

FIG. 25–9 Forces on the poles of a small compass placed at the center of a circular loop of wire whose plane is in the magnetic meridian.

used for determining the direction of the magnetic field relative to the current which produces it. If the fingers of the right hand are curled in the direction of the current in the coil, the thumb will extend in the direction of the magnetic field (see also Figures 25–4 and 25–5).

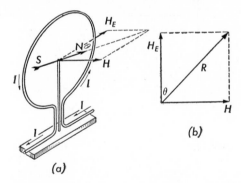

(b)

(a)

FIG. 25–10   (a) Tangent galvanometer. The plane of the circular coil is parallel to the earth's magnetic field. (b) The two magnetic fields which act on the N-pole of the small compass needle. H_E is the horizontal component of the earth's magnetic field; H is the intensity of the magnetic field produced by the current I. R is the resultant of these two field intensities. $H = H_E \tan \theta$.

One of the earliest forms of standard current-measuring instruments, the so-called *tangent galvanometer*, consisted of a single circular loop of wire with a very small compass needle placed at its center (see Figure 25–10). The plane of the coil was set parallel to the direction of the compass needle at the place where the instrument was used. When a current I was sent through the loop, it set up a magnetic field of strength H at the center, producing a force Hp on each pole of the magnet, the force on the north pole directed toward the right, that on the south pole toward the left. These two forces produced a torque causing the compass needle to rotate out of the plane of the coil. The horizontal component of the earth's magnetic field produced an opposite torque on the compass needle. The compass needle came to rest at some angle θ with the plane of the loop, at which angle the two opposing torques were equal in magnitude. A simple calculation shows that the current in the loop is proportional to the tangent of the angle θ, hence the name tangent galvanometer. The modern type of galvanometer will be described in Section 25–13.

25-6 MAGNETIC FIELD INTENSITY OF A CURRENT IN A LONG STRAIGHT LINE

We have already shown that the magnetic field around a straight wire carrying current is circular in every plane at right angles to the wire. The intensity of this magnetic field at any point in the neighborhood of the wire can be evaluated with the aid of Equation (5). The mathematics required for this is beyond the scope of this book. Because of its impor-

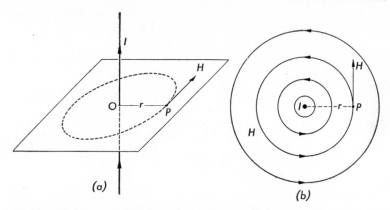

Fig. 25–11   (a) Magnetic field intensity H at a point P at a distance r from a straight wire carrying current is circular in a plane at right angles to the current.   (b) The magnetic field viewed in a plane perpendicular to I. The current is coming out of the paper toward the reader.

tance, we shall merely give its value here. If the current in the wire is I and if the wire is very long, then the magnetic field intensity H at a point a distance r from the wire is given by

$$H = \frac{2I}{10r} \, . \tag{9}$$

Figure 25–11(a) shows a part of the long wire carrying current I going through a point O in a plane perpendicular to it. A circular line of force is drawn through P, with O as its center. The direction of H can always be found with the aid of the right-hand rule. H is tangent to the circle of radius r drawn in a plane at right angles to the wire, with the wire at the center of the circle. Figure 25–11(b) shows the circles drawn in the plane of the paper to represent the magnetic field intensity. The current is assumed to be coming out of the paper toward the reader; the lines of force are circular in a counterclockwise direction. This means that at any point P the force on a north pole of a magnet placed there is tangent to the circle in the direction of the arrow shown.

Illustrative Example. A long straight wire has a current of 40 amp in it. Determine the magnetic field intensity at a point 60 cm from the wire.

Using Equation (9) and substituting the values $I = 40$ amp, and $r = 60$ cm, we get

$$H = \frac{2 \times 40}{10 \times 60} = 0.133 \text{ oersted.}$$

25-7 MAGNETIC FIELD INTENSITY INSIDE A SOLENOID

A solenoid is made by winding wire on a cylindrical form; the length L of the cylinder should be much larger than its radius R. The adjacent turns of wire should be very close together [see Figure 25–12(a)]. The

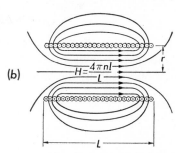

(a)

(b)

FIG. 25–12 (a) Windings of a solenoid. (b) Magnetic field intensity inside a solenoid. Current is coming out of the wires on top and going into the wires on bottom.

magnetic field inside the solenoid is the sum of the contributions of the current in each turn of wire to this field. Calculation of the intensity of the magnetic field, using Equation (5), shows that the field is uniform over the entire region inside the solenoid except near the ends [see Figure 25-12(b)]. The intensity H of the uniform portion of the magnetic field inside the solenoid is found to be

$$H = \frac{4\pi nI}{10L}, \tag{10}$$

where I is the current in amperes, in the wire wound around the cylindrical form and n is the total number of turns of wire. The solenoid is frequently used as a standard for measuring magnetic field intensities and as a convenient method of getting known uniform magnetic fields.

Illustrative Example. A solenoid 80 cm long with a radius of 3 cm is wound with 500 turns of wire and carries a current of 4 amp. Determine the intensity of the magnetic field inside the solenoid at points near its center.

Since the length of the solenoid is much greater than its radius, the magnetic field intensity can be determined with the aid of Equation (10) for points near the center. Thus

$$H = \frac{4\pi \times 500 \times 4}{10 \times 80} \text{ oersteds,}$$

so that $\qquad\qquad H = 31.42$ oersteds.

25-8   FORCE ON A CURRENT ELEMENT IN A MAGNETIC FIELD

Ampère's work, in 1825, on the forces experienced by wires carrying currents in magnetic fields forms the foundation of the subject of electrodynamics. Let us start with the fundamental Equation (4) for the magnetic field intensity ΔH produced by a current element $I\Delta s$ at a point A at a distance r from it, and imagine a very long thin magnet of pole strength p with its north pole at this point A. It will experience a force

$$\Delta F = p\Delta H \tag{11}$$

in the direction of ΔH. According to Newton's third law, the magnetic pole at A will exert an equal and opposite force on the current element $I\Delta s$. Substituting the value of ΔH from Equation (4) into the above equation yields

$$\Delta F = K \frac{I\Delta s \cdot p \sin \theta}{r^2} \tag{12}$$

for the value of this force. Its direction is in a plane perpendicular to the plane containing $I\Delta s$ and r, as shown in Figure 25-13.

Now the current element $I\Delta s$ is in the magnetic field of the long thin magnet of pole strength p. Let us assume that the south pole of this magnet is sufficiently far away so that the magnetic field produced by the north pole is radial. We have shown that the intensity H_p of such a field is given by

$$H_p = \frac{p}{\mu r^2} \; ; \quad \text{[Equation (3) in Chapter 20]}$$

H_p is the value of the intensity of the magnetic field at the current element $I \Delta s$ at a distance r from p, and μ is the permeability of the medium.

From the above equation, we get

$$\frac{p}{r^2} = \mu H_p.$$

Substituting this value in Equation (12), we get

$$\Delta F = K I \Delta s \mu H_p \sin \theta \qquad \qquad \text{(13)}$$

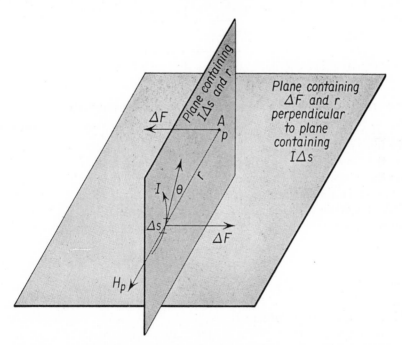

FIG. 25–13   Equal and oppositely directed forces are experienced by the north magnetic pole at A and by the current element $I \Delta s$.

for the force on the current element when it is in a magnetic field of strength H_p. Since H_p is radial, its direction is along r from A to $I \Delta s$, and θ is the angle between r and $I \Delta s$, as shown in Figure 25–13. The force ΔF, produced by the interaction of the magnetic field and the current element, is at right angles to the plane containing H_p and $I\Delta s$, as shown in Figure 25–13.

The force on the current element will be the same for a given field intensity, no matter what the source of the magnetic field may be. Hence, dropping the subscript $_p$, the fundamental equation for the force on a current element in a magnetic field becomes

$$\Delta F = KI\Delta s\mu H \sin \theta. \tag{14}$$

It will be convenient at this stage to define a new quantity called the *magnetic flux density*, B, or the *magnetic induction*, by the equation

$$B = \mu H. \tag{15}$$

The magnetic induction B is a vector quantity in the same direction as H. When H is in oersteds, B is expressed in *gauss*.

Substituting the value of B into Equation (14) yields

$$\Delta F = KI\Delta s B \sin \theta. \tag{16}$$

This equation is sometimes known as *Ampère's law*.

25-9   FORCE ON A WIRE CARRYING CURRENT IN A MAGNETIC FIELD

If a wire of length L, carrying current I, is placed in a magnetic field, the force on it can be evaluated with the aid of Equation (16) by calculating the force on each current element and summing these forces vectorially for the entire wire. In general this is a rather difficult thing to do. In some special cases of interest to us, this can readily be done. For example, if the magnetic field is uniform throughout the length of the wire and if the wire is straight so that the angle θ is constant, then Equation (16) yields

$$F = KILB \sin \theta \tag{17}$$

for the force on a wire carrying current I in a constant magnetic field of flux density B, where L is the length of the wire in the magnetic field and θ is the angle between B and L.

In the special case where B and L are at right angles to each other, as in Figure 25–14, $\theta = 90°$ and $\sin \theta = 1$, so that Equation (17) becomes

$$F = KILB. \tag{18}$$

We have shown that if the current is expressed in electromagnetic units, $K = 1$, so that Equation (18) becomes

$$F = I_m LB; \tag{19}$$

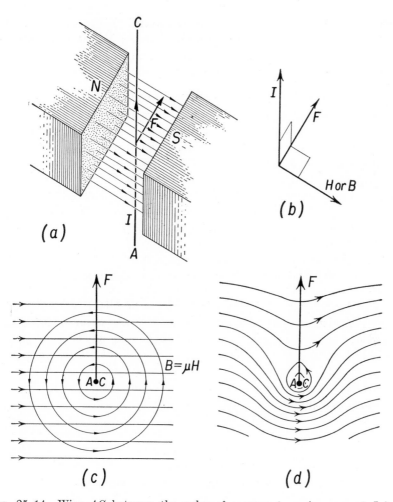

Fig. 25-14   Wire AC between the poles of a magnet carries current I in a magnetic field of strength H and flux density B.   (a) Direction of force F on wire is at right angles to the wire and the direction of the magnetic field. (b) Relative directions of I, B, and F; these vectors are mutually perpendicular.   (c) The two magnetic fields, that due to I and the field B of the magnet; (d) the resultant of these two fields is stronger below AC and weaker above AC.   The wire is forced from the stronger to the weaker field.

if the current is expressed in amperes, $K = 1/10$, so that Equation (18) becomes

$$F = \tfrac{1}{10}ILB. \tag{20}$$

The relative directions of F, B, and I are shown in Figure 25–14(b).

For example, if a wire has a length of 10 cm in a magnetic field of 3,000 gausses and is at right angles to this field, then, when the current in it is 6 abamperes, it will experience a force

$$F = 3,000 \times 6 \times 10 = 18 \times 10^4 \text{ dynes.}$$

Just as the magnetic field intensity H is represented by lines of force, so can the magnetic influx density or the magnetic induction B be represented by *lines of induction*. The scale of the drawing can be chosen so that the number of *lines of induction per unit area* at any point is equal to the value of B at that point. Although Equation (20) suggests a method of measuring B by measuring the force on a current element in a magnetic field, more practical methods will be described in Chapter 27. We shall defer until then a discussion of the factors which determine the permeability μ of a substance.

A simple method for determining the direction of the force on a wire carrying current when placed in a magnetic field is to examine the relative directions of this magnetic field of flux density B and the magnetic field produced by the current in the wire. Figure 25–14(c) shows these two magnetic fields in a plane at right angles to the wire when viewed from A toward C. Since the current in the wire is coming out of the paper, its magnetic field is circular around the wire and counterclockwise. Below the wire, the two magnetic fields are in the same direction, thus producing a more intense magnetic field; above the wire, the two fields are in opposite directions, thus producing a weak field, as shown in Figure 25–14(d). Experiment shows that the force on AC is upward; that is, the wire is forced from the stronger magnetic field toward the weaker magnetic field. The method outlined above is perfectly general; *whenever a wire carrying current is placed in a magnetic field, the force on the wire will always be directed from the stronger toward the weaker part of the resultant field.*

25-10 FORCE BETWEEN TWO PARALLEL WIRES CARRYING CURRENTS

Two parallel wires carrying currents will exert forces on each other owing to the interaction of their respective magnetic fields. If the two currents are in the same direction, the force between them will be one of attraction; if the two currents are in opposite directions, the force will be one of repulsion. Figure 25–15 shows the magnetic fields in a plane at right angles to the wires. In Figure 25–15(a), the currents are assumed to be coming out of the paper toward the reader. The magnetic field is circular in a counterclockwise direction around each wire. The two fields are in opposite directions in the space between the wires. The resultant magnetic field is thus weakened in this region, as shown in Figure 25–15(b), and the wires are forced toward each other, each wire going from the stronger to the weaker part of the field. Figure 25–15(c) shows the two

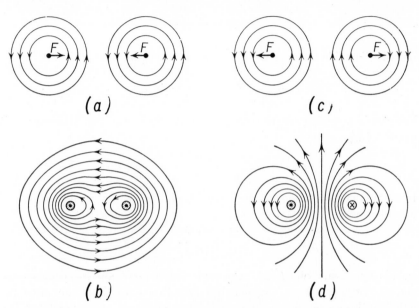

(a)

(c)

(b)

(d)

FIG. 25–15   Magnetic field of two parallel wires in a plane at right angles to them (a) when currents are in the same direction out of the paper, (b) the resultant field; (c) currents are in opposite directions, and (d) the resultant field.

magnetic fields between two parallel wires carrying currents in opposite directions. These fields, again, are drawn in a plane perpendicular to the two wires. It will be seen that the fields between the wires are in the same direction, and hence reinforce each other in this region, as shown in Figure 25–15(d). The wires are therefore forced away from each other, the force on each wire being directed from the stronger to the weaker field.

We have already shown that the force on a wire carrying current I in a magnetic field of flux density B is given by

$$F = \tfrac{1}{10}ILB, \tag{20}$$

when I and B are at right angles to each other. We can apply this equation to determine the force between two parallel wires. Let us consider a length L of one wire carrying current I to be in the magnetic field B of the second wire carrying current I' at a distance r from it. The value of

B can be found by combining the equations

$$B = \mu H \tag{15}$$

and

$$H = \frac{2I'}{10r}, \tag{9}$$

obtaining

$$B = \frac{2\mu I'}{10r}.$$

Substituting this value of B into Equation (20) yields

$$F = \frac{2\mu L I I'}{100r}.$$

From this equation we can obtain the equation for the force per unit length of wire as

$$\frac{F}{L} = \frac{2\mu I I'}{100r}.$$

In a vacuum $\mu = 1$, so that the force per unit length between two parallel wires becomes

$$\frac{F}{L} = \frac{2I I'}{100r}. \tag{21}$$

In this equation, I and I' are expressed in amperes, L and r in centimeters, and F in dynes. It is obvious that Equation (21) gives the force per unit length on each of the two wires. If $I = I' = 1$ amp, $r = 1$ cm, and $L = 1$ cm, then $F = 0.02$ dyne.

Equation (21) suggests a method for the accurate measurement of current in terms of the force exerted by two parallel currents. An instrument based upon this effect is called a *current balance*. For convenience, circular coils of wire, rather than straight wires, are used in actual current balances.

25-11   A CHARGE MOVING IN A MAGNETIC FIELD

Rowland's experiment showed that, as far as its magnetic effect is concerned, a moving charge is equivalent to a current. We have already shown that if a charge q is moving with a velocity v, it can be considered the equivalent of a current element IL; that is,

$$qv = IL. \tag{3}$$

If we are dealing with the motions of charged particles in magnetic fields, then Ampère's law

$$F = \tfrac{1}{10}BIL \tag{20}$$

can be written in the form

$$F = \tfrac{1}{10}Bqv, \qquad (22)$$

where B is the magnetic flux density at the place where the charge q is moving with velocity v, and the direction of v is at right angles to the direction of B. The force F is at right angles to both B and v. Figure 25-16(a) shows the relative directions of B, v, and F when the charge q is positive, while Figure 25-16(b) shows the directions of these vectors

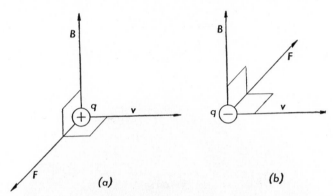

(a)   (b)

Fig. 25-16 Force on a charge moving in a magnetic field. (a) When the charge is positive, the force F is directed out of the paper toward the reader; (b) when the charge is negative, F is directed into the paper away from the reader.

when q is negative. It will be observed that when the velocities of the two charges are in the same direction in the same magnetic fields, the force on the positive charge is opposite to that on the negative charge. If the charge q has a mass m and is acted upon by a force F, then, applying Newton's second law, we get

$$F = ma. \qquad (23)$$

Substituting this value in Equation (22), we get, for the acceleration of the charge,

$$a = \frac{Bqv}{10m}. \qquad (24)$$

The acceleration will also be directed at right angles to the directions of B and v. But we have already seen that in the case of uniform circular motion, the acceleration is always at right angles to the velocity. Hence a charge q, moving with velocity v at right angles to the lines of induction in a uniform magnetic field, will move with uniform circular motion in a

path of radius r, given by

$$a = \frac{v^2}{r},$$

which, combined with Equation (24), yields

$$m\frac{v^2}{r} = \frac{Bqv}{10},$$

from which

$$r = \frac{10mv}{Bq}, \qquad (25)$$

also

$$\frac{q}{m} = \frac{10v}{Br}. \qquad (26)$$

Fig. 25-17 Cloud chamber photograph showing curved paths of particles moving at right angles to a magnetic field. The magnetic field is directed into the paper, and the particles originate from a source at the left. The three heavy tracks are those of protons; the numerous light tracks curved in the opposite direction are those electrons. (Photograph by H. R. Crane.)

Equation (25) shows that the radius of the circular path of a charged particle moving at right angles to the lines of induction in a uniform magnetic field is proportional to the momentum of the particle and inversely proportional to the magnetic flux density. Figure 25–17 is a photograph of the paths of charged particles traveling at right angles to the direction of a uniform magnetic field.

Nowadays many instruments, constructed for both scientific and industrial work, make use of charged particles moving in magnetic and electric fields. Among these are the cathode-ray tubes used in television; the electron microscope; the mass spectrograph for determining the masses of ions and, from these, atomic masses; the cyclotron for getting charged particles of very high energy for use in nuclear disintegration processes; and the magnetron used in ultra-high-frequency radio transmission. A few of the simpler examples will be considered in this text.

Illustrative Example. An electron moves with a speed of 6×10^9 cm/sec at right angles to the direction of a uniform magnetic field of 30 gausses. Determine the radius of its path.

The charge of an electron is $e = 1.60 \times 10^{-19}$ coul, and its mass is 9.11×10^{-28} gm. Putting these values into Equation (25), we get

$$r = \frac{10 \times 9.11 \times 10^{-28} \times 6 \times 10^9}{30 \times 1.6 \times 10^{-19}} \text{ cm},$$

from which $r = 11.4$ cm.

25-12   RATIO OF CHARGE TO MASS OF AN ELECTRON

Historically, J. J. Thomson, in 1897, first successfully determined the nature of the cathode rays by measuring the ratio of the charge e of a cathode ray to its mass m. This involved sending the cathode rays through electric and magnetic fields. Since then, many other experimenters have

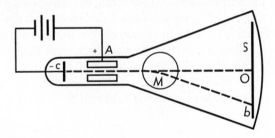

Fig. 25–18   Tube for measuring the ratio e/m of cathode rays.

performed similar experiments on cathode rays and on electrons from other sources. These experiments showed that cathode rays and electrons are identical.

One method for measuring the ratio e/m for cathode rays is illustrated in Figure 25–18. The cathode consists of a circular disk C, while the anode

A is a metal cylinder with a small circular hole drilled along its axis. The gas in the tube is at a pressure of about 0.001 mm of mercury. When a high-voltage discharge is maintained between A and C, some of the cathode rays which go from C to A pass through the small circular hole in the anode and then enter a magnetic field of flux density B which is directed into the paper. The positions of the circular pole pieces of the magnet providing this magnetic field are indicated by the circle marked M.

In going from the cathode to the anode under a difference of potential V, each electron of charge e had an amount of work Ve done upon it by the electric field and therefore acquired an amount of kinetic energy, given by

$$Ve = \tfrac{1}{2}mv^2, \tag{27}$$

in which m is the mass of the electron and v is its speed. In Equation (27), the assumption is made that when the electron left the cathode it had no kinetic energy. When the electron, moving with velocity v, enters the magnetic field of flux density B, it will experience a force Bev, expressed in electromagnetic units; this will cause it to move in a circular path of radius r, given by

$$r = \frac{mv}{Be}. \tag{28}$$

When the electron leaves the region of the magnetic field, there is no longer any force acting on it; it will therefore continue to move with the same velocity that it had at the end of its path in the magnetic field. It will continue moving in a straight line from the edge of the magnetic field until it strikes the fluorescent screen S at some point b. This fluorescent screen, usually made of powdered zinc sulphide crystals pasted on a glass plate, emits a bluish light wherever electrons strike it. The point b can therefore be observed readily. When the magnetic field is removed, the cathode rays, after passing through the hole in the anode, continue to move in the same straight line until they strike the fluorescent screen at O. It is a matter of simple geometry to determine the radius r of the circular path from a measurement of the displacement Ob on the fluorescent screen.

By eliminating v from Equations (27) and (28), we get

$$\boxed{\frac{e}{m} = \frac{2V}{B^2r^2}.} \tag{29}$$

Since all the quantities on the right-hand side of the equation are measurable, e/m can be determined. Measurements of e/m for electrons from all sources yield practically the same value. if the velocity v is small in comparison with the velocity of light. The present accepted value of e/m is

$$\frac{e}{m} = 1.7589 \times 10^7 \frac{\text{abcoul}}{\text{gm}},$$

or

$$\frac{e}{m} = 1.7589 \times 10^8 \frac{\text{coul}}{\text{gm}}. \tag{30}$$

The mass of the electron can be calculated by combining the value of e/m and the value of the electronic charge e determined by independent methods (see Section 24–5). Since

$$e = 1.602 \times 10^{-19} \text{ coul},$$

$$m = 9.106 \times 10^{-28} \text{ gm}. \tag{31}$$

To get an idea of just how small this mass is, let us compare it with the mass of the lightest atom known, the hydrogen atom. The atomic mass of hydrogen is 1.00814; we know that Avogadro's number $N_0 = 6.023 \times 10^{23}$ is the number of atoms in a gram-atomic mass. Therefore the mass M of 1 atom of hygrogen is

$$M = \frac{1.00814}{6.023 \times 10^{23}} \text{ gm},$$

from which

$$M = 1.673 \times 10^{-24} \text{ gm}.$$

The ratio of the mass of the hydrogen atom to the mass of the electron is therefore

$$\frac{M}{m} = \frac{1.673 \times 10^{-24}}{9.106 \times 10^{-28}},$$

from which

$$\frac{M}{m} = 1,837. \tag{32}$$

The mass of the lightest known atom is more than 1,800 times the mass of the electron.

25-13 GALVANOMETER: MOVING-COIL TYPE

The force experienced by a wire placed in a magnetic field is the basis for the design of a moving-coil type of galvanometer or current-measuring instrument. The essentials of such a galvanometer are a strong permanent magnet shaped so that the two poles face each other across a gap in which the magnetic field intensity is fairly uniform, a rectangular coil of many turns of fine wire, and a fine spring attached to the coil. This spring may

be wound in the form of a spiral like a fine watch spring, in which case the
coil is pivoted in jeweled bearings, or the spring may be in the form of a
long wire, one end of which is rigidly attached to the top of the frame housing the coil and the other end is attached to the coil and is part of the conductor leading current into the coil.

The action of the galvanometer can be understood by referring to
Figure 25–19, which shows one turn of the galvanometer coil with its plane
parallel to the lines of induction of a uniform magnetic field of flux density B.

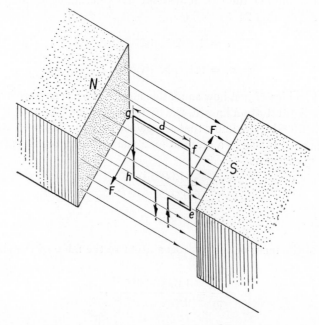

FIG. 25–19 Forces on a single turn of a galvanometer coil carrying current I;
the magnetic field is parallel to the plane of the coil *efgh*.

If a current I goes through this coil in the direction shown, the force
on the wire *ef* is directed into the paper, and the force on the wire *gh* is
directed out of the paper. The resultant force on the coil is zero, but the
torque produced by these two forces is $F \times d$, where d is the width of the
coil. This torque will produce a rotation of the coil about an axis in its
plane passing through the center of gravity of the coil. Since

$$F = \tfrac{1}{10}BIL, \tag{20}$$

where L is the length of *ef* or *gh*, the torque G is

$$G = Fd = \tfrac{1}{10}BILd = \tfrac{1}{10}BIA, \tag{33}$$

in which $A = Ld$ is the area of the coil. Since B and A are constants, the torque is proportional to the current I through the galvanometer coil.

If there were no spring attached to the coil, it would turn until it set itself at right angles to the magnetic field, in which position the torque on it would be zero. As a matter of fact, it would probably oscillate in this magnetic field just as though it were a magnet of magnetic moment $M = \frac{1}{10}IA$ [see Equation (8) in Chapter 20].

In the D'Arsonval type of galvanometer, such as that shown in Figures 25-20 and 25-21, the movable coil is suspended from a very fine elastic fiber which may be made of gold or some other conductor. The

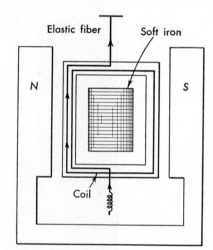

FIG. 25-20   Essentials of a D'Arsonval type of galvanometer.

latter also acts as one of the conducting leads for the current entering or leaving the coil. In the portable type of galvanometer shown in Figure 25-22, a fine hairspring H is attached to the coil. As the coil rotates, it twists the spring, causing it to exert an opposing torque on the coil. The coil will come to rest at that angle at which the torque caused by the spring is just equal to that produced by the action of the magnetic field on the current in the coil. The angle of twist of a spring depends upon the torque acting on it and upon the elastic constants of the substance used in making it. Hence the angle through which a galvanometer coil will rotate when a current I flows through it will be determined by the kind of spring used. But, once the spring is put into the instrument, the angle of deflection will be proportional to the current I, providing the angle is not too large. In actual practice, the magnetic field is made radial by hollowing out the pole pieces into cylindrical form and using a soft iron cylinder inside the coil. This makes it possible to use a larger angle of deflection and still have the direction of the magnetic field remain parallel to the

plane of the coil.   Figure 25–22 shows a galvanometer coil in a magnetic
field due to a permanent magnet with a soft iron cylinder inside the coil.

The angle of deflection of the galvanometer is usually indicated by
means of a pointer moving over a scale or by means of a beam of light

Fɪɢ. 25–21   D'Arsonval type of galvanometer of great sensitivity.   The cover
has been removed to show details of the construction.   (Courtesy of Leeds
and Northrup Company.)

reflected from a mirror which turns with the coil.   The beam of light may
fall directly on a scale on the wall of a laboratory, or the scale may be
viewed with the aid of a telescope.   Whatever method is used, the scale
has to be calibrated if measurements are to be made.   These galvanometers
can be made very sensitive; some of the suspended-coil type of galvanometers will give measurable deflections when the current through the

coil is of the order of 10^{-10} amp.   If the resistance R_i of the galvanometer
coil is known, the potential difference across the terminals of the coil when
a current I flows through it is $V = IR_i$.   For example, if the current

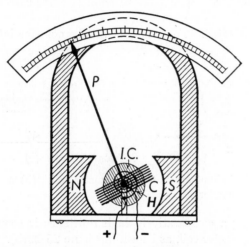

FIG. 25-22   Essentials of a moving-coil galvanometer. C is the moving coil,
N and S are the poles of a permanent magnet, $I.C.$ is the soft iron core, P is
the pointer, and H is the hairspring.

through a galvanometer is 10^{-10} amp for a deflection of one scale division,
and the resistance of the coil is 500 ohms, the voltage across the coil is
5×10^{-8} volt.

25-14 AMMETERS AND VOLTMETERS

The ammeter and voltmeter used in d-c circuits are modified forms of
the galvanometer.   An ammeter is connected in series in the circuit in
which the current is to be measured; it should therefore have negligible
resistance so as not to affect the current in the circuit.   Most galvanometers
have appreciable resistance, varying from about 10 ohms to about 1,000
ohms.   Furthermore, the galvanometer coils are made of very fine wire so
that it would not be safe to send large currents through them.   The simple
transformation required to convert a galvanometer into an ammeter is to
connect a wire of low resistance in parallel with the galvanometer coil, as
shown in Figure 25-23(a), or, in the language of the laboratory, to connect
a *shunt* across the galvanometer coil.   When the ammeter is put into a
circuit to measure the current in it, the current divides when it enters the
instrument, the major portion of the current going through the shunt,
while the remaining small fraction of the current goes through the moving

coil. The scale, however, is calibrated in terms of the total current flowing through the instrument, that is, through both the shunt and the coil.

A voltmeter is used to measure the difference of potential between any two terminals of a circuit. It should be designed to draw as little current as possible so that the original conditions of the circuit will not be noticeably affected. To transform a galvanometer into a voltmeter,

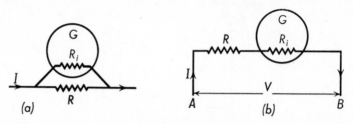

Fɪɢ. 25–23   (a) A shunt across a galvanometer coil.   (b) A resistor in series with a galvanometer coil.

a resistor having a comparatively high resistance is connected in series with the galvanometer coil, as shown in Figure 25–23(b). When the two terminals of the voltmeter are connected across two points A and B of a circuit, a small current I flows through the resistor and the galvanometer coil. The voltage V indicated by the instrument is given by

$$V = I(R + R_i),\qquad(34)$$

in which R is the resistance of the resistor and R_i is the resistance of the moving coil. Good voltmeters generally have resistances of the order of 1,000 ohms/volt. That is, an instrument designed to measure 150 volts, when the deflection of the pointer is a maximum, would have a resistance of 150,000 ohms.

Illustrative Example. A galvanometer coil has a resistance of 50 ohms and requires a current of 0.002 amp for a full-scale deflection; that is, the maximum scale reading. What must be done to transform this galvanometer into an ammeter which will give a full-scale deflection when a current of 1 amp flows through the instrument?

To transform a galvanometer into an ammeter, a resistor of low resistance R must be connected in parallel with the galvanometer coil. When 1 amp flows through this instrument, 0.002 amp will go through the galvanometer coil, and the remainder, 0.998 amp, will flow through the shunt R. Since the difference of potential across the coil is the same as that across the shunt, we have

$$0.002 \times 50 = 0.998 \times R,$$

from which
$$R = \frac{0.1}{0.998} \text{ ohm} = 0.1002 \text{ ohm}.$$

Illustrative Example. What must be done to a galvanometer which requires 0.001 amp for a full-scale deflection, and whose coil has a resistance of 50 ohms, to transform it into a voltmeter which will give a full-scale deflection when the voltage is 150 volts?

To transform a galvanometer into a voltmeter, a resistor having a high resistance R must be connected in series with the galvanometer coil. The same current, 0.001 amp, therefore flows through both resistor and coil so that the potential difference of 150 volts is registered when this current flows through them; therefore

$$150 = 0.001(R + 50),$$

from which $\qquad\qquad\qquad R = 149{,}950 \text{ ohms}.$

25-15   THE ELECTROMAGNETIC TELEGRAPH

The first practical device for electrical communication was the electromagnetic telegraph, which was invented by Samuel F. B. Morse in 1838 and put into practical operation in 1844 with the construction of the telegraph line between Washington and Baltimore. The operation of the telegraph is based upon the fact that a bar of iron is attracted to an electromagnet whenever a current is sent through it.

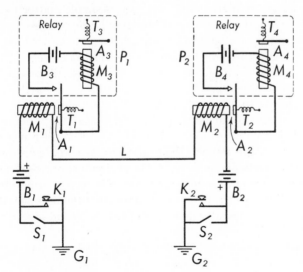

Fig. 25–24   Simple electromagnetic telegraph circuit with relays.

The essentials of an electromagnetic telegraph are shown in the circuit diagram of Figure 25–24. The two distant stations P_1 and P_2 have identical telegraph sets which are connected by the single metallic wire L; the second conductor, to complete the circuit, is the ground G_1G_2. Each side can receive or transmit signals. With the switch S_2 closed, P_2 is set to receive signals transmitted by P_1. The side which is transmitting signals keeps the switch open and uses a key K_1 to open and close the circuit. When the key K_1 is closed, current from the battery B_1 flows through the coils of the electromagnet M_1 and the line L to the electromagnet M_2, the battery B_2, the switch S_2, to the ground at G_2, and through the ground back to G_1 and the battery B_1. Each electromagnet has a coil of fine wire wound around a soft iron core. When current flows through the electro-magnets M_1 and M_2, the strong magnetic fields thus established attract the soft iron armatures A_1 and A_2, respectively. A sound is produced as the armature strikes the core of the electromagnet. As long as the key K_1 is closed, the armatures will remain in contact with the cores of the electro-magnets. When the key K_1 is opened, a spring attached to each armature pulls it back to its original position. These springs are labeled T_1 and T_2.

In the original Morse telegraph, a piece of paper was drawn past a pencil attached to the armature so that when the key was closed for a short time, a "dot" appeared on the paper; when it was closed for a longer time, a "dash" appeared. Shortly the telegraph operators acquired suffi-cient skill to hear the dots and dashes so that the paper and pencil arrange-ment could be dispensed with, but the terms *dot* and *dash* still remain part of the language of telegraphy. It was a simple matter to arrange a code of dots and dashes to transmit messages by telegraphy.

In general, the resistance of a telegraph circuit is rather high, and very small currents flow through the line and the electromagnets. This means that the force on each armature is comparatively small, and only a very faint sound is audible when the armature strikes the core. A *relay*, an invention credited to Joseph Henry, is usually added to each telegraph station. By means of an additional battery this relay operates a local circuit consisting of a sounder, which is simply another electromagnet and a heavy armature. When the armatures A_1 and A_2 are pulled over to the electromagnets M_1 and M_2, the local circuits are closed, and a loud sound is heard when each sounder pulls down its heavy armature.

When station P_1 has completed transmitting the message, the switch S_1 is closed, and the operator at P_2 opens switch S_2 and is ready to trans-mit messages to P_1.

QUESTIONS

1. A horizontal wire is set up so that it is parallel to the direction of the earth's magnetic field as indicated by a neighboring compass needle. A current is sent through the wire from south to north. Which way will the compass needle be deflected if it is placed (a) below the wire and (b) above the wire?

2. Referring to Rowland's experiment, determine the direction of the magnetic field produced by the rotation of the charged disk when it is rotating in a counter clockwise direction (a) if the disk is charged positively and (b) if the disk is charged negatively.

3. Show that any two adjacent turns of a helical coil, such as that sketched in Figure 25–5, will attract each other when there is a current in the coil.

4. Consider the magnetic field around a circular coil and show that any portions of the coil which are diametrically opposite will repel each other whenever there is a current in the coil.

5. Compare the magnetic field of a bar magnet with that of a long solenoid (a) for similarities and (b) for differences.

6. Does the ratio e/m for cathode rays depend upon the nature of the gas in the tube?

7. An electron moves in a circular path in a magnetic field under the action of a constant force. How much work is done on the electron during each revolution?

8. Suppose that a stream of electrons is moving downward in a horizontal magnetic field directed toward the right. Determine the direction of the force on each electron and compare it with the force on a wire carrying current in the same direction.

9. Ammeters and voltmeters frequently are mounted in cases which are identical; it is necessary to read the label to determine which instrument it is. Suppose you mistook an ammeter for a voltmeter and connected the ammeter across the terminals of a 110-volt lamp while it was in operation. Can you predict what would be likely to happen?

10. Suppose you mistook a voltmeter for an ammeter and connected the voltmeter in the circuit. Can you predict what would happen?

11. What is the function of a relay in a telegraph circuit?

PROBLEMS

1. Determine the intensity of the magnetic field at the center of a circular coil consisting of a single turn of 8 cm radius when it carries a current of 15 amp.

2. Determine the intensity of the magnetic field at the center of a closely wound circular coil of 75 turns whose average radius is 9 cm, when the coil carries a current of 5 amp.

3. A circular coil of 20 cm radius consists of a single turn of wire and has a small compass needle suspended at its center so that it can swing freely about a vertical axis. The plane of the coil is set parallel to the earth's magnetic field. If the horizontal component of the intensity of the earth's magnetic field is 0.2 oersted, determine the angle through which the compass needle is deflected when a current of 4 amp is sent through the coil.

4. Determine the magnetic field intensity at the center of a closely wound circular coil of 600 turns whose average radius is 35 cm if it carries a current of 8.0 amp.

5. Determine the magnetic field intensity at a distance of 25 cm from a long straight wire in which there is a current of 24 amp.

6. A small compass needle whose magnetic moment is 40 pole cm and whose moment of inertia is 6.0 gm cm², is placed at a point 15 cm from a long straight wire. When a current is sent through the wire, the needle oscillates with a period of 7.2 sec. Determine (a) the strength of the magnetic field at the position of the compass, and (b) the current in the wire.

7. A solenoid 75 cm long and 8 cm in diameter is wound with 800 turns of wire. Determine the magnetic field intensity inside this solenoid when it carries a current of 6.5 amp.

8. A long straight wire carries a current of 25 amp. The north pole of a long bar magnet is placed 5 cm from this wire. If the pole strength of the magnet is 80 unit poles, (a) determine the magnitude and direction of the force on this north pole. (b) Using Newton's third law, determine the magnitude and direction of the force exerted by this north pole on the wire carrying current.

9. Two long straight wires are 18 cm apart and carry currents of 30 amp each. Determine the intensity of the magnetic field at a point midway between them (a) when these currents are in the same direction and (b) when these currents are in opposite directions.

10. Two long, straight parallel wires are 16 cm apart. One wire carries a current of 12 amp, the other a current of 24 amp. Determine the intensity of the magnetic field at a point midway between them (a) when the currents are in the same direction and (b) when the currents are in opposite directions.

11. In the Oersted experiment, a long straight wire placed 4 cm above a compass needle carries a current of 28 amp directed toward the north. Determine the torque acting on the compass needle if its magnetic moment is 150 pole cm.

12. A rectangular coil of 25 turns, 4 cm by 6 cm, is suspended in a uniform magnetic field of 5,000 gausses. The plane of the coil is parallel to the direction of the magnetic field. Find the torque which acts on it when it carries a current of 0.04 amp.

13. The magnetic flux density between the poles of a large electromagnet is 1,000 gausses in a direction from east to west. The field extends vertically for a distance of 5 cm. A wire is suspended vertically in this field and a current of 12 amp is sent upward through it. Determine the magnitude and direction of the force on the wire.

14. A current of 12 amp flows downward in a vertical wire 80 cm long which is suspended in a place where the intensity of the earth's magnetic field has a horizontal component of 0.25 oersted and a vertical component 0.75 oersted. Determine the magnitude and direction of the force on the wire.

15. A straight wire 12 cm long is placed in a magnetic field of 350 gausses directed at right angles to the length of the wire. A delicate spring balance attached to the wire measures a force of 180 dynes when a current is sent through the wire. Determine the current in the wire.

16. Two long straight parallel wires 4 cm apart carry currents of 12 amp and 40 amp, respectively, in the same direction. Determine the force per unit length on each wire.

17. Electrons from a heated filament are accelerated by a difference of potential of 1,500 volts between the filament and the plate. Determine the maximum kinetic energy of each electron (a) in electron volts and (b) in ergs.

18. A stream of electrons, each one moving with a velocity of 9×10^9 cm/sec, enters a uniform magnetic field whose flux density is 125 gausses directed at right angles to the velocity of the electrons. Determine (a) the force which acts on each electron and (b) the radius of its path in the magnetic field.

19. A rectangular coil of 150 turns of fine wire is suspended in a uniform magnetic field with its plane parallel to the direction of the field. The dimensions of the coil are 2 cm by 4 cm. When a current of 0.25 amp is sent through the coil, a torque of 18,000 dyne cm acts on it. Determine the flux density of the magnetic field.

20. An electron moves in a circular path of 3.0 cm radius in a uniform magnetic field whose flux density is 60 gausses. Determine (a) the velocity of the electron and (b) its kinetic energy. (c) How much work is done by the magnetic field on the electron?

21. The following data were obtained in an experiment on the determination of e/m for cathode rays, similar to the experiment illustrated in Figure 25-18. The difference of potential between the anode and cathode was 25,000 volts, the intensity of the magnetic field was 8.0 gausses, and the radius of the circular path in the magnetic field was determined from the deflection to be 66.8 cm. Calculate e/m from these data.

22. A proton whose mass is 1.65×10^{-24} gm travels in a circular path of 35 cm radius in a magnetic field whose flux density is 12,000 gausses. Determine (a) the velocity of the proton and (b) its period of revolution.

23. A rectangular galvanometer coil has 500 turns wound on a frame 2 cm by 4 cm. It hangs between the poles of a magnet where the flux density is 800 gausses. Determine the torque which acts on this coil when the current in it is 3×10^{-8} amp.

24. The coil of a galvanometer has a resistance of 75 ohms, and the instrument gives a full-scale deflection for a current of 0.002 amp. Compute the resistance needed and show how it should be connected to change this instrument into an ammeter which will give a full-scale deflection for 5 amp.

25. The coil of a galvanometer has a resistance of 60 ohms and gives a full-scale deflection when a current of 0.001 amp flows through it. Compute the resistance needed and show how it should be connected to change this instrument into a voltmeter which will give a full-scale deflection when the voltage across it is 250 volts.

26

Electromagnetic Induction

26-1 INDUCED ELECTROMOTIVE FORCES

One of the most important discoveries in electricity and magnetism, known as *electromagnetic induction*, was made independently by Michael Faraday (1791–1867) in England and Joseph Henry (1797–1878) in the United States, in 1831. Faraday's apparatus consisted essentially of two neighboring circuits, shown in Figure 26–1: one circuit, which we shall call the

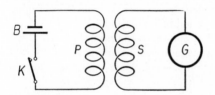

Fig. 26–1 Faraday's experiment on electromagnetic induction.

primary circuit, contained a battery B, a coil P, and a key K, for opening and closing the circuit; the second circuit, or secondary circuit, consisted of a coil S and a galvanometer G. Faraday observed that when the key was closed, the galvanometer in the S circuit gave a momentary deflection and then returned to its zero position and remained there as long as the key was closed. When the key was opened, there was another momentary deflection of the galvanometer, opposite in direction to the previous deflection, and then the galvanometer needle returned to its zero position.

Analyzing this simple experiment, we find that when the key in the primary circuit was closed, a current started flowing through the primary coil P. This current produced a magnetic field in the neighborhood of P and also around the coil S; that is, a change was produced in the magnetic field around the coil S in the secondary circuit. The fact that the galvanometer showed only a momentary deflection can be interpreted by saying that a current was *induced* in the secondary circuit momentarily and that this induced current was due to the *change* in the magnetic field around the secondary circuit. As long as the current in the primary circuit remained constant, the magnetic field around both P and S remained constant, but the galvanometer read zero during this time. But when the magnetic field was again changed, say by opening the key, a current was again induced in the secondary circuit, this time in a direction opposite to that produced when the key was closed.

The results of the above experiment on electromagnetic induction can be explained qualitatively by stating that the change in the magnetic field around the secondary coil *induced an electromotive force* in the coil, and, since the coil is part of a closed circuit, this induced emf produced a current in the secondary circuit.

There are many ways in which the magnetic field around the coil S may be varied. Suppose, for example, that the key of the primary circuit is kept closed so that a steady current flows through the coil P. As long as the magnetic field around the secondary coil S remains constant, there will be no emf induced in it, and the galvanometer will read zero. But if we move S away from P so as to decrease the magnetic field around S, the galvanometer will show a deflection; similarly, if we move S toward P, the galvanometer will show a deflection but now in the opposite direction.

If we put a variable resistor in the primary circuit so that the current in it may be varied, and keep the distance between S and P constant, there will be an induced emf and hence an induced current in the secondary circuit whenever the current in the primary circuit is changed. When the current in the primary coil is increased, the induced current in the secondary coil will be in one direction; when the current in the primary coil is decreased, the induced current in the secondary coil will be in the opposite direction.

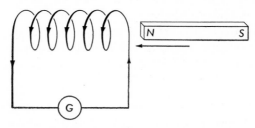

FIG. 26-2   An emf is induced in the coil by the motion of a bar magnet. Direction of the induced current is shown by the arrows on the wire.

So that there will be no doubt that it is the change in the magnetic field which gives rise to the induced emf in the secondary coil, suppose we perform an experiment using a bar magnet instead of the primary coil, as sketched in Figure 26–2. When the north pole of the bar magnet approaches coil S, the galvanometer registers a current in one direction; when the magnet is removed from coil S, the galvanometer registers a current in the opposite direction.

26-2 FARADAY'S LAW OF ELECTROMAGNETIC INDUCTION

From the results of very careful experiments, it has been found that the *electromotive force induced in each turn of a coil of wire is proportional to the time rate of change of the number of magnetic lines of induction passing through each turn of the coil.* Let us designate the total number of lines of induction through a coil, or the *magnetic flux* through it, by the letter Φ (capital Greek phi). If $\Delta\Phi$ is the change in magnetic flux through the coil in a time interval Δt, then the average emf E induced in a single turn of wire can be written as

$$E \propto - \frac{\Delta\Phi}{\Delta t}$$

or, in the form of an equation,

$$E = -k\frac{\Delta\Phi}{\Delta t}, \tag{1}$$

where k is a factor of proportionality depending upon the system of units used. The negative sign is used to show that the emf is positive when the flux is decreasing; that is, the direction of the emf is such that it tends to set up a current whose magnetic flux would oppose this decrease. Equation (1) is one method of expressing *Faraday's law of electromagnetic induction.*

We have already introduced the concept of magnetic induction or magnetic flux density and represented it by the vector B. One method of expressing B is in terms of the number of lines of induction per unit area perpendicular to that area. If B is constant over a given area A and everywhere perpendicular to it, then the total magnetic flux through this area, or the total number of lines of induction through this area, is

$$\Phi = BA. \tag{2}$$

In the cgs electromagnetic system of units, k is set equal to 1, so that Equation (1) becomes

$$E_m = -\frac{\Delta\Phi}{\Delta t}. \tag{3a}$$

In this system, the unit of emf or potential difference is the *abvolt.* The unit of magnetic flux is the *maxwell*, and, since B is expressed in gausses and A in square centimeters, we have 1 gauss = 1 maxwell/cm^2. From Equation (3a) we note that a change in magnetic flux of 1 maxwell/sec will induce an emf of 1 abvolt in a single turn of a coil.

The abvolt is a small unit in comparison with the practical unit, the volt; thus

$$1 \text{ abvolt} = 10^{-8} \text{ volt}.$$

Hence, to express the induced emf in volts, we set the constant $k = 10^{-8}$, and the fundamental equation becomes

$$E = -10^{-8} \frac{\Delta \Phi}{\Delta t}. \qquad \text{(3b)}$$

If a coil of wire has n turns, an emf will be induced in each turn by the changing magnetic flux. The turns of a coil may be considered as

FIG. 26-3 Michael Faraday (1791–1867). Chemist and physicist. Discovered the laws of electrolysis and electromagnetic induction. Introduced the concept of lines of force to help understand the phenomena associated with electric and magnetic fields. (Courtesy of *Scripta Mathematica*.)

connected in series; hence the emf induced in a coil will be the sum of the induced emf's in the separate turns. If the change in magnetic flux is the same through each turn, then the induced emf, in volts, will be given by

$$E = -10^{-8} n \frac{\Delta \Phi}{\Delta t}. \qquad \text{(4)}$$

Illustrative Example. A flat coil of wire containing 50 turns is thrust over the north pole of a very strong magnet so that 200,000 lines of induction pass through the coil at the end of 0.5 sec. Determine the magnitude of the induced emf.

Assuming that originally there was no flux through the coil, the change in magnetic flux through each turn is 200,000 maxwells. The average emf E is, from Equation (4),

$$E = 10^{-8} n \frac{\Delta\Phi}{\Delta t},$$

so that

$$E = 50 \frac{200,000}{0.5} \times 10^{-8} \text{ volt}$$

or

$$E = 0.2 \text{ volt}.$$

26-3 LENZ'S LAW FOR INDUCED CURRENTS

The method for determining the direction of the current in a coil produced by an induced emf was first clearly stated by Lenz in 1834 and is based upon the application of the principle of the conservation of energy to the process of electromagnetic induction. *Lenz's law states that the induced current is in such a direction as to oppose, by its magnetic action, whatever change produces the induced current.*

For example, in the case illustrated in Figure 26–2, if the north pole of a bar magnet is brought near one end of a coil, the induced current in the coil will be in such a direction as to set up a magnetic field which will oppose the motion of the north pole toward it; that is, the magnetic field caused by the induced current will repel the north pole of the bar magnet. If the north pole of the bar magnet is moved away from one end of the coil, the induced current will set up a magnetic field so as to attract the north pole of the bar magnet and oppose its motion away from the coil. Thus work must be done in moving the bar magnet with respect to the coil because of the force which exists between the bar magnet and the magnetic field of the induced current. This work is transformed into electric energy, as evidenced by the existence of an induced current in the coil.

That Lenz's law is a consequence of the principle of conservation of energy can be seen from the fact that when an induced current i flows for a time t in a circuit in which an emf E has been induced, a quantity of electric energy Eit has been supplied to the circuit. Reasoning from the principle of conservation of energy, we can state that this electric energy Eit must come from some outside source. For example, in moving a bar magnet toward the coil, forces must be set up to oppose this motion so that work will have to be done by some outside agency to move the magnet toward the coil. This means that the direction of the induced current must be such as to set up a magnetic field which will oppose the motion of the magnet toward the coil. If the current were in the opposite direction, it would attract the magnet to it, thus itself doing the work to create the electric energy in it; this, however, is contrary to the principle of conservation of energy. Hence the induced current must always be in such a direction as to oppose, by its magnetic action, whatever change produces the induced current. This is Lenz's law.

Another way of stating Lenz's law is that *the direction of the induced current is such as to oppose the change in the magnetic flux through the circuit.* If, for any reason whatever, there is an increase in the magnetic flux through the circuit, the induced current will set up a magnetic field to oppose the increase in the magnetic flux through it. Similarly if there is a decrease in the magnetic flux through the circuit, the induced current will be in such a direction that it will set up a magnetic field which will oppose the decrease in the flux through it.

26-4 MOTION OF A WIRE IN A MAGNETIC FIELD

A very simple and instructive example of electromagnetic induction is that illustrated in Figure 26–4, in which a wire AC is moving through a magnetic field with constant velocity v at right angles to the direction of

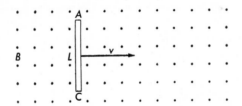

FIG. 26–4 Wire AC moving with constant velocity v with its length L at right angles to lines of magnetic induction. Flux density B directed out of the paper.

the lines of induction B. The direction of its motion is also at right angles to the length L of the wire. Because of this motion, there will be an electromotive force induced in the wire. This can be shown in two different ways, each one illustrating a different aspect of the subject. Suppose that we want to explain it with the aid of Equation (1) and Lenz's law. In this case, let us make the wire AC part of a circuit consisting of a rectangular frame $ACDG$, as shown in Figure 26–5, with the plane of this frame at right angles to the direction of the magnetic flux B. Let us assume that this flux density B is uniform and directed out of the paper toward the reader. The lines of induction are represented by the dots in the diagram. Now let the wire AC move along the frame with velocity v toward the end

DG. As it does so, it will decrease the area of the rectangle *ACDG* and thus decrease the total flux through it. During a time interval Δt, the wire will have moved a distance $v\Delta t$ to position $A'C'$ and will have de-

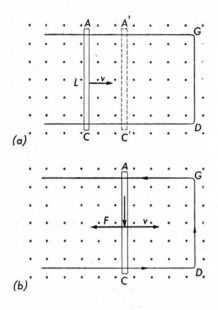

(a)

(b)

FIG. 26–5   Determining direction of the current induced by the motion of the wire *AC* through a uniform magnetic field.

creased the area by $Lv\Delta t$, which is that represented by $ACC'A'$. If *B* is the magnetic flux density through this frame, then the change in magnetic flux is

$$\Delta\Phi = BLv\Delta t,$$

and the induced emf in this frame is, from Equation (3a),

$$E_m = BLv.$$
                                                                             (5)

The direction of the induced current, and hence the induced emf, can be found by applying Lenz's law to this case. In order to oppose the motion of the wire *AC* toward the right, the induced current in *ACDG* will have to be in such a direction as to increase the magnetic field inside the frame, that is, to the right of *AC*, and decrease the magnetic field to the left of *AC*. The wire will then experience a force directed from the stronger to the weaker part of the field, as shown in Figure 26–5(b).

In the above analysis, we used the macroscopic point of view to determine the emf induced in the wire. It will be worth while considering the same problem from the microscopic point of view. Figure 26–6(a) shows the wire, enlarged to some extent, with some of its positive and negative charges. As the wire moves toward the right with velocity v, the charges within the wire have this velocity superposed on any other motions they may have within the wire. We have shown (Section 25–11) that a charge q, moving with velocity v in a magnetic field of flux density B in a direction at right angles to B, will experience a force F given by

$$F = \tfrac{1}{10}Bqv. \quad \text{[Equation (22) in Chapter 25]}$$

This force F is at right angles to both B and v and is along the length of the wire; it is directed from A to C for the positive charges and from C to A for the negative charges. There will thus be relative motion, momen-

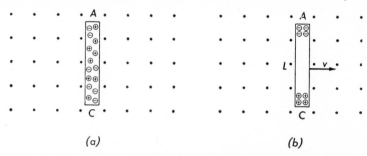

(a)   (b)

Fɪɢ. 26–6   Motion of a wire through a magnetic field causes a separation of the positive and negative charges, so that one end becomes positively charged and the other end negatively charged.

tarily, of the negative with respect to the positive charges in the wire, with the end A becoming negatively charged and C becoming positively charged, as shown in Figure 26–6(b). Thus an electric field is produced within the wire which separates the charges within AC, maintaining C at a higher potential than A. If the wire AC is made part of a circuit, it will supply current to it; the direction of the current will be from C through the external circuit to A and then through the wire to C.

Many practical devices such as electric generators and motors are designed so that conductors move across magnetic fields. In such cases, it is often very convenient to discuss their operation in terms of the emf induced in these conductors. Equation (5) is therefore a very useful equation. In using this equation, it must be remembered that B, L, and v are considered to be perpendicular to one another. If they are not, then only those components of all three which are mutually perpendicular are to be considered. As the wire moves through the magnetic field, it is often described as "cutting" the lines of magnetic induction. Equation (5) may be considered a special statement of Faraday's law of electromagnetic induction, applicable to cases in which conductors are in motion through magnetic fields. It states that *whenever a conductor cuts across a magnetic field, the emf induced in the conductor is equal to the number of lines of induction cut per unit time.*

26-5 ELECTRIC DYNAMO OR GENERATOR

An electric dynamo or generator is a device for transforming mechanical energy into electric energy. In its simplest form, the generator consists of a permanent magnet or an electromagnet, a coil which can rotate between the poles of the magnet, and brush contacts so that connection can be made between the ends of the coil and the external circuit. In Figure 26–7, N and S are the north and south poles of an electromagnet

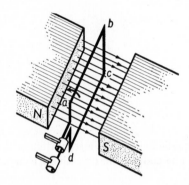

FIG. 26–7   Essentials of an electric generator.

and *abcd* is a rectangular coil which rotates about an axis in its plane and is perpendicular to the plane of the paper. The two ends of the coil are connected to two insulated rings mounted on the axis and rotating with the coil. Two blocks of carbon, called brushes, press against these rings as they rotate and provide electrical contact with the external circuit.

Let us assume that the magnetic field between the two poles is uniform and that the coil is rotating counterclockwise with uniform angular speed. As the coil rotates, the magnetic flux through it changes; the rate of

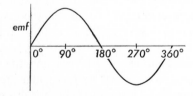

FIG. 26–8   Graph of the alternating emf induced in the coil of the generator during one revolution.

change of magnetic flux through the coil depends upon the particular position of the coil at any instant. The emf induced in the coil will consequently depend upon the particular position of the coil. Figure 26–8 is a graph showing the emf induced in the coil plotted against the position of the coil, with the zero position taken as the one in which the plane of the coil is perpendicular to the direction of the magnetic field and *ab* is at the top. It will be noted that the induced emf changes direction after half a revolution of the coil; the emf is said to be an *alternating* emf. It will also be observed that the maximum value of the induced emf occurs when the coil passes through the horizontal position, that is, when the plane of the coil is parallel to the magnetic field; and that the induced emf is zero when the coil passes through the vertical position, that is, when the plane of the coil is perpendicular to the magnetic field. The rate of change of the magnetic flux through the coil is greatest when it is passing through the position where it is parallel to the field and is zero when it is passing through the position where it is perpendicular to the field.

Instead of talking about the rate of change of the magnetic flux through the coil, it is sometimes more convenient to discuss the emf induced in each wire of the coil in terms of the *rate at which each wire cuts across the lines of magnetic induction*. The two methods yield the same results. For example, consider the motion of the wire *ab* of this coil. As the wire moves down in a circular path from the top position past the north pole of the magnet, it will cut the greatest number of lines of induction in a given time when it is moving perpendicular to these lines, that is, when it is moving vertically downward. The emf induced in the wire will therefore be a maximum when it is halfway down. At the bottom of its path, it is moving parallel to the lines of induction, and hence the rate of cutting these lines is zero; the induced emf will also be zero in this position. As it moves past its lowest position in this circular path and starts moving upward, the induced emf will be reversed in direction. The induced emf will of course again be reversed when the wire *ab* passes the highest point, and at this point the emf will again be zero.

The direction of the induced current in the wire can be determined with the aid of Lenz's law. As the wire *ab* moves down, the magnetic field due to the induced current will have to be in such a direction as to strengthen the magnetic field below the wire and weaken the field above it, thus giving rise to a force in the upward direction. The induced current will therefore be from *b* to *a*, out of the plane of the paper toward the reader. On the upward motion, the induced current will be in the opposite direction, so that the magnetic field above it will be strengthened and the force on the wire will be downward. Work will therefore have to be done by the device which rotates the coil in order to deliver electric energy to the outside circuit.

In some small generators, such as those operated by hand and used for supplying current to ring bells in telephones, the magnetic field may be due to a permanent magnet; these generators are usually called *magnetos*. In most generators, the magnetic field is maintained by current flowing through coils wound around a soft iron core which terminates in two pole pieces. This current may be supplied by a battery, or else it may be supplied by the generator itself. Instead of a single coil of wire, there are usually several coils, each of many turns, rotating in the magnetic field. The coils, usually wound on an iron core, may be wound by one of several different methods. This whole assembly is called the *armature* of the generator. In very large *alternating-current* (abbreviated a-c) *generators*, the armature is usually kept stationary and the magnetic field coils are rotated. In these generators, there are always more than two pole pieces.

The induced emf in the coils of an armature is always an alternating emf, and the current flowing through these coils is always an *alternating current;* this means that the current changes direction every half cycle in a manner similar to that of the emf shown in Figure 26–8.

There are many different types of devices which can be operated with alternating currents; among these devices are several types of electric motors, all electric heating devices, and radio receivers and transmitters. There are some devices which cannot function with alternating current; these are electroplating baths which require direct current and electric motors specifically designed to operate on direct current. For such cases it is necessary to change the alternating current developed in the armature to current which always flows in the same direction in the outside circuit R. One of the simplest ways of doing this is to construct a device which will switch the outside connections to the two ends of each coil of the armature each time that the coil makes half a revolution. This device is known as a *commutator.* When provided with a commutator, the generator is called a *direct-current* (abbreviated d-c) *generator.* It must be remembered that the current which flows in the armature coils of this type of electric generator is always an alternating current; in the a-c generator the current delivered to the external circuit is also alternating current, while in the d-c generator the current delivered to the external circuit is direct current.

26-6   EMF INDUCED IN AN A-C GENERATOR

The emf induced in an armature of an a-c generator can be calculated with the aid of Equation (5). Figure 26–9 shows the traces of the wires *ab* and *dc* of Figure 26–7 in cross section in the magnetic field of flux density B. Assume that the armature is rotating with a constant angular velocity ω and let θ be the angle through which the coil has rotated from the vertical position in a time t, so that

$$\theta = \omega t.$$

Since the wire *ab* moves in a circular path of radius r, where $2r$ is the width *ad* or *cb* of the coil, its linear velocity v is

$$v = \omega r.$$

The angle between v and the flux density B is also θ; hence the component of v perpendicular to the field is $v \sin \theta$. Therefore the instantaneous emf induced in the wire ab is

$$E_1 = 10^{-8} \, Blv \sin \theta,$$

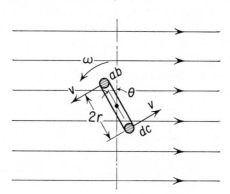

Fig. 26–9

where l is the length of the wire. An equal emf in the opposite direction is induced in the wire dc. Since the two wires are in series, the instantaneous emf induced in the coil $abcd$ is

$$E_2 = 2 \times 10^{-8} \, Blv \sin \theta$$

or

$$E_2 = 2 \times 10^{-8} \, Blr\omega \sin \theta. \tag{6}$$

Since $2r$ is the width of the coil and l its length, its area is

$$A = 2lr;$$

hence the emf induced in the coil can be written as

$$E_2 = 10^{-8} \, BA\omega \sin \theta. \tag{7}$$

If there are n turns in this coil, the instantaneous value of the emf induced in it is

$$E = 10^{-8} nBA\omega \sin \theta \tag{8}$$

or

$$\boxed{E = E_{\max} \sin \theta,} \tag{9}$$

where

$$E_{\max} = nBA\omega \times 10^{-8} \tag{10}$$

is the maximum induced emf. Figure 26–8 is a graph of Equation (9).

A more common method of expressing the alternating emf is in terms of the frequency f of the alternations. The angular velocity ω and the frequency f are related by the equation

$$\omega = 2\pi f$$

and, since

$$\theta = \omega t.$$

we can write the alternating emf as

$$E = E_{max} \sin 2\pi ft.$$ (11)

Illustrative Example.   The armature of an a-c generator is rotating at
a constant speed of 1,800 rpm in a horizontal magnetic field whose flux
density is 8,000 gausses. The diameter of the armature is 15 cm and its
length is 30 cm. Determine (a) the maximum emf induced in a coil of
the armature having 25 turns and (b) the instantaneous emf when the coil
has moved 30° from the vertical position.

From the above data,

$$B = 8{,}000 \text{ gausses,}$$

$$A = 2lr = 15 \times 30 \text{ cm}^2 = 450 \text{ cm}^2,$$

$$\omega = \frac{2\pi \times 1{,}800}{60} \text{ rad/sec} = 60\pi \text{ rad/sec,}$$

$$n = 25 \text{ turns;}$$

hence $$E_{max} = 25 \times 8{,}000 \times 450 \times 60\pi \times 10^{-8} \text{ volt,}$$

or $$E_{max} = 170 \text{ volts.}$$

When $\theta = 30°$,

$$E = E_{max} \sin 30°,$$

or $$E = 85 \text{ volts.}$$

26-7   DIRECT-CURRENT GENERATOR

In the simple form of d-c generator in which the armature consists of
a single coil of several turns of wire, the commutator consists of a single

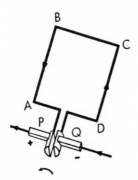

Fig. 26-10   Split-ring commutator.

ring split in half, with the two halves insulated from each other. These
two halves of a single ring replace the two rings of the a-c generator; that

is, the two ends of the armature coil are connected to these two insulated halves of a single ring, as shown in Figure 26–10. The two brushes P and Q make contact with the two commutator halves, and, as the coil rotates, the brushes automatically change halves every time the coil goes through 180°. The effect of this is that the brush P is always connected to that part of the coil which is moving down in the magnetic field, while the brush Q is always connected to that part of the coil which is moving upward in the magnetic field. Since the terminals of the external circuit are connected to the brushes P and Q, the current in this circuit will always be in the same direction, but not necessarily constant. As a matter of fact, if the armature has only a single coil, the current in the external circuit will have

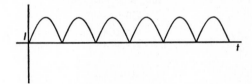

FIG. 26–11   Direct current from a single coil.

the appearance shown in Figure 26–11, in which the current is plotted as a function of the time. The current supplied by an a-c generator of similar design is shown in Figure 26–12. The commutator of the d-c generator has the effect of *rectifying* the voltage and current, that is, converting the negative half of each cycle into a positive half, so that both the emf and the current are always in the same direction.

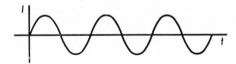

FIG. 26–12   Alternating current from a single coil.

In modern d-c generators, the armature consists of several coils connected in series. The commutator of such a generator consists of a single ring divided into as many pairs of segments as there are coils on the armature. The segments of the commutator are all insulated from each other. A typical commutator is shown in Figure 26–13. The coils are spaced uniformly around the iron core and are placed in slots cut in the iron parallel to the axis of the armature. Since the coils are connected in series, the emf induced in the armature is the sum of the emf's induced in the individual coils. The brushes are placed opposite each other in contact with the commutator. The effect of having a commutator with a large number of segments is to maintain a fairly constant emf between the brushes whose value at any instant is practically equal to the average value of the emf induced in the entire armature. This is due to the fact

Fig. 26-13   A commutator with many segments.   (Courtesy of General Electric Company.)

that as the armature rotates, the brushes always make contact with two segments of the commutator which are in the same position relative to the magnetic field through the armature.   There is a slight variation in the

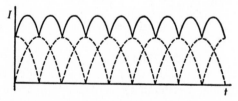

Fig. 26-14   Direct current from a d-c generator having a commutator with four segments.

induced emf, however, during the short time that the brushes are in contact with one pair of segments due to the variation in magnetic flux which occurs while the armature rotates through the corresponding small angle. Figure 26-14 is a graph showing the current supplied by a d-c generator which has a commutator consisting of several segments. The slight variations in this current are sometimes referred to as the commutator *ripple*.

26-8 DIRECT-CURRENT MOTOR

The d-c motor is a device for transforming electric energy into mechanical energy. This, of course, is the reverse of the d-c generator. As a matter of fact, the d-c generator can be used as a d-c motor by merely reversing the processes, that is, by sending current into the machine and having it perform mechanical work as it rotates. The essentials of a d-c motor are an armature of one or more coils, each containing several turns of wire; an electromagnet consisting of an iron core properly shaped with coils of wire wound around it, known as the *field coils;* a commutator with the proper number of insulated segments; and two brushes for contact with the external source of direct current (see Figure 26–15). The field

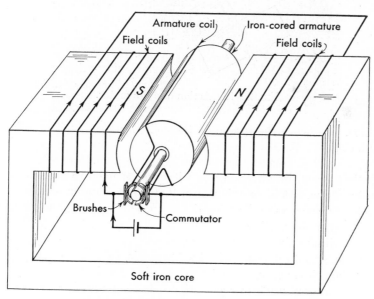

FIG. 26–15   Essentials of a shunt-wound d-c motor.

coils may be connected in parallel with the armature, in which case the motor is usually referred to as a *shunt-wound* motor; or they may be connected in series with the armature, giving us a *series-wound* motor; or there may be two sets of field coils, one in series and one in parallel with the armature, giving us a *compound-wound* motor.

Consider the single coil of wire *abcd* in the magnetic field and suppose that current from a battery is sent through it in the direction shown in

Figure 26–16. In the position shown, the force on the wire *ab* will be directed downward, while the force on *cd* will be directed upward. This will produce a torque on the coil in a counterclockwise direction, causing the coil to rotate. When the coil is perpendicular to the magnetic field— say *ab* is at the bottom and *dc* at the top—the two forces will be in the

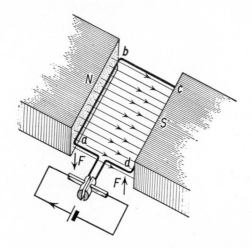

FIG. 26–16 Action of a d-c motor.

same line, and hence the torque on the coil will be zero. The coil may, because of its inertia, continue to rotate beyond this position; but, unless the direction of the current in the coil is reversed, the torque on the coil will be in a clockwise direction and will cause the coil to go back to the vertical position. It is for this reason that a commutator is needed in a d-c motor to reverse the direction of the current in the coil every time it passes through the vertical position. In other words, the current in the armature coil must be an alternating current.

As the armature rotates in the magnetic field, the magnetic flux through the coil changes, so that an emf is induced in the coil. In other words, the motor also acts as a generator. By comparing it with the generator shown in Figure 26–7, it will be found that the emf induced when the coil is in contact with the brushes is opposite to the voltage impressed upon the terminals of the coil from the outside source. This induced emf is usually called the *counter electromotive force* of the motor. If R is the resistance of the armature coil, the current I through it is given by

$$I = \frac{V - E}{R},$$

(12)

where V is the voltage impressed upon the terminals and E is the counter emf developed in the armature.

The armature of the motor is usually coupled to some machinery and delivers mechanical power to operate this machinery. The power P supplied to the armature is

$$P = VI. \tag{13}$$

From Equation (12),

$$V = IR + E;$$

therefore

$$\boxed{P = I^2R + IE.} \tag{14}$$

The power supplied to the armature consists of two terms: the term I^2R represents the power converted into heat, while the term IE represents the mechanical power developed by the armature. There is an additional, though small, amount of power supplied to the field coils. If I_c is the current through the field coils and R_c is the resistance of these coils, then $I_c^2R_c$ is the power delivered to the field coils; this power is all transformed into heat. In general, the power transformed into heat is small, so that the efficiency of the motor in converting electrical power into mechanical power is large; it may be as high as 95 per cent in some of the very large motors.

A full discussion of the electric motor is beyond the scope of this book, but one additional fact will be mentioned here. The coils of the armature are usually wound on an iron core. As the armature rotates, this iron also cuts across lines of force so that there is an emf induced in it, giving rise to induced currents in the iron. These induced currents are usually called *eddy currents;* they represent a waste of energy. To reduce the eddy currents as much as possible, the iron is cut into thin sheets or *lamina,* covered with some insulating material, and then put together to form the armature core. A laminated iron core has a much greater electrical resistance than a solid iron core of the same dimensions; in this way the eddy currents in the armature are reduced.

26-9 SELF-INDUCED ELECTROMOTIVE FORCE

The law of electromagnetic induction is that an emf is induced in any circuit in which the magnetic field is changing. The manner in which the change in the magnetic field around a circuit is produced does not matter; it may be produced by external circuits or magnets, or it may be produced by changes in the current in the circuit itself. Consider, for example,

the simple circuit sketched in Figure 26–17 and consisting of a coil of wire
C, an ammeter *A*, a switch *S*, and a battery *B*.   While the switch *S* is
open, no current flows through the circuit, and there is no magnetic field
around it.   The moment the switch *S* is closed, current starts flowing in

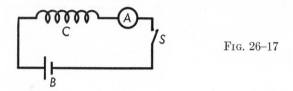

Fɪɢ. 26–17

the circuit, setting up a magnetic field around it.   This change in the
magnetic field induces an emf in this circuit itself.   This emf is referred to
as the *self-induced electromotive force*.   According to Lenz's law, the direction of the induced current due to this self-induced emf must be such as to
oppose the change which produced it; in this case, the change which produced it is an increase in the current through the circuit.   To oppose this
increase, the induced current must be opposite to the direction of the current from the battery, and hence the self-induced emf *E* must be opposite
to the voltage *V* of the battery.   If *R* is the resistance of the circuit, the
current *I* flowing in it is given by

$$I = \frac{V - E}{R}.$$ (12)

The magnitude of the self-induced emf *E* varies from a maximum
value equal to *V* when the switch is first closed, to zero when the steady
condition is reached.   The current *I*, therefore, will vary from zero at the
instant when the switch is closed to its maximum value given by Ohm's

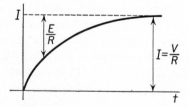

Fɪɢ. 26–18   Growth of the current in a
circuit containing inductance.

law, which holds when the steady state is reached.   Figure 26–18 is a curve
of the current in the circuit plotted against time.   The current takes some
time to reach its value in the steady state.

As long as the current in the circuit is constant, the magnetic field
remains unchanged, so that there is no self-induced emf in the circuit.
But when the switch is opened, the current decreases to zero and so does

the magnetic field. This decrease in the magnetic field induces an emf in the circuit, this time in the same direction as that of the original impressed emf. Sometimes this self-induced emf is large enough to cause a spark to pass between the blades of the switch. A simple demonstration of the existence of a self-induced emf when the switch is opened can be made with the arrangement shown in Figure 26–19. A lamp L is connected in

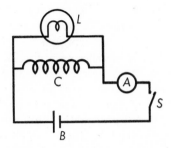

FIG. 26–19   A circuit for demonstrating the existence of a self-induced emf.

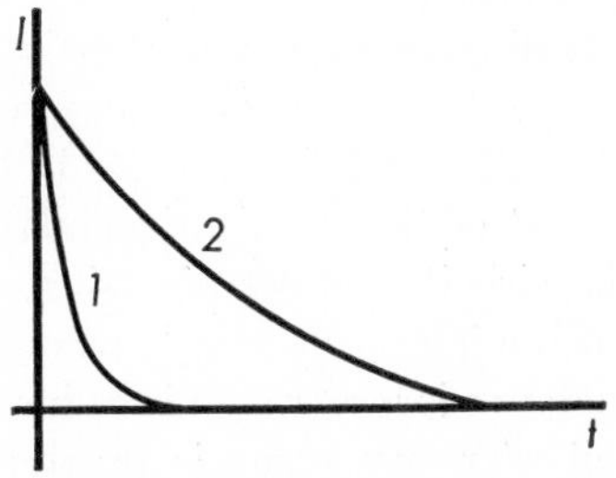

FIG. 26–20   Graphs of the decay of the current in circuits containing inductance; (1) no iron in the circuit, (2) iron in the circuit.

parallel with the coil C, containing many turns of wire. The resistance of the lamp filament should be large in comparison with the resistance of the coil, and the lamp should be of such size that it will glow dimly while the switch S remains closed. It will be observed that when the switch S is opened, the brightness of the lamp will suddenly increase and then drop. At the instant that the switch is opened, the emf induced in the coil C keeps the current flowing in the circuit, which now consists of the lamp L and the coil C. The emf induced in the coil can be greater than the normal operating voltage of the lamp, and, when this is the case, the lamp will flash brilliantly for an instant. If the coil has an iron core, the effect will last for a longer time. Figure 26–20 is a graph of the current in the circuit after the switch S has been opened. Curve 1 is for a coil without iron and curve 2 is for a coil with iron. In each case, the initial value of the current is the value it had just before the switch was opened.

The magnitude of the self-induced emf is proportional to the rate of change of magnetic flux through the circuit, and this, in turn, is proportional to the rate of change of the current in the circuit provided there is no iron in the neighborhood; that is,

$$E \propto \frac{\Delta I}{\Delta t},$$

in which ΔI is the change in the current in a small time interval Δt. Or, in the form of an equation,

$$E = L \frac{\Delta I}{\Delta t},$$ (15)

where L is the factor of proportionality and is known as the *coefficient of self-inductance* of the circuit or simply the *inductance* of the circuit. In the practical system of units, L is expressed in *henrys*. When the current changes at the rate of 1 amp/sec and the self-induced emf is 1 volt, the coefficient of self-inductance is 1 henry. The inductance of a circuit, or any part of the circuit, depends mainly upon its geometry. For example, if the circuit consists of a single loop of wire, its inductance is small; if the same length of wire is wound in the form of a coil of many turns, its inductance is larger. This is due to the fact that the magnetic flux through a coil of many turns is greater than that through a single large turn; furthermore, the emf induced in the coil is the sum of the emf's induced in each of the turns. The inductance of the coil can be increased still further by putting a soft iron core inside the coil, since the effect of this iron core is to increase the magnetic flux through the coil.

QUESTIONS

1. Referring to Faraday's experiment, illustrated in Figure 26–1, determine the direction of the current induced in S (a) when the key is closed and (b) when the key is opened.

2. The illustration in Figure 26–2 shows the direction of the induced current when the north pole approaches the coil from the right. Suppose the experiment were repeated with the north pole of the magnet made to approach the coil from the left. What would be the direction of the induced current?

3. Suppose the bar magnet of Figure 26–2 were placed inside the coil. What would be the direction of the current induced in the coil if the bar magnet were moved out of the coil (a) toward the right and (b) toward the left?

4. Suppose that the angular speed of the armature of an a-c generator were increased. What effect would it have on the emf of the generator?

5. What happens to the counter emf of a d-c motor as its speed increases?

6. An electric generator is running at constant speed but supplying no current. A load is then put across the line so that the generator supplies a current I. What happens to the speed of the generator at the instant it supplies power? Where does this power come from?

7. Compare the value of the current through the armature of a d-c motor when it is started and after it has acquired full speed.

8. Why is there frequently a spark across the terminals of a switch when it is opened?

9. The self-inductance of a circuit is frequently compared to inertia and is spoken of as "electrical inertia." Use this analogy in discussing the experiments on self-induction described in Section 26–9.

10. A long piece of wire in the form of a single loop is connected to a 6-volt battery. An identical piece of wire, wound in the form of a small coil of several hundred turns, is connected in parallel to the same battery. Compare the times required for the currents to reach their steady-state values in the two cases.

PROBLEMS

1. The magnetic flux in a coil having 60 turns changes steadily from zero to 20,000 maxwells in 2 sec. Find the induced emf in the coil.

2. A square coil, 5 cm on a side, having 800 turns, is turned from a position perpendicular to a magnetic field to a position parallel to the field in 0.02 sec. If the value of B is 5,000 gausses, what is the average value of the induced emf in volts?

3. A straight wire 6 cm long is rotated around one of its ends through an angle of 90° in 0.02 sec. If, during this motion, it always lies perpendicular to a uniform magnetic field of flux density of 3,000 gausses, what is the emf induced between its ends?

4. (a) A short solenoid, connected to a galvanometer, stands on one end upon a table. The north pole of a long bar magnet is brought down from above into the solenoid. Apply Lenz's law to find the direction of the current induced in the solenoid. Write out the steps in your reasoning and give the direction, viewed from above, as either clockwise or counterclockwise.

(b) If the vertical component of the earth's magnetic field is 0.5 oersted, what average voltage is induced in the coil of (a) above if it is rotated through 90° about a horizontal axis? The coil has 1,000 turns, a cross-sectional area of 40 cm², and the rotation takes place in 0.02 sec about a north-south axis.

5. Referring to Figure 26–2, assume the magnetic flux in each turn to be changing at a rate of 15 maxwells/sec. Calculate the induced emf in the coil.

6. Assume a rectangular coil of wire having 10 turns with dimensions of (20×30) cm² to be rotating at a constant speed of 600 rpm in a magnetic field in which the flux density is 6,000 gausses. The axis of rotation is perpendicular to the field. Find the value of the maximum emf produced.

7. Part of a closed circuit consists of a straight wire 150 cm long moving at a speed of 200 cm/sec perpendicular to a magnetic field of 10,000 gausses. (a) What is the emf induced in the circuit? (b) What is the force on the wire when the induced current is 4 amp?

8. A coil of 300 concentrated turns and an area of 800 cm² is lying flat on a horizontal table. When the coil is turned over through 180° in 0.15 sec, the average induced emf is 0.024 volt. What is the strength of the vertical component of the earth's magnetic field?

9. A rectangular coil 12 cm by 25 cm, containing 15 turns, is rotating at a constant speed of 1,800 rpm in a magnetic field in which the flux density is 1,500 gausses. The axis of rotation is perpendicular to the field. (a) Determine the maximum emf induced in this coil. (b) Plot a graph, to scale, showing the

emf induced as a function of time; start the zero of time when the plane of the coil is parallel to the lines of induction.

10. Find the efficiency of a certain motor from the following data, given on its name plate: 5 hp, 230 volts, 18 amp, 1,200 rpm.

11. When the current in a coil is changed at the constant rate of 8 amp/sec, the emf induced in the coil is 0.25 volt. Determine the self-inductance of the coil.

12. The coefficient of self-inductance of a coil is 32 millihenrys (1 millihenry $= 10^{-3}$ henry). Determine the average value of the self-induced emf when the current in the coil is increased from 2 amp to 8 amp in 0.05 sec.

13. In the shunt-wound d-c motor sketched in Figure 26–21, the resistance of the field coils is 150 ohms and the resistance of the armature is 2 ohms. When a

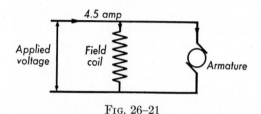

Fig. 26–21

difference of potential of 120 volts is applied to the brushes, and the motor is running at full speed delivering mechanical power, the current supplied to it is 4.5 amp. (a) What is the current in the field coils? (b) What is the current in the armature? (c) What is the counter emf developed by the motor? (d) How much mechanical power is developed by this motor?

14. The armature of a shunt-wound d-c motor has a resistance of 1.0 ohm. When the motor is running at normal speed and developing 2 hp, the current in the armature is 7.0 amp when the impressed voltage is 220 volts. (a) What is the counter emf of the motor? (b) At what rate is heat developed in the armature?

15. A shunt-wound d-c motor is delivering 4 hp. The voltage impressed on the brushes is 240 volts, and the current supplied to it is 13 amp. What is its efficiency?

16. A coil of wire contains 8 turns and has a resistance of 24 ohms. The coil is connected to a ballistic galvanometer which has a resistance of 60 ohms. If the magnetic flux through the coil is changed from zero to 3×10^5 maxwells, (a) determine the charge which flows through the circuit. (b) If the sensitivity of the galvanometer is 25 μcoul/cm, determine the galvanometer deflection in centimeters.

27

Magnetic
Properties

27-1 MEASUREMENT OF MAGNETIC FIELDS

The phenomenon of electromagnetic induction provides a simple way of measuring the magnetic field in any region by the use of a coil of several turns connected to a galvanometer. If the coil has n turns and if $\Delta\Phi$ is the change in the number of lines of induction through it, then the average value of the emf induced in this coil is given by

$$E = 10^{-8}n\frac{\Delta\Phi}{\Delta t}. \qquad \text{[Equation (3b) in Chapter 26]} \qquad (1)$$

If R is the combined resistance of the coil and the galvanometer, the induced current I in the circuit is, from Ohm's law,

$$I = \frac{E}{R}.$$

Putting in the value of E from Equation (1), we get

$$I = 10^{-8}\frac{n}{R}\frac{\Delta\Phi}{\Delta t}.$$

But $I\Delta t$ is the charge Q which flows through the circuit during this brief process, so that

$$Q = I\Delta t = 10^{-8}\frac{n}{R}\Delta\Phi. \qquad (2)$$

Suppose that the coil used for exploring the magnetic field is rotated through 180° and that $\Delta\Phi$ is the change in the magnetic flux through the coil; a quantity of charge Q will flow through the coil and the galvanometer in the short time interval Δt. This will produce a deflection in the galvanometer which can be measured, and, if the galvanometer has been calibrated, the quantity of charge Q can be determined. Hence the change in magnetic flux through the coil can be measured. A galvanometer used in this manner is called a *ballistic* galvanometer; its coil should have

579

a sufficiently large moment of inertia so that all of the charge Q flows through it while its deflection is still small.

If the exploring coil is placed in a uniform magnetic field of flux density B so that the lines of induction pass perpendicularly through the area A of the coil, the total flux through it is AB. If the coil is turned through 90° so that no lines of force pass through this area, the change in flux is AB. If the coil is turned through another 90°, the change in flux is again AB. Or if the coil is turned through 180° from the first position, the change in flux will be $2AB$. (Compare this with the generator coil.) Since the area of the coil is known, the magnetic flux density can be determined from the galvanometer deflection.

27-2   MAGNETIC FIELD INTENSITY AND FLUX DENSITY

At the start of the subject of magnetism, we described the magnetic field around a permanent magnet and introduced the term magnetic field intensity H at any point in a magnetic field, defined by the equation

$$H = \frac{F}{p}, \qquad \text{[Equation (2) in Chapter 20]} \qquad \text{(3)}$$

where F is the force produced by this magnetic field on the pole of strength p of a magnet placed at this point. In discussing Oersted's discovery and the work of Biot and Savart, we continued to describe the magnetic field accompanying the current in a circuit in terms of the magnetic field intensity H in the space outside the conductor. For example, the field intensity inside a long solenoid containing n turns wound on a cylinder of length L and of comparatively small radius R was given by

$$H = \frac{4\pi nI}{10L}, \qquad \text{[Equation (10) in Chapter 25]} \qquad \text{(4)}$$

where I is the current in the solenoid, provided the point in question was not close to the ends of the solenoid.

In discussing Ampère's work on the forces acting on wires carrying currents in magnetic fields and in discussing the work of Faraday and Henry on electromagnetic induction, we introduced a new concept, that of magnetic flux density B, defined by the equation

$$B = \mu H, \qquad \text{[Equation (19) in Chapter 25]} \qquad \text{(5)}$$

where μ is the permeability of the medium in which the wire is situated. In the electromagnetic system of units, $\mu = 1$ for a vacuum, by definition. In this system of units, B is measured in gausses and H in oersteds. For material substances, μ differs from 1: it is slightly less than 1 for a certain class of substances known as *diamagnetic* substances; it is slightly larger than 1 for another class known as *paramagnetic* substances; it is much larger than 1 for a few substances known as *ferromagnetic* substances, among which are iron, steel, nickel, and cobalt.

In this chapter we shall consider a method for measuring the permeability of a substance and describe some of the magnetic properties of different materials.

27-3　MEASUREMENT OF PERMEABILITY

One method of measuring the permeability of a substance is illustrated in Figure 27-1. The substance, in this case iron, is made in the form of a ring of average radius R, having a circular cross section of area A, as shown in Figure 27-1(a). Such a ring is sometimes called a *toroid*. A coil of n turns of wire is then wound uniformly around this toroid, forming a ring solenoid or a toroidal solenoid. This constitutes the primary winding; it is connected in series with a switch, a battery, an ammeter, and a rheostat. If current I is sent through this coil, the field inside it is approximately uniform throughout its cross-sectional area A; the lines of force are circles inside the toroid, and there is no field outside. The field intensity H inside the ring is given by

$$H = \frac{4\pi n I}{10L}, \tag{6}$$

where n is the number of turns of wire wound around the toroid and L is its average length. The length L can be found to a close approximation by taking the average of the inside and outside radii of the ring and setting $L = 2\pi R$, where R is the average of the two radii. The dotted circle represents the average length L of the toroid.

A small secondary coil S is wound over the toroid and connected directly to a ballistic galvanometer. A change in the magnetic flux through S will produce a deflection in the galvanometer; the galvanometer in this secondary circuit can be calibrated so that the change in magnetic flux, and hence the change in magnetic flux density, can be obtained from its deflection. The magnetic flux through the secondary coil is the same as that through the toroidal iron core. If we start with an unmagnetized iron toroid and send a known current through the primary coil, a *magnetizing force H* will be produced inside the coil and hence inside the iron core.

The value of this magnetizing force can be computed from Equation (6). The effect of this magnetizing force is to produce a flux density $B = \mu H$ inside the iron core and a total flux $\Phi = BA$ through it. When the primary

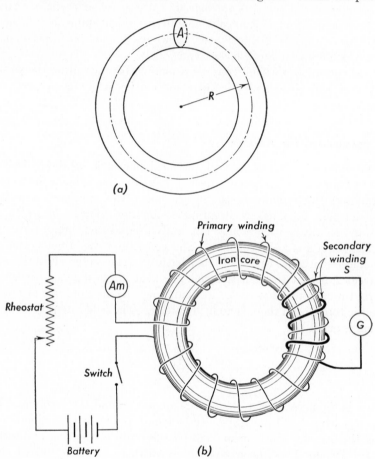

(a)

(b)

Fɪɢ. 27–1   Toroidal solenoid and circuits for measuring the permeability of the iron core.

switch is closed, the change in magnetic flux will be from zero to Φ and will produce a deflection of the galvanometer. The value of the flux density B can be calculated from this deflection.

The relationship between the flux density B and the magnetizing force H can best be represented with the aid of a graph such as that shown in Figure 27–2. We start with an unmagnetized iron core and magnetize it by starting with a small value of H, varying the magnetizing force in small steps with the aid of the variable resistor in the primary; the flux density B is measured for each value of H by closing the switch in the primary circuit and noting the deflection of the galvanometer in the secondary circuit. Each of these points is then plotted on the graph, yielding the magnetization curve shown in Figure 27–2. The flux density B

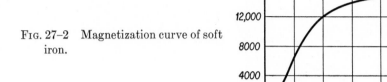

FIG. 27–2   Magnetization curve of soft iron.

at first increases slowly with increasing H; then it increases more rapidly until it reaches the flat portion of the curve OA. Along this flat portion of the curve, the iron is said to be *saturated*. The permeability μ can be determined from this curve for different values of H by taking the ratio of B to H at various points. Its value will also depend upon the particular type of iron used. For some types of soft iron, its value may be as high as 8,000. Because of its high permeability, soft iron is used in electrical machinery where large flux densities are required.

Special alloys have been developed which have interesting and valuable magnetic properties. Permalloy, which is made of iron and nickel, has a very great permeability for low values of the magnetizing force and a small permeability for high values of the magnetizing force. Alnico, made of iron, aluminum, nickel, cobalt, and copper, becomes a very strong permanent magnet when placed in a magnetic field.

27-4 HYSTERESIS

Let us take a piece of unmagnetized steel in the form of a ring of circular cross section, wind a toroidal solenoid around it, as in Figure 27–1, and then put a second coil S around it connected to a ballistic galvanometer to study its magnetic properties. If we send current through the coil and magnetize the steel until the flux density in it has reached its saturation value, as shown in Figure 27–3, the variation of B with H will follow the magnetization curve OA. If we now decrease the current through the magnetizing coil in small steps, it will be found that the curve of B against H will not coincide with the original curve OA, but will follow the curve AC. OC is the value of the magnetic flux density still remaining in the

steel when the current in the solenoid has been reduced to zero.   The steel
is now a permanent magnet, and the value of the flux density *OC* is called
its *retentivity*.   To reduce the flux density to zero, that is, to demagnetize

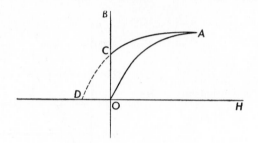

FIG. 27-3   Hysteresis.

the steel, it is necessary to reverse the current in the magnetizing coil and
increase its value until *H* has reached the negative value given by *OD*.
The value of *H* needed to reduce *B* to zero is called the *coercive force*.   This
property of a magnetic substance, in which *B* lags behind its previous
value while *H* returns to its former value, is called *hysteresis*.

All ferromagnetic materials exhibit the phenomenon of hysteresis;
one of the effects of hysteresis is that the value of *B* for any given value of
H is not always the same, but depends upon the previous treatment that
the ferromagnetic material received.   If an alternating current is sent
through the solenoid which is wound around a ferromagnetic core, the
B-H curve will be similar to that shown in Figure 27–4 for each cycle of

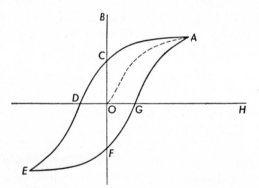

FIG. 27-4   Hysteresis loop in cycle of magnetization of iron.

the current.   While the current in the coil, and hence the magnetizing
force, goes from its maximum value to zero, the corresponding value of *B*
goes from its maximum or saturation value at point *A* to its value at

point C. As the current in the coil reverses, the flux density decreases to zero at D and then reverses and reaches its saturation value at E which is equal in magnitude to that at A. As the current in this direction is decreased to zero, the flux density decreases to the value OF, equal in magnitude to OC. The current now reverses its direction, and the value of the flux density drops to zero when H has the value OG, and, as H increases to its maximum value, B reaches its saturation value at A. The cycle then repeats itself; during this cycle the curve never goes through the origin.

It can be shown that the area inside the $B\text{-}H$ loop is a measure of the work done per unit volume on the ferromagnetic material in one cycle. The work done is converted into internal energy in the material, and this usually produces a rise in its temperature. Care must be taken in the design of machinery such as motors, generators, and transformers, in which alternating currents are used, to keep the rise in temperature to a reasonable value by conducting heat away from the machine.

A simple way of demagnetizing a substance is to place it inside a coil and send alternating current through the coil. If the amplitude of the alternating current is decreased slowly, then the hysteresis loop will get smaller and smaller during successive cycles until finally, when the current in the coil is zero, the values of B and H will be zero.

27-5　MAGNETIC PROPERTIES OF MATTER

A careful study of the permeability of different substances shows that all substances have magnetic properties. For most substances, the permeability differs only slightly from the value 1. Substances which have very large permeabilities and behave very much like iron are called *ferromagnetic* substances. Among these, in addition to iron and steel, are nickel, cobalt, and the different magnetic alloys. All other substances can be divided into two groups: one known as *diamagnetic,* and the other known as *paramagnetic.* Diamagnetic substances, of which bismuth is typical, have permeabilities slightly less than 1. If a ring of bismuth forms the core of a toroidal solenoid, such as that shown in Figure 27–1, and the value of the flux density B is measured for different values of H, it will be found that B is slightly less than H. When a sphere of bismuth is placed in a magnetic field, it will experience a force which will cause it to move from the stronger to the weaker part of the field; this is just the opposite of the behavior of ferromagnetic materials.

Paramagnetic materials have permeabilities slightly larger than 1. Aluminum, platinum, and oxygen are paramagnetic. If a ring of aluminum, for example, is used as a core in a solenoid, such as that shown in Figure 27–1, the value of the flux density B will be found to be slightly greater than the value of the magnetizing force H.   When placed in a magnetic field, paramagnetic substances are forced from the weaker to the stronger part of the field;   this is similar to the behavior of ferro-magnetic materials.

A very important characteristic of paramagnetic substances is that their permeability increases as their temperature decreases.   Paramagnetic substances have been used to obtain temperatures below 1° abs, for a study of the properties of matter at very low temperatures.   The para-magnetic substance is first cooled to a temperature of about 1° abs by placing it in contact with liquid helium which is evaporating rapidly. The paramagnetic substance is magnetized isothermally at this temper-ature by placing it in a strong magnetic field.   The liquid helium is then removed completely, and the paramagnetic substance is demagnetized adiabatically by removing it from the magnetic field.   In this process of demagnetization, the internal energy of the paramagnetic substance is reduced and its temperature drops well below 1° abs.   The temperature of the substance is calculated from the measured value of its permeability. When other materials are mixed with the paramagnetic substance, the properties of these materials can be studied at these low temperatures.

We have seen the intimate relationship between electric currents and magnetism.   It is therefore reasonable to look for an explanation of mag-netism in terms of the motion of the electric charges in the atoms.   Dia-magnetism is explained satisfactorily in terms of the motion of electrons in orbits around the nucleus.   For simplicity, let us assume that the electron is moving in a circular orbit around the nucleus;   this is equivalent to a current in a circular loop of wire.   We can speak of a magnetic moment due to the orbital motion of the electron just as we speak of the magnetic moment of a current in a wire.   When the magnetic field through a circular loop is increased, a current is induced in the loop which is in such a direction as to set up a magnetic field which will oppose the increase in the magnetic field through the loop.   In a similar manner, when a substance is brought into a magnetic field, we can think of the action of this magnetic field on the orbital electrons as exerting forces on them which will cause them to move so as to decrease the total field through the substance.   This will make the permeability of the substance less than 1, which is the case for diamagnetic substances.

Since all substances contain electrons which move in orbits, the above explanation would lead to the conclusion that all substances are diamag-netic.   But since there are paramagnetic substances, there must be some additional source of magnetism in the atom.   This additional source is the *spin* of the electron.   A spinning electron behaves very much like a small magnet with a definite magnetic moment.   In most atoms these small magnets are so oriented that, as far as any outside effect goes, they neutralize each other so that only the orbital motion is effective. In other substances, these small magnets, because of the spin of the electrons, are so oriented that they do have a resultant magnetic moment. When placed in a magnetic field, these small magnets line up with the field, thus adding to the external field. Thus the permeability of these substances is greater than 1; these substances are paramagnetic.

27-6 FERROMAGNETISM

In an early theory of ferromagnetism (see Section 20-8), it was assumed that magnetic materials contained small magnets of molecular size. The results of modern investigations have caused this view to be modified considerably. Here we can only briefly sketch the new theory.

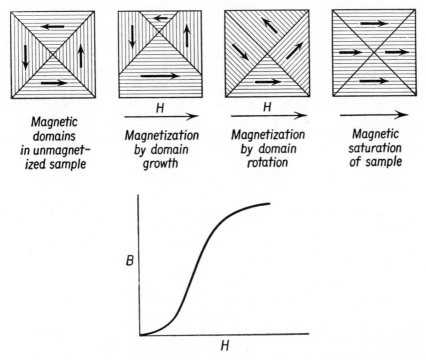

| Magnetic domains in unmagnetized sample | Magnetization by domain growth | Magnetization by domain rotation | Magnetic saturation of sample |

F*IG.* 27-5 Schematic representation of changes in magnetic domains of a ferromagnetic substance during magnetization.

In ferromagnetic materials the atoms are grouped into fairly large aggregates called *ferromagnetic domains*. In such a domain the maximum number of electrons in the atoms, consistent with the requirement of stable equilibrium, are oriented with their spins parallel, so that the domain is magnetically saturated and has a large magnetic moment. The size of the domain depends, among other factors, upon the manner in which the substance was fabricated, for example, upon the rate of cooling from the liquid to the solid phase, upon the manner in which the solid was worked, and so forth.

In the unmagnetized state of the substance, the magnetic domains are oriented at random, so that, as far as external magnetic effects are concerned, the net magnetic moment is zero. This is illustrated schematically in Figure 27-5. When an external magnetic field is applied, two things may occur. (1) At low values of the field, some of the domains whose magnetic moments are favorably oriented to this field may grow in size at the expense of the other domains, thus contributing to the external field, so that the flux density B increases with H, as shown by the lower part of the *B-H* curve. (2) As the external field is increased, some of the domains are rotated, so that their magnetic moments have components in the direction of H giving rise to the upper part of the *B-H* curve. Magnetic saturation is reached when the magnetic moments are all parallel to H, after which B increases linearly with H. When the magnetic field H is decreased, these magnetic domains rotate in the opposite direction but not to their original orientations; they return to a certain orientation which leaves a resultant magnetic moment, so that the substance remains permanently magnetized. It is necessary to reverse the direction of H in order to demagnetize this ferromagnetic substance.

QUESTIONS

1. Describe a method for measuring the intensity of the earth's magnetic field at your location.

2. Outline a method for determining whether a given sample of a substance is paramagnetic or diamagnetic.

3. Distinguish clearly between the flux density B and the magnetizing force H for a magnetic substance placed in the magnetic field of an electric current.

4. Why is soft iron rather than steel commonly used in electric machinery?

5. Soft iron becomes saturated when the magnetic flux density is 13,000 gausses. If it were necessary to create a magnetic field with a flux density of 100,000 gausses, would there be any advantage in using iron?

PROBLEMS

1. A small circular coil of 50 turns of fine wire has a plane area of 3 cm² and a resistance of 80 ohms. It is connected to a ballistic galvanometer having a resistance of 16 ohms. The flux through the coil is changed from zero to 30,000 maxwells. (a) Determine the charge flowing through the galvanometer. (b) If the galvanometer deflection is 2.8 cm on a scale a distance 1 meter from it, deter-

mine its sensitivity. (c) The coil is moved to a new position; the flux through it is changed from zero to a new value, producing a galvanometer deflection of 4.0 cm. Determine the flux density through the coil.

2. A small coil of 200 turns of wire, having a circular area of 5 cm^2 and a resistance of 12 ohms, is used as an exploring coil to measure the magnetic field between the poles of a magnet. This coil is connected to a ballistic galvanometer whose resistance is 36 ohms and whose sensitivity is 0.18 μcoul/cm. (a) The coil is thrust into the magnetic field with the plane of the coil perpendicular to the lines of induction; the observed galvanometer deflection is 6.30 cm. Determine the flux density of this magnetic field. (b) While the coil is in this field, it is rotated through 180° about a diameter as an axis. Determine the deflection of the galvanometer.

3. A toroidal solenoid of 200 turns of wire has an average radius of 12 cm and a circular cross section of 3.0 cm^2. (a) Determine the magnetizing force H when a current of 3 amp is sent through it. (b) A core of soft iron inside the toroid has a permeability of 800 at this value of H. Determine the total magnetic flux in the iron core.

4. The toroidal solenoid of Figure 27–1 has a primary coil of 600 turns of wire, an average radius of 16 cm, and a circular cross section of 4.0 cm^2 area. The secondary coil has 20 turns of wire whose resistance is 3.5 ohms and is connected to a ballistic galvanometer which has a resistance of 26.5 ohms. (a) What is the magnetizing force when the current in the primary coil is 0.25 amp? (b) The permeability of the iron core at this value of the magnetizing force is 650. Determine the charge sent through the galvanometer. (c) Determine the flux density in the iron core.

28

Alternating Currents

28-1 MEASUREMENT OF ALTERNATING CURRENT

Alternating currents are used so extensively that it is worth while considering a few of the simpler phenomena associated with them. For example, when the terminals of a resistor are connected to a source of alternating emf, the current in the resistor will vary continually. The instantaneous value of the current can be determined with the aid of a device known as an oscillograph, but for many practical purposes it is sufficient to know the *effective value* of the alternating current. This value can be determined by having the alternating current produce the same effect in a circuit that a known direct current would produce. The heating effect produced by the flow of current through a resistor is used for defining the effective value of an alternating current. *An alternating current has an effective value of one ampere when it produces the same heating effect in a resistor as that produced by a direct current of one ampere.*

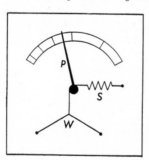

Fig. 28–1 Essentials of a hot wire ammeter; W is the wire, S is a spring, and P is a pointer.

One form of an a-c ammeter uses the change in length of a wire produced by the heating effect of the current which passes through it. As this wire is heated, its temperature rises and its length changes. A pointer attached to this wire moves over a scale which can be calibrated by sending a known direct current through the instrument. Since the heating effect depends upon the square of the current, the scale will not be uniform (see Figure 28–1).

590

28-2 INSTANTANEOUS AND EFFECTIVE VALUES

The simplest type of alternating current is one which varies sinusoidally with a constant frequency f. Let us first consider the current in a resistor which is connected to an a-c generator. The instantaneous value of the voltage v across the resistor at any instant t is given by

$$v = V_m \sin 2\pi ft, \qquad (1)$$

where V_m is its maximum value. The graph of this equation is shown in Figure 28-2. If R is its resistance, the instantaneous value i of the current in the resistor will be given by Ohm's law

$$i = \frac{v}{R}. \qquad (2)$$

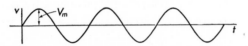

FIG. 28-2   Instantaneous values of an alternating emf.

Combining this with Equation (1) yields

$$i = \frac{V_m}{R} \sin 2\pi ft \qquad (3)$$

or

$$i = I_m \sin 2\pi ft, \qquad (4)$$

where

$$I_m = \frac{V_m}{R}. \qquad (5)$$

The instantaneous value of the current is plotted in Figure 28-3. If the source of supply is a 60-cycle source, one complete cycle takes

FIG. 28-3   Instantaneous values of the alternating current in a resistor.

$\frac{1}{60}$ sec. The current in a resistor is said to be *in phase* with the alternating emf; that is, both the current and the voltage reach their maximum values and their zero values at the same time, and also reverse direction at the same time.

The instantaneous value of the power p supplied to the resistor is

$$p = vi,$$ (6)

which, with the aid of Equation (2), becomes

$$p = i^2R;$$ (7)

that is, the rate at which heat is developed in the resistor depends upon the square of the current. Figure 28–4 is a graph of the square of the

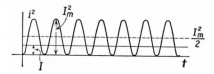

FIG. 28–4   Instantaneous squared values of an alternating current, the average of the squared values of this current, $I_m^2/2$, and its effective value I.

current in the resistor.   It will be noted that the square of the current is always positive, and the curve representing it has twice the frequency of the alternating current.   Since the effective value of an alternating current is defined in terms of its heating effect, this effective value can be determined by averaging the squares of the current and then taking the square root of this average value.   This is sometimes called the *root mean square* value, or the *rms* value of the current, as well as the effective value. The average value of the square of the current is $I_m^2/2$; hence the effective value I of the current is

$$I = \frac{I_m}{\sqrt{2}} = 0.707\, I_m,$$ (8)

where I_m is the maximum value of the alternating current.   Similarly the effective value V of a sinusoidally varying emf is

$$V = \frac{V_m}{\sqrt{2}} = 0.707\, V_m,$$ (9)

where V_m is the maximum value of emf applied to the terminals of the resistor.

From the definition of the effective value of the current, the average power supplied to the resistor can be written as

$$P = I^2R.$$ (10)

Ohm's law holds not only for the instantaneous values of the current and voltage but also for their effective values; that is,

$$I = \frac{V}{R},$$ (11)

so that the average power supplied to a resistor can be written as

$$P = IV.$$ (12)

In the above equations, capital letters such as I, V, and P are used to represent effective values of quantities which vary with time, while lower-case letters i, v, and p represent their instantaneous values.

Illustrative Example. A 120-volt, 60-watt lamp is connected to a 120-volt, 60-cycle a-c source. Determine the effective and maximum values of the current in the lamp and the resistance of the lamp.

The filament of a lamp can be considered a resistor. The rating of the source as 120 volts gives its effective value. From Equation (12), the effective value of the current in the lamp is

$$I = \frac{P}{V} = \frac{60}{120} = 0.5 \text{ amp},$$

and, from Equation (10), the resistance R of the filament is

$$R = \frac{P}{I^2} = \frac{60}{0.25} = 240 \text{ ohms}.$$

The same value could have been obtained from Equation (11).

The maximum value of the current is, from Equation (8),

$$I_m = \sqrt{2}\, I = 1.414 \times 0.5 = 0.707 \text{ amp}.$$

28-3 INDUCTANCE IN AN A-C CIRCUIT

If the terminals of a coil of wire are connected to a source of alternating emf, an alternating current will flow in this coil. This alternating current will be accompanied by an alternating magnetic field around the coil. As shown previously, this alternating magnetic field will induce an emf in this coil known as the self-induced emf. Because of the self-induction of the coil, the current in it *lags* behind the emf impressed on the coil; that is, the current reaches its maximum value after the impressed emf has reached its maximum value. If the resistance of the coil is negligible, the current i in the coil is found to lag behind the impressed emf v by a quarter of a period; this is illustrated in Figure 28–5. If the coil has appreciable resistance, then the lag between the current and the impressed emf is less than a quarter of a period. In the special case in which the inductance of the coil is negligible in comparison with its resistance, the current and the impressed voltage are in phase with each other.

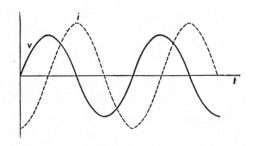

Fig. 28–5   The current lags behind the voltage by 90° in an inductance.

The effective value I of the current in a coil which has a resistance R and a coefficient of self-inductance L can be shown to be given by

$$I = \frac{V}{\sqrt{R^2 + (2\pi f L)^2}},\qquad (13)$$

where V is the effective value of the impressed emf and f is the frequency of the alternating current. The quantity $2\pi f L$ is called the *inductive reactance* of the coil and is usually designated by the symbol X_L; thus

$$X_L = 2\pi f L. \qquad (14)$$

The inductive reactance X_L is expressed in ohms, if the inductance L is expressed in henrys and the frequency f is expressed in cycles per second. Thus the simplified form of Ohm's law $I = V/R$ is not generally applicable to an a-c circuit when effective values of the current and potential difference are used. Instead, a more generalized form of Ohm's law, such as that given by Equation (13), must be used for a-c circuits. Equation (13) may be written in a simplified form as follows:

$$I = \frac{V}{Z},\qquad (15)$$

in which Z is called the *impedance* of the a-c circuit and is also measured in ohms. In the above circuit,

$$Z = \sqrt{R^2 + (2\pi f L)^2} \tag{16}$$

or

$$Z = \sqrt{R^2 + X_L^2}. \tag{17}$$

The effect of an inductance in an a-c circuit can be shown by means of the circuit illustrated in Figure 28–6, in which a coil of many turns of wire is placed in series with a 110-volt lamp, and 120 volts from a 60-cycle

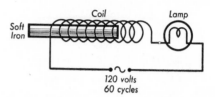

Fig. 28–6   An iron core inside a coil increases its impedance.

source are impressed across the circuit. The lamp will glow with fair brightness. If now a soft iron core is inserted slowly into the coil, the lamp will grow dimmer, showing that the current in the circuit has been decreased. Placing an iron core inside the coil increases the changing magnetic flux in the coil and hence increases its inductance. The impedance of the circuit is thus increased, and the current in it is decreased. Changing the inductance of a circuit forms a convenient way of controlling the current in an a-c circuit.

28-4   VECTOR DIAGRAM FOR AN A-C CIRCUIT

For convenience in making calculations, a coil may be considered as having an inductance L in series with a resistance R, as shown in Figure 28–7. The effective voltage across R is then IR, and the effective voltage

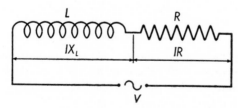

Fig. 28–7   A circuit containing inductance and resistance.

across L is IX_L. Since the voltage across the resistor R is in phase with the current I and since the voltage across the inductance L leads the current I by one quarter of a period, the voltages IR and IX_L are also out of phase by a quarter of a period and hence cannot be added algebraically. A convenient method for adding them is illustrated in Figure 28–8, in which a vector along the x-axis, drawn to some convenient scale, represents the effective value I of the current in the circuit. The voltage drop

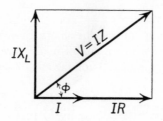

Fig. 28–8   Vector diagram for a circuit containing inductance and resistance; the current lags behind the voltage.

$V_R = IR$ is in phase with this current and is represented by a vector drawn from the same origin along the x-axis. The potential difference V_L across the inductance differs in phase from the current I by 90°; hence it is also out of phase by 90° with IR, the voltage drop across R. The voltage $V_L = IX_L$ is drawn along the positive y-axis. The total voltage V across the terminals of the circuit is then given by the vector sum of the two voltages; thus

$$V = \sqrt{(IR)^2 + (IX_L)^2}$$
$$= I\sqrt{R^2 + X_L^2},$$

or $$V = IZ,$$

in agreement with Equations (13) and (15).

In this type of vector diagram two quantities which are out of phase by a quarter of a period are drawn at right angles to each other; they are said to be 90° out of phase. The angle ϕ between I and V is called the *phase angle* and is given by the equation

$$\tan \phi = \frac{X_L}{R}.$$

(18)

This angle represents the lag between the current and the voltage, or the phase difference between them, when measured in a clockwise direction from the vector representing the impressed voltage V to the vector representing the current I.

Illustrative Example. A coil having an inductance of 200 millihenrys (abbreviated mh) is placed in series with a resistor having a resistance of 30 ohms. (a) Determine the current in the circuit when 120 volts from a 60-cycle source are impressed across its terminals. (b) Determine the voltage across the coil and also across the resistor.

The inductive reactance X_L of the coil is

$$X_L = 2\pi f L = 2\pi \times 60 \times 0.2 \text{ ohms}$$
$$= 377 \times 0.2 = 75.4 \text{ ohms}.$$

The impedance Z of the circuit is

$$Z = \sqrt{R^2 + X_L^2}$$
$$= \sqrt{(30)^2 + (75.4)^2} \text{ ohms}$$
$$= 81 \text{ ohms}.$$

(a) The current in the circuit is

$$I = \frac{E}{Z} = \frac{120}{81} = 1.48 \text{ amp}.$$

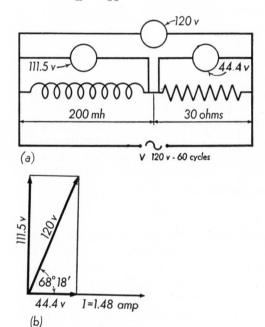

(a)

(b)

Fig. 28–9

(b) The voltage across the coil is

$$V_L = IX_L = 1.48 \times 75.4$$
$$= 111.5 \text{ volts},$$

and the voltage across the resistor is

$$V_R = IR = 1.48 \times 30$$
$$= 44.4 \text{ volts}.$$

These voltages are drawn to scale in the vector diagram of Figure 28–9(b). The phase angle between the current and voltage is determined from the equation

$$\tan \phi = \frac{X_L}{R} = \frac{75.4}{30} = 2.51,$$

yielding $\phi = 68°18'.$

The current lags behind the impressed voltage by $68°18'$.

Voltmeters connected across the resistor, the coil, and the terminals of the circuit, as shown in Figure 28–9(a), would read the values 44.4 volts, 111.5 volts, and 120 volts, respectively.

28-5   POWER IN AN A-C CIRCUIT

The power delivered to an a-c circuit by an a-c generator is, at any instant, given by Equation (6)

$$p = vi, \tag{6}$$

where v is the instantaneous value of the emf and i is the instantaneous value of the current. When the circuit consists of a resistance only, the current and voltage are in phase at all times. This means that the product of the voltage and the current is always positive, and power is actually transformed from the electrical form into heat and leaves the circuit. As shown previously, the average power delivered to the resistor can be written in terms of the effective values of the current and voltage,

$$P = IV. \tag{12}$$

If the circuit consists of a pure inductance, the current and voltage are always out of phase by one quarter of a period or by 90°. This means that the power, as given by Equation (6), is sometimes positive and sometimes negative. The interpretation of this is that in that part of the cycle during which the current is increasing in one direction, energy is being supplied to build up the magnetic field around the current. During the next quarter of a cycle, while the current is decreasing, the magnetic field is decreasing and returning energy to the circuit by inducing an emf in the circuit to oppose the decrease. The net result is that no energy is actually removed from the circuit; it is merely being stored in the magnetic field while the magnetic field is being increased and then returned to the circuit when the magnetic field is decreasing.

If the circuit contains both inductance and resistance, power is removed from the circuit only by that portion of the current which remains in phase with the voltage across the circuit. In the vector diagram of Figure 28–8, the component of V in the direction of I is $V \cos \phi$, so that the power delivered to an a-c circuit is, on the average,

$$P = VI \cos \phi.$$ (19)

The factor $\cos \phi$ is called the *power factor* of the circuit. When ϕ is 90°, the power factor is zero, and no power is delivered to the circuit. When ϕ is 0°, the power factor is 1, and the power delivered to the circuit is VI.

28-6 CAPACITANCE IN AN A-C CIRCUIT

Capacitors, or condensers, are widely used in a-c circuits. To understand the behavior of a capacitor in a circuit, let us first consider a capacitor C connected in series with a battery B and a switch S, as shown in Figure 28–10. When the switch is closed, the plates of the capacitor become

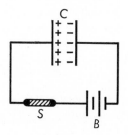

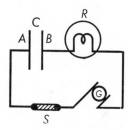

Fig. 28–10 Capacitance in a d-c circuit.   Fig. 28–11 Capacitance and resistance in an a-c circuit.

charged positively and negatively, as shown. Since the plates initially were not charged, this means that there was a momentary current in the circuit in which electrons were transferred from one plate to the other until the net charge Q on each plate was

$$Q = CV,$$ (20)

in which C is the capacitance of the capacitor and V is the electromotive force of the cell. If the switch S is now opened, the capacitor remains charged. It can be used as a source of electric energy. For example, if a resistor is connected across the terminals of the capacitor, the charge Q will flow through the resistor. A current will thus have been established in this circuit, and the electric energy which was stored in the capacitor while it was being charged has now been transformed into heat.

The behavior of a capacitor in an a-c circuit can be shown with the aid of the circuit illustrated in Figure 28–11, in which the capacitor C is connected in series with a lamp R, a switch S, and an a-c generator G.

When the switch is closed, the lamp will glow, showing that there is a current in the circuit. Since the current is alternating, the plate A of the capacitor becomes charged positively during one half of the cycle and negatively during the opposite half of the cycle. Conversely, the plate B of the capacitor acquires a charge opposite to that of A at every instant. In the connecting wires leading to the plates of the capacitor, the current consists of the motion of electrons to and from the plates. In the space between the plates, which may be a vacuum or may contain air or some other dielectric, there is an electric field which is also alternating in direction as well as changing in magnitude. The instant the switch is closed, charges begin to build up on the two plates, positive on one, negative on the other. The rate of charging is greatest initially, and, as charges accumulate on the plates, a counter emf equal to q/C, where q is the instantaneous value of the charge, is set up which decreases the rate of charging. Thus the current is a maximum initially when the impressed voltage is zero, and decreases in value while the voltage is increasing, the current becoming zero when the voltage reaches its maximum value (see Figure 28–12). The current reverses direction when the impressed voltage

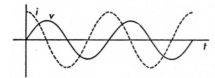

FIG. 28–12   The current in a capacitor leads the voltage across the capacitor by 90°.

across the capacitor starts decreasing; that is, the charges on the plates are being fed back to the source. When the impressed voltage reverses direction, charges opposite in sign to that in the first half of the cycle build up on the plates, rapidly at first and at a diminishing rate as the voltage builds up to a maximum in the negative direction. It will thus be seen that the current reaches its maximum value before the voltage across the capacitor reaches its maximum value; one way of saying this is that the current *leads* the voltage. Neglecting resistance, the current leads the voltage across a capacitor by 90° or a quarter of a period.

The effective value I of the current in a circuit containing only a capacitance C is given by

$$I = \frac{V}{X_C},$$
(21)

in which V is the voltage across the terminals of the capacitor and X_C is the *capacitive reactance* given by the equation

$$X_C = \frac{1}{2\pi f C},$$ (22)

in which f is the frequency of the alternating current. Thus the higher the frequency and the greater its capacitance, the smaller is the capacitive reactance. The capacitive reactance X_C is expressed in ohms when C is expressed in farads and f in cycles per second.

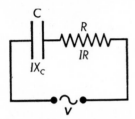

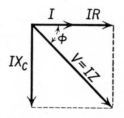

Fig. 28–13   Capacitor in series with a resistor in an a-c circuit.

Fig. 28–14   Vector diagram for a circuit containing a capacitance and resistance in series; the current leads the voltage.

If an a-c voltage is impressed across the terminals of a circuit consisting of a capacitor and a resistor in series, as shown in Figure 28–13, the current I in the circuit is given by

$$I = \frac{V}{\sqrt{R^2 + X_C^2}} = \frac{V}{Z},$$ (23)

in which V is the voltage across the terminals of the circuit, and Z is the impedance of this circuit, given by

$$Z = \sqrt{R^2 + X_C^2}.$$ (24)

Figure 28–14 is the vector diagram showing the relationship between the current I in the circuit, the voltage IR across the terminals of the resistor, and the voltage IX_C across the terminals of the capacitor. The vector representing IX_C is drawn in the negative y-direction to show that the current leads the voltage by 90° or a quarter of a period. The phase angle ϕ by which the current leads the impressed voltage V is, from the figure,

$$\tan \phi = \frac{X_C}{R}.$$ (25)

Illustrative Example. A circuit, containing a capacitor of 4.0 μfd capacitance and a resistor of 250 ohms, is connected in series with a 60-cycle, 120-volt source. Determine (a) the current in the circuit, (b) the voltage across the terminals of the resistor, (c) the voltage across the terminals of the capacitor, (d) the phase angle, and (e) the power supplied to the circuit.

The capacitive reactance of the capacitor is

$$X_C = \frac{1}{2\pi f C} = \frac{1}{2\pi \times 60 \times 4 \times 10^{-6}} \text{ ohms}$$

$$= 663 \text{ ohms.}$$

The impedance of the circuit is

$$Z = \sqrt{(250)^2 + (663)^2} \text{ ohms}$$

$$= 709 \text{ ohms.}$$

(a) The current I in the circuit is

$$I = \frac{120}{709} \text{ amp} = 0.17 \text{ amp.}$$

(b) The voltage V_R across the resistor is

$$V_R = IR = 0.17 \times 250 \text{ volts}$$

$$= 42.4 \text{ volts.}$$

(c) The voltage V_C across the capacitor is

$$V_C = IX_C = 0.17 \times 663 \text{ volts}$$

$$= 113 \text{ volts.}$$

(d) The phase angle can be found from the equation

$$\tan \phi = \frac{X_C}{R} = \frac{663}{250} = 2.65,$$

so that $\phi = 69°20'.$

(e) The power delivered to the circuit is

$$P = VI \cos \phi = 120 \times 0.17 \times \cos 69°20'$$

$$= 7.2 \text{ watts.}$$

28-7 CAPACITANCE, INDUCTANCE, AND RESISTANCE IN SERIES

The most general type of series a-c circuit will contain capacitance, inductance, and resistance elements. Figure 28–15 shows an a-c circuit containing a capacitance C, an inductance L, and a resistance R in series with an a-c generator. If V is the voltage at the terminals of the generator, the current I supplied to the circuit is given by the generalized form of Ohm's law

$$I = \frac{V}{Z},$$

(26)

in which the impedance Z is given by

$$Z = \sqrt{R^2 + (X_L - X_C)^2},$$

(27)

and

$$X_L = 2\pi f L,$$

$$X_C = \frac{1}{2\pi f C}.$$

FIG. 28–15   Circuit containing resistance, inductance, and capacitance in series.

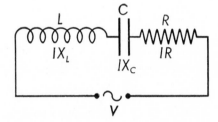

The reason for the negative sign with the capacitive reactance X_C is that the current in a capacitor leads the voltage by a quarter of a period, while the current in the inductance lags behind the voltage by a quarter of a

FIG. 28–16   Vector diagram of the voltages and currents in a series circuit containing resistance, inductance, and capacitance.

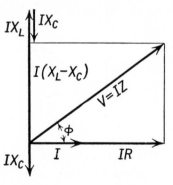

period, so that the voltage IX_C is 180° out of phase with the voltage IX_L. This is illustrated in the vector diagram shown in Figure 28–16, in which IX_L is drawn in the positive y-direction and IX_C is drawn in the negative y-direction.   The difference between these two voltages is then added to the voltage IR across the resistance R to obtain the total voltage V impressed on the circuit. The phase angle between V and I is obtained from the equation

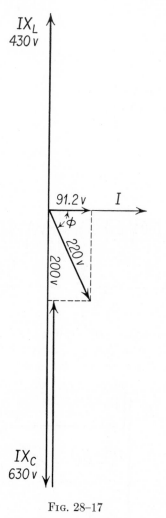

Fig. 28–17

$$\tan \phi = \frac{X_L - X_C}{R} ; \qquad \textbf{(28)}$$

if this value is positive, the current I lags behind the voltage V; if this value is negative, the current I leads the voltage V.

Illustrative Example. A series a-c circuit consists of a capacitor of 8 μfd, an inductance of 600 millihenrys, and a resistor of 48 ohms resistance. Determine (a) the current in the circuit, (b) the voltage across each element in the circuit, (c) the phase angle, and (d) the power supplied to the circuit when the terminal voltage of the 60-cycle generator is 220 volts.

The capacitive reactance is

$$X_C = \frac{1}{2\pi \times 60 \times 8 \times 10^{-6}} \text{ ohms}$$
$$= 332 \text{ ohms.}$$

The inductive reactance is

$$X_L = 2\pi \times 60 \times 0.60 \text{ ohms}$$
$$= 226 \text{ ohms.}$$

The total impedance is

$$Z = \sqrt{(48)^2 + (226 - 332)^2} \text{ ohms}$$
$$= 116 \text{ ohms.}$$

(a) The current in the circuit is

$$I = \frac{220}{116} = 1.90 \text{ amp.}$$

(b) Constructing the vector diagram as shown in Figure 28–17, with the current I along the x-axis, we find that the voltage across the resistor is

$$V_R = IR = 1.90 \times 48 \text{ volts} = 91.2 \text{ volts}$$

in phase with the current and therefore drawn along the x-axis; the voltage across the capacitance is

$$V_C = IX_C = 1.9 \times 332 \text{ volts} = 630 \text{ volts}$$

in the negative y-direction, since the current leads the voltage by 90°; the voltage across the inductance is

$$V_L = IX_L = 1.9 \times 226 \text{ volts} = 430 \text{ volts}$$

in the positive y-direction, since the current lags behind the voltage by 90°.

The impressed voltage V is the vector sum of these individual voltages and is given by

$$V = \sqrt{(91.2)^2 + (630 - 430)^2} = 220 \text{ volts.}$$

This is a convenient way of checking the calculations.

(c) The phase angle is determined from the equation

$$\tan \phi = \frac{X_L - X_C}{R} = \frac{226 - 332}{48},$$

so that

$$\tan \phi = \frac{-106}{48} = -2.21$$

and

$$\phi = -65°40';$$

hence the current leads the voltage by 65°40'.

It will be noted that the voltage across a capacitor or an inductance in an a-c series circuit may be much greater than the voltage across the terminals of the circuit.

(d) The power supplied by the generator is

$$\begin{aligned} P &= VI \cos \phi \\ &= 220 \times 1.9 \times \cos 65°40' \\ &= 173 \text{ watts.} \end{aligned}$$

28-8 RESONANCE IN AN A-C CIRCUIT

A case of very great interest is one in which the current and the voltage are in phase in an a-c circuit containing resistance, inductance, and capacitance. This can be established by adjusting the values of C and L so that

$$X_L = X_C, \tag{29}$$

in which case the phase angle ϕ will be zero, since

$$\tan \phi = \frac{X_L - X_C}{R}. \tag{28}$$

Putting in the values for X_L and X_C in Equation (29), we get

$$2\pi f L = \frac{1}{2\pi f C},$$

from which

$$f = \frac{1}{2\pi\sqrt{LC}} \cdot$$

(30)

When this condition is fulfilled, the current in the circuit will be a maximum and will be given simply by

$$I = \frac{V}{R},$$

since for this case $Z = R$.

A circuit for which Equation (30) holds is said to be in *resonance* at the frequency f. When the frequency of the a-c supply is that given by Equation (30), there is a maximum transfer of energy from the generator to the circuit, since the phase angle ϕ is zero and the power factor is 1. For example, if, in the illustrative example of the previous section, sufficient inductance is added to the circuit either by inserting more iron in the inductance coils or by adding additional inductance coils so that the circuit is in resonance at 60 cycles/sec, then the current in the circuit would be increased to its maximum value, given by

$$I = \frac{V}{R} = \frac{220}{48} \text{ amp} = 4.58 \text{ amp.}$$

To determine the new value of the inductance, we can solve Equation (30) for L and get

$$L = \frac{1}{4\pi^2 f^2 C} = \frac{1}{4\pi^2 \times 3{,}600 \times 8 \times 10^{-6}} \text{ henry}$$

$$= 0.88 \text{ henry} = 880 \text{ millihenrys.}$$

Illustrative Example. A capacitance of 0.2 μfd, an inductance of 32 millihenrys, and a resistance of 300 ohms are connected in series. (a) Determine the resonance frequency for this circuit. (b) What will be the current in this circuit when a generator supplies power to it at a terminal voltage of 6.0 volts at the resonance frequency?

(a) The resonance frequency is given by

$$f = \frac{1}{2\pi\sqrt{LC}},$$

and, substituting 32×10^{-3} henry for L and 2×10^{-7} farad for C, we get

$$f = \frac{1}{2\pi\sqrt{32 \times 2 \times 10^{-10}}} \text{ cycle/sec}$$

$$= \frac{10^5}{2\pi \times 8} = 2{,}000 \text{ cycles/sec.}$$

(b) The current in this circuit will be a maximum when the frequency of the source is 2,000 cycles/sec, and in this case will be

$$I = \frac{V}{R} = \frac{6}{300} \text{ amp} = 0.02 \text{ amp.}$$

28-9 THE TRANSFORMER

The electric energy which is transmitted from the generating station to the consumer is transmitted during a certain time interval, and, in designing a transmission system, it is the power or the rate at which the energy is transmitted that is of importance. If the terminal voltage of a d-c generator is V, the power delivered to the transmission line is

$$P = VI, \tag{12}$$

where I is the current in the line. If the transmission line has a resistance R, then the rate at which heat is developed in the line is I^2R; hence the power P delivered to the consumer is

$$\boxed{P = VI - I^2R.} \tag{31}$$

A greater amount of power can be transmitted to the consumer by reducing the resistance of the power line, that is, by using wires of larger diameters, or else by transmitting the power using smaller currents. The latter method means stepping up the voltage at the generating station.

It has been found difficult to build d-c generators which will develop emf's greater than about 3,000 volts. Hence, to transmit direct current at higher voltages, it would be necessary to connect several generators in series. This practice is not commonly followed in this country. Another difficulty is that, for safe handling, the voltage at the consumer's end of the line must be comparatively low—not more than a few hundred volts—and no efficient methods have been developed for stepping down the voltage of a d-c line. For a-c generating stations, however, the problem is entirely different. With the aid of a device known as a *transformer*, it is possible to step up the voltage at the transmission line to any desired value and then to use another transformer at the consumer's end of the line to step down the voltage to a safe, usable value, the power meanwhile having been transmitted at a high voltage and low current. Modern transmission lines are operated at voltages as high as 300,000 volts.

A transformer consists of two coils near each other. In most transformers these coils are wound on closed iron cores, such as that shown in Figure 28–18(a). The conventional diagram of an iron-core transformer is shown in Figure 28–18(b). For special uses, particularly in some radio circuits, transformers are made without iron cores; these are usually called air-core transformers.

Suppose that the primary coil P of an iron-core transformer is connected to an a-c source and that the effective voltage across its terminals is E. Let us suppose initially that the terminals of the secondary coil are left open. The current that now flows through the primary coil sets up

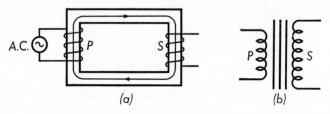

(a)   (b)

Fig. 28–18   (a) Iron-core transformer.   (b) Conventional diagram; lines between the coils indicate an iron core.

a magnetic field in the iron core. Because of the high permeability of the iron, practically the entire magnetic flux is inside the iron core. Since the current is alternating, the magnetic flux in the iron core is also alternating. This alternating magnetic flux induces an emf in each turn of the secondary coil, and hence the induced emf E_S in the secondary coil is proportional to the number of turns of wire n_S in the secondary coil. Since the same magnetic flux goes through each turn of the primary coil, an emf will be induced in each turn of the primary coil so that the total self-induced emf in the primary coil E_P will be proportional to the number of turns n_P in the primary coil. Since the magnetic flux is changing at the same rate inside each coil, we can write that

$$\frac{E_S}{E_P} = \frac{n_S}{n_P}.$$

(32)

Equation (32) holds for both the instantaneous values of the emf's and for their effective values.

In a well-designed transformer, E_P will differ very slightly from the impressed voltage E. Thus to a very close approximation, Equation (32) may be written as

$$\frac{E_S}{E} = \frac{n_S}{n_P}.$$

(33)

If the number of turns n_S in the secondary coil is greater than the number of turns n_P in the primary coil, the transformer is called a *step-up* transformer; if the reverse is the case, it is a *step-down* transformer. For example, if the secondary coil has 1,000 times as many turns as the primary coil, the emf E_S induced in the secondary will be 1,000 times the voltage impressed across the primary.

When a load is connected to the terminals of the secondary coil, a current will flow in the secondary circuit and power will be supplied by it. This power must, of course, come from the source of power connected to the primary coil. This transfer of power takes place through the interactions of the magnetic fields because of the current in the primary coil and that in the secondary coil. In well-designed transformers the efficiency is as high as 98 or 99 per cent. Neglecting the slight loss of power in heating the coils and the iron core, we find that the power drawn from the secondary coil must equal the power supplied to the primary coil; that is,

$$ei_P = e_S i_S, \tag{34}$$

where the symbols refer to the instantaneous values of the voltage and current in the primary and secondary coils, respectively. Or,

$$\frac{e}{e_S} = \frac{i_S}{i_P}. \tag{35}$$

Since Equation (35) holds at any instant, it also holds for the maximum values and hence for the effective values, so that we can write

$$\frac{E}{E_S} = \frac{I_S}{I_P}, \tag{36}$$

which, combined with Equation (33), yields

$$\frac{I_S}{I_P} = \frac{n_P}{n_S}. \tag{37}$$

Thus the effective values of the currents in the primary and secondary circuits are in the inverse ratio of the numbers of turns in the two coils.

If we rewrite Equation (37) as

$$n_S I_S = n_P I_P, \tag{38}$$

we note that if the current in the secondary is increased, as in the case when the load on the secondary is increased, the current in the primary is also increased.

In a step-up transformer, the emf induced in the secondary is large, but the current I_S is small, while the voltage across the primary is small

and the current I_P through it is large. Both step-up and step-down transformers are used in transmitting power. A simplified version of a transmission system is shown in Figure 28–19. At the powerhouse, the a-c
generator develops electric power at, say, 120 volts; the terminals of this
generator are connected to the terminals of the primary coil of a step-up

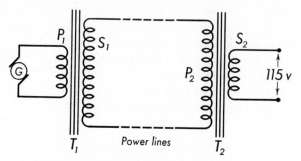

Fig. 28–19   Simple transmission line.

transformer T_1 which steps up the voltage to 12,000 volts at the terminals
of the secondary coil. The two wires of the transmission line, which may
be several miles long, connect the terminals of this secondary coil to the
primary of a step-down transformer T_2 at the consumer's end of the line.
Because of the voltage drop in the transmission line, the difference of potential at the primary of the step-down transformer may be only 11,500 volts,
say. If the ratio of turns between P_2 and S_2 is 100:1, the emf at the
terminals of S_2 will be about 115 volts, suitable for use with a great many
electric appliances.

28-10   THE INDUCTION COIL

An induction coil is a device for obtaining electrical energy at high
voltage from a low-voltage d-c source such as a battery. An induction
coil consists of a primary coil of a few turns of heavy wire wound on a soft
iron core and a secondary coil of a great number of turns of fine wire wound
over the primary but insulated from it (see Figure 28–20). An interrupter,
that is, a device for automatically making and breaking the circuit once
the switch is closed, is put into the primary circuit. A mechanical type of
interrupter is shown in the figure. When the primary switch is closed, the
current in the primary circuit builds up to its maximum value, as shown
in the graph of Figure 28–21. This primary current produces a strong
magnetic field in the iron core which attracts the soft iron armature of the
interrupter, pulling it away from the contact C, thus breaking the primary
circuit and producing a spark at the contact point. The current in the
primary decreases very rapidly to zero.

As the current in the primary increases, the magnetic field in the iron core also increases. This increase in magnetic field produces a changing magnetic flux in each turn of the secondary coil and hence induces an emf

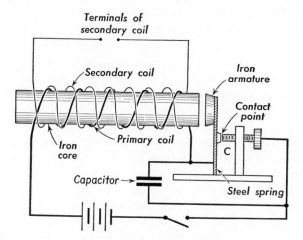

FIG. 28–20   An induction coil.

in each turn. If there are thousands of turns of fine wire in the secondary coil and only a few turns of wire in the primary, the induced emf in the

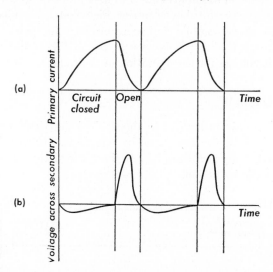

FIG. 28–21   Graphs showing (a) current in primary circuit as a function of the time and (b) the corresponding voltage induced in the secondary of the induction coil.

secondary will be very much larger than the potential difference across the primary. When the primary circuit is broken, the magnetic flux in the iron core decreases very rapidly and induces a very large emf in the second-ary. The direction of the induced emf when the magnetic flux is decreasing is opposite to that produced when the magnetic flux is increasing. Thus an alternating emf is induced in the secondary coil by a varying direct current in the primary. However, the emf induced when the primary circuit is broken is much greater than that induced when the circuit is closed owing to the shorter time taken by the primary current to decrease to zero.

When the iron armature is pulled over to the soft iron core and the circuit is thus broken, the steel spring attached to it pulls it back so that it again makes contact at C and thus starts the chain of events over again. When the current in the primary is changing, there is also an induced emf in it owing to the self-inductance of the primary. This back emf is large enough to produce a spark at the gap left when the contact at C is broken. This spark is objectionable both because it represents a loss of energy and because of its destructive action on the contact points. A capacitor is usually connected in parallel with the contact points so that when the circuit is broken, the capacitor is charged by the back emf, thus reducing the size of the spark. When the contact is closed, the capacitor is dis-charged. There is an additional effect produced by the presence of a capacitor in the circuit containing inductance; that is, it produces rapid oscillations of the current. Such effects will be discussed in Chapter 29.

An induction coil has many practical uses; for example, it can be used to operate gas-discharge tubes requiring high voltage. It is used in the ignition system of automobile engines to produce the high voltage needed to operate the spark plugs; it is used in automobile radios to supply the necessary high voltage for the operation of the radio tubes.

28-11 THE TELEPHONE

One of the major advances in the field of electrical communications was the invention of the telephone by Alexander Graham Bell in 1876. The fundamental physical principle at the basis of this invention is that of electromagnetic induction.

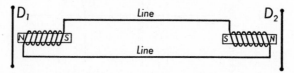

FIG. 28-22 Early form of telephone and telephone circuit.

In the early form of the practical telephone, the receiver and trans-mitter were identical, as shown in Figure 28-22. The receiver or trans-mitter consisted of a permanent magnet with a coil of fine wire wound around it near one end and a thin, soft iron diaphragm D held firmly a short distance from it. The two coils were connected by two wires which constituted the transmission line. There was no battery or other electric generator in the circuit. The power was supplied by the voice of the speaker. The diaphragm D_1 was set into vibration by the sound waves coming from the speaker. As the diaphragm vibrated in the magnetic field of the permanent magnet, it changed the magnetic flux through the coil; that is, when the center of the diaphragm went closer to the magnet, the magnetic flux was increased, and when it moved away from the magnet, the magnetic flux was decreased. This induced an alternating current in the coil around the magnet, and this alternating current was transmitted through the line to the receiver. At the receiver, the magnetic field caused by this alternating current alternately strengthened and weakened the magnetic field acting on the diaphragm D_2, causing it to vibrate in a manner similar to that of the transmitter diaphragm D_1. The vibrations of the diaphragm D_2 produced sound waves in the air which could be detected by the ear of the listener.

One of the chief difficulties with the old type of telephone circuit was that there was an insufficient amount of electric power available. In the modern telephone, the receiver and transmitter are different types of instruments, and batteries and generators are used as sources of electric power. The modern telephone receiver does not differ appreciably from the early type except that the permanent magnet is bent in the form of a U; it has two soft iron pole pieces on which coils are wound and connected in

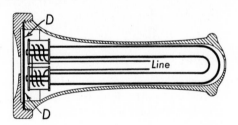

Fig. 28–23   Modern form of the telephone receiver.

series, as shown in Figure 28–23. Alternating current flowing through these coils alternately strengthens and weakens the magnetic field which acts on the diaphragm D, causing it to vibrate and produce sound waves in the air.

The modern form of transmitter or *microphone*, sketched in Figure 28–24, consists of a cylindrical box containing granules of carbon C in contact with the two faces of the cylinder. Direct current supplied by a battery B flows through these carbon granules and through the primary coil P of a step-up transformer. The secondary coil S is connected to the

transmission line.   The diaphragm D is fastened to one face of the cylinder
containing the carbon granules.   Sound waves striking the diaphragm
cause it to vibrate, and this, in turn, varies the pressure on the carbon

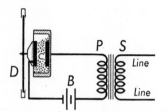

Fig. 28–24   Telephone transmitter or microphone.

granules.   The resistance of the conducting path containing the carbon
granules varies with the pressure; hence the direct current through this
circuit fluctuates in value as the disk vibrates.   These fluctuations in the

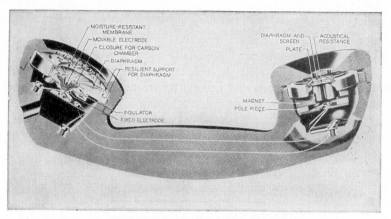

Fig. 28–25   Photograph showing in cross section the Bell system modern telephone hand set.   The transmitter is at the left and the receiver is at the
right.   (Courtesy of Bell Telephone Laboratories.)

current through the primary coil produce fluctuations in the magnetic
field through the secondary coil S and induce *alternating currents* in it
which are transmitted through the line to the receiver.

The modern telephone hand set, shown in cross section in Figure
28–25, contains the receiver and transmitter in a single unit.

QUESTIONS

1. What effect does the self-inductance of a coil have on the current (a)
when connected to a d-c source and (b) when connected to an a-c source?

2. Discuss the effect of putting a capacitor (a) in a d-c circuit and (b) in
an a-c circuit.

3. A lamp rated at 120 volts, 60 watts is placed in a circuit containing both inductance and capacitance. Under what conditions would it be possible for the lamp to operate at normal brightness when the circuit is connected to a 120-volt a-c source?

4. What properties of an electric circuit determine the resonance frequency of the circuit?

5. When a circuit is operating at its resonance frequency, what is the relationship between the voltage across the resistors and the voltage impressed on the terminals of the circuit?

6. Under what conditions can the voltage across an inductance in a series a-c circuit exceed the total voltage impressed across the terminals of the circuit?

7. Under what conditions can the voltage across the terminals of a capacitor in a series a-c circuit exceed the total voltage applied to the terminals of the circuit?

8. Under what conditions can current be supplied to an a-c circuit without delivering power to it?

9. Alternating-current generators are usually rated in kilovolt-amperes instead of kilowatts to designate their output. Can you give a reason for this? Under what conditions would the number of kilovolt-amperes be the same as the number of kilowatts supplied by the generator?

10. Suppose you have a lamp which is to be operated at 32 volts and that you have two power sources available: one is a 110-volt d-c source and the other is a 110-volt a-c source. With the aid of appropriate diagrams, show how you could operate this lamp (a) on the d-c source and (b) on the a-c source.

PROBLEMS

1. An inductance of 64 millihenrys is connected in series with a resistance of 48 ohms. Determine the impedance of this circuit (a) when a 60-cycle alternating emf is applied to the circuit and (b) when a 2,000-cycle alternating emf is applied to the circuit.

2. A coil has an inductance of 600 millihenrys and a resistance of 25 ohms. Determine the effective value of the current in the coil when it is connected to a 60-cycle, 120-volt a-c source.

3. A coil with an inductance of 0.020 henry and a resistance of 8 ohms is supplied with a current of 8 amp from an a-c source with a frequency of 60 cycles/sec. Determine (a) the voltage across the terminals of the coil and (b) the power supplied to the coil.

4. An inductance of 0.25 henry is connected in series with a resistance of 65 ohms. The terminals of this circuit are connected to a 60-cycle generator with a terminal voltage of 120 volts. Determine (a) the current in the circuit, (b) the phase angle, and (c) the power supplied to the circuit.

5. Determine the capacitive reactance of a 5-μfd capacitor when it is connected in a circuit supplied by (a) 60-cycle alternating current and (b) 2,000-cycle alternating current.

6. (a) What is the effective value of the current supplied to a 3-μfd capacitor by a 60-cycle, 32-volt a-c generator? (b) How much power is supplied to the capacitor?

7. A 2-μfd capacitor is connected in series with a 400-ohm resistor, and the circuit is supplied with power from a 240-volt, 60-cycle generator. Determine (a) the impedance of the circuit, (b) the current in the circuit, and (c) the power supplied to the circuit.

8. A 6-μfd capacitor is connected in series with a 300-ohm resistor, and 220 volts are applied to the terminals from a 60-cycle source. Determine (a) the current in the circuit, (b) the phase angle, and (c) the power supplied to the circuit.

9. An alternator furnishes 80 amp at 240 volts to an inductive circuit in which 17.6 kw are being used. Determine the power factor of this circuit.

10. A lamp rated at 60 watts, 220 volts is connected in series with a capacitor of 16 μfd capacitance to a 60-cycle, 220-volt source. (a) Determine the current in the circuit. (b) Will the lamp be lighted to its normal brightness?

11. A 50-ohm resistor is connected in series with an inductance of 1.8 henrys and a capacitance of 10 μfd. (a) Determine the impedance of this circuit when it is supplied with power from a 60-cycle, 220-volt source. (b) Determine the current.

12. A 30-ohm resistor is connected in series with a capacitance of 8 μfd and an inductance of 0.06 henry. A 60-cycle alternating current of 3 amp flows in the circuit. Determine (a) the voltage across each element of the circuit, (b) the total voltage applied to the terminals of the circuit, and (c) the phase angle between the current and the applied voltage.

13. A 48-ohm resistor is connected in series with an inductance of 450 milli-henrys and a capacitance of 9 μfd. (a) What is the resonance frequency of this circuit? (b) What current will flow in this circuit when it is supplied from a 240-volt source operating at this frequency? (c) Determine the voltage across either the inductance or the capacitance under these conditions.

14. An iron-core transformer has 100 turns in the primary winding and 800 turns in the secondary winding, and is operated from a 120-volt, 60-cycle generator. Determine (a) the emf induced in the secondary, (b) the current in the secondary circuit when it is taking 2.4 kw of power with a power factor of 0.75, and (c) the current in the primary.

15. A transformer is used to step down the voltage of a transmission line from 13,200 volts to 240 volts. (a) What is the ratio of the turns on the two windings? (b) If the secondary supplies 25 amp, determine the current in the primary.

29

Radio

29-1 ELECTRICAL OSCILLATIONS AND WAVES

Both the telegraph and the telephone use conducting wires to connect the receiving station and the transmitting station. But electric energy can also be transmitted through space without the use of wires; this energy travels through space in the form of *electromagnetic waves* with the same speed as light; that is, about 186,000 miles per second or 3×10^8 m/sec. The existence of these electromagnetic waves was first predicted theoretically by James Clerk Maxwell, in 1864, in his work on electricity and magnetism,

FIG. 29-1 James Clerk Maxwell (1831–1879). Mathematician and physicist. He put the laws of electricity in mathematical form. These equations form the foundations of electromagnetic theory. He predicted the existence of electromagnetic waves and originated the electromagnetic theory of light, and also made outstanding contributions to the molecular theory of heat. (Courtesy of *Scripta Mathematica*.)

though it was not until 1887 that Heinrich Hertz (1857–1894) succeeded in producing these electromagnetic waves and thus laid the foundation for the practical development of modern wireless telegraphy and radio. The first wireless signals were transmitted across the Atlantic Ocean in 1901 through the inventive efforts of G. Marconi. Accompanying these developments was the discovery by Thomas A. Edison, in 1883, of the emission of electrons by hot wires, the so-called *thermionic emission* of electrons.   This discovery became the basis of the invention of the two-element thermionic tube by A. J. Fleming in 1904 and of the three-element thermionic tube by Lee De Forest in 1907.   Progress in radio then proceeded at an accelerated pace.

Energy in the form of electromagnetic waves is radiated from a circuit in which the current is alternating rapidly.   The greater the frequency of these alternations, the greater is the percentage of the energy which is radiated from the circuit.   The method of producing electromagnetic waves consists essentially of setting up and maintaining an alternating current of high frequency in a circuit.   These *electrical oscillations* in the circuit produce alternating electric and magnetic fields which travel out into space with the speed of light.   The electric field is always at right angles to the magnetic field; that is, the vector E representing the intensity of the electric field in the electromagnetic wave is always at right angles to the vector H representing the intensity of the magnetic field, and they are both always at right angles to the direction in which the wave is traveling.   This is illustrated in Figure 29–2 for an electromagnetic wave of a single wavelength λ moving in the x-direction with a velocity c.   To simplify it still

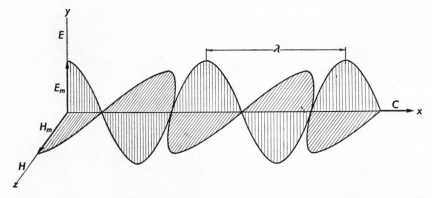

Fɪɢ. 29–2 Propagation of an electromagnetic wave in the x-direction. The electric and magnetic fields are at right angles to each other; the E curve is wholly in the xy plane and the H curve is wholly in the xz plane.

further, only a wave with its electric intensity in the xy plane is shown. Such a wave is called a *linearly polarized wave* (see Section 35–1).   The magnetic field H of the wave is in time phase with the electric field E, but is in the zx plane.   The relationship between the wavelength λ, the frequency f, and the velocity c of the wave is

$$c = f\lambda.$$
(1)

The frequencies of the electromagnetic waves used in broadcasting range from about 500,000 cycles/sec to 1,600,000 cycles/sec. For example, at a frequency of 1,000,000 cycles/sec, the length of the wave radiated from the antenna of the transmitting station is, from Equation (1),

$$\lambda = \frac{c}{f} = \frac{3 \times 10^8 \text{ m/sec}}{10^6 (1/\text{sec})}$$

or $\lambda = 300$ m.

The ordinary a-c generator used for developing power usually generates 25-, 50-, or 60-cycle alternating current. Although it is possible to develop high-frequency alternating current with a generator which has a rotating armature, a much simpler method is to set up electrical oscillations in a circuit consisting of a capacitor and an inductance coil. In Hertz's experiments on electromagnetic waves, the oscillator consisted of a circuit containing a capacitor of capacitance C, a coil of inductance L, and a spark gap S, as shown in Figure 29–3. When a sufficiently high voltage was

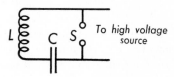

Fig. 29–3   Spark-gap type of oscillator circuit.

applied to the terminals of the spark gap to produce a spark in the air between the terminals, electrical oscillations were set up in this circuit of frequency, given by

$$f = \frac{1}{2\pi\sqrt{LC}}, \tag{2}$$

and electromagnetic waves of this frequency were radiated by these oscillations. The spark-gap method for producing oscillations in a circuit was in practical use for many years but has since been replaced by the thermionic-tube method.

29-2   RESONANT CIRCUITS

We have already shown (Section 28–8) that if a circuit, consisting of a capacitance C, an inductance L, and a resistance R in series, has an alternating emf of frequency f applied to it, then the current in this circuit will be a maximum if

$$f = \frac{1}{2\pi\sqrt{LC}}.$$

The above frequency is called the *natural* or *resonant frequency* of the circuit.

In our study of sound (Section 19–3) it was shown that resonance can occur between any two elastic bodies which can vibrate with the same natural frequency. It was suggested by Sir Oliver Lodge, in 1890, that the same type of phenomenon could be produced with electrical circuits which had the same natural frequency. He succeeded in setting up oscillations in one circuit containing a spark gap and in receiving the electromagnetic waves radiated from it in a neighboring circuit by *tuning* it to the same frequency. He detected this wave by observing a spark produced across a small spark gap in the same circuit. If the first circuit has an inductance L_1 and capacitance C_1 and the second circuit has an inductance L_2 and capacitance C_2, then the condition for electric resonance is

$$\frac{1}{2\pi\sqrt{L_1 C_1}} = \frac{1}{2\pi\sqrt{L_2 C_2}},$$

or if

$$\boxed{L_1 C_1 = L_2 C_2.} \tag{3}$$

When the condition represented by Equation (3) is satisfied, the two circuits are said to be in resonance. This idea is at the basis of the method for *tuning* a receiving set. When an electromagnetic wave of frequency f strikes a conductor, it sets up an emf which produces a current in the conductor. If the conductor is part of a circuit containing inductance L and a variable capacitor, then the circuit can be tuned by varying the capacitance until the resonant frequency of the circuit is equal to the frequency of the incident electromagnetic wave. In most radio receiving sets, the capacitance is varied by rotating one set of plates of the capacitor with respect to the other set.

29-3 THERMIONIC EMISSION

The development of modern radio depends to a very great extent on a discovery made by Edison, in 1883, in his study of methods for improving the electric light bulb. Edison put a metal plate into a glass tube containing a filament and evacuated the tube. The filament was heated by means of a battery A, as shown in Figure 29–4. Another battery B and a galvanometer G were connected in series between the plate P and one side of the filament F. When the positive terminal of B was connected to the plate, a current flowed through the galvanometer; but, when the battery was reversed so that the negative terminal of B was connected to the plate, no current flowed through the galvanometer. Edison merely noted this effect but made no use of it. The explanation of this effect is that the heated filament emits negative electrons; this is known as *thermionic emission* of electrons. When the plate is positive with respect to the filament, the electrons are attracted to the plate and flow through the circuit back to the filament. When the plate is negative with respect to the filament, the electrons are repelled by the plate, and no current flows in the circuit from F to P, G, and B.

When the filament is heated to a temperature T, some of the free electrons of the metal evaporate from the solid into the space around it,

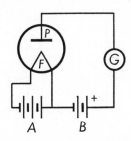

Fig. 29–4   Circuit for showing thermionic emission.

forming what may be called an *electron gas* around the solid. Equilibrium is reached when just as many electrons leave the filament as re-enter it from the electron gas around it. When a difference of potential is established between the filament and plate, electrons are attracted to the plate, and other electrons evaporate from the filament to replace them. When the plate voltage is made sufficiently large, the electrons are moved to the plate as fast as they are emitted by the filament. A further increase in the plate

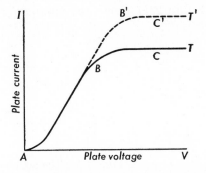

Fig. 29–5   Curves showing the thermionic current as a function of the voltage at different filament temperatures.

voltage does not increase the current through the tube. Figure 29–5 shows the plate current I as a function of the difference of potential V between plate and filament. At first, the current I increases as V increases, but, beginning at point B, an increase in V does not affect the current. This value of the current is called the *saturation current*, and, for any one filament, the saturation current depends upon the temperature. If the temperature of the filament is increased from T to T', the saturation value of the current is increased. It is to be noted that Ohm's law does not apply in this case.

29-4 THE RECTIFIER TUBE

A vacuum tube containing a filament and a plate is called a *diode* and can be used to rectify alternating current. Figure 29–6 shows one method

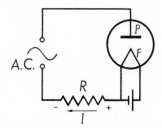

FIG. 29–6   The diode tube used as a rectifier; direct current is supplied to the external load R.

for using a diode as a rectifier. The filament is heated to the required temperature by current from a battery, and the plate is connected to one end of an a-c generator. The external load R, which is to be supplied with direct current, is connected to the other end of the generator and to one of the filament terminals. Whenever the plate becomes positive with respect to the filament, electricity will flow through the circuit; no electricity will flow when the plate is negative with respect to the filament. Thus electricity will flow through the circuit only during the positive half of the cycle. Figure 29–7 shows the alternating difference of potential from the a-c

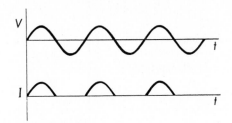

FIG. 29–7   The action of the diode as a rectifier.

generator, and directly underneath it is the graph of the rectified current through the external load R. The diode so used is sometimes called a *half-wave rectifier*.

Another method for using the rectifier is illustrated in Figure 29–8. In this case no battery is required; the filament is heated by alternating current obtained from the secondary of a step-down transformer. The secondary coil of a step-up transformer is connected between the plate and one terminal of the load. These two coils may both be wound on the same iron core and supplied by a single primary coil, as shown in the figure. The ad-

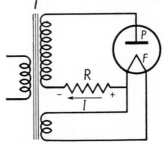
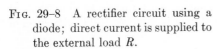

FIG. 29–8   A rectifier circuit using a diode; direct current is supplied to the external load *R*.

vantages of this circuit are that no battery is used and that any desired voltage may be applied to the load.

The direction of the current through the external load *R* is shown in both figures. It must be remembered that the direction of the current is

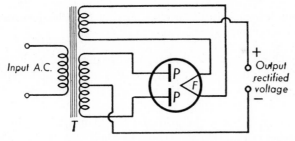

FIG. 29–9   Full-wave rectifier using tube with two plates.

the direction in which positive charges would flow; the negative electrons flow in the opposite direction.

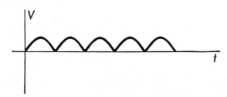

FIG. 29–10   Output voltage of a full-wave rectifier.

When full-wave rectification is desired, either two diodes are used or else a single tube is built containing one filament and two plates. Figure 29–9 shows a circuit using the latter type of tube as rectifier, and Figure 29–10 shows the rectified output voltage of this circuit.

29-5   THE TRIODE

The three-electrode tube, in addition to the filament and plate, has an electrode in the form of a wire mesh, usually called a *grid*. The grid is generally placed between the filament and the plate. The introduction of the grid into the electron tube opened up many new uses for these tubes. Only a few such uses can be sketched. To understand the operation of such a tube, consider the diagram shown in Figure 29–11. Because of the

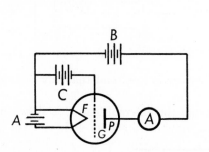

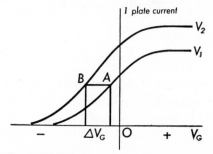

Fɪɢ. 29–11   Triode and circuit for ob-   Fɪɢ. 29–12   Characteristic curves of a
taining the characteristic curves.   triode.

position of the grid G, a small change in its potential with respect to the filament will produce a big change in the current in the plate circuit. The electrons go right through the spaces in the wire mesh on their way to the plate. If the plate voltage is kept fixed at some value V_1 and the potential difference between the grid and the filament is varied, we get the characteristic curve labeled V_1, shown in Figure 29–12, in which the plate current I is plotted against the grid voltage V_G. A similar curve is obtained for a higher value of the plate voltage V_2. It will be observed that each characteristic curve has a central portion which is straight and curved portions near the ends. The variations in the grid voltage are restricted to values lying on the straight portion of the characteristic curve when the tube is operated as an *amplifier*, while grid voltages restricted to values on the lower curved portion are used when the tube is operated as a *detector*.

Since radio tubes are normally operated at less than the saturation value of the plate current, the electrons are not drawn to the plate as fast as they are emitted by the filament. They constitute what is known as a *space charge* in the neighborhood of the filament. The amplifying property of a triode is due to the position of the grid in the region of the space charge. As we have seen, a small change in the potential of the grid produces a large change in the plate current if the plate voltage is kept constant. The normal method of rating a tube is in terms of its voltage amplification. The *voltage amplification constant* μ of a tube is defined as the ratio of the change in plate voltage to the change in the grid voltage needed to keep the current in the plate circuit constant. This can be determined from the voltage characteristic curves of Figure 29–12. Thus if the grid voltage is changed by an amount ΔV_G, the plate voltage will have to be changed from V_1 to V_2 to keep the plate current constant; hence

$$\mu = \frac{V_2 - V_1}{\Delta V_G}. \tag{4}$$

In many tubes, the voltage amplification factor is 10. This means that if the grid voltage is decreased by 1 volt, the plate voltage will have to be increased by 10 volts to maintain the plate current at a constant value.

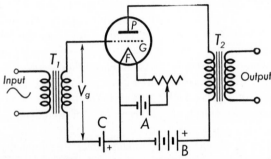

FIG. 29–13   Single-stage, transformer-coupled triode amplifier.

The use of a triode as an amplifier is shown in the circuit illustrated in Figure 29–13. The grid is kept at a negative potential with respect to the filament by means of a battery C; this potential is usually referred to as the *grid bias*. The value of this grid bias is chosen so that the steady current in

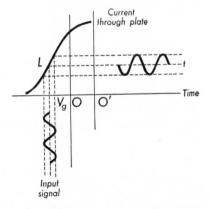

FIG. 29–14   Action of the triode as an amplifier; an alternating voltage applied to the grid produces similar variations in the plate current.

the plate circuit has a value which is in the center of the straight portion of the characteristic curve; this is the point L on the curve, shown in Figure 29–14. If an alternating potential difference is applied between grid and filament, the current in the plate circuit will fluctuate in value; these fluctuations will follow the alternations impressed on the grid. This fluctuating current, in going through the primary of the transformer T_2, will produce a fluctuating magnetic field which, in turn, will induce an alternating emf in the secondary coil which will have a form similar to that impressed on the grid of the tube. In addition to the voltage amplification produced by the tube, additional amplification is obtained if T_2 is a step-up transformer. The terminals of the secondary coil of T_2 can be connected to another tube amplifier circuit, thus increasing the amplification still further. Two or three stages of amplification are quite common. When transformers are used between the various stages, we speak of the amplifier as a transformer-coupled amplifier. Resistors or capacitors may be used instead of transformers to couple the different stages. When the frequency of the voltage is less than 20,000 per second, that is, in the so-called *audio-frequency range*, iron-core transformers are used as the coupling between the stages. But when the frequency is much higher, that is, in the radio-frequency range, air-core transformers are used. One reason is that the permeability of iron is practically 1 at these high frequencies, and another is that the secondary voltage is different for different frequencies because of the induced currents in the iron.

One of the most important uses of the triode is as a generator of oscillations in electric circuits. There are many different types of oscillator circuits, one of which is shown in Figure 29–15. The grid bias is obtained

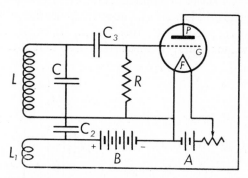

Fig. 29–15   A triode oscillator circuit using a tickler coil L_1.

from the difference of potential between the terminals of the resistor R through which a very small current is flowing. The grid circuit has a coil of inductance L and a capacitor of capacitance C. An additional coil of inductance L_1 is in the plate circuit, and its position with respect to coil L can be varied. Suppose that there is a change in the grid potential owing to a change in current in the circuit: this will produce a change in the current in the plate circuit, and, because of the magnetic coupling between the coils L_1 and L, an additional change will be produced in the grid circuit. In this way energy is fed back from the plate circuit to the grid circuit. If the amount of energy fed from the plate circuit into the grid circuit is greater than the energy lost by this circuit, oscillations will be set up in this circuit of frequency

$$f = \frac{1}{2\pi\sqrt{LC}} \cdot$$

To start the original changes in the current in the circuit in order to be able to feed energy from the plate circuit to the grid circuit through the coils L_1 and L is a simple matter. For example, there are always small variations in the current flowing through the circuit, particularly when the circuit is first closed. No matter how small these variations are, they are quickly amplified until oscillations are set up in the circuit.

It is interesting to note that the source of power for the oscillating circuit is the B battery in the plate circuit, which, of course, supplies direct current. The function of the triode, therefore, is to convert the d-c form of energy into a-c energy. When oscillations are set up, both direct and alternating currents flow in the plate circuit and also in the grid-to-filament circuit. The capacitor C_2 is put into the circuit as a shunt across the battery to provide a low-impedance path for the alternating current in the plate circuit; the direct current cannot flow through the capacitor. The capacitor C_3 in the grid-to-filament circuit prevents the direct component of the grid-to-filament current from flowing in the coil L, so that it must flow through the grid resistor R. This ensures the proper bias of the grid with respect to the filament. A fraction of the alternating current flows in R also, thus providing the variations in the grid potential needed to produce the variations in the plate current.

29-6   MODULATED WAVES

The oscillations set up in circuits used in radio transmitting sets are of high frequency and constant amplitude. The electromagnetic waves emitted by such oscillators are continuous waves of the type shown in Figure 29–16. These waves are used as the *carrier* of the signals which are transmitted. One method of producing these signals is to interrupt the oscillations by opening and closing the circuit for short or long periods, causing groups of waves to be emitted of the type shown in Figure 29–17. This will give effects similar to the dots and dashes of telegraphy.

Another way is to vary the amplitude of these high-frequency waves by impressing audio-frequency alternating voltages, such as that produced in a telephone line, on the high-frequency oscillations in the circuit.   The wave emitted by the transmitter, known as an *amplitude-modulated wave,*

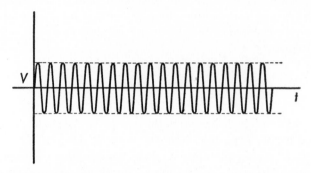

Fig. 29–16   Continuous waves generated in an oscillator circuit.

then has the form shown in Figure 29–18.   This is the method used in radio broadcasting by stations whose carrier waves are in the range of frequencies

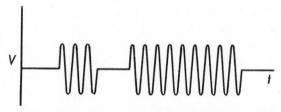

Fig. 29–17   Interrupted continuous waves used in wireless telegraphy.

from 500 to 1,700 kc.   One method for modulating a wave is shown in simplified form in Figure 29–19.   The high-frequency voltage from an

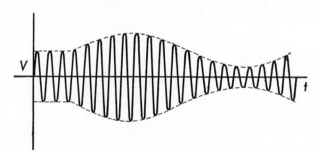

Fig. 29–18   An amplitude-modulated wave.

oscillator is fed into the grid circuit of an amplifier, while the audio-frequency voltage from a telephone circuit is fed into the plate circuit. This produces changes in the amplitude, but not the frequency, of the alternating current in the plate circuit. These oscillations passing through the primary of an air-core transformer T_1 induce similar oscillations in

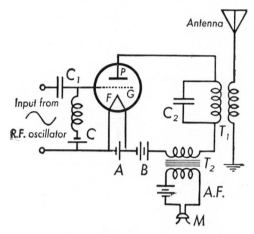

FIG. 29–19 Plate modulation circuit.

the secondary coil which is in the antenna circuit. The modulated wave is then radiated from the antenna and may be picked up by the antenna of a receiving set some distance away.

29-7 TRANSMISSION OF ELECTROMAGNETIC WAVES

The path followed by an electromagnetic wave, once it leaves the antenna of the transmitter, depends to a great extent upon the wavelength or frequency of the wave and upon the structure of the atmosphere. It is possible to direct the wave by proper design of the antenna and by the use of waves of the right frequency. Waves whose frequencies are in the ordinary broadcast range, that is, the type used for amplitude-modulated, or AM, broadcasting, generally follow two paths after leaving the antenna. One part travels near the surface of the earth, with the ground acting as a guide for these waves. They can be received by radio receivers not too far removed from the transmitter (see Figure 29–20). The reception of waves from local AM stations depends almost entirely on these surface-guided waves. Another part of the energy radiated from such a transmitter travels up into the atmosphere and is reflected from the first layer of ionized air, the so-called *E-layer* or *Kennelly-Heaviside layer*. After reflection, this wave returns to the earth and may be picked up by radio receivers. Part of this reflected wave may again be reflected from the surface of the earth, travel up into the atmosphere, and then be reflected once more from the Kennelly-Heaviside layer to the earth. Thus distant receivers may pick up these AM waves, while intermediate stations will not be able to receive them.

The heights of the ionized layers in the atmosphere, such as the E-layer and the F-layer, vary with the time of day, with the time of the year, and with the amount of radiation incident upon them from the sun and other

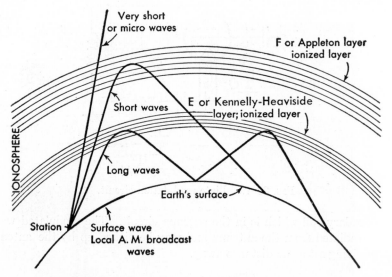

Fɪɢ. 29–20 Different paths traveled by electromagnetic waves of different wavelengths.

regions of the sky. Hence the points on the earth to which the radio waves are reflected will vary from time to time. Signals may be received at a given point from a distant transmitter during the daytime but not at night, and vice versa.

Short electromagnetic waves, such as those used in high-frequency broadcasts to foreign or very distant stations, travel to the higher ionized layers, such as the F-layer, before being reflected to the earth. The frequencies of these waves are of the order of 10^7 cycles/sec, or as sometimes stated, about 10 megacycles/sec. Since the speed of these waves is 3×10^8 m/sec, their wavelengths are of the order of 30 m. Very short waves, of the order of a few meters or less, or very-high-frequency waves, that is, about 100 megacycles/sec or higher, are used in the broadcast of frequency-modulated or FM waves and television. A negligible amount of the energy of these waves is reflected from the ionized layers. Such waves travel in straight lines from the transmitter to the receiver; hence the practice of putting the transmitting antenna on a tall building or on high ground to cover as wide an area in its neighborhood as possible.

Radar signals are transmitted by waves less than 1 m long; these waves are sometimes called *microwaves*. They also travel in straight lines from the transmitter to the receiver. Microwaves penetrate the atmosphere very readily. In one experiment, radar waves were transmitted to the moon and reflected from it back to a receiver on the earth (see Figure 29–21). Modern sensitive short-wave receivers have been detecting short

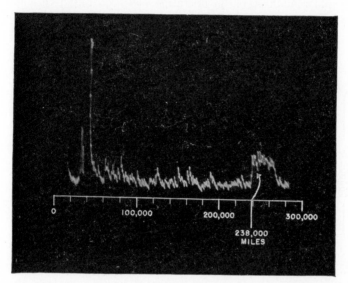

FIG. 29–21   Reflection of radar signal from the moon. The high peak on the left of the pattern as seen on the oscillograph shows the transmitted pulse, and the small peak on the right shows the pulse reflected from the moon to the radar receiving set. (Courtesy of U.S. Army Photographs.)

electromagnetic waves of a few centimeters wavelength, which come from some source in the sun. An analysis of these waves will undoubtedly enable us to determine the nature of the processes in the sun which emit such waves.

29-8   THE CRYSTAL DETECTOR

One of the simplest circuits used for the detection of radio waves is that shown in Figure 29–22 in which the detecting element is a special type of crystal, such as galena (lead sulphide), silicon, or germanium. This type of crystal, known as a *semiconductor*, possesses the interesting property of having a very great resistance when the direction of the current through it is one way and a much smaller resistance when the current is in the opposite direction. It thus acts essentially as a half-wave rectifier. In the early days of radio, crystal receiving sets were very popular since they required no batteries of any kind for their operation. However, it required a great deal of skill and patience to find a sensitive area on the crystal by probing with a very fine wire and maintaining the wire at this position. With the advent of the diode and the triode, crystal sets lost their popularity. Within the past few years, however, the art of making sensitive crystals which would remain stable in operation has been raised to a very high level, and crystals are once more being used as components of radio circuits.

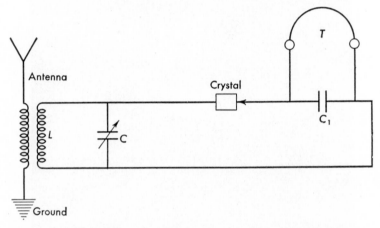

Fig. 29–22   A simple radio receiving circuit using a crystal detector.

Let us return now to a consideration of the detecting circuit shown in Figure 29–22. When an amplitude-modulated wave strikes the antenna, an electromotive force is induced in it, giving rise to a current of the same frequency as the carrier wave but of varying amplitude. The alternating magnetic field which accompanies this current induces a similar alternating emf in the neighboring coil of inductance L. This coil is part of a circuit containing a variable capacitor. By varying its capacitance until it reaches a value C such that the natural frequency of this circuit, which is $1/2\pi\sqrt{LC}$, is equal to the frequency of the carrier wave, the alternating current of this frequency will attain its maximum value. Currents of different frequencies produced by carrier waves from different stations will, in general, have negligible values. Thus this LC part of the circuit acts as a *selector* or *tuner* of the incoming waves.

The voltage across the capacitor C will have the form similar to that sketched in Figure 29–23(a). This is also the voltage across that part of the circuit in parallel with it; the latter contains the crystal and the telephone receiver T with its bypass capacitor C_1. Because of the rectifying action of the crystal, the current through it, although of the same frequency as the voltage, will be much greater when in the positive direction than in the negative direction, as shown in Figure 29–23(b). It will be recalled that the original amplitude-modulated wave was produced by superposing an audio-frequency current on the high-frequency carrier current. The

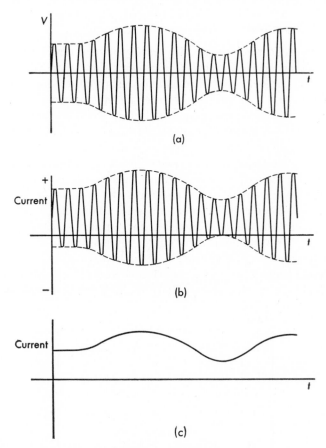

(a)

(b)

(c)

FIG. 29–23   Action of a crystal in a detecting circuit. (a) Graph of the incoming modulated wave. (b) Rectified current delivered by crystal; that is, the current in the positive direction is much greater than in the negative direction. (c) The current through the telephone.

current through the crystal may also be considered as consisting of an audio-frequency current superposed on the high-frequency carrier current. In its passage through the telephone receiver T, the alternating current produces an alternating magnetic field which acts on the diaphragm of the receiver; but, because of its inertia, it responds only to the variations in magnetic fields produced by the audio-frequency component of the current, which has the form shown in Figure 29–23 (c). This is similar in form to the original impressed audio-frequency current. The bypass capacitor C_1 provides a path of low impedance for the high-frequency component of the current.

29-9 A SIMPLE RECEIVER

Modern radio receivers usually employ several circuits and different types of tubes designed for special purposes. For our purposes, however, we shall consider only simplified circuits using either diodes or triodes. The radio wave which strikes the receiving antenna sets up oscillatory currents in it. These currents are usually very small, so that it is common to amplify them by means of one or more stages of radio-frequency amplifiers. The amplified currents then go to a detector circuit where they are *demodulated*. Demodulation, or detection, is essentially a method for separating the audio-frequency current from the radio-frequency wave. This is usually accomplished by rectifying the modulated current either by means of a diode rectifier or by a special adaptation of a triode. The audio-frequency current may then be sent through a telephone receiver, or it may be further amplified by one or more stages of audio-frequency amplification and then sent through a telephone receiver or loud-speaker.

A simple type of receiver is shown in Figure 29–24. Any modulated wave striking the antenna sets up currents in it which induce currents in

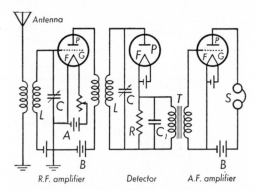

FIG. 29–24   A simple type of radio receiver.

the coil L which is connected across the grid and filament of the tube in the radio-frequency amplifying circuit. There are waves from many radio stations striking the antenna at the same time; it is desirable, however, to select the waves from one station only. This is accomplished by placing a variable capacitor across the coil L and by *tuning* the circuit by varying the capacitance C, until the natural frequency of the circuit is equal to the frequency of the carrier wave emitted by the transmitting station whose signal is desired. This signal is then amplified by the single-stage radio-frequency amplifier. This amplifier is coupled to the detector circuit by means of an air-core transformer. The detector circuit can also be tuned to the proper frequency by means of a variable capacitor across the secondary of the air-core transformer.

The action of the diode as a detector is illustrated in Figure 29–25. The high-frequency voltage applied across the plate and filament of the diode is shown in Figure 29–25(a) in light line. The voltage across the

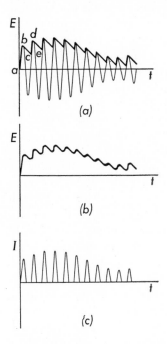

Fig. 29–25 Action of a diode as a rectifier. (a) High-frequency voltage applied across the plate and filament of the diode. (b) Rectified voltage across the capacitor C_1. (c) Pulse of current through the diode.

capacitor C_1 is shown in the heavy line of the figure, and, since R and C_1 are in parallel, this is also the voltage across R, as shown in Figure 29–25(b). The small jagged edges in this voltage curve are due to the action of the capacitor. When the impressed voltage increases in value from a to b, the capacitor is charged to the peak value of the voltage at b, and current flows through the diode. As the high-frequency voltage decreases in value, the charged capacitor keeps the filament more positive than the plate, and no current flows through the diode. During this time, part of the charge of the capacitor goes through the resistance R until the high-frequency voltage builds up to a point c, at which time the plate becomes more positive than the filament, and current again flows through the diode, charging the capacitor to the voltage shown at d. The pulses of current flowing through the diode are shown in Figure 29–25(c). The voltage across the diode resistor R thus has the same form as the audio-frequency modulating voltage of the incoming waves. The small jagged edges are greatly exaggerated in the figure.

The rectified audio-voltage is again amplified by the audio-frequency amplifier and made to operate a loud-speaker S.

29-10 TRANSISTORS

An increase in our knowledge of the electronic configurations of atoms, and particularly the manner in which atoms are grouped to form crystals, has led to the development of certain semiconductors, particularly silicon and germanium, so that they can be used to replace the three-element thermionic tube. A crystal so used is called a *transistor*. The interesting properties of such a crystal depend upon the presence of minute amounts of impurities in it. These impurities can be introduced in controlled amounts to get the desired characteristics. For example, atoms of germanium have four outer electrons each which they share with one another in the crystal. But if one atom of antimony, Sb, which has five outer electrons, replaces one atom of germanium, there will be one excess electron in this region. This electron may be set in motion by the application of a small electric field. A germanium crystal with this type of impurity is called an n-type crystal, the n standing for negative charge. On the other hand, if an atom of indium, In, which has only three outer electrons, replaces a germanium atom, there will be a deficiency of electrons, or a "hole" left in this part of the crystal. If an electric field is applied to such a crystal, electrons from other parts of the crystal flow toward the holes, leaving holes in the other parts of the crystal. Thus the current in this type of crystal may be considered as the motion of these holes. A hole in a region which normally would be occupied by an electron is equivalent to the presence of a positive charge at this place. A germanium crystal with a type of impurity which produces holes is called a p-type crystal, where p stands for positive charge.

A transistor is a crystal having either two p-type regions separated by an n-type region, in which case it is known as a p-n-p transistor, or it may have two n-type regions separated by a p-type region, in which case it is called an n-p-n transistor. Figure 29–26 is a schematic diagram of an n-p-n transistor; the electrode connected to the p-region is called the base, one wire or electrode connected to an n-region is called the *emitter*, and the other wire or electrode is called the *collector*.

A transistor behaves as a power amplifier. Its action can be demonstrated by connecting one battery B_1 so that the base is positive with respect to the emitter while a second battery B_2 puts an opposite bias on the collector. The electric field in the left half of the crystal is directed so that electrons and holes move toward the common junction and electrons move into and through the p-region. The conductivity of the crystal is thus large for current in this direction. If the battery terminals of B_1 were reversed, the electrons and holes would move away from the common

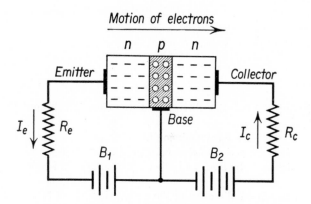

FIG. 29–26   Schematic diagram of an n-p-n transistor.

junction so that only a small current would result; the conductivity of the crystal would thus be small for current from base to emitter. Thus this crystal has a low resistance for current in one direction and a high resistance for current in the opposite direction.

It will be noted from the figure that the voltage bias on the collector with respect to the base is opposite to that of the emitter with respect to the base; hence the collector region will have a high resistance when the emitter region has a low resistance. If the thickness of the intermediate p-region is very small, many electrons from the n-region on the left will go through the p-region to the n-region on the right and toward the collector. In addition, there will be the small current due to the motion of electrons and holes of the region on the right.

If we call the current in the emitter branch I_e and the resistance of this branch R_e, the power developed in it is $I_e^2 R_e$. Similarly, the power developed in the collector branch is $I_c^2 R_c$, where I_c is the current in the collector branch and R_c is its resistance. The value of R_c is usually much greater than R_e, mainly because of the way the electric fields produced by the batteries B_1 and B_2 are biased in the different sections of the crystal. The ratio of the power delivered to the collector to that in the emitter is

$$\frac{I_c^2 R_c}{I_e^2 R_e}.$$

Even though I_c may be only slightly larger than I_e, there will still be a large gain in power in the ratio R_c/R_e.

Transistors are very small in size; the largest dimension is usually less than one inch. They are rapidly replacing thermionic tubes in many different types of circuits. One of the greatest advantage of a transistor is its low power requirements, mainly because no heating elements are needed to supply electrons as is the case with thermionic tubes. Transistors have also been developed with four electrodes, analogous to the four element thermionic tube.

QUESTIONS

1. What are the relative directions of the electric field and the magnetic field in a plane electromagnetic wave?

2. Will a 60-cycle a-c transmission line emit electromagnetic waves?

3. What is the function of the spark gap in the circuit of Figure 29–3?

4. What is meant by *tuning* a radio circuit? Mention two ways of tuning a circuit.

5. (a) What is the direction of the current in a diode tube? (b) What is the nature of the charge flowing through the tube?

6. Explain what is meant by the *saturation current* in a diode tube.

7. Explain why the straight-line portion only of the characteristic curve of a triode should be used when the tube is operated as an amplifier.

8. What is the source of the energy radiated from the oscillator circuit of Figure 29–15?

9. Explain what is meant by the *modulation of the amplitude of a carrier wave*.

10. Trace the flow of energy, and its modifications, from the transmitter, essentially the circuit of Figure 29–19, to the loud-speaker of the receiver of Figure 29–24.

PROBLEMS

1. A broadcasting station operates on a frequency of "860 kilocycles." What is the length of the radio wave emitted by its antenna?

2. The wavelength of ship-to-shore radio communication is 1,500 m. Determine the frequency of oscillation.

3. Determine the frequency of oscillation of a circuit consisting of an inductance of 0.3 millihenry in parallel with a capacitor of 4 μfd capacitance.

4. Determine the frequency of oscillation of a circuit consisting of an inductance of 8 millihenrys and a capacitance of 2 μfd.

5. A radio-frequency oscillator consists of an inductance of 0.30 millihenry and a capacitor of 80 micromicrofarads (80×10^{-12} farad). Determine the frequency of the oscillations.

6. The radio-frequency amplifier of a radio set has a fixed inductance of

0.25 millihenry.   At what value of its capacitance must a capacitor be set to be in tune with a radio wave of 1,560 kilocycles/sec?

7. What is the frequency of an oscillating circuit which emits short radio waves of 3 cm wavelength?

8. A series circuit has an inductance of 450 microhenrys and a capacitance of 300 micromicrofarads.   The resistance of this circuit at its natural frequency is 5 ohms.   A difference of potential whose effective value is 3 volts is applied to this circuit.   Determine (a) the resonance frequency of the circuit, (b) the impedance of the circuit, (c) the current in the circuit, and (d) the voltage across the capacitor.

9. The voltage amplification factor of a triode is 8.   When the grid voltage is −2 volts, the plate voltage is 100 volts and the current is 4 milliamperes.   To what value must the plate voltage be raised to keep the current at 4 ma when the grid voltage is changed to −4 volts?

Part Five

LIGHT

30

Light and
Its Measurement

30-1 THE NATURE OF LIGHT

The word *light*, as commonly used, refers to the radiant energy emitted by certain sources which produces a visual effect. As we shall show later, light is propagated from its source in the form of waves which travel with a speed of 186,000 miles per second or 3×10^{10} cm/sec through empty space. Maxwell, as a result of his work on electricity and magnetism, showed that electromagnetic waves are propagated through space with the speed of light. Using this result as a basis, Maxwell formulated the *electromagnetic theory of light*. This theory has been very successful in explaining many of the phenomena associated with the propagation of light. Light waves are now understood to be electromagnetic waves of shorter wavelength and higher frequency than the electromagnetic waves used in radio.

If light is propagated as an electromagnetic wave, its origin must ultimately be traced to the electric charges in the solids, liquids, and gases which emit the light; hence an analysis of the light emitted by a substance should yield valuable information concerning the structure of the atom and of aggregates of atoms such as molecules and crystals. The emission of light by a source involves an interaction between matter and radiant energy. To explain the phenomena observed as a result of the interaction between matter and radiant energy, Maxwell's electromagnetic theory of propagation had to be supplemented by what is now known as the *quantum theory*. Radiant energy, in its interaction with matter, behaves as though it consisted of bundles of energy, the amount of energy in each bundle or *quantum* of energy being given by the simple expression

$$\mathcal{E} = hf,$$ (1)

where $\mathcal{E}$ is the quantum of energy, f is the frequency of the radiation, and h is a universal constant known as the Planck constant and equal to

$$h = 6.62 \times 10^{-27} \text{ erg sec.}$$

A quantum of light energy hf is also called a *photon*. We shall return to the quantum theory later in discussing the analysis of light and atomic structure. For the present we shall concern ourselves with the propagation of radiant energy, particularly that form which produces a visual effect.

The normal human eye is capable of responding to those waves whose lengths lie in the range between 3.8×10^{-5} cm and 7.6×10^{-5} cm. We have already mentioned the radio waves as electromagnetic radiation. The lengths of these waves vary from about a centimeter for the very short radio waves to several thousand meters for the very long radio

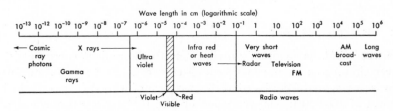

Fig. 30–1   The complete electromagnetic spectrum. Because of the wide range in wavelengths, the latter have been drawn to a logarithmic scale.

waves. Between the longest visible waves and the shortest radio waves are the *infrared* waves. The principal sources of infrared rays are bodies at high temperatures. Beyond the shortest waves visible are the *ultraviolet* waves. Their wavelengths extend below 3.8×10^{-5} cm down to about 10^{-7} cm. Shorter than these are the *x-rays, gamma rays* and *cosmic-ray photons* (see Figure 30–1).

30-2 SOURCES OF LIGHT

Our principal source of light is the sun, but, when sunlight is not available, other sources of light must be used. Before electric power became generally available, the sources of light widely used were the kerosene lamp, the candle, and illuminating gas. Light is emitted from these sources as a result of chemical action; that is, the burning of a fuel. With the development of large sources of electric power, many new sources of light were invented and developed to convert electric energy into light. Edison's incandescent electric light consisted of a carbon filament sealed into a glass bulb with two leads through the glass for connection to a source of electric power. The glass bulb was evacuated to prevent the carbon from being oxidized by the oxygen of the air. The carbon filament was heated to a high temperature and radiated heat as well as light.

The modern incandescent lamp contains a tungsten filament which, in some cases, is heated to a temperature of 3000°C. The glass bulbs, instead of being evacuated, are filled with an inert gas such as argon. This not only prevents oxidation of the filament but also prevents rapid evaporation of the tungsten from the hot filament and thus keeps the inside walls of the glass bulb comparatively free of tungsten. In most tungsten lamps, the filament consists of a double helix of fine tungsten wire; the wire is first wound in the form of a long helix, and this helix is then wound again. Special forms of filaments are used for specific purposes; for example, a ribbon filament is used when a surface of uniform brightness is desired.

The *carbon arc* has long been in use as an intense source of light, for example, in motion-picture projectors and in searchlights. The carbon arc consists of two carbon rods connected to a source of power through a series resistor. To start the arc, the carbon rods are brought into contact and then separated. The carbon rods are heated by the current passing through them, becoming very hot at the points of separation. Some of the carbon vaporizes and becomes ionized and acts as the conducting path for the current between the carbon electrodes. The positive terminal is white hot, and its temperature is about 3700°C. The positive terminal is the main source of light in a carbon arc, although the vapor and the negative terminal also contribute some light.

Some carbon arcs, used either for spectroscopic purposes or therapeutic purposes, have the cores of the positive electrodes filled with materials other than carbon. The light obtained from cored carbons is characteristic of the core material and is superposed on the white light from the hot carbon.

Sunlight comes to us from an envelope around the sun known as the *photosphere*, which is at a temperature of about 6000°C. Sunlight is whiter than the light from either the tungsten lamp or the carbon arc. The hotter the source, the closer will the light emitted by it approach the color of sunlight.

Fig. 30-2   Mercury arc.

Another important source of light is the mercury arc. In the low-pressure mercury arc, a pool of mercury is placed at the bottom of a glass or quartz tube containing two metal electrodes sealed into the ends (see Figure 30-2). The mercury is in contact with one electrode, and mercury vapor at a low pressure fills the rest of the space in the tube. To start the arc, the tube is tilted so that liquid mercury makes momentary contact with both electrodes, and then the tube is returned to its vertical position. Some of the mercury vapor is ionized by the passage of the current through it and is the conducting path for the current from the top electrode, which is positive, to the mercury in contact with the negative electrode. The electric discharge through the mercury vapor is similar to the electric discharge through a gas at low pressure; the light emitted is characteristic of the mercury and comes from the positive column; it is rich in blue, green, and violet light.

The high-pressure mercury arc contains a small amount of liquid mercury which is completely vaporized by the heat developed by the passage of the current through the tube. It starts as a low-pressure arc and changes to a high-pressure arc as the temperature of the vapor rises. The vapor temperature is of the order of 5000° abs. Pressures of 50 to 100 atmospheres are common in such arcs. The tube is always made of quartz. High-pressure mercury arcs are used when intense sources of light suitable for photographic work are desired. They are also good sources of ultraviolet radiation.

Fluorescent lamps, which are very good sources of light, have recently been developed. A fluorescent lamp is essentially a mercury-vapor lamp in a long glass tube which has a coating of some fluorescent material on the inside surface. Some argon gas is also put into the tube to make it easier to start the lamp. Details of the construction of one such lamp are shown in Figure 30–3. Two filaments are built into the ends of the tube; when

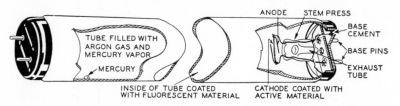

Fig. 30–3 Details of the construction of a fluorescent lamp. (Courtesy of Westinghouse Electric Company.)

heated, these filaments emit electrons, which, in their motion through the tube under the action of the electric field, ionize the gas and vapor, thus starting the arc.

A special starting arrangement must be used with fluorescent lamps, because the difference of potential needed to start the lamp is higher than that needed to keep it operating after it has been started. A simplified version of a starting arrangement is illustrated in Figure 30–4. When the lamp is switched on, alternating current flows through the two filaments in series, through the inductance L, and through the switch S. After a short time, the switch S is opened, producing a large induced emf across the filaments which now act as electrodes and start the arc in the tube. Once the arc is started, the discharge current through the tube keeps the filaments hot. There are several types of starters for fluorescent lamps, designed so that the closing and opening of the switch S is performed automatically. These are usually incorporated in the lamp housing.

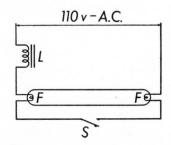

FIG. 30–4   Starting arrangement for a fluorescent lamp. S is the switch, F and F are filaments, and L is the inductance.

There are essentially two sources of light in a fluorescent lamp; the primary source is the low-pressure mercury vapor in the tube. As already stated, this light is rich in green, blue, and violet wavelengths. In addition, mercury vapor emits a large amount of ultraviolet light, part of which is absorbed by the fluorescent material which coats the wall of the tube. The fluorescent material acts as a secondary source of light and reradiates some of the energy in the form of visible radiation.

There are many substances which fluoresce under the action of ultra-violet light. By a suitable choice of fluorescent material, many different wavelengths such as red, orange, yellow, can be added to the light coming from the mercury and thus produce sources of light which can have any desired color such as white, yellow, red, and so forth.

30-3 ELECTRIC DISCHARGE THROUGH GASES

For the study of the passage of an electric current through a gas, let us put the gas into a very long glass tube which has a circular electrode sealed into each end and which is provided with a small side tube which can be

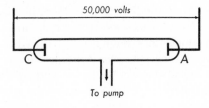

FIG. 30–5   A gas-discharge tube.

connected to a pumping system, as sketched in Figure 30–5. This will make it possible to control the pressure of the gas in the tube.

Suppose that there is air in the tube and that the two electrodes A and

C are connected to the positive and negative terminals, respectively, of a source of high potential, say 50,000 volts. When the pressure of the air inside the tube is reduced to a few millimeters of mercury, the passage of the electric current through the gas will be accompanied by the emission of light from the gas; at this pressure, the entire space between the electrodes will be filled with a pink or reddish glow. The light emitted is character-istic of the gases in the tube. Such tubes are in commercial use as sources of light for various purposes and are very valuable in the physics laboratory as a means of studying the spectra of various elements and compounds.

When the pressure of the air in the tube is reduced to about 0.1 mm, there is no longer a uniform glow between the electrodes, but a series of dark and light regions, as shown in Figure 30–6. A bluish velvety glow,

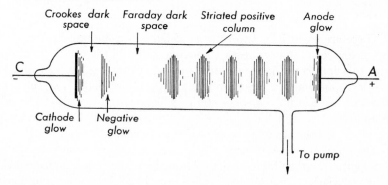

FIG. 30–6   Appearance of the electrical discharge when the pressure of the air in the tube is about 0.1 mm.

known as the *cathode glow*, covers the entire negative electrode or cathode C. This is followed by a dark space called the *Crookes dark space* which ends at the *negative glow*. This is separated by the *Faraday dark space* from the luminous column, known as the *positive column*, which extends up to the anode. The positive column usually appears to be striated; that is, it consists of a series of bright and dark regions equally spaced. Covering the entire anode or positive terminal is the *anode glow*.

Experiments show that there are always some ions present in the air. These ions may have been produced by the action of light or as the result of collisions between molecules, or by ionizing agents which are always present at the earth's surface and are known as *cosmic rays*. Whatever the original source of these ions may be, when a difference of potential of several thousand volts is put across the electrodes A and C, these ions will be set into motion—the positive ions toward C, the negative ions toward A. If the pressure of the gas is in the neighborhood of 1 atm, these ions will, on the average, move through very short distances before colliding with neutral atoms or molecules. Under these conditions, they will have acquired very little energy before making a collision. But when the pressure is reduced to about 1 mm of mercury, these ions will travel comparatively longer distances between collisions, and, under the action of the electric field, they will acquire more energy during their motion. When an ion with sufficient energy collides with a neutral atom or molecule, it may succeed in knocking out an electron from the neutral atom or molecule and still have enough kinetic energy left to move away, leaving two additional charges in the gas: the electron, and the ionized atom or molecule. This process is called *ionization by collision*. As the pressure is lowered, a greater number of collisions result in the production of ions and electrons. At the same time, of course, some of the positive and negative charges recombine to form neutral atoms or molecules. When the pressure of the gas in the tube gets very low, the average distance that an ion or electron travels between collisions becomes comparatively large, and the number of collisions it can make becomes small. Some of the charges may even travel the entire length of the tube without making any collisions with molecules of the gas. At such low pressures, in the neighborhood of 0.001 mm of mercury, the positive ions which reach the cathode have a great deal of energy. One of the results is that the cathode, under the bombardment of the positive ions, emits electrons; they are sometimes called *cathode rays* because of their origin. These cathode rays leave the cathode in a direction at right angles to its surface, since the cathode is an equipotential surface and the electric field is perpendicular to it near the surface.

An electric discharge can be maintained through any gas at a low pressure; the light emitted is characteristic of the gas and comes principally from the positive column. Electric discharges through different gases can be used to obtain light of different colors; for example, neon gives out red light, argon gives out blue light, and so forth. The light, when examined with a spectroscope, yields information concerning the structure of the atoms and molecules of the gas. As sources of light, these gases are used chiefly for display purposes.

30-4 INTENSITY OF A SOURCE OF LIGHT

It should be possible to express the intensity of a source of light in terms of the rate at which it emits radiation, that is, in terms of the power emitted by the source in the form of radiation. However, since all sources emit some radiation to which the eye is not sensitive, and furthermore, since the eye is not equally sensitive to all the wavelengths usually present in visible radiation, a special unit has to be used to express the rate at which a source emits such radiation. The rate at which visible radiation is emitted by a source is usually called the *luminous flux*, and the unit of luminous flux is the *lumen*. Now, the eye is most sensitive to wavelengths in the region of $5,550 \times 10^{-8}$ cm, or 5,550 Angstrom units (A) where

$$1 \text{ A} = 10^{-8} \text{ cm.}$$

Light of this wavelength appears green in color to the normal eye. In terms of light of this wavelength, a lumen is equivalent to 0.00147 watt.

The luminous flux from any source of light can be measured by some types of *photometers*, and these sources can be rated in terms of this luminous flux, that is, in lumens. Although this is done in some cases, it has not yet become standard practice. The luminous flux from a typical 25-watt tungsten-filament lamp, for example, is 260 lumens, while the luminous flux from a 1,000-watt tungsten-filament lamp is 21,500 lumens. The *luminous efficiency* of a source is the ratio of the total luminous flux emitted to the total power supplied and is expressed in lumens per watt. The luminous efficiencies of some sources of light are listed in Table 30–1.

Table 30-1   Luminous Efficiencies of Sources of Light

Source	Input in Watts	Luminous Efficiency in Lumens per Watt
Tungsten lamp	25	10.4
" "	100	16.3
" "	1,000	21.5
Carbon arc, 10-mm diameter	1,000	60
High-pressure mercury arc in quartz	100	35
" "	250	40
" "	1,000	65
White fluorescent lamp	40	58
Ideal monochromatic source; $\lambda = 5,550$ A	1	680

The luminous intensity of a source is sometimes expressed in terms of a unit called *candle power* (abbreviated cp). In the early days of this subject, the light emitted from a spermaceti candle which burned 120 grains per hour was used as a standard of intensity; the intensity of this source, when viewed in a horizontal plane, was defined as one candle power. Recently the National Bureau of Standards developed a new standard of luminous intensity. This consists of a hollow enclosure which is maintained at the temperature of the melting point of platinum and is defined as having an intensity of sixty candle power per square centimeter of opening. The relationship between the luminous intensity of a source, expressed in candle power, and the total luminous flux emitted by this source, in lumens, is obtained as follows. Imagine that the source of light of 1 cp is so small that it can be considered a point source and that it emits radiation uniformly in all directions. If we put this source at the center of a sphere of 1 ft radius, the amount of luminous flux which falls on 1 sq ft of this sphere is defined as 1 lumen. Since the surface area of this sphere is 4π sq ft, the total luminous flux coming from a source of 1 cp is 4π lumens. In general, if I is the luminous intensity of a source, expressed in candle power, and F the total luminous flux from this source, expressed in lumens, then

$$F = 4\pi I.$$ (2)

For example, a 32-cp source emits 402 lumens and could be rated in this manner.

30-5 COLOR SENSITIVITY OF THE EYE

The problem of color vision embraces three distinct fields—physics, psychology, and physiology—and each has made important contributions to our present state of knowledge of this subject. Here we shall touch only upon a few important aspects of the subject. It has already been mentioned that the normal eye is sensitive only to a short range of wavelengths from 3,800 A to 7,600 A; but even in this range, the sensitivity of the eye to different wavelengths is not uniform. Figure 30-7 is a graph of the sensitivity of the average human eye, under normal daylight illumination

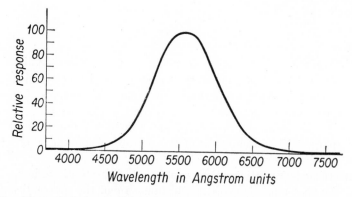

Fig. 30-7   Relative brightness sensitivity of the average human eye.

levels, plotted against wavelengths from 4,000 to 7,500 A. A point on this curve shows the relative response or sensitivity of the eye to a given amount of energy at that particular wavelength. The eye is most sensitive to light of 5,550 A; its response to a given amount of energy at this wavelength is called 100. For the same amount of energy of 5,000 A incident on it, the eye is only about one third as sensitive; that is, three times as much energy at a wavelength of 5,000 A is required to produce the same response as that produced by light of 5,550 A. A very narrow band of wavelengths constitutes a spectral color; the color identification ranges from violet for the shortest wavelengths to blue, green, yellow, orange, and red as the wavelength of the light increases toward the maximum wavelengths visible. Light of any given color as perceived by the eye may be analyzed into its component wavelengths by means of a spectroscope, and the intensity at each wavelength, or more commonly within a very narrow band of wavelengths, can be measured with an appropriate instrument.

30-6 ILLUMINANCE

The *illumination* of a surface is called the *illuminance* and is *the rate at which a unit area of the surface receives visible radiation, or the amount of luminous flux per unit area reaching the surface*. To determine the illuminance of a small surface at a distance r from a point source of light, imagine a sphere of this radius surrounding the point source located at the center of this sphere. The total luminous flux F coming from this point source will illuminate the entire inner surface of this sphere. If the source emits luminous flux uniformly in all directions, then the illuminance E of the inner surface of the sphere will be given by

$$E = \frac{F}{4\pi r^2},$$ (3)

since the surface area of a sphere of radius r is $4\pi r^2$. Thus the illuminance of a surface will vary inversely as the square of its distance from the point source. In Figure 30–8, for example, two concentric spheres of radii 1 ft and 2 ft, respectively, are drawn around the source of light I. A cone of light which fills an area A of the first sphere will cover an area $4A$ of the second sphere. The illuminance of the second sphere will be one fourth that of the first sphere.

Referring to Equation (3), we find that if the total luminous flux F emitted by the source is expressed in lumens and the perpendicular distance r from the point source to the illuminated surface is expressed in feet, then the illuminance E of the surface will be expressed in lumens per square foot. An older unit of illuminance, known as the *foot candle*, is still being used. A foot candle is the illuminance produced when light from a source of one candle power falls at right angles upon a surface one foot away. Since a sphere of 1 ft radius has a surface area of 4π sq ft and one candle emits 4π lumens, the illuminance of a surface 1 ft from a source of 1 cp is also 1 lumen/sq ft. Thus a foot candle represents the same illuminance

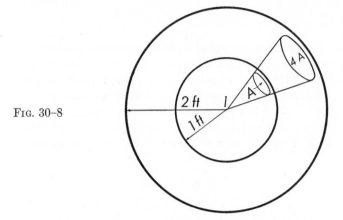

Fig. 30–8

as a lumen per square foot. In terms of Equation (3), if I is the luminous intensity of the source expressed in candle power and F is the total luminous flux from this source, then, since

$$F = 4\pi I, \tag{2}$$

Equation (3) becomes

$$E = \frac{4\pi I}{4\pi r^2}$$

or

$$E = \frac{I}{r^2}. \tag{4}$$

Illustrative Example. A street lamp is rated at 1,600 lumens. Determine the illuminance at a distance of 20 ft from the lamp.

If we imagine a surface placed at right angles to a line from the lamp and assume the lamp to be small enough so that it can be considered as a point source, then the illuminance E is, from Equation (3),

$$E = \frac{1,600 \text{ lumens}}{4\pi \times 400 \text{ ft}^2},$$

$$E = \frac{0.32 \text{ lumen}}{\text{ft}^2},$$

or

$$E = 0.32 \text{ ft candle.}$$

Proper illumination has come to be considered essential not only for comfort and enjoyment but also for safety and efficiency. For example, it is now considered desirable to have an illuminance of 10 lumens/sq ft on library reading desks and 75 lumens/sq ft in hospital operating rooms.

30-7 PHOTOMETRY

The measurement of illuminance and luminous intensity of light is called *photometry*, and instruments used for such measurements are called *photometers*. A Bunsen photometer is very simple in design and illustrates the principle used in many photometers for determining the intensity of a source of light. The Bunsen photometer has a screen S which consists of a white sheet of paper with a translucent grease spot G in its center, as shown in Figure 30–9. This screen is mounted in a box containing two mirrors

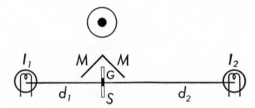

Fɪɢ. 30–9   Bunsen grease-spot photometer.

MM so arranged that both sides of the screen can be viewed simultaneously. This box is mounted on a long rod, at the ends of which are two light sources of intensities I_1 and I_2. Most of the light which strikes the screen from each of these sources is diffusely reflected from the white paper, while a small fraction is transmitted through it. On the other hand, most of the light from each of these sources is transmitted through the grease spot, while a small fraction is reflected from it. The experimental procedure is to move the screen S until the grease spot cannot be distinguished from the white section; then the illumination of the grease spot is equal to that of the rest of the screen.

If d_1 is the distance of the screen from the source of intensity I_1, the illuminance of the left side of the screen is I_1/d_1^2. If d_2 is the distance of I_2 from the screen, then the illuminance of the right side of the screen is I_2/d_2^2. When the grease spot disappears, the two surfaces have the same illuminance, so that

$$\frac{I_1}{d_1^2} = \frac{I_2}{d_2^2}. \tag{5}$$

If I_2 is a standard lamp, that is, a lamp whose intensity is known, then the intensity I_1 of any other lamp can be determined with this photometer.

The only measurements made are the distances of the lamps from the screen.

The Lummer-Brodhun photometer is an improvement on the Bunsen photometer; the grease spot is replaced by the photometer head shown in Figure 30–10. Light, from the two sources S_1 and S_2 of intensities I_1 and

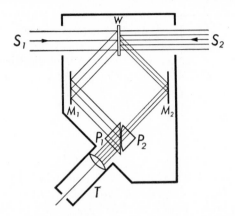

FIG. 30–10   Diagram of a Lummer-Brodhun photometer head.

I_2, falls on a rough white surface W. Some of the light which is scattered by this surface is reflected from the mirrors M_1 and M_2 into two right-angled prisms P_1 and P_2. Part of the hypotenuse of P_2 is ground away so that only that portion of the light which strikes the surface of contact passes through it into the telescope T. The light entering P_1 which strikes that part of the hypotenuse face not in contact with P_2 is totally reflected into the telescope. The field of view seen through the telescope is sharply divided into two sections, one brighter than the other except when their illuminations are equal, in which case the dividing line disappears. When this position is reached, the distances d_1 and d_2 are measured, and the intensities I_1 and I_2 can then be compared with the aid of Equation (5), provided the distances are large in comparison with the dimensions of the sources.

30-8 PHOTOELECTRIC PHOTOMETERS

Besides the photometers which usually depend upon the matching of illuminated surfaces, other photometers are used which are based upon some electrical effect resulting when light is incident upon a surface. There are several types of such *photoelectric* effects. In one type of photoelectric effect, light incident upon a metallic surface causes the ejection of electrons from the surface. A typical photoelectric tube which utilizes this effect is shown in Figure 30–11 together with an appropriate circuit. The semi-cylindrical cathode *C* has its inner (concave) surface coated with a substance such as potassium or cesium, which has a very good photoelectric

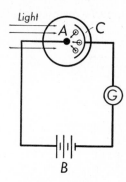

Fig. 30–11   A photoelectric tube used for measuring illuminance.

response. The anode *A* is a wire parallel to the axis of the cylinder passing down the center of the tube. Some photoelectric tubes have high vacua; others have small amounts of some inert gas to increase the sensitivity of the tube. Let us consider only high-vacuum photoelectric tubes. A galvanometer *G* is connected in series with a battery *B*; the positive end of the battery is connected to the wire anode *A*.

When light falls on the photoelectric surface of the cathode, electrons are ejected from its surface and are attracted to the anode because of the difference of potential between the anode and the cathode. The number of electrons per second, and hence the current through the galvanometer, is proportional to the intensity of the light incident on the surface. However, the sensitivity of the surface to the various wavelengths is different from the sensitivity of the normal eye to these wavelengths. Light filters have been developed for use with photoelectric cells so that the response will accurately match that of the normal eye. The photoelectric current can then be calibrated to read the illuminance produced by the light incident on the cell.

These photoelectric tubes have a wide variety of uses, not only as photometers but also in sound reproduction from tracks on films and for the control of many industrial processes where the variation in the intensity of a beam of light can be used as an indicator of quality or quantity. The photoelectric currents are very small, but they can be amplified with the use of tube amplifier circuits and made to control large power outputs.

Another type of photoelectric effect which has wide applications in photometry is the *photovoltaic* effect. The Weston photronic cell is a type of photovoltaic cell. It consists of a very thin film of selenium formed on an iron plate. When light shines on the selenium, it passes through it to the iron and produces an emf between the two, with the iron as the positive terminal and the selenium as the negative terminal. If a galvanometer is connected across these two surfaces, as shown in Figure 30–12, a current will

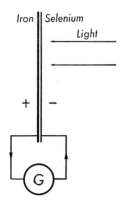

Iron | Selenium

Light

Fig. 30–12 A photovoltaic cell used for measuring illuminance. The selenium film is deposited on the iron.

flow through the circuit because of this emf. No outside battery is required. Since the iron is the positive electrode, the action of the light must be such as to cause the electrons to go from the iron to the selenium. If the resistance of the galvanometer is less than about 100 ohms, the current through the photronic cell is directly proportional to the illuminance of the surface. Many types of exposure meters used in photography consist of photovoltaic cells connected to galvanometers whose readings are calibrated for proper exposure conditions. The response of the photovoltaic cell to different wavelengths of light differs from that of the eye, but suitable light filters have been developed which, when placed over the cell, will make it respond in a way very similar to the response of the normal eye.

30-9 SPEED OF LIGHT

We have mentioned several times that the speed of light and the speed of other electromagnetic waves through space are the same, and the value of this speed is 186,000 mi/sec or 3×10^{10} cm/sec, or 3×10^8 m/sec. The earliest determinations of the speed of light were based upon astronomical observations. In 1675, Roemer, a Danish astronomer, observed that the time of occurrence of the eclipse of one of Jupiter's moons differed from that calculated on the assumption that light travels instantaneously, that is, with infinite speed. He explained this discrepancy by asserting that light travels with a finite speed, and calculated its speed with the data then available. Referring to Figure 30–13, suppose that the time of occurrence of an eclipse of one of Jupiter's moons is observed when the earth is at E_1, and a calculation is then made as to the time of occurrence of an eclipse of this same moon of Jupiter 6 months later, when the earth is at E_2. If this calculation, which takes into consideration the motion of Jupiter as well as the earth, is made using the assumption that the speed of light

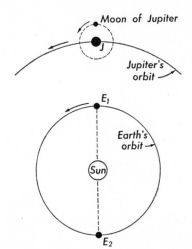

Fig. 30–13   Roemer's method of determining the speed of light.

is infinite, observation will show that the eclipse occurs about 1,000 sec later than the calculated time. The distance from E_1 to E_2 is the diameter of the earth's orbit around the sun; this is about 186,000,000 miles. If the difference between the observed time and the calculated time is ascribed to the fact that the speed of light is finite, then it must take 1,000 sec to travel the diameter of the earth's orbit. Hence the speed of light is about 186,000 miles per second.

One of the earliest terrestrial determinations of the speed of light was made in 1849 by Fizeau who timed the passage of a beam of light a distance of 8.633 km from the source to a mirror and then back to the source. On its way from the source, the light passed through the space between two teeth on the rim of a wheel whose speed was adjusted so that, on its return, the light failed to pass through this space but hit the adjacent tooth and was thus eclipsed. In this experiment, the wheel had 720 teeth, and the light was eclipsed when the speed of the wheel was 12.6 rps. Hence the wheel moved only 1/1,440 revolution, while the light traveled a distance of 17.266 km; the time required to traverse this distance was $1/1{,}440 \times 12.6$ sec. Foucault, in 1850, also measured the speed of light, using a rotating mirror to measure the time required for a beam of light to go from it to a second mirror several meters away and back to the source. The mirror used in Foucault's experiment had a speed of about 800 rps. Some of the best determinations of the speed of light were made by Albert A. Michelson (1852–1931). He began his experiments about 1878 and continued them for about 50 years. We shall describe the arrangement used in the last experiments.

In Michelson's experiment, a beam of light was sent from Mt. Wilson to Mt. San Antonio and back again. The distance between the two points was measured very accurately by the United States Coast and Geodetic Survey, a distance of about 22 miles. The essential arrangement for this experiment is shown in Figure 30–14. M_1 is an octagonal mirror which is

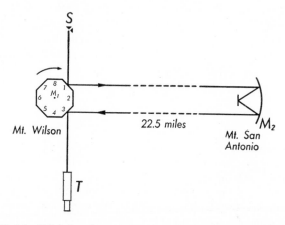

Fɪɢ. 30–14   Michelson's method for measuring the speed of light.

mounted on the shaft of a variable-speed motor so that it rotates about an axis through its center. Light from a source S strikes mirror M_1 at an angle of 45° and is reflected from it to the distant mirror M_2. It is reflected back from this mirror to the octagonal mirror in such a way that when M_1 is stationary, the reflected ray strikes section 3 at an angle of 45° and is reflected into the telescope T. When the mirror M_1 is set into rotation, the reflected beam will, in general, strike section 3 at an angle other than 45° because section 3 has turned to a new position in the time required for the light to travel from M_1 to M_2 and back again. The reflected beam will not enter the telescope if it strikes a section of the mirror at an angle other than 45°. By increasing the speed of the motor, however, it is possible to bring section 2 of the octagonal mirror into the place formerly occupied by section 3 in the time required by the beam of light to go from M_1 to M_2 and back to M_1. When the motor reaches this angular speed, the light will again enter the telescope. The experiment consists in varying the speed of the motor until the reflected light comes into view again in the telescope. The speed of the motor is then measured accurately. The time taken to travel the distance $2M_1M_2$ is one eighth the time required for 1 rev. In these experiments the angular speed of the motor was about 530 rps.

As a result of many careful experiments, Michelson determined the speed of light c, in air, as

$$c = 299,711 \text{ km/sec.}$$

From this value, the speed of light c, in a vacuum, was calculated to be

$$c = 299,776 \text{ km/sec.}$$

For most calculations, the speed of light can be taken as 3×10^{10} cm/sec.

The speed of light in a material medium is less than its speed in a vacuum. Foucault placed a tube of water between the two mirrors used in measuring the speed of light and found that the speed of light in water is less than in a vacuum. Michelson used a tube 3 ft long containing carbon bisulphide and found that the speed of light in carbon bisulphide was about four sevenths of its speed in a vacuum.

QUESTIONS

1. If a source of light could be designed to emit only light of the wavelength to which the eye is most sensitive, what would be its rated intensity, in watts, if it had an intensity of 600 lumens?

2. Why is quartz rather than glass used for high-pressure mercury arcs?

3. Can you suggest why the first determinations of the speed of light were made from astronomical observations?

4. Can you suggest a modification of the Michelson experiment which would make it possible to measure the speed of light with the distances available in the average laboratory room?

5. How long does it take a radio signal transmitted from New York to reach San Francisco?

6. Why are electric light bulbs "frosted"? Are they frosted on the inside or the outside?

7. A large ballroom has mirrors on all the walls. If the lights in the room were suddenly extinguished, would there be any light traveling back and forth between the mirrors? Explain your answer.

8. If possible, use a portable photometer or illuminometer and determine the illumination at various places in the classroom. Discuss the adequacy of this illumination.

PROBLEMS

1. What is the illuminance of a surface placed 4 ft from a 25-watt tungsten lamp?

2. What is the illuminance of a surface placed 6 ft from a 100-watt tungsten lamp?

3. If, by means of properly placed mirrors, all of the light from a 1,000-watt tungsten lamp could be concentrated in a parallel beam 1 ft in diameter, what would be the illuminance of any surface placed perpendicularly in the beam?

4. Two sources of light are mounted 2 m apart on an optical bench and a grease-spot photometer head is placed between. One source is rated as 41.6 cp. Determine the intensity of the second source if the grease spot is observed to vanish when at a distance of 120 cm from it.

5. A lamp whose intensity is to be measured is placed 200 cm from a standard lamp rated at 450 lumens. Equal illuminances are produced by the two lamps when the Lummer-Brodhun photometer head is 60 cm from the standard lamp. Determine the intensity of the test lamp.

6. (a) Calculate the illuminance at a distance of 12 ft from a 60-cp lamp. (b) At what distance would a 40-cp lamp have to be placed to produce the same illuminance?

7. (a) At what distance would a 100-watt tungsten lamp have to be placed to produce an illuminance of 15 lumens/ft²? (b) At what distance would a 100-watt high-pressure mercury arc have to be placed to produce the same illuminance?

8. A 40-cp lamp and a 60-cp lamp are placed at the ends of a photometer bench 200 cm long. (a) At which place will the photometer head show equal illuminances from these two lamps? (b) Determine this illuminance.

9. A 25-watt tungsten lamp and a 100-watt tungsten lamp, each operated at its rated power, are placed 200 cm apart at the ends of a photometer bench. (a) Determine the position at which the photometer head will show equal illuminances. (b) Determine the illuminance produced by each lamp.

10. Calculate the speed of light from the data obtained by Fizeau as given in Section 30–9.

11. The sun is approximately 93,000,000 miles from the earth. How long does it take light from the sun to reach us?

12. Light from the bright star Sirius takes 8.8 years to reach the earth. Its distance can be said to be 8.8 light years. What is this distance in (a) kilometers and (b) miles?

13. The distance between Mt. Wilson and Mt. San Antonio is 35.426 km and the angular speed of the motor in one of Michelson's experiments was 528.76 rps. Calculate the speed of light from these data.

31

Reflection and Refraction

31-1 PASSAGE OF LIGHT THROUGH A MEDIUM

In the passage of a beam of light through a medium, some of the radiant energy is absorbed and transformed into heat; some of the radiant energy is also scattered in all directions. Light, because of its electromagnetic character, sets the electrons of the medium into vibration, thus giving up some of its energy. These electrons re-emit some of this energy in the form of radiation, either of the same wavelength as the incident radiation or of different wavelengths. Fluorescent radiation is of the latter type. The fluorescent materials coating the walls of the fluorescent lamps absorb some of the ultraviolet radiation emitted by the mercury vapor and then transform this energy into visible radiation.

Absorption and scattering of light take place even in the most transparent media such as air and glass. The *color of the sky*, for example, is due to the small amount of scattering of sunlight by the molecules of the air. These molecules are more effective in scattering the shorter wavelengths such as the violet and blue light. When we look away from the sun, we see this scattered light, and the sky thus appears blue. If we were in the stratosphere, where there are fewer scattering particles, the sky would appear much darker, almost black. Since blue and violet light are scattered from the direct beam, sunlight should appear redder as it goes through thicker layers of air. It is for this reason that the setting sun looks redder than the noonday sun.

When a beam of light strikes the surface separating one medium from another—for example, the surface between air and glass—some of the light is reflected back into the first medium at the surface of separation, and the remainder enters the second medium. The light which passes from one medium into another is said to be *refracted*. If the surface of separation between the two media is smooth, the light which is thrown back into the first medium is said to be *regularly reflected;* if the surface is rough, the light is *diffusely reflected*. Unless otherwise stated, we shall assume that the surface between two media is smooth.

662

In general, smooth, polished metal surfaces will reflect about 90 per cent of the incident light, while smooth, polished glass surfaces will reflect from 4 to 10 per cent for angles of incidence from 0° to 60°. In the case of a metal, the light which is refracted through the surface is absorbed in a small thickness of the substance. Glass, on the other hand, is transparent; that is, very little light is absorbed in its passage through reasonable thicknesses of glass.

Although reflection and refraction can be studied by considering the detailed interaction between the light and the individual particles of the medium through which it travels, we can get sufficiently valuable and interesting results by assuming that light travels along straight lines through optically homogeneous media, the direction of motion being indicated by *rays* of light. These rays of light are drawn at right angles to the *wave front;* the wave front is the envelope of the waves emitted by the particles in the medium, and all points on a wave front are in the same phase. This method of treating reflection and refraction is a first approximation only; later, in the discussion of *interference* and *diffraction,* we shall consider some of the modifications that must be made because of the wave character of light. The simpler treatment is called *geometrical optics.*

31-2 LAWS OF REFLECTION

When a narrow beam of light strikes a smooth surface separating two media, such as air and glass, part is reflected and part is refracted (see Figure 31–1). The angles of incidence, reflection, and refraction are all

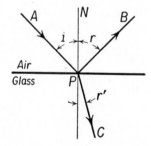

Fig. 31–1 Light reflected and refracted at a surface separating two media.

measured from a *normal* to the surface; a *normal* to a surface at a given point is a line drawn perpendicular to the surface at that point. In the figure, NP is the normal to the surface at P, AP is the incident ray, PB is the reflected ray, and PC is the refracted ray. The angle of incidence i is the angle between the incident ray and the normal, the angle of reflection r is the angle between the reflected ray and the normal, and the angle of refraction r' is the angle between the refracted ray and the normal.

The two laws of reflection are as follows:

(a) *The incident ray, the normal, and the reflected ray all lie in one plane.*

(b) *The angles of incidence and reflection are equal.*

These two laws can easily be verified experimentally. These laws enable us to construct the reflected rays when the incident rays and the position and shape of the reflecting surface are given.

The two laws of reflection are empirical laws and have been known since the tenth century. The equality of the angles of incidence and reflection can be readily derived by considering the motion of the wave fronts associated with these rays and using Huygens' principle (see Section 18–5). Suppose that AB is a wave front of the incident wave and that it is advancing toward the surface and that it is inclined at an angle i to it (see Figure 31–2). When A reaches the surface, that point on the

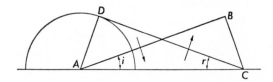

FIG. 31–2 AB is the incident wave front; CD is the reflected wave front.

surface sends out a wave which travels with the same speed and for the same length of time as point B does in going toward point C. Hence, to determine the position of the reflected wave front, draw a circle with A as a center and with a radius equal to BC, and then draw a line from C tangent to this circle at D. The line CD represents the position of the reflected wave front at the time that point B reaches C. CD makes an angle r with the reflecting surface. Since the triangles ADC and ABC are right triangles with a common side AC, they are congruent. Hence angle i equals angle r. Thus, for a plane wave, the angle of incidence is equal to the angle of reflection. If the wave front is spherical, we can always take a sufficiently small portion of it and treat it as a plane wave. The above law of reflection can thus be extended to other than plane waves.

31-3   ROTATING MIRROR

Rotating mirrors provide an interesting application of the laws of reflection. Such mirrors are used for measuring the deflection of a galvanometer coil and other rotating devices. When the mirror turns through a small angle, say 1°, the angle of incidence is increased by 1° and so is the angle of reflection. If the incident beam comes from a stationary source, the reflected beam will travel through 2°. In general, if a plane

mirror in position M, as shown in Figure 31–3, rotates through an angle
α and if the incident beam remains stationary, the reflected beam will
rotate through an angle 2α.

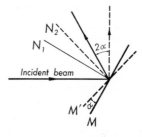

Fig. 31–3   The angle through which
the reflected beam rotates is twice
the angle through which the mirror
rotates.

31-4 IMAGES FORMED BY A PLANE MIRROR

The method for determining the position of the image of any point of
an object placed in front of a plane mirror is illustrated in Figure 31–4.
MM' is a plane mirror and O is any point of an object.   Since a point is
determined by the intersection of two lines, it will be sufficient to take any

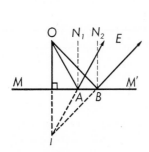

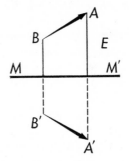

Fig. 31–4   Method of determining the
position of the image formed by a
plane mirror.

Fig. 31–5   The image formed by a
plane mirror appears reversed to
an observer at E.

two rays from O which strike the mirror and are reflected from it.   Normals
are drawn at the points of incidence A and B, and the angles of reflection
are made equal to the respective angles of incidence.   The two reflected
rays do not meet in front of the mirror, but when produced backward they
meet in a point I. I is the *image* of point O.   It is easy to prove, by simple
geometry, that I lies just as far behind the mirror as O does in front of it.
Further, the line OI is perpendicular to the plane of the mirror.

The image I is called a *virtual image* because the rays of light do not
actually pass through this point but only appear to do so.

This method of image construction can be extended to an object of
finite size.   Figure 31–5 shows the image $A'B'$ of an object AB.   It will

be noted that to an observer at E, the head of the arrow AB appears on the right, while when viewed in the mirror, the head of the arrow $A'B'$ appears on the left. The image is said to be *reversed* from right to left. The size of the image formed by a plane mirror is the same as the size of the object.

31-5   REFRACTION OF LIGHT

Refraction occurs whenever light goes from one medium into another and is due to the fact that light travels with different speeds in different media.   Refraction was studied, and the laws of refraction were derived empirically long before the cause of refraction was known.   When a ray of light goes from air into glass, for example, the ray is bent toward the normal, as shown in Figure 31–1.   When the ray of light goes from glass into air, it is bent away from the normal.   Using different values for the angles of incidence, measurements can be made of the corresponding angles of refraction.   It is on such measurements that the following *laws of refraction* are based:

(a) *The incident ray, the normal, and the refracted ray are in the same plane.*

(b) *The ratio of the sine of the angle of incidence to the sine of the angle of refraction is a constant;* or, stated in the form of an equation,

$$\frac{\sin i}{\sin r'} = n, \tag{1}$$

in which i is the angle of incidence, r' is the angle of refraction, and n is a constant known as the *relative index of refraction* of the second medium with respect to the first one. This law is sometimes referred to as *Snell's law.*

It can be shown, on the basis of the wave theory, that n is the ratio of the speed of light in the first medium to its speed in the second medium. It is convenient, in constructing tables of values, to assume that light goes from a vacuum into the substance; the index of refraction n is then called the *absolute index of refraction* of the substance. Since the speed of light in air is almost the same as that in a vacuum, for most purposes the values given in tables can be used for the refraction of light from air into the substance.

To show that the index of refraction is equal to the ratio of the speeds of light in the two media, consider a beam of light going from medium I in which its speed is v_1 into medium II in which its speed is v_2. It must be remembered that the wave fronts travel at right angles to the rays. Consider a wave front such as MP traveling in the first medium at an angle i to the surface, as shown in Figure 31–6. We can use Huygens' construction to determine the position and direction of motion of the wave front in the second medium in a manner similar to that used in Section 18–6. Suppose that the wave sent out by point P travels for a time t in the first medium with a speed v_1 to reach the point N on the surface.

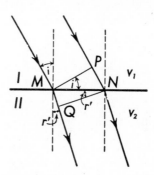

Fɪɢ. 31–6   Refraction of light.

Simultaneously a wave starting from point M on the surface will travel with a speed v_2 for the same time t. If we draw a circle of radius v_2t, with M as a center, and draw a line from N tangent to this circle at Q, we shall obtain the position of the new wave front NQ. The wave front NQ and succeeding wave fronts in the second medium travel forward at an angle r' to the surface. Now, since it took the same time for the light to travel from P to N as from M to Q, the distances PN and MQ are in the ratio of the speeds of light in the two media, or

$$\frac{PN}{MQ} = \frac{v_1}{v_2}.$$

(2)

Now, from the figure,

$$\sin i = \frac{PN}{MN}$$

and

$$\sin r' = \frac{QM}{MN} ;$$

therefore

$$\frac{\sin i}{\sin r'} = \frac{PN}{QM} = \frac{v_1}{v_2}.$$

But, from Snell's law,

$$n = \frac{\sin i}{\sin r'} ;$$

therefore

$$\boxed{n = \frac{v_1}{v_2}.}$$

(3)

If the speed of the wave v_2 in the second medium is less than its speed v_1 in the first medium, the rays are bent toward the normal when entering the second medium. If v_2 is greater than v_1, the wave is bent away from the normal when it goes from medium I to medium II.

Illustrative Example. A narrow beam of light travels from air into water at an angle of incidence of 40°. The index of refraction of water relative to air is 1.33. Determine (a) the angle of refraction and (b) the speed of light in water.

(a) Using Snell's law

$$n = \frac{\sin i}{\sin r'}$$

and solving for $\sin r'$, we get

$$\sin r' = \frac{\sin i}{n} \cdot$$

Since $i = 40°$ and $n = 1.33$, we have

$$\sin r' = \frac{\sin 40°}{1.33},$$

so that

$$\sin r' = \frac{0.6428}{1.33} = 0.4833,$$

from which

$$r' = 28°54'.$$

(b) The velocity v_2 of light in the second medium is, from Equation (3),

$$v_2 = \frac{v_1}{n} \cdot$$

Now $v_1 = 3 \times 10^8$ m/sec, and $n = 1.33$;

hence

$$v_2 = \frac{3 \times 10^8 \text{ m/sec}}{1.33},$$

so that

$$v_2 = 2.26 \times 10^8 \text{ m/sec.}$$

31-6   REFRACTION AND DISPERSION

The *absolute index of refraction* of a medium is the ratio of the speed of light in a vacuum to its speed in the medium. Now the speed of light in a vacuum is the same for all colors, but this is not true in a material medium. The speed of light depends not only on the nature of the medium but also on the particular color or wavelength of light. This can easily be demonstrated by sending the light through some transparent substance arranged so that the surface through which the light enters the medium is inclined at an angle A to the surface through which the light leaves the medium (see Figure 31–7). A triangular prism of the material is a very convenient form for this experiment. If a very narrow beam of white light is incident on side AB, it will be observed that the emergent beam is not white but consists of an array of colors extending from red through orange, yellow, green, blue, and violet. The prism is said to *disperse* the incoming radiation into its *spectrum*.

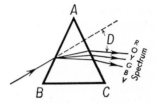

Fig. 31–7   Deviation and dispersion of a beam of white light by a triangular prism.

This dispersion is due to the fact that each particular color or wavelength travels with a different speed through the glass. The white light incident upon the surface AB at some angle i is refracted and dispersed. The different wavelengths or colors which constitute the white light travel through the material at different speeds and are refracted again at the surface AC. The ray entering the prism is bent toward the normal, and when it leaves the prism it is bent away from the normal, thus deviating it still further from its original direction. The angle of deviation D for any one color depends upon the material of the prism, the angle A of the prism, and the angle of incidence of the light.

Table 31-1   Absolute Indices of Refraction

Wavelength Substance	7,682 A	6,563 A	5,893 A	4,861 A	4,047 A
Borosilicate Crown glass	1.5191	1.5219	1.5243	1.5301	1.5382
Dense Flint glass	1.6441	1.6501	1.6555	1.6691	1.6901
Water 20°C	1.3289	1.3311	1.3330	1.3371	
Carbon disulphide 18°C		1.6198	1.6255	1.6541	
Diamond			2.417		

It will be observed that red light is deviated least, while violet light shows the greatest deviation. Thus red light travels fastest through the glass. The index of refraction of glass for red light is smallest. In specifying the index of refraction of a substance, it is also necessary to specify the color or the wavelength of the light used. Table 31–1 lists the absolute indices of refraction for a few substances for several wavelengths; the latter are expressed in angstroms.

If a very narrow beam of *monochromatic light*, that is, light of a single wavelength such as the yellow light from a sodium flame or a sodium arc, is sent through a triangular prism ABC which is made of some transparent substance, the beam will be deviated from its original direction through an angle D, the angle of deviation. This angle may be found experimentally, or it may be computed with the aid of Snell's law, provided the index of refraction of the substance is known. If the angle of incidence is changed by rotating the prism with respect to the incident beam, for example, the angle of deviation will also change. It may increase or decrease in value, depending upon the direction of rotation of the prism. Suppose that the prism is rotated so that the angle of deviation decreases; it will be found that the angle of deviation will reach a minimum value D_m, and any further rotation of the prism will produce an increase in the angle of deviation (see Figure 31–8). When the angle of deviation is a minimum, the angle of incidence i and the angle of emergence e are equal.

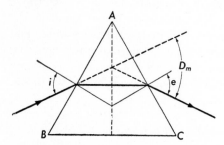

FIG. 31–8   Angle of minimum deviation.

There is a simple relationship connecting the angle of minimum deviation D_m, the angle A between the two refracting faces of the prism, and the index of refraction n of the material of the prism for the particular wavelength of light used. This relationship can be derived from simple geometrical considerations. The necessary angles are shown in Figure 31–9. Since D_m is an exterior angle to the isosceles triangle whose base angles are each $i - r'$, we get

$$D_m = i - r' + i - r' = 2i - 2r'.$$

The angle opposite A in the quadrilateral formed by the sides of the prism and the normals is equal to $\pi - A$. Since the sum of the angles of a triangle is equal to π, we can write

$$r' + r' + \pi - A = \pi,$$

so that $\qquad\qquad\qquad 2r' = A.$

Hence $$D_m = 2i - A,$$

or $$i = \frac{D_m + A}{2}.$$

Using Snell's law $$n = \frac{\sin i}{\sin r'},$$

we get

$$n = \frac{\sin \frac{1}{2}(A + D_m)}{\sin \frac{1}{2}A}. \qquad (4)$$

If a transparent substance is fashioned in the form of a prism of refracting angle A, its index of refraction for any desired wavelength can
be determined by measuring the angle of minimum deviation for this
particular wavelength.

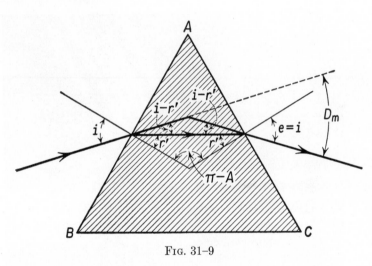

FIG. 31-9

Illustrative Example. When a narrow beam of sodium light was sent
through a particular glass prism whose refracting angle was 60°, the angle
of minimum deviation was found to be 51°. Determine the index of refraction of this glass for yellow sodium light.

In this case, $A = 60°$ and $D_m = 51°$; substituting these values in
Equation (4), we obtain

$$n = \frac{\sin 55°30'}{\sin 30°},$$

from which $$n = 1.65.$$

31-7 REFRACTION EFFECTS

When light goes through a transparent medium with parallel surfaces, as shown in Figures 31–10 and 31–11, the light is *displaced* but not *deviated;*

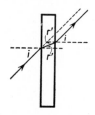

FIG. 31–10   Displacement of a ray of light by a transparent plate with parallel surfaces.

when the light emerges, it travels parallel to its original direction.   When white light is used, rays of different colors are refracted by different amounts upon entering the glass, but they become parallel again after emerging

FIG. 31–11   Photograph of a beam of light incident upon a rectangular plate of glass.   Note the reflected rays at both surfaces.   The transmitted rays are parallel to the incident rays but displaced slightly.   (Courtesy of Bausch & Lomb Optical Company.)

from it.   When viewed by the eye, these rays are brought to a focus in a single point, and the effect produced is the same as that of a single beam of white light.

When a divergent beam of light passes through a plate of glass with parallel surfaces, the rays, on emerging, are displaced by different amounts, as shown in Figure 31–12. If the divergence is not too large, the rays seem

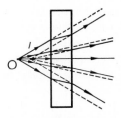

FIG. 31–12   The point of divergence of a beam of light appears displaced after passing through a plate of glass with parallel faces.

to come from a point I displaced from the original point O by an amount depending on the thickness of the glass. By reversing the directions of the rays in this diagram, we get the effect produced by the plate of glass on a bundle of rays which are converging toward a point or focus. The focal point or point of convergence of the rays is shifted away from the plate of glass. This method has been used to change the focal length of camera lenses.

Another interesting effect produced by the refraction of a narrow bundle of rays is illustrated in Figure 31–13. Rays from some point O

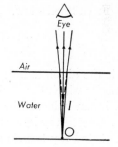

FIG. 31–13   Shallowing effect produced by refraction.

at the bottom of a pool of water are viewed by an observer whose eye is vertically above this point in air. The narrow bundle of rays entering the eye appears to come from a point I above point O. The pool of water seems shallower; its apparent depth is equal to the depth of the water divided by its index of refraction, which is 1.33.

It will be left as an exercise for the student to show that if an object is at a distance d below the surface of a homogeneous transparent substance of index of refraction n, the apparent depth d_a of this object is given by

$$d_a = d/n.$$

(5)

31-8 CRITICAL ANGLE. TOTAL REFLECTION

A ray of light traveling in a region of high index of refraction toward one of smaller index of refraction—from water toward air, for example—may penetrate through the surface of separation, providing the angle of incidence r' in the water is less than a certain value called the *critical angle* of incidence and denoted by c. If the angle of incidence is greater than this critical angle, the light will not be able to penetrate the surface but will be *totally reflected* back into the water.

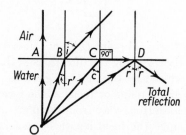

Fig. 31–14   Critical angle of refraction; total reflection.

A few typical rays from a point source O in water are shown in Figure 31–14. The ray OA strikes the surface normally and is not deviated. The ray OB strikes the surface at an angle r' and enters the air at a larger angle i. From Snell's law,

$$\frac{\sin r'}{\sin i} = \frac{1}{n},$$

where n is the absolute index of refraction of the medium. The limiting case is one for which the angle $i = 90°$; the sine of i for this case is 1 and is its maximum value. The ray OC strikes the surface at such an angle that the refracted ray in air makes an angle of 90° with the normal; that is, the refracted ray travels along the surface. The angle which this ray OC makes with the normal is called the *critical angle* of incidence and is denoted by c. Applying Snell's law to this case, we get

$$\frac{\sin c}{\sin 90°} = \frac{1}{n}$$

or

$$\boxed{\sin c = \frac{1}{n} \cdot}$$ (6)

The value of the sine of the critical angle for any substance is the reciprocal of its index of refraction. Taking $n = 1.33$ for water, the critical angle is 48°46′. If the angle of incidence is greater than the critical angle, the ray is totally reflected back into the medium. The ray *OD* illustrates the case of total reflection. For rays which are incident at angles greater than the critical angle, the surface acts as a perfectly reflecting surface. It is for this reason that, wherever possible, glass prisms arranged for total reflection are used instead of silvered surfaces as reflectors in optical instruments.

31-9 TOTALLY REFLECTING PRISMS

Totally reflecting glass prisms have found wide applications in such optical instruments as binoculars, periscopes, and range finders. The index of refraction of the glass used in making these prisms ranges from 1.50 to 1.65. When $n = 1.50$, the critical angle is 41°50′. If a ray of light going through the glass strikes the surface at an angle greater than this critical angle, the ray of light will be totally reflected. Figure 31–15 shows

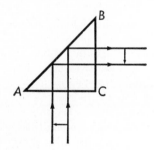

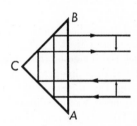

Fig. 31–15 A totally reflecting prism.

Fig. 31–16 Two reflections and an inversion by a totally reflecting prism.

total reflection in a 45° prism. The rays enter one face normally, strike the hypotenuse at an angle of 45°, and are reflected through an equal angle, leaving the other face of the prism normally. Since the rays enter and leave normally, no dispersion takes place.

Another way of using this prism is shown in Figure 31–16. The rays enter the hypotenuse face normally, undergo two total reflections, and leave the same face normally. Not only is the path of the rays reversed, but the rays themselves are reversed from top to bottom. Prism binoculars use two such prisms at right angles to each other. One produces a reversal from right to left, the other a reversal or, better, an inversion from top to bottom. Other varieties of shapes of prisms are used in optical instruments to displace the path of light around obstacles and to invert and reverse images.

QUESTIONS

1. Using a plane mirror near a sheet of paper, print in capital letters the words CHOICE QUALITY so that they appear upright when viewed in the mirror. Examine the appearance of these words on the sheet of paper; account for the difference in appearance of these two words.

2. What is the smallest length of mirror that you can use to see your whole figure imaged in it?

3. Explain why white light, after passing through a plate of glass with parallel faces, is not dispersed into its component colors.

4. How do you *see* the virtual image formed by a plane mirror?

5. A beam of light is converging toward a point on a screen. A plane parallel plate of glass is put in the path of this converging beam. In which direction will the point of convergence be shifted? Justify your answer with the aid of a diagram.

6. Totally reflecting prisms are usually designed so that the light enters and leaves the prism at an angle of 90° with respect to a surface. Can you account for this?

7. Why are totally reflecting prisms preferred to silvered mirrors in optical instruments?

8. Draw a diagram showing two plane mirrors at right angles to each other. Consider as an object a point on the line midway between these two mirrors and construct the image of this object formed by each of these mirrors. Now consider one of these images as the virtual object for the other mirror. These three images and the object should form the corners of a square. Try this with two small mirrors. Also use different angles and see the formation of multiple images.

9. Draw two plane mirrors at right angles to each other. Let a ray which is in a plane perpendicular to the planes of the mirrors strike one mirror at such an angle that it is also reflected from the second mirror. Show that the ray is exactly reversed in direction, although slightly displaced, as a result of these two reflections.

10. Refer to Figure 31–4 and give the geometrical proof that the image I is just as far behind the mirror as the object O is in front of the mirror.

11. Refer to Figure 31–4 and show that the size of the image formed by a plane mirror is the same as the size of the object.

PROBLEMS

1. What is the velocity in water (a) of red light of wavelength 6,563 A and (b) of blue light of wavelength 4,861 A?

2. What is the velocity in silicate flint glass (a) of red light of wavelength 7,600 A and (b) of violet light of 4,000 A?

3. A narrow beam of light from a sodium lamp (wavelength is 5,893 A) is incident on the surface of water at an angle of 40°. Determine the angle of refraction in the water.

4. A narrow beam of white light is incident on a crown-glass surface at an

angle of 45°. What is the angle of refraction (a) for the deep red light of wavelength 7,600 A and (b) for the violet light of wavelength 4,000 A?

5. Water is placed in a flat-bottom jar made of crown glass. Trace the path of a ray of light which is incident on the top of the surface of the water at an angle of 45° and passes through both the water and the glass. (a) What is the angle of refraction in the water? (b) What is the relative index of refraction of the glass with respect to the water?

6. The angle between the two refracting surfaces of a crown-glass prism is 60°. Trace the path of a ray of yellow sodium light through the prism, assuming that the angle of incidence is 30°. (a) What is the angle of refraction at the first surface? (b) What is the angle of deviation of the emergent ray?

7. The angle between the two refracting surfaces of a flint-glass prism is 60°. Trace the path of a ray of yellow sodium light through the prism such that its angle of refraction is 25°. (a) What is the angle of incidence? (b) What is the angle of deviation of the emergent beam?

8. What is the critical angle for yellow sodium light, wavelength 5,893 A, in diamond?

9. What is the smallest possible value of the index of refraction for the glass used in making a totally reflecting prism of the type shown in Figure 31–15?

10. A hollow glass prism, whose cross section is an equilateral triangle, is filled with carbon disulphide. Trace the path of a ray of sodium light through it such that its angle of refraction is 25°. (a) What is the angle of incidence? (b) What is the angle of deviation of this ray?

11. (a) Determine the angle of minimum deviation for a beam of yellow light passing through a 60° prism if its index of refraction is 1.65. (b) Determine the angle of incidence of this beam when its deviation is a minimum.

12. (a) Determine the angle of minimum deviation for a beam of light of wavelength 5,893 A passing through a 60° thin-walled glass prism filled with carbon disulphide at 18°C. (b) Determine the angle of incidence of this beam when its deviation is a minimum.

13. A low-power microscope is used to measure the index of refraction of a sample of glass which has parallel surfaces and is 1.20 cm thick. The microscope is first focused on a small dot on the lower surface; the microscope tube is then raised until a small dot on the upper surface is in focus. The distance the microscope tube has been raised is found to be 0.80 cm. Determine the index of refraction of this glass.

14. Calculate the critical angle for light going from diamond into air. Discuss the relationship of this value for the critical angle to the brilliance of a diamond.

15. When the refracting angle A of a prism is small, the angle of minimum deviation D_m is also small. Show that for a prism of small angle, the angle of deviation is given by $D_m = A(n - 1)$.

(Hint: For small angles, the sine of the angle is equal to the angle.)

16. Using the equation derived in Problem 15, calculate the deviation of a ray of light going through a glass prism having a 5° refracting angle if the index of refraction of the glass is 1.65.

32

Lenses and Mirrors

32-1 LENSES

Lenses, either singly or in combinations, are used for the formation of images of objects which send light to them. Lenses are most frequently made of transparent material with spherical surfaces. Spherical surfaces are used because they are easiest to make. For certain special cases, other surfaces may be made to eliminate certain defects of spherical lenses or to provide certain needed effects. A plane surface is a special case of a spherical surface; a plane can be considered a sphere of infinite radius. Spherical lenses are classified as either *converging lenses* or *diverging lenses*. Three common forms of converging lenses are shown in Figure 32–1(a), (b), (c),

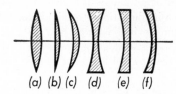

(a) (b) (c) (d) (e) (f)

FIG. 32–1   Spherical lenses; (a), (b), and (c) are converging lenses; (d), (e), and (f) are diverging lenses.

and three common forms of diverging lenses are shown in Figure 32–1(d), (e), (f). It will be observed that a converging lens is thicker at the center than at the edges, while a diverging lens is thinner at the center than at the edges.

A beam of parallel light incident on a converging lens will be converged toward a point F, known as the *principal focus* of the lens (see Figure 32–2). A beam of parallel light incident upon a diverging lens will diverge after passing through the lens as though it came from a point F', its principal focus, as shown in Figure 32–3. F' is called a *virtual focus*, since the rays do not actually pass through it.

The action of the lens is due to the refraction of the light as it enters and leaves the spherical surfaces bounding the lens. Figure 32–4 shows the effect of a converging lens on the wave fronts of the parallel beam. The wave fronts incident on the first surface of the lens are plane and parallel.

678

The part of the wave front which passes through the center of the lens is retarded more than the part which goes through the outer part of the lens. The emerging wave front is not plane; it can be shown that it is spherical

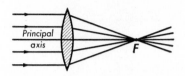

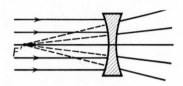

FIG. 32–2   Rays parallel to the principal axis are converged toward the
principal focus by the converging
lens.

FIG. 32–3   Rays parallel to the principal axis are diverged by the diverging lens. After passing through
the lens, the rays appear to come
from the virtual focus at F'.

with its center at the focus. Since the wave fronts travel perpendicular to their surfaces, they converge toward the center F. Parallel wave fronts incident on a diverging lens, as shown in Figure 32–5, are retarded more at

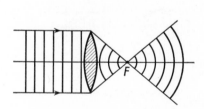

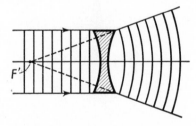

FIG. 32–4   Change in wave front produced by a converging lens on a
parallel beam of light incident
upon the lens.

FIG. 32–5   Change in wave front produced by a diverging lens on a
parallel beam of light incident
upon the lens.

the thicker edge of the lens than at the center. The emerging wave front is spherical, with its center at F'. These wave fronts travel perpendicularly to their surfaces, diverging from the center F'.

32-2   THIN LENSES

A thin lens is one whose thickness is small in comparison with its diameter. Only thin lenses will be considered in this book. Figure 32–6 shows a section of a thin converging lens whose two surfaces are parts of spheres, one of radius R_1, the other of radius R_2, with the centers of these spheres at C_1 and C_2, respectively. The line passing through these centers of curvature is called the *principal axis*. A *principal focus* of a lens is a point of convergence of a beam of light which is parallel to the principal

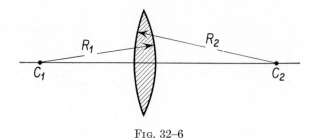

FIG. 32–6

Fig. 32–6

axis. F and F' in Figure 32–7 are principal foci. There are two principal foci, one on each side of the lens. The focal length f of a thin lens is the distance from the lens to either principal focus measured along the principal axis. The focal length of a lens depends upon the kind of glass used

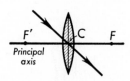

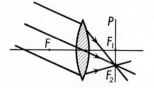

Fig. 32–7   Principal axis, principal foci, and optical center of a thin lens.

Fig. 32–8   A parallel beam of light inclined to the principal axis is focused at a point F_2 in the focal plane P.

and upon the radii of the spherical surfaces of the lens. We shall assume that the lens is so thin that all distances can be measured from a line through the center of the lens perpendicular to the principal axis. The *optical center C* of a lens is a point such that any ray passing through it will not be deviated. In the case of a thin lens whose surfaces have the same curvature, the optical center coincides with the geometrical center.

A plane drawn through a principal focus perpendicular to the principal axis is called a *focal plane* of the lens. A beam of parallel light which is inclined at a small angle to the principal axis, as shown in Figure 32–8, after passing through a converging lens, will be focused at a point in the focal plane. To determine the position of the focal point F_2, it is merely necessary to trace that ray in the beam which passes through the optical center of the lens. Since this ray goes through the lens without deviation, the point F_2 at which it intersects the focal plane is the point of convergence of all the other rays in the parallel beam.

32-3   IMAGE FORMATION BY CONVERGING LENSES

With the aid of a few well-chosen rays, it is a comparatively simple matter to construct graphically the image formed by a converging lens. Figure 32–9 shows an object AB at a distance from the converging lens

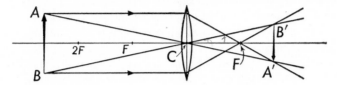

FIG. 32–9   Image formed by a converging lens when the object distance is greater than $2f$.

greater than $2f$, where f is its focal length. Two rays from any one point on the object, traced through the lens, are sufficient to determine the image of this point. In the figure, one ray from point A is chosen parallel to the principal axis; it is deviated by the lens so that it passes through the principal focus F. A second ray from point A is taken so that it passes through the optical center and travels on without deviation. These two rays intersect at a point A' which is the image of A. A similar construction yields B', the image of B. We could do this for other points on the object and obtain their images as well. These points would lie along $A'B'$, which is the image of AB. It will be observed that this image is *smaller* than the object, is *inverted*, and is *real;* that is, light rays actually pass through the image. This image can be seen by looking along the axis from a point beyond the image, or the image may be formed on a screen placed where the image is, and then the image may be viewed from any convenient position.

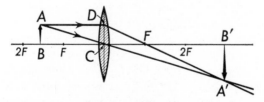

FIG. 32–10   Real, enlarged image formed by a converging lens when the object distance is greater than f and less than $2f$.

Figure 32–10 shows another type of image formation by a converging lens. In this case the object lies between the focus F and a point distant $2f$ from the lens. The image is *real, inverted,* and *larger* than the object. Point B is chosen on the axis in order to simplify the diagram.

A special case intermediate between the two just discussed occurs when the object is at a distance from the lens equal to twice the focal length. The image in this case is the same distance from the lens on the other side. It is real, inverted, and the same size as the object. It can be shown that this is the minimum distance between object and real image for any position of the object from the converging lens. This forms a convenient method for determining the focal length of a converging lens: when the object and image are the same size, the focal length of the lens is one fourth the distance between them.

Figure 32–11 shows a third type of image which is formed by a converging lens. The object distance is less than the focal length of the lens.

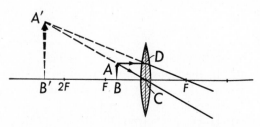

Fɪɢ. 32–11   Virtual, enlarged image formed by a converging lens when the object distance is less than *f*.

It will be observed that the rays from A do *not* meet after passing through the lens, but, when projected back, they meet in point A' on the same side as the object. The image in this case is *virtual, erect,* and *larger* than the object. The virtual image can be seen only by looking through the lens; it cannot be formed on a screen.

32-4   THE LENS EQUATION

In the preceding section, we showed how to determine by graphical means the relative positions of the image produced by a thin converging lens for different positions of the object. These same diagrams enabled us to determine the relative sizes of image and object, and also the nature of the image, that is, whether it was real or virtual. The graphical method is applicable to all cases; the same results can also be obtained by means of a simple equation called the *lens equation,* which can be derived most readily from the graphical representation. Referring to Figure 32–12, AB is an object situated at a distance s to the left of the lens of focal length f, and $A'B'$ is the image formed by this lens at a distance s' to the right of the lens. All distances are measured from a line through the center C of the lens perpendicular to the principal axis; the latter passes through the two principal foci F and F'. Triangles ABC and $A'B'C$ are right triangles by construction; further, angle ACB = angle $A'CB'$, since they are vertex angles. Hence

$$\frac{A'B'}{AB} = \frac{CB'}{CB} = \frac{s'}{s}.$$ (1)

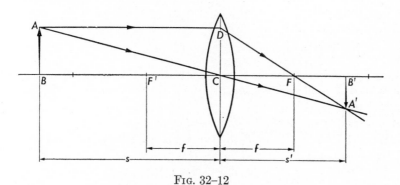

Fɪɢ. 32–12

Triangles CDF and $A'B'F$ are similar since they are both right triangles with vertex angles DFC and $B'FA'$ which are equal. Therefore

$$\frac{A'B'}{CD} = \frac{B'F}{CF} = \frac{s'-f}{f}.$$

Now $CD = AB$ by construction;

therefore $$\frac{A'B'}{AB} = \frac{s'-f}{f}.$$ (2)

From Equations (1) and (2), we get

$$\frac{s'}{s} = \frac{s'-f}{f},$$

so that $$s'f = ss' - sf,$$

and, dividing by $ss'f$, this becomes

$$\frac{1}{s} = \frac{1}{f} - \frac{1}{s'}$$

or

$$\boxed{\frac{1}{s} + \frac{1}{s'} = \frac{1}{f}.}$$ (3)

Equation (3) is the *lens equation*. In using this equation, we start with light coming toward the lens from the left; s is positive when the object is to the left of the lens; s' is positive when the image is to the right of the lens; f will then be positive for a converging lens and will be negative for a diverging lens.

Equation (1) gives the relative sizes of image and object when they are at right angles to the principal axis. We now define a term called the *magnification m* as follows:

$$m = -\frac{s'}{s}, \tag{4}$$

where s' is the image distance and s is the object distance. The negative sign is used to indicate that when s' and s are both positive, the image is inverted relative to the object. *The positive and negative signs are to be used only when numerical values are substituted for s, s', and f.*

We shall illustrate the method of using Equations (3) and (4) in a few typical cases.

Illustrative Example. An object 6 cm tall is situated 45 cm from a converging lens of 15 cm focal length. Determine the position, size, and nature of the image.

This case is illustrated in Figure 32–9. Let us solve Equation (3) for s':

$$\frac{1}{s} + \frac{1}{s'} = \frac{1}{f}, \tag{3}$$

from which

$$\frac{1}{s'} = \frac{1}{f} - \frac{1}{s}$$

$$= \frac{s - f}{sf},$$

so that

$$s' = \frac{sf}{s - f}. \tag{5}$$

In this case, $s = 45$ cm and $f = 15$ cm;

hence

$$s' = \frac{45 \times 15}{45 - 15},$$

or

$$s' = 22.5 \text{ cm}.$$

Since s' is positive, the image is real and on the right side of the lens.

Using Equation (4) for the magnification produced by the lens

$$m = -\frac{s'}{s}, \tag{4}$$

we get

$$m = -\frac{22.5}{45} = -\frac{1}{2};$$

that is, the height of the image is half that of the object, or 3 cm high. The negative sign indicates that the image is inverted. Thus the image is real, inverted, and smaller than the object.

Illustrative Example. Suppose that the object of the above example is moved to a position 20 cm from the converging lens; determine the position, size, and nature of the image.

This case is illustrated in Figure 32–10. Using $s = 20$ cm and $f = 15$ cm, Equation (5) yields, for the position of the image,

$$s' = \frac{20 \times 15}{20 - 15} = 60 \text{ cm.}$$

The magnification produced by this lens is now

$$m = -\frac{60}{20} = -3.$$

Thus the image is real, three times larger than the object, and inverted.

Illustrative Example. Suppose that the above object is now moved to a position 10 cm from the lens; determine the position, size, and nature of the image.

This case is illustrated in Figure 32–11. Using $s = 10$ cm and $f = 15$ cm, Equation (5) yields, for the position of the image,

$$s' = \frac{10 \times 15}{10 - 15} = -30 \text{ cm.}$$

The magnification produced by this lens is now

$$m = -\frac{-30}{10} = +3.$$

The fact that s' is negative means that the image is to the left of the lens, that is, on the same side as the object; hence the lens now forms a virtual image. The magnification is now $+3$; that is, the image is upright with respect to the object, and its height is three times that of the object.

32-5 IMAGE FORMATION BY DIVERGING LENSES

Figure 32–13 shows the image $A'B'$ formed by the diverging lens of the object AB. The rays from any point such as A, after passing through the lens, diverge and do not meet; when projected back, they meet in point A', which is the virtual image of A. A diverging lens cannot form a real image of a real object. This statement can be verified by experiment, or by graphical construction using a variety of positions for the object, or by an analysis of Equation (5). The experiment would consist of attempting to focus the image formed by the diverging lens on a screen. A lamp or an illuminated arrow can be used as an object. No position of the diverging lens will be found which will give an image on the screen. One might inquire how such images can be seen; the answer, of course, is that they are

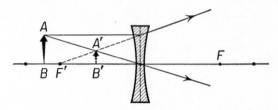

FIG. 32–13   Virtual image formed by a diverging lens.

seen with the aid of the eye which can be considered an optical instrument containing a converging lens. The eye forms a real image with the diverging light coming from the lens. Optical instruments constructed for visual use generally form virtual images.

In Equation (5), using our sign convention, f for a diverging lens will always be a negative number. For a real object, s is positive. The numerator of the fraction in Equation (5) will therefore always be negative, while the denominator will always be positive, so that s' will always be negative; that is, the image will be virtual. The graphical proof, if needed, is left to the student.

Suppose that, in the case illustrated in Figure 32–13, s is 25 cm and $f = -15$ cm; then, from Equation (5),

$$s' = \frac{25(-15)}{25 - (-15)} = -\frac{25 \times 15}{40} = -9.4 \text{ cm.}$$

Since s' is negative, the image is virtual.

The magnification produced by this lens is

$$m = -\frac{-9.4}{25} = +0.38.$$

The image is thus smaller than the object and is upright with respect to the object.

32-6   COMBINATIONS OF LENSES

Two or more lenses are frequently used in combination to produce a desired result. Although a general discussion of this topic is beyond the scope of this book, a few simple combinations of two lenses will be discussed here and in the next chapter because of their importance in the design of many optical instruments.

If two thin lenses are placed in contact so that their principal axes coincide, and if the thickness of the combined lens system is still sufficiently small so that it may be treated as a single thin lens, then the focal length f of this system is given by

$$\frac{1}{f} = \frac{1}{f_1} + \frac{1}{f_2},$$ (6)

where f_1 and f_2 are the focal lengths of the individual lenses. For example, if a converging lens of 15 cm focal length is placed in contact with another converging lens of 10 cm focal length with their principal axes coinciding, then the focal length f of this system is given by

$$\frac{1}{f} = \frac{1}{15} + \frac{1}{10} = \frac{2+3}{30},$$

so that $f = 6$ cm.

If a converging lens of focal length 10 cm is placed in contact with a diverging lens of -15 cm focal length with their principal axes coinciding, then the focal length of the combination is given by

$$\frac{1}{f} = \frac{1}{10} - \frac{1}{15} = \frac{3-2}{30},$$

so that $f = 30$ cm.

If the two lenses are separated, the simplest method is to treat each lens separately, first determining the image formed by the lens nearest the object, and then using the image thus formed as the object for the second lens. Either the graphical method or the lens equation can be used in the solution of this problem.

Illustrative Example. An object is placed 14 cm in front of a converging lens of 10 cm focal length. Another converging lens of 7 cm focal length is placed at a distance of 40 cm to the right of the first lens. Determine the position and character of the final image.

The graphical solution is shown in Figure 32–14. $A'B'$ is the image formed by the first lens and is real, inverted, and larger than the object AB. $A'B'$ is used as the object for the second lens which forms the final image $A''B''$. The latter is virtual, larger than $A'B'$, and upright with respect to it; hence the final image is inverted with respect to the original object.

We can solve this problem by two successive applications of the lens equation. For the first lens L_1, $f_1 = 10$ cm and $s_1 = 14$ cm; hence

$$s_1' = \frac{14 \times 10}{14 - 10} = 35 \text{ cm.}$$

The subscripts 1 refer to the first lens. Since the two lenses are 40 cm apart, the image $A'B'$ is 5 cm from the second lens L_2. Using $A'B'$ as the object for the second lens, then $s_2 = 5$ cm and $f_2 = 7$ cm, so that

$$s_2' = \frac{5 \times 7}{5 - 7} = -17.5 \text{ cm};$$

that is, the final image is virtual and to the left of the second lens.

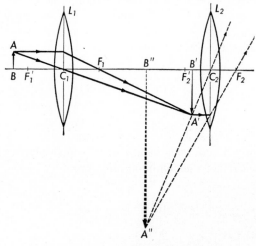

FIG. 32–14

Since the second lens magnifies the image produced by the first lens, the total magnification m is the product of the magnification m_1 produced by the first lens and the magnification m_2 produced by the second lens; that is,

$$m = m_1 m_2,$$

or

$$m = \frac{s_1'}{s_1} \cdot \frac{s_2'}{s_2},$$

which in this case becomes

$$m = -\frac{35}{14} \cdot \frac{17.5}{5},$$

so that

$$m = -8.75.$$

The negative sign shows that the final image is inverted with respect to the original; the magnification produced by this lens system is 8.75.

Illustrative Example. Two converging lenses L_1 and L_2 are placed 40 cm apart, their principal axes coinciding. An object AB is placed 15 cm in

front of L_1. Determine the position and character of the final image. The
focal length of L_1 is 12 cm and the focal length of L_2 is 10 cm.

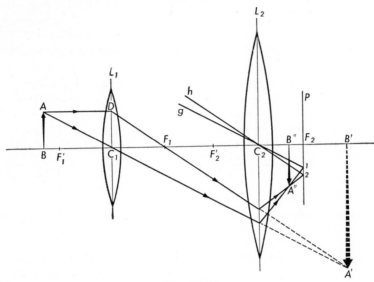

The graphical solution is shown in Figure 32–15. The image $A'B'$
formed by the lens L_1 would have appeared at $A'B'$ if lens L_2 had not
intercepted the rays. The image distance s_1' from L_1 is

$$s_1' = \frac{15 \times 12}{15 - 12} = 60 \text{ cm.}$$

Thus $A'B'$ is 20 cm to the right of lens L_2; $A'B'$ is thus a *virtual object* for
the lens L_2. Its distance s_2 is 40 cm − 60 cm, or $s_2 = -20$ cm. The position of the image formed by L_2 is at a distance s_2' from it, given by

$$s_2' = \frac{-20 \times 10}{-20 - 10} = 6.7 \text{ cm;}$$

that is, the final image is real and to the right of L_2, 6.7 cm from it. The
magnification produced by this combination of lenses is

$$m = \frac{s_1'}{s_1} \cdot \frac{s_2'}{s_2} = \frac{60}{15} \cdot \frac{6.7}{(-20)} = -1.34.$$

The negative sign shows that the final image is inverted with respect to the
original object.

In the graphical solution, the positions of points along $A''B''$ are
located with the aid of rays which are parallel to those going *toward* L_2.

It will be recalled that a bundle of parallel rays inclined to the principal axis is focused at a point in the focal plane of the lens. To determine this point in the focal plane, it is necessary simply to choose one of these parallel rays to pass through the center of the lens. Since a ray through the center of the lens is not deviated, its intersection with the focal plane is the point at which all rays parallel to it are focused. The line PF_2 is in the focal plane passing through F_2, the principal focus of lens L_2. Line gC_2 is parallel to the ray C_1A' and intersects the focal plane at point 1. Hence the lens L_2 bends the ray C_1A' so that it passes through point 1. Similarly the line hC_2 is drawn parallel to the ray DA' and strikes the focal plane at point 2; hence the lens L_2 bends the ray DA' so that it passes through point 2. The rays going to points 1 and 2 intersect at A'', which is the image of A' and of A. All other points of the image $A''B''$ can be found in a similar manner.

32-7 SPHERICAL MIRRORS

A spherical mirror consists of a small section of the surface of a sphere with one side of the surface covered with a polished reflecting material, usually silver or aluminum. If the outside or convex surface is silvered, we have a *convex mirror*, shown in Figure 32–16; if the inside or concave surface is silvered, we have a *concave mirror*, shown in Figure 32–17. Most

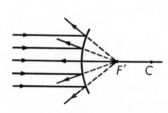

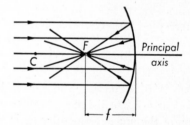

FIG. 32–16   A beam of light parallel to the principal axis is reflected from a convex spherical mirror. The reflected beam appears to diverge from the virtual focus F'.

FIG. 32–17   A beam of light parallel to the principal axis is reflected from a concave spherical mirror. The reflected beam converges toward the principal focus F.

mirrors used commercially are made of glass, with the rear surface silvered and then covered with a coating of lacquer or paint for protection. Mirrors for astronomical telescopes and for other accurate scientific work are silvered on the front surface. In a mirror silvered on the back surface, light is reflected not only from the silvered surface but also from the front glass surface, giving rise to two images, one fainter than the other. There is also absorption of some of the light which enters the glass on its way to and from the silvered surface. With front-surface mirrors, these difficulties are avoided. In the following discussion, only front-surface mirrors will be considered.

The principal axis of the mirror is a line through the center of curvature C of the mirror and the vertex or center of the portion of the spherical surface used. A bundle of rays parallel to the principal axis, when reflected from a concave mirror, will go toward the principal focus F. The distance from F to the vertex or center of the mirror is its focal length f. A bundle of rays parallel to the principal axis, when reflected from a convex mirror, will diverge as though it came from the principal focus F'; F' is a virtual focus.

It can readily be shown that the principal focus F of a spherical mirror is halfway between the center of curvature C and the vertex V when the angles of incidence are small. In Figure 32–18, a ray AN is drawn parallel

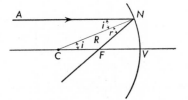

FIG. 32–18   The principal focus of a concave mirror is halfway between the center of curvature C and the vertex V.

to the principal axis CFV of a concave mirror of radius R. The line CN is a radius of the sphere and hence is normal to the spherical mirror at N. The angle ANC is the angle of incidence i, and the angle CNF is the angle of reflection r. The angle r is thus equal to the angle i. Further, the angle NCF is also equal to i, since CN is a transversal to two parallel lines. Hence the triangle CFN is an isosceles triangle. Thus $CF = FN$. When the angle i is small, FN does not differ appreciably from FV, so that, for small angles of incidence, F is halfway between the center C of the mirror and the vertex V. Since $CV = R$, the radius of the sphere, $FV = CF = R/2$. Rays parallel to the principal axis are reflected through point F, the principal focus; hence the focal length of the mirror is

$$f = R/2. \qquad\qquad (7)$$

32-8 IMAGE FORMATION BY CONCAVE MIRRORS

Just as in the case of a converging lens, so in the case of a concave mirror, three positions of the object are chosen to illustrate the three types of images formed from real objects. In Figure 32–19, the object distance s

is greater than the radius R of the sphere or greater than $2f$. One ray from point A of the object is taken parallel to the principal axis; this ray is reflected from the mirror through the principal focus. A second ray from

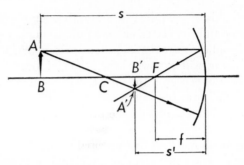

Fig. 32–19   A real, inverted, smaller image is formed by a concave mirror when the object distance is greater than $2f$.

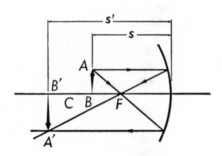

Fig. 32–20   A real, inverted, enlarged image is formed by a concave mirror when the object is between C and F.

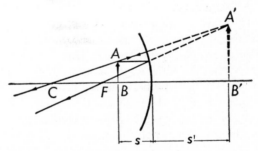

Fig. 32–21   A virtual, erect, enlarged image is formed by a concave mirror when the object distance is less than f.

point A is drawn through the center of curvature C; this ray strikes the mirror normally and is reflected back on itself. The two reflected rays meet in A', which is the image of A. The image $A'B'$ is real, inverted, and smaller than the object.

Figure 32–20 shows an enlarged, real, inverted image formed by a concave mirror when the object is placed between the principal focus and the center of curvature. One ray from A is taken parallel to the principal axis and is reflected back through the principal focus. The second ray from A is taken through the principal focus and is reflected back parallel to the principal axis. They meet in A', the image of A. The image $A'B'$ is real, inverted, and larger than the object.

When the object distance is less than the focal length, as illustrated in Figure 32–21, the rays from A, when reflected by the mirror, do not meet; when projected on the other side of the mirror, they meet in A', which is the virtual image of A. The image in this case is virtual, erect, and enlarged.

32-9 THE MIRROR EQUATION

An equation relating the distance s of the object from the mirror to the distance s' of the image from the mirror in terms of its focal length f or its

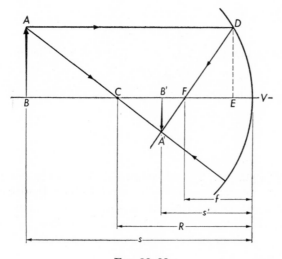

Fɪɢ. 32–22

radius of curvature R, can be derived in a manner analogous to that used in deriving the lens equation. Referring to Figure 32–22, since triangles ABC and $A'B'C$ are similar, we can write

$$\frac{AB}{A'B'} = \frac{BC}{B'C} = \frac{s - R}{R - s'}.$$

If we drop a perpendicular from D to E onto the principal axis, then, since the triangles DEF and $A'B'F$ are similar,

$$\frac{DE}{A'B'} = \frac{EF}{B'F}.$$

Now $DE = AB$, and, if we restrict this discussion to rays which make very small angles with the principal axis and if the section of the sphere used for a mirror is very small, then E may be considered to coincide with the vertex V, so that $EF = f$ and $B'F = s' - f$.

Substituting these values in the above equation, we get

$$\frac{AB}{A'B'} = \frac{f}{s' - f}.$$

Equating the two expressions for the ratio $AB/A'B'$, we have

$$\frac{s - R}{R - s'} = \frac{f}{s' - f}.$$

Now, since $$R = 2f,$$

we can write $$\frac{s - 2f}{2f - s'} = \frac{f}{s' - f}.$$

Clearing fractions and rearranging terms, we obtain the equation

$$s'f + sf = ss',$$

and, dividing each term by $ss'f$, we get

$$\boxed{\frac{1}{s} + \frac{1}{s'} = \frac{1}{f}} \tag{8}$$

for the mirror equation. It will be noticed that this is identical with the lens equation; however one must be careful about the sign convention. In the mirror equation as in the lens equation, the light is assumed to come from the left; the distance s is positive when the object is to the left of the mirror. Since a mirror reflects light, the image distance s' will also be considered positive when the image is on the left. If s' is negative, the image is virtual and on the right, that is, behind the mirror. The focal length f is positive for a concave mirror and negative for a convex mirror. *The positive and negative signs are to be used only when numerical values are substituted for s, s', and f.*

The mirror equation may also be written in terms of the radius R of the spherical mirror. Since $f = R/2$, the mirror equation becomes

$$\boxed{\frac{1}{s} + \frac{1}{s'} = \frac{2}{R}.} \tag{8a}$$

The magnification m produced by a mirror is defined in the same manner as that produced by a lens and is given by

$$m = -\frac{s'}{s}. \tag{4}$$

Illustrative Example. An object is placed 50 cm from a concave mirror of 30 cm radius. Determine the position and character of the image.

The graphical solution of this problem is shown in Figure 32–19. The focal length f of this mirror is $R/2$ or 15 cm. If we solve Equation (8) for the distance s', we get

$$s' = \frac{sf}{s-f}.$$

Since $s = 50$ cm and $f = 15$ cm,

$$s' = \frac{50 \times 15}{50 - 15} = 21.4 \text{ cm}.$$

The magnification produced by this mirror is

$$m = -\frac{s'}{s} = -\frac{21.4}{50} = -0.43.$$

The image is 21.4 cm from the mirror; it is real, inverted, and smaller than the object.

Illustrative Example. An object is placed 25 cm in front of a concave mirror whose focal length is 15 cm. Determine the position and character of the image.

The graphical solution of this problem is shown in Figure 32–20. Solving the mirror equation for s' yields

$$s' = \frac{sf}{s-f}.$$

Since $s = 25$ cm and $f = 15$ cm,

$$s' = \frac{25 \times 15}{25 - 15} = 37.5 \text{ cm}.$$

The magnification produced by this mirror is

$$m = -\frac{s'}{s} = -\frac{37.5}{25},$$

from which $\qquad m = -1.5.$

The image is real and at a distance of 37.5 cm from the mirror. The image is inverted and magnified 1.5 times.

Illustrative Example. An object is placed 7.5 cm from a concave mirror whose focal length is 15 cm. Determine the position and character of the image.

The graphical solution is shown in Figure 32–21. The image distance s' can be obtained from the equation

$$s' = \frac{sf}{s - f},$$

Using the values $s = 7.5$ cm and $f = 15$ cm,

we get
$$s' = \frac{7.5 \times 15}{7.5 - 15} = -15 \text{ cm.}$$

The magnification produced by this mirror is

$$m = -\frac{s'}{s} = -\frac{-15}{7.5} = +2$$

Since s' is negative, the image is behind the mirror; that is, the image is virtual and at a distance of 15 cm from the mirror. The fact that the magnification is positive shows that the image is upright with respect to the object. In this case, the image is twice the size of the object.

32-10 IMAGE FORMATION BY CONVEX MIRRORS

No matter where the object is placed in front of a convex mirror, its image will always be virtual, erect, and smaller than the object, as shown in Figure 32–23. A ray from A parallel to the axis is reflected back as

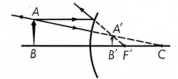

Fig. 32–23 A virtual, erect, smaller image is formed by a convex mirror for any position of a real object.

though it came from the virtual focus F'. A second ray, taken normal to the mirror, is reflected back on itself. These two rays do not meet; when projected behind the mirror, they meet in point A', which is the virtual image of A. The image $A'B'$ is virtual, erect, and smaller than the object.

Suppose that the focal length of the convex mirror is -15 cm and that the object is placed 45 cm in front of the mirror. The distance of the image from the mirror is

$$s' = \frac{sf}{s - f} = \frac{45(-15)}{45 - (-15)} = -11.25 \text{ cm.}$$

The magnification produced by this mirror is

$$m = -\frac{s'}{s} = -\frac{-11.25}{45} = +0.25.$$

The image is virtual and is situated 11.25 cm behind the mirror. Since the magnification is positive, the image is upright and, in this case, is one fourth the size of the object.

32-11 SPHERICAL ABERRATION OF LENSES AND MIRRORS

In the discussion of spherical mirrors, it was stated that the mirror should be a small portion of the surface of the sphere. If the mirror surface is a large portion of the sphere, the images formed are blurred. This blurring of the image is due to *spherical aberration;* that is, rays from one point of an object reflected by different portions of the spherical surface do not meet in a point but cover a sizable area. Spherical aberration can be reduced by using a diaphragm to limit the rays to the central portion of the mirror. This will make the image clearer and sharper but will reduce its brightness.

When a beam of parallel rays is incident upon a large mirror, the reflected rays do not all pass through the principal focus, as shown in Figure 32–24; the rays which are reflected from the outer portion of the mirror

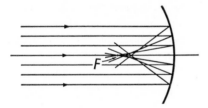
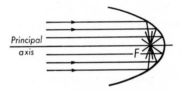

FIG. 32–24 Spherical aberration produced by a mirror.

FIG. 32–25 A beam of light parallel to the principal axis is focused in a point by a parabolic mirror.

cross the principal axis closer to the mirror than those which are reflected from the central portion. Instead of a sharp focal point, there is a sizable focal spot.

A sharp focus can be obtained with a large mirror if the surface is parabolic in shape instead of spherical. It is a property of the parabola that any ray from the focus which strikes the parabolic surface is reflected parallel to the principal axis, as shown in Figure 32–25. If a very small source of light is placed at the focus, a parallel beam is reflected from the parabolic mirrors. Such mirrors are commonly used in automobile head lamps and in searchlights. The very large astronomical telescopes are of the reflecting type; a very large parabolic mirror is used as the objective of such a reflecting telescope to focus the rays from distant stars. Parabolic mirrors are used only in cases in which the incident or emergent beam is parallel to the principal axis of the mirror; otherwise even parabolic mirrors will show "spherical aberration."

The images formed by lenses also show spherical aberration. To eliminate additional errors owing to the dispersion of white light by the glass, we can use monochromatic light such as the yellow light from a sodium lamp. Figure 32–26 shows a set of rays of monochromatic light

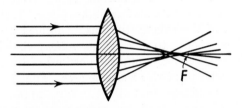

F IG . 32–26   Spherical aberration of a lens.

parallel to the principal axis passing through a lens. The rays which go through the edge of the lens are deviated so that they cross the principal axis closer to the lens than those which go through the center portion. This produces a blurring of the focal spot. One method of reducing spherical aberration is to use a diaphragm to limit the light from the object to the central portion of the lens. This, of course, reduces the amount of light available for producing the image.

32-12 CHROMATIC ABERRATION OF A LENS

A ray of white light, upon entering the lens, is dispersed into its component colors, and, upon leaving the lens, the different colors are deviated by different amounts. A lens may be considered equivalent to a very large number of prisms of varying angles; the action of the lens on white light is the same as that of a prism of appropriate angle for each incident ray. When a beam of parallel white light goes through a lens, the different colors cross the principal axis at different points; that is, the different colors are brought to different foci (see Figure 32–27). The red light is focused farthest from the lens, and the violet light is focused closest to the lens. This is known as *chromatic aberration*. Lenses which are not properly corrected for chromatic aberration produce images which show colors around the edges.

The method of correcting for chromatic aberration is to use two lenses specially designed for this purpose. Two converging lenses of the same kind of glass can be used to correct for chromatic aberration for the special case in which parallel light is either incident on the lens and brought to a

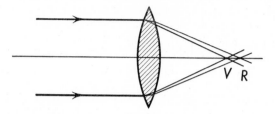

FIG. 32–27   Chromatic aberration of a lens.

focus, or else the light which emerges is parallel. The special condition that must be satisfied by these two lenses is that the distance d between them must be half the sum of the focal lengths of the two lenses. Ramsden and Huygens eyepieces used with telescopes and microscopes are built this way (see Section 33–4).

If the two lenses are in contact, they must be of different kinds of glass and properly designed to correct for chromatic aberration. The basic idea in the design of such an *achromatic* lens is illustrated in Figure 32–28, which

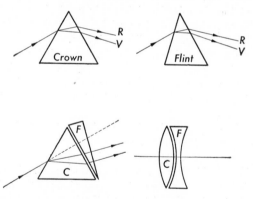

FIG. 32–28   The design of an achromatic lens.

shows light passing through a prism of crown glass and a prism of flint glass. The angles of the prism have been chosen so that each one forms a spectrum of the same angular width, but each deviates the light by a different amount. When these two prisms are placed in contact with their vertex angles opposed, the different colors come out parallel and produce a beam of white light deviated from its original direction. Such a combination of prisms produces *deviation without dispersion*. A converging achromatic lens combination can therefore be made by combining a crown-glass lens of short positive focal length and a flint-glass lens of longer negative focal length. These may be cemented together to form *a single achromatic lens*.

1. Does spherical aberration depend upon the fact that the surfaces are spherical or upon the fact that the rays used make large angles with the axis of the lens or mirror?

2. Can a parabolic mirror show spherical aberration?

3. Draw a parallel beam inclined at a small angle to the principal axis of a diverging lens and locate the focal point from which the beam appears to diverge after passing through the lens.

4. Draw a parallel beam of light inclined at a small angle to the principal axis of a concave mirror and locate the focal point to which the beam converges after reflection from the mirror.

PROBLEMS

1. An object 2 cm long is placed 32 cm in front of a converging lens whose focal length is 20 cm. Find (a) the position and (b) the size of the image, algebraically and graphically. Describe the image.

2. An object 6 cm long is placed 60 cm in front of a converging lens whose focal length is 20 cm. Find (a) the position and (b) the size of the image, algebraically and graphically. Describe the image.

3. An object 3 cm long is placed 15 cm in front of a converging lens whose focal length is 20 cm. Find (a) the position and (b) the size of the image, algebraically and graphically. Describe the image.

4. A convenient, though approximate, method for obtaining the focal length of a converging lens is to measure the distance of the image formed of a very distant object. What percentage error would be made if the distant object used were the windows of the laboratory about 6 m from the lens whose focal length is known to be 10 cm?

5. An object 5 cm long is placed 20 cm in front of a diverging lens whose focal length is -10 cm. Find (a) the position and (b) the size of the image, algebraically and graphically. Describe the image.

6. An illuminated object and a screen are 6 m apart. A converging lens is placed between them so that an image 15 times as long as the object is formed on the screen. (a) Determine the distance of the lens from the object. (b) Determine the focal length of the lens.

7. An object is placed 20 cm from a concave spherical mirror whose radius is 24 cm. Determine the position of the image, algebraically and graphically. Describe the image.

8. An object 4 cm long is placed 60 cm from a concave spherical mirror whose radius of curvature is 40 cm. Determine (a) the position and (b) the size of the image. Describe the image.

9. An object 3 cm long is placed 4 cm from a concave spherical mirror whose focal length is 12 cm. Determine (a) the position and (b) the size of the image. Describe the image.

10. An object 6 cm long is placed 20 cm in front of a convex spherical mirror

whose focal length is 24 cm. Determine (a) the position and (b) the size of the image. Describe the image.

11. A concave spherical mirror has a radius of curvature of 50 cm. A square object 3 cm on edge is placed 10 cm in front of the mirror. Determine (a) the position of the image and (b) the area of the image.

12. A lens placed 40 cm from an object forms a real inverted image 16 cm from the lens. (a) What is the focal length of the lens? (b) Is it a converging or diverging lens?

13. A converging lens forms a real image which is exactly the same size as the object at a distance of 50 cm from the object. What is the focal length of the lens?

14. A spherical mirror forms a virtual image of a real object. The image is four times as large as the object and is 48 cm from the mirror. Find (a) the object distance and (b) the radius of curvature of the mirror. (c) Is it a convex or concave mirror?

15. A real image is formed 80 cm from a lens when the object is 24 cm from the lens. Determine the focal length of the lens.

16. A thin converging lens of 6 cm focal length is placed in contact with a thin diverging lens of −16 cm focal length with their principal axes coinciding. Determine the effective focal length of this system.

17. A thin converging lens of 24 cm focal length is placed in contact with a thin diverging lens of −16 cm focal length with their principal axes coinciding. Determine the effective focal length of this system.

18. Two thin converging lenses, each of 10 cm focal length, are spaced 15 cm apart, their principal axes coinciding. A beam of parallel light is incident on the first lens. Trace the beam in its passage through this system to determine the position of the focal point. How far from the second lens is this focal point?

19. Two thin converging lenses, each of 10 cm focal length, are spaced 5 cm apart, their principal axes coinciding. A beam of parallel light is incident on the first lens. Trace this beam in its passage through the system and determine the position of the focal point. How far from the second lens is this focal point?

20. An object is placed 40 cm from a thin converging lens of 8 cm focal length. A second thin converging lens of 12 cm focal length is placed 20 cm behind the first lens. (a) Determine the position of the final image, both graphically and algebraically. (b) Determine the magnification produced by this lens combination.

21. An object is placed 32 cm from a thin converging lens of 16 cm focal length. A second thin converging lens of 6 cm focal length is placed 20 cm behind the first lens. (a) Determine the position of the final image, both graphically and algebraically. (b) Determine the magnification of this lens combination.

22. A converging lens forms an image on a screen 60 cm from it. A thin diverging lens is interposed between them at a distance of 40 cm from the converging lens. It is now found necessary to move the screen 10 cm away from the lens in order to produce a sharp image. Determine the focal length of the diverging lens.

33

Optical Instruments

33-1 THE CAMERA

The photographic camera uses a converging lens to form a real, inverted image of an object which usually is at a distance from the lens greater than twice its focal length. The image then is smaller than the object. The image is focused on a film or plate which is coated with an emulsion containing silver bromide crystals. The light dissociates the silver bromide, and later, when the film or plate is developed, the bromine is removed, leaving only silver at the places where light struck the film or plate. In most cameras, the converging lens consists of two or more lenses designed and arranged to reduce several of the objectionable aberrations to a minimum. The word *design* is used advisedly, because it is a matter of optical engineering to choose the proper lenses and arrange them for the special purposes desired.

Figure 33–1 shows a lens system used in some fairly good cameras. Two achromats are spaced the proper distance apart, and a diaphragm *D*

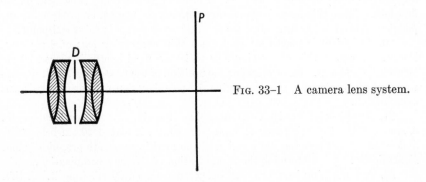

FIG. 33–1   A camera lens system.

is placed between them. The diaphragm is of the *iris* type so that the diameter of the opening can be adjusted. A shutter is usually placed near the diaphragm to admit light into the camera for a known time interval. When the object to be photographed is very far away, the image is formed

702

in the principal focal plane, and hence the photographic plate or film P must be placed at this position. When the object is closer to the lens but at a distance from it greater than twice its focal length, the image will be formed between the principal focus and a point at a distance twice the focal length of the lens (see Figure 32–9). The distance between the lens and the film must be changed to have the image focused on the film. This is usually accomplished by moving the lens away from the film.

In some of the box or "fixed focus" type of cameras, there is no way in which to move the lens with respect to the film. The lens used in such a camera has a short focal length, and, as long as the object is at a distance greater than about 6 ft from the lens, its image will be focused close enough to the principal focus so that the image on the film will not be blurred too much.

The amount of light entering the camera in a given time interval can be controlled by varying the diameter of the opening in the iris diaphragm. The diameter of this aperture is usually given as a fraction of the focal length. Thus an $f/8$ lens means that the diameter of the aperture is an eighth of the focal length of the lens. The amount of light which enters in a given time interval is proportional to the square of the diameter of the aperture; thus twice as much light will enter the camera in the same time interval with the aperture open to $f/4.5$, say, as compared to $f/6.3$, since the ratio of $(6.3)^2$ to $(4.5)^2$ is $2:1$; the time of exposure at $f/4.5$ will be just one half that at $f/6.3$, other conditions remaining unchanged. Two lenses of different focal lengths, set at the same f-number, will require the same times of exposure under identical conditions.

33-2 PROJECTION LANTERN

The projection lantern forms a real, inverted, and enlarged image on a screen at a great distance from the projection lens when the object is placed very close to the principal focus of the lens (see Figure 33–2). The most common use of a projection lantern is for the projection of lantern slides and films. The focusing is done by moving the lens with respect to the slide until a clear, sharp image is obtained. The slide must be properly illuminated so that its enlarged image will be uniformly bright over its whole area. This is accomplished by using a very intense source of light such as a carbon arc or a specially designed tungsten-filament lamp and directing the light by means of a condenser lens so that every point of the source sends light to each point of the object and toward the projection lens. In Figure 33–2, a small section AB of the object is shown illuminated by light from the two extreme points of the source. Rays of light from all intermediate points may be traced in a similar manner through the condensing lens system and through AB. These rays converge and form an image of the source of light at, or very close to, the projection lens. The latter should be large enough so that all of the light goes through it. The projection lens forms a real, inverted, and enlarged image $A'B'$ of the

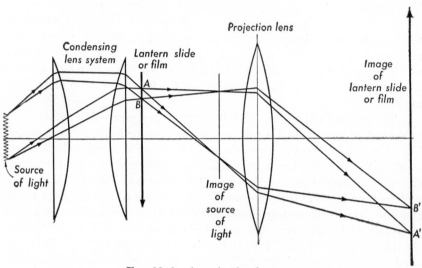

Fɪɢ. 33–2   A projection lantern.

section AB. The image of every other section of the object may be traced in a similar manner. Focusing of the image on the screen is usually accomplished by moving the projection lens, keeping the object in a fixed position relative to the source of light.

The projection lantern can also be used for opaque projection, that is, for projecting pictures on opaque backings, by interposing mirrors between the condenser and the projection lens so that light is reflected properly from the opaque object.

33-3   THE EYE

Many optical instruments are designed to be used in conjunction with the eye; it will therefore be worth while to discuss briefly some of the properties of the eye. Figure 33–3 shows the general structure of the eye. Light enters the eye through the *cornea C*, which is a transparent coating of refractive index 1.376. It then passes through a region A containing a salt solution known as the *aqueous humor* of refractive index 1.336. It then passes through the *pupil P*, which is the opening in the *iris* diaphragm I,

and through the *crystalline lens L.* This is a lens-shaped transparent organ
suspended in the eyeball by a ring of tissue attached to the walls. The
index of refraction of the lens varies from 1.388 for the outer layers to
1.411 for the inner layers. After passing through the lens, the light goes

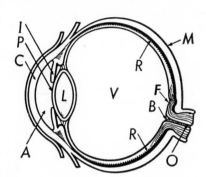

FIG. 33-3 Longitudinal section of a
human eye.

through a transparent jellylike substance called the *vitreous humor V* of
refractive index 1.336, until it strikes the *retina R*, which is the light-
sensitive part of the eye. The retina is composed mainly of nerve tissue,
which is connected with the brain by the optic nerve *O*. The image formed
on the retina is real, inverted, and smaller than the object. The *optic
axis* of the eye is a line passing through the vertex of the cornea and the
center of the pupil.

The retina is a transparent membrane situated between the outer
coating of the vitreous humor and the choroid membrane *M*. A section
of the human retina is shown in Figure 33-4. It consists of eight fairly
well defined layers; the outermost layer consists of rods and cones; the
innermost layer consists of nerve fibers which lead from the rods and cones
through the other layers to the optic nerve; the latter carries the impulses
to the visual center in the brain. The retina is not uniformly sensitive to
light throughout its area. At the place where the optic nerve enters the
eye is the blind spot *B*; there is no vision when light falls on this spot.
A short distance away there is a small indentation called the *fovea F*, which
is the most sensitive part of the retina. The fovea is approximately in the
center of the retina and is about 0.5 mm in diameter. The fovea contains
over 30,000 cones, each with a separate nerve; that part of the image on
the retina which falls on the fovea is seen most distinctly. Proceeding
out from the fovea, it is found that the retinal surface contains a mixture
of rods and cones, with the percentage of cones decreasing continuously
until, at the outer edges, only rods are present. The results of many
experiments show that the rods respond primarily to different intensities
of light without regard to its color, while the cones are color sensitive.

Objects at various distances from the eye must form images on the retina if they are to be seen clearly. Since the image distance from the cornea to the retina is fixed, the only way this can be done is through a change in the effective focal length of the eye. This is called the *accommodation* of the eye and is accomplished by changing the shape of the crystalline lens through a change in the tension of the circular ligament supporting it.

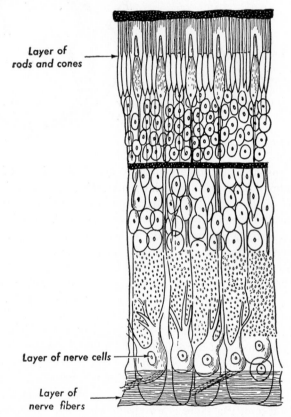

Layer of
rods and cones

Layer of nerve cells

Layer of
nerve fibers

Fɪɢ. 33–4   Diagrammatic section of the human retina.

In discussing the optics of the eye and the correction of certain defects with the use of lenses, it is common to talk about the *power* of the eye or the *power* of the lens instead of the focal length. *The power of a lens is expressed in* diopters *and is defined as the reciprocal of the focal length expressed in meters.* For example, if the focal length of a lens is 50 cm, that is, 0.5 m, its power is 2 diopters.

Each eye has a certain *range of accommodation*. This is the distance measured along the optic axis, between the *near point* and the *far point* of the eye. The *far point* is that point on the optic axis which is sharply

imaged on the retina when the eye is in its most relaxed state and when
the power of the eye is least.   The *near point* is that point on the optic axis
which is sharply imaged on the retina when the accommodation is most
strongly exerted or when the power of the eye is greatest.   Eyes are classified according to the positions of the far and near points and to the range
of accommodation.

The *emmetropic* eye or normal eye is one whose far point is at infinity,
and whose near point is close to the eye; this near point is generally taken
to be about 25 cm or 10 in.

The *myopic* or *nearsighted* eye has its far point at a finite distance
from the eye; its near point is usually about the same as in the normal

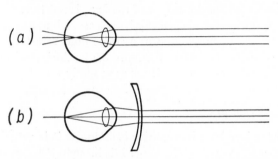

FIG. 33–5   (a) Myopia.   (b) Myopia corrected by a lens of negative power.

eye.   An eye is usually myopic because it is longer than an emmetropic
one.   Myopia is usually corrected by the use of spectacles of negative
power, that is, divergent lenses, as illustrated in Figure 33–5.

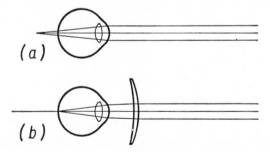

FIG. 33–6   (a) Hyperopia.   (b) Hyperopia corrected by a positive lens.

The *hyperopic* or *farsighted* eye has a far point which is virtual; that
is, its far point is situated behind the eye.   An eye is usually hyperopic
because it is too short.   Hyperopia is corrected by the use of spectacles of
positive power, as illustrated in Figure 33–6.

The *presbyopic* eye is one which has lost some of its power of accommodation because of the decrease in the elasticity of the lens tissue due to

age.   In particular, the near point has moved inconveniently far from
the eye.   The usual correction for presbyopia is a positive lens to be used
for reading or viewing objects close to the eye.

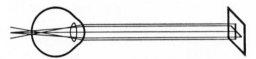

FIG. 33–7   Astigmatism of the eye.

A common defect of the eye, known as *astigmatism*, is due to the fact
that the curvature of the cornea, or of the lens, is not the same in all directions about the optic axis.   When this is the case, a bundle of rays refracted
by the surface cannot be focused in a single point; instead, the rays are
focused in two lines, as shown in Figure 33–7.   Astigmatism is corrected
by the use of cylindrical lenses with axes properly oriented.

33-4   THE MAGNIFYING GLASS

When an object is to be examined minutely, it is usually brought as
close as possible to the eye.   The closer it is brought, the larger is the *visual
angle a* which it subtends at the eye, and the larger is its image on the retina
(see Figure 33–8).   But, of course, it cannot be seen in sharp focus if it is

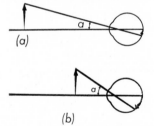

FIG. 33–8   The visual angle determines
the apparent size of the object.

brought closer than the near point; this fact imposes a limit on the size
of the retinal image and the smallness of the detail which can be seen.

The visual angle can be increased and a magnified retinal image
obtained with the aid of a converging lens used as a *magnifying glass*.   The
most common way of using a magnifying glass is to place the object at or
within the principal focus F of the lens so that parallel light enters the eye
from each point of the object, as shown in Figure 33–9; that is, the image
formed by this lens is at infinity.   Either a hyperopic or emmetropic eye
can use such an image.

The *angular magnification M* of a converging lens used in this manner is the ratio of the two visual angles a and A, or

$$M = \frac{A}{a} \cdot \quad\quad (1)$$

As to the emmetropic eye, to a close approximation,

$$a = \frac{S}{25 \text{ cm}}, \quad\quad (2)$$

where S is the size of the object in centimeters and the near point is expressed in centimeters, and

$$A = \frac{S}{f}, \quad\quad (3)$$

where f is the focal length of the magnifying lens.

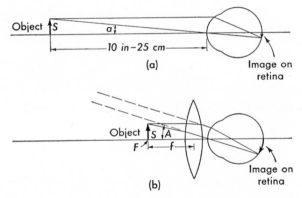

FIG. 33–9   Use of a converging lens as a simple magnifying glass.

Therefore

$$M = \frac{A}{a} = \frac{25 \text{ cm}}{f} \quad\quad (4)$$

if f is expressed in centimeters, or

$$M = \frac{10 \text{ in.}}{f} \quad\quad (4a)$$

if f is expressed in inches.

Another way of using a converging lens as a magnifier is to place the object between the principal focus and the lens, as shown in Figure 33–10.

In this case the image will be virtual and will be in focus when it is at the near point, that is, 25 cm from the eye. If S' is the size of the image, the visual angle it forms at the eye is $S'/25$ cm. If S is the size of the object,

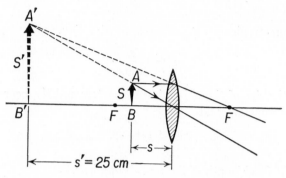

Fɪɢ. 33–10   Use of magnifying glass.

then, when it is viewed from the near point by the unaided eye, the visual angle formed by it is $S/25$ cm. The angular magnification M, which is the ratio of these two visual angles, is thus

$$M = \frac{S'}{S}.$$

Hence, in this particular case, the angular magnification is the same as the linear magnification m, so that we can write

$$M = -\frac{s'}{s}.$$

The value of s can be found from the lens equation, yielding

$$s = \frac{s'f}{s' - f}.$$

Hence

$$M = \frac{s' - f}{f} = \frac{-s'}{f} - 1.$$

Now

$$s' = -25 \text{ cm},$$

so that

$$M = \frac{25 \text{ cm}}{f} + 1 \qquad\qquad (5)$$

A simple converging lens used as a magnifier will produce a magnification of 25 cm/f when the object is placed at the principal focus and will produce a magnification of 25 cm/f + 1 when the object is placed inside the focus to produce an image at the near point. For intermediate cases, the magnification will lie between these two values. For example, if the focal length of a thin lens used as a magnifier is 5 cm, its magnification will be 5, or 6, or some intermediate value. For lenses of very short focal length and therefore of high power, there is very little difference between the two extreme values and may be taken as 25 cm/f.

A single lens is seldom used for magnifications greater than about 5 because of the amount of spherical and chromatic aberration produced. Two common types of eyepieces or *oculars* used in optical instruments, such as the telescope, microscope, and spectroscope, are the *Ramsden ocular* and the *Huygens ocular*. These are designed to reduce spherical and chromatic aberrations to a minimum while using lenses made of the same type of glass. The Ramsden ocular, shown in Figure 33–11, consists of

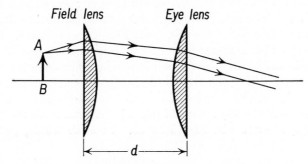

FIG. 33–11   Ramsden ocular consists of two plano-convex lenses of equal focal lengths separated a distance equal to about 2/3 the focal length of either one.

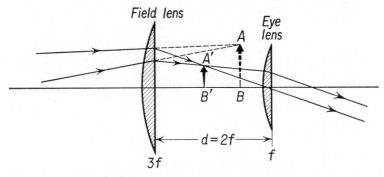

FIG. 33–12   Huygens ocular. Field lens has a focal length three times that of the eye lens. The distance between the lenses $d = 2f$, where f is the focal length of the eye lens.

two converging lenses of equal focal lengths separated by a distance equal to two thirds of the focal length of either. The lenses are plano-convex and mounted so that the curved surfaces face each other. If f is the focal length of either lens, the effective focal length of the eyepiece is $\frac{3}{4}f$.

The Huygens ocular, shown in Figure 33–12, consists of two plano-convex lenses, the focal length of one being three times that of the other.

The two lenses are mounted with their curved surfaces facing in the same direction; the distance between the lenses is half the sum of their focal lengths, the lens with the shorter focal length to be used nearer the eye. If f is the focal length of this *eye lens*, then the effective focal length of the combination is $3f/2$.

33-5   THE ASTRONOMICAL TELESCOPE

The astronomical telescope, used for viewing distant objects, consists of two converging lenses: an objective lens L_1, and an eye lens L_2.   Points from a distant object can be considered as sending sets of parallel rays to the objective.   If the rays from one point come in parallel to the principal axis, they are converged at the principal focus of the objective.   If the rays from some other point of the object come in inclined at some small angle to the principal axis, they are focused in a point which is in the *focal plane* of the objective.   When the eye lens L_2 is placed at a distance equal to its focal length f from the principal focus of the objective, rays which come from the image in the focal plane of the objective will leave the eye lens as parallel rays, as shown in Figure 33–13.   In other words, parallel rays

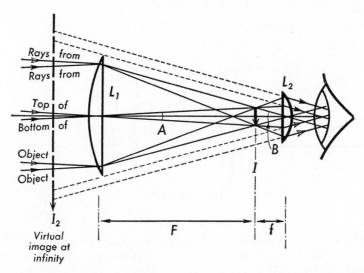

FIG. 33–13   Optical diagram of a simple astronomical telescope.

entering the objective lens leave the eye lens as parallel rays.   This is the normal adjustment of the telescope for distant objects.   The distance between the two lenses is, of course, $F + f$, where F is the focal length of the objective.

It will be observed that rays which come from object points above the axis of the telescope enter the eye as though they came from below the axis. This type of telescope therefore gives an inverted and reversed image. To see this image, the eye must be focused for infinity. If the distant object subtends a visual angle A as seen with the unaided eye, it will subtend a visual angle B when viewed with the aid of the telescope. The ratio of these angles determines the ratio of the retinal images and is therefore the *magnification* M produced by the telescope. Thus

$$M = \frac{B}{A} \cdot \qquad\qquad (6)$$

In Figure 33–13, the limiting rays from the object enter the center of the objective lens, making an angle A with each other; upon emerging from the objective lens, they still make an angle A with each other. These two rays go to the end points of the image I, a distance F from the objective. The rays from the end points of the image I make an angle B with each other at the center of the eye lens and when they enter the eye. This image is at a distance f from the eye lens. From Figure 33–13, it can be seen that

$$\boxed{M = \frac{B}{A} = \frac{F}{f} \; ;} \qquad\qquad (7)$$

that is, the magnification of a telescope is the ratio of the focal lengths of the objective lens and the eye lens. By using eyepieces of different focal lengths, different magnifications can be obtained with the same objective.

33-6 THE TERRESTRIAL TELESCOPE

Since the astronomical telescope produces inverted and reversed images, it is unsuitable for most terrestrial uses. The astronomical telescope can be modified to produce an erect image by inserting a converging lens between the focal plane of the objective and the eye lens (see Figure 33–14). If f_1 is the focal length of this converging lens, it should be placed at a distance of $2f_1$ from the focal plane of the objective to produce an erect image, without magnification, at a distance $4f_1$ from the focal plane. The eyepiece is then placed at a distance f from this image. The length of the terrestrial telescope formed this way has been increased by four times the focal length of the erecting lens. Usually, terrestrial telescopes use an erecting system consisting of two converging lenses with a diaphragm or stop between them to correct for spherical aberration.

A better way to make a terrestrial telescope is to use two 90° prisms, one for inverting the image and the other for reversing it, as shown in

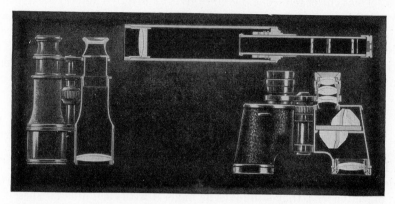

Fɪɢ. 33–14   Cutaway sections for comparison of the three types of terrestrial telescopes.   (Courtesy of Bausch & Lomb Optical Company.)

Figure 33–15.   This method is used for getting erect images in prism binoculars.   A pair of prism binoculars consists of two telescopes joined together.   Each telescope contains a pair of right-angled prisms arranged to invert and reverse the image formed by the telescope.

Fɪɢ. 33-15   Prism binoculars.   Two 90° prisms are used for reversing and inverting the image.   (Courtesy of Carl Zeiss, Inc.)

A third method for producing erect images is to make a Galilean type of telescope.   This uses a diverging lens for the eyepiece, as shown in Figure 33–16.   The distance between the objective and the eyepiece is $F - f$, where F is the focal length of the objective and f is the numerical value of the focal length of the eyepiece.   Parallel rays which enter the objective are converged toward its focal plane; however, the diverging lens intercepts them and deviates them so that they emerge as parallel rays.

From the figure, it will be noted that rays which come from object points above the axis appear to come from above the axis after passing through the telescope; the image as seen by the eye, therefore, is erect. Galilean telescopes are used extensively in opera glasses (see Figure 33–14).

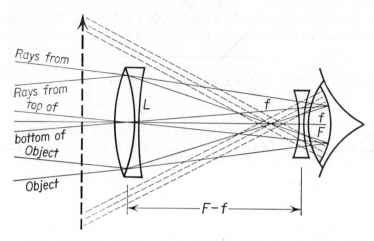

Rays from

Rays from
top of

bottom of
Object

Object

L

f

f
F

$F-f$

FIG. 33–16   Optical diagram of a Galilean telescope or opera glass.

33-7   THE COMPOUND MICROSCOPE

The compound microscope consists of two systems of converging lenses; in the diagram sketched in Figure 33–17, they are shown as single converging lenses. The objective lens L_1 has a very short focal length and the object is placed very close to, but just outside, the principal focus of this lens. A real, inverted image I_1 is formed at a distance s' from the objective lens. The eye lens L_2 is then used as a simple magnifying glass for viewing this image. If the eye is focused for parallel light, the eye lens L_2 is moved until the image I_1 is at its principal focus F_2, so that parallel rays enter the eye as though coming from a virtual image I_2 at infinity.

The magnification m_1 produced by the objective lens is

$$m_1 = \frac{s'}{s},\tag{8}$$

where s is the distance of the object from the lens. To a very close approximation, the object distance s can be taken as the focal length F of the object lens, so that

$$m_1 = \frac{s'}{F}.\tag{9}$$

The magnification m_2 produced by the eye lens is

$$m_2 = \frac{25 \text{ cm}}{f},$$ (4)

where f is the focal length of the eye lens, in centimeters. Hence the total magnification M of the compound microscope is

$$M = m_1 m_2 = \frac{s'}{F} \times \frac{25 \text{ cm}}{f}.$$ (10)

Magnifications of several hundred diameters are common with compound microscopes. Thus, if the magnification is 400 diameters, the area

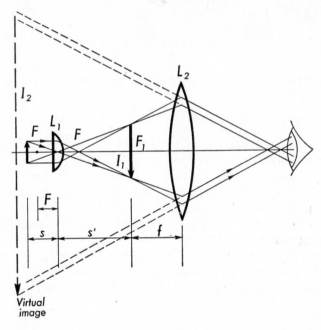

Fig. 33–17   Simplified optical diagram of a compound microscope.

of the object is magnified 160,000 times. The object must therefore be strongly illuminated to provide sufficient illumination so that the image can be seen. This is usually accomplished by focusing onto the object light from a source by means of a mirror and a condensing lens (see Figure 33–18).

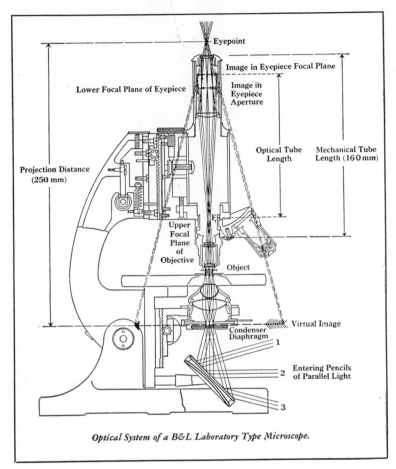

Eyepoint

Image in Eyepiece Focal Plane

Lower Focal Plane of Eyepiece

Image in
Eyepiece
Aperture

Optical Tube
Length

Mechanical Tube
Length (160 mm)

Projection Distance
(250 mm)

Upper
Focal
Plane
of
Objective

Object

Virtual Image

Condenser
Diaphragm

1

2 Entering Pencils
of Parallel Light

3

Optical System of a B&L Laboratory Type Microscope.

Fɪɢ. 33–18   Complete optical system of a compound microscope.   (Courtesy of
Bausch & Lomb Optical Company.)

33-8   THE PRISM SPECTROSCOPE

A prism spectroscope is used for determining the composition of the
light which comes to it from any source.   The light enters a narrow slit S
placed at the principal focus of a converging lens and emerges from the
lens as a parallel beam, as shown in Figure 33–19.   The light is said to be
collimated by this lens; the slit and lens are mounted at the ends of a light
tight tube called the *collimating tube*.   The collimated light enters a prism
made of some suitable transparent material, such as glass, rock salt, or
quartz, and is dispersed into its component wavelengths.   Rays of any one
wavelength are deviated through the same angle and hence emerge from

the prism as a parallel beam.   There is, therefore, a parallel beam emerging from the prism at a different angle for each wavelength present.   The telescope T can be rotated so that its axis is parallel to any one beam. The beam will be converged to the principal focus of the telescope objective, while other beams will be converged to foci in the focal plane of the

Table 33-1   Wavelengths of Some Spectral Lines

Element in Gaseous State	Color of Line	Wavelength in Angstrom Units
Hydrogen	Red	6,562.8
	Blue	4,861.3
	Violet	4,340.5
	Violet	4,101.7
Helium	Red	7,281.3
	Red	7,065.2
	Red	6,678.5
	Yellow	5,875.6
	Green	5,015.7
	Blue	4,921.9
	Blue	4,471.5
	Violet	4,143.8
	Violet	4,120.8
Sodium	Yellow	5,895.9
	Yellow	5,890.0
Mercury	Yellow	5,790.7
	Yellow	5,769.6
	Green	5,460.7
	Blue	4,916.0
	Violet	4,358.3
	Violet	4,077.8
	Violet	4,046.6

objective.   Each converged beam is an image of the slit formed by monochromatic light.   These images are then viewed with the eyepiece of the telescope. A scale in a side tube is sometimes brought into the field of view by reflecting it from one face of the prism.   This scale can be calibrated in terms of known wavelengths.   The spectroscope can then be used for determining the wavelengths of light emitted by other sources.

Known wavelengths for the calibration of prism spectroscope scales can be obtained by using the light emitted by elements in the vapor state. These elements emit light consisting of a series of definite wavelengths whose values are known and listed in tables. The lights emitted by sodium vapor, by hydrogen, by mercury vapor, and by helium are commonly used for calibration purposes (see Table 33–1). Unless calibrated, a prism

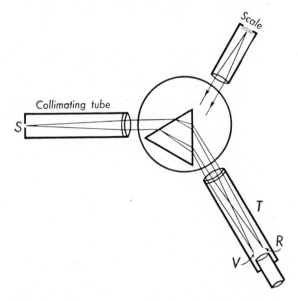

Fɪɢ. 33–19   A prism spectroscope.

spectroscope cannot be used for determining wavelengths. Wavelengths can be measured by instruments making use of the phenomena of interference and diffraction. These will be discussed in the next chapter.

QUESTIONS

1. Compare the indices of refraction of the various parts of the eye with the index of refraction of water.

2. A camera lens is rated at $f/1.9$. Discuss the meaning of this term.

3. The diameter of the pupil of the eye depends upon the intensity of the light entering the eye. Look at the pupil of your eye in a mirror in a dimly lighted room. Now turn on some bright lights and observe the diameter of the pupil. Make an estimate of the diameters of the pupil under these two conditions.

4. Mention some of the advantages of using a lens of large diameter for the objective of a telescope.

5. Very large astronomical telescopes use mirrors for their objectives rather than lenses. Can you suggest some of the advantages of a mirror over those of a lens as a telescope objective?

6. What is the nature of the final image formed by (a) an astronomical telescope and (b) a terrestrial telescope?

7. What is the nature of the final image formed by a compound microscope?

8. What would be the effect of putting a thin parallel plate of glass between the lens of a camera and the film?

PROBLEMS

1. A lantern slide 3 in. wide is to be projected on a screen 6 ft wide at a distance of 25 ft from the projection lens. The picture should fill the whole screen. What should be the focal length of the projection lens?

2. An object and a screen are 20 ft apart. A lens is to be used to project an image on the screen 50 times as large as the object. A lens of what focal length should be used?

3. A lantern slide is to be projected on a screen situated 24 ft from the projection lens. If the width of the image is to be 5 ft while the width of the slide is 2 in., what must be the focal length of the projection lens?

4. Determine the magnification produced by a converging lens used as a magnifier if its focal length is 4 in.

5. Determine the magnification produced by a converging lens used as a magnifier if its focal length is 5 cm.

6. A camera lens has a focal length of 12 cm. What is the diameter of its aperture when it is set at (a) $f/3.5$ and (b) $f/4.5$? (c) What are the relative areas of these two apertures?

7. What is the focal length of a spectacle lens of -1.5 diopters?

8. What is the focal length of a spectacle lens of $+2.25$ diopters?

9. A small laboratory telescope has an objective whose focal length is 18 cm and an eye lens whose focal length is 3 cm. (a) What is the magnification of this telescope? (b) How far apart are the lenses?

10. An astronomical telescope has an objective lens whose focal length is 8 ft, and is used with an eye lens whose focal length is 0.5 in. Determine its magnification.

11. A compound microscope has an objective of 4 mm focal length which forms an image 15 cm from it. The eye lens has a focal length of 2.5 cm. Determine its magnification when it is adjusted so that parallel light enters the eye.

12. A high-power compound microscope has an objective whose focal length is 2 mm which forms an image 15 cm from it. It is used with an eye lens of 2.5 cm focal length. Determine its magnification when it is adjusted so that parallel light enters the eye.

13. The distance between the objective lens and the eye lens of an astronomical telescope when adjusted for parallel light is 80 cm. The measured value of the magnification is 12. Determine the focal lengths of the lenses.

14. A box camera of the so-called "fixed focus" type has a lens whose focal length is 4 in. Determine the positions of the images formed when the objects are (a) 6 ft, (b) 15 ft, and (c) 25 ft from the lens.

15. A camera lens whose focal length is 3 in. has its position relative to the film adjustable for object distances from 3.5 ft to infinity. Determine the maximum displacement of the lens for these extreme positions.

16. The field lens of a Huygens ocular has a focal length of 9 cm, and the eye lens has a focal length of 3 cm; they are spaced 6 cm apart. Determine the effective focal length of this ocular. Trace two parallel rays through this ocular assuming (a) that they enter through the field lens, and (b) that they enter through the eye lens. Determine the focal point in each case.

17. The lenses of a Ramsden ocular have focal lengths of 9 cm each and are placed 6 cm apart. Determine the effective focal length of this ocular. Trace two parallel rays through this ocular and determine the position of the focal point.

34

Light as a
Wave Motion

34-1 INTERFERENCE OF LIGHT FROM TWO SOURCES

We showed, in our study of sound, that interference phenomena can be produced by waves. If light is propagated as a wave, then it should be possible to produce interference effects with light. For example, suppose we could arrange two monochromatic sources of light S_1 and S_2 of the same wavelength, as shown in Figure 34–1, suppose that they start sending out

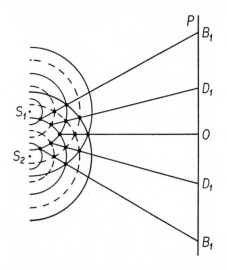

FIG. 34–1 Interference of light from two sources.

waves simultaneously, and then suppose that we examine the effect that is produced by these waves on a distant screen P; we should find a series of bright and dark regions. Viewed in one plane, the light spreads out in the form of circles; the distance between two successive full circular arcs is drawn equal to a wavelength of the monochromatic light; so is the distance between two successive dotted circular arcs. We may think of the full circular arcs as the crests of the waves and the dotted ones as the troughs of the waves. The distance between a dotted and the neighboring full circular arc is half a wavelength.   Wherever two crests meet or wherever two troughs meet, the waves from the two sources are *in phase;* they reinforce each other at these points, producing relatively great intensity of illumination.   Wherever a trough meets a crest, the waves from the two sources are out of phase by 180°, and these points are always dark or of zero intensity of illumination.   Therefore on the screen *P* there will be bright spots where waves from the two sources meet *in phase,* and dark spots where waves from the two sources meet out of phase by 180°.   It is easy to see that, wherever there is a bright spot, the difference in path of the two rays of light is a whole number of whole wavelengths or zero;   also, wherever there is a dark spot, the difference in path of the two rays of light is either half a wavelength or an odd number of half wavelengths.   At other points the intensity of illumination lies between zero and the maximum value. The total energy reaching the screen from these two sources is the sum of the energies reaching the screen from each source.   The distribution of this energy is nonuniform.

   To produce this interference effect with light, it is not possible to use two separate, independent sources of light, because we have no way of controlling the phase relationships of these two sources.   The atoms and molecules of each light source emit light at random with arbitrary phase relationships.   However, it is possible to produce interference by taking

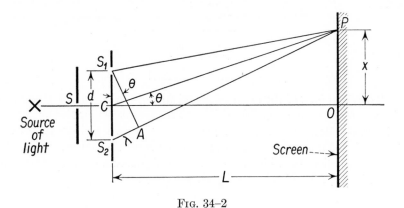

Fig. 34–2

light from a single source *S* and dividing it into two narrow beams by sending it through two narrow slits S_1 and S_2 in an opaque board, as shown in Figure 34–2.   According to Huygens' principle, these two slits S_1 and S_2 then act as new sources which emit light simultaneously and in phase.

   The positions of the light and dark regions on the screen can be determined with the aid of Huygens' principle.   Figure 34–2 shows light from a source *S* going through two narrow slits S_1 and S_2 toward a screen a distance L from them. Let us assume that the light is monochromatic with a wavelength λ. For a point P on the screen to be bright, light reaching it from the two slits must be in phase; that is, the light path from S_2 to P must exceed that from S_1 to P by an integral number of wavelengths, or

$$S_2P - S_1P = S_2A = n\lambda,$$

where n is an integer ($n = 0, 1, 2, 3 \ldots$) and S_2A is the path difference.

The angle at A can be considered to be a right angle when the distance to the screen is very large. For this case,

$$S_2A = d \sin \theta,$$

where d is the distance between the slits and θ is the angle between S_1S_2 and S_1A. From the figure, it can be seen that the angle PCO is equal to θ; hence

$$\tan \theta = \frac{OP}{CP} = \frac{x}{L},$$

where x is the distance from the central image to P and, for the small angles involved, $CP = L$. For such small angles, $\tan \theta = \sin \theta$ to a very good approximation;

hence

$$\frac{x}{L} = \frac{n\lambda}{d}$$

or

$$\boxed{x = n\frac{\lambda L}{d}.} \tag{1}$$

To get an idea of the order of magnitude of the quantities involved in this type of experiment, suppose that the source is a sodium lamp emitting an intense yellow line of wavelength 5,893 A, that the distance between the slits is 0.5 mm or 0.05 cm, and that the screen is 200 cm away. The first bright region, for which $n = 1$, will be displaced a distance x from the central image, for which $n = 0$ by an amount

$$x = \frac{5,893 \times 10^{-8} \times 200}{0.05} \text{ cm,}$$

or

$$x = 0.24 \text{ cm} = 2.4 \text{ mm.}$$

This will also be the spacing between successive bright spots.

If white light is used instead of sodium light, each color will produce its own set of interference bands, and these will overlap. The central image at O will be very bright, and there will be a series of colored bands on either side of O. These interference bands can be viewed very easily by the reader if he looks at the light from the bulb of an automobile lamp through two pinholes punched close together in a piece of cardboard.

Figure 34–3 is a reproduction of an interference pattern produced by two narrow slits. The source of light S of Figure 34–3 was a slit which was illuminated by light from an intense mercury arc.

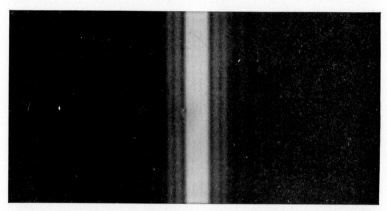

FIG. 34–3   Photograph of the interference pattern produced by the passage of light from a high-pressure mercury arc through two slits which are close together. No lens was used; the light was allowed to fall directly on a photographic plate. (Courtesy of Central Scientific Company.)

34-2 INTERFERENCE FROM THIN FILMS

Interference phenomena are very common; for example, the colors that are observed on soap bubbles are due to interference of light reflected from the two film surfaces. The colors observed on wet pavements are due to the interference effects produced by thin films of oil which reflect light from their two surfaces.

FIG. 34–4   Interference from thin films.

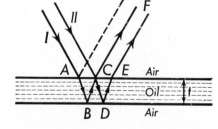

Consider monochromatic light incident on a thin film of oil at almost normal incidence, as shown in Figure 34–4. Ray I strikes the first surface at A; it is partly reflected into the air and partly refracted into the oil toward B, at which point part of the light is again reflected to C and some of it is refracted out into the air. Ray II, which strikes point C of the top surface, undergoes similar reflections and refractions. Now at C two rays meet and travel on into the air along CF: part of ray II which is reflected at C, and part of ray I which traveled through the oil and was reflected at B. The difference in path between these two rays is $AB + BC$, or approximately twice the thickness t of the oil film. If these two waves meet in phase at C, it will be a bright spot; if they meet out of phase by 180°, C will be a dark spot.

If the thickness of the film varies from point to point, there will be some points in which the two waves will reinforce each other, producing bright spots, and other points in which the waves meet out of phase and produce dark spots. If yellow sodium light is the source of illumination, the film will show yellow regions separated by dark spaces. If white light is used, each component wavelength will produce its own interference pattern. For example, where the thickness of the film is just right to produce a dark spot for yellow light, the other wavelengths will be present because the thickness of the film is not sufficient to cause the two reflected portions to be completely out of phase. What is observed at this point is a mixture of all the colors in varying intensities except yellow. This spot may appear blue. At a different point in which interference completely removes the red light, a composite of all the other colors will be seen; this may appear green. In this manner a thin film of oil on the pavement, when reflecting white light from the sky, shows a variety of colors.

Newton observed and studied the interference effects produced by the thin film of air between the convex surface of a lens and the flat surface of a plane piece of glass. Figure 34–5 shows the experimental arrangement.

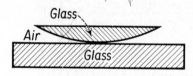

Fig. 34–5   Formation   of   Newton's rings.

The two pieces of glass make contact only at the center so that the thin film of air has a wedge-shaped cross section. Suppose that monochromatic light is incident on the convex surface of the lens; part of it is reflected and part refracted into the air and reflected from the flat glass plate. Wherever the two waves meet in phase, they will reinforce each other, and those points will be bright spots; wherever the two waves meet out of phase by half a wavelength, they will annul each other, and those points will be dark spots. Because of the circular symmetry of the arrangement, a series of dark and bright rings will be seen; these are called *Newton's rings*. If a source of white light is used, the rings will appear colored.

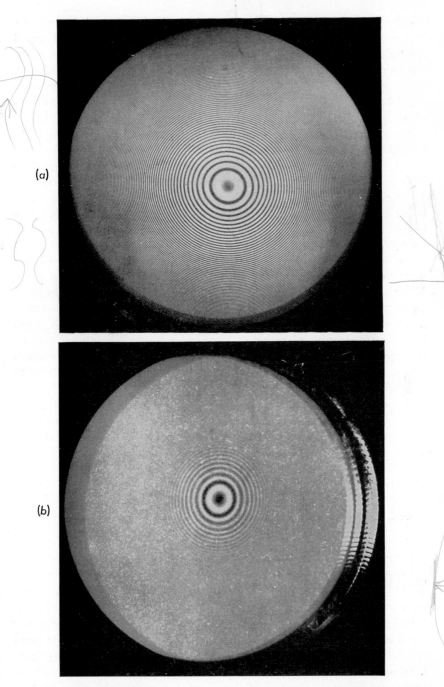

(a)

(b)

Fig. 34–6   (a) Photograph of Newton's rings made with sodium light.   (Courtesy of Bausch & Lomb Optical Company.)   (b) Photograph of Newton's rings made with white light.   (Courtesy of Bausch & Lomb Optical Company.)

If we try to determine the positions of the bright regions from the difference in path of two waves, we find the surprising result that, where the thickness of the film is such that two waves meeting at a point would be expected to produce a bright spot, this point is found to be a dark spot. Conversely, where the thickness of the film is such that two waves meeting would be expected to produce a dark spot, that point is found to be a bright spot. The reason for this interchange of the expected positions of the dark and bright rings is due to the difference in the reflections of the two waves. One wave is reflected from a glass-air surface, while the other wave is reflected from an air-glass surface. This difference in reflections introduces a change of phase of half a wavelength. The waves reflected at the glass-air surface suffer no change in phase, while those reflected at the air-glass surface suffer a change in phase of half a wavelength. This conclusion receives further verification by noting that the central spot in Newton's rings is black. In this region the thickness of the air film is negligible; hence the only change in phase is that produced on reflection from the second surface. Thus a dark spot will be observed in the center no matter what the wavelength of the light is. This can be seen clearly in Figure 34–6(a) and 34–6(b). Figure 34–6(a) is a photograph of Newton's rings made with sodium light, and Figure 34–6(b) is a photograph of Newton's rings made with white light.

Thomas Young, the first one to give the above explanation of Newton's rings on the wave theory of light, proceeded to show the correctness of the interpretation of the central black spot. He reproduced the Newton ring experiment by using an oil film between a crown-glass lens and a flint-glass plate. The oil had an index of refraction intermediate between that of crown glass and that of flint glass; hence the light underwent the same change of phase at each surface, and these phase changes thus canceled each other. In this case, the center spot was white, and the other bright and dark regions were shifted in a corresponding manner.

Interference bands can be easily produced by making a wedge-shaped air film between two plane pieces of glass, as shown in Figure 34–7. If

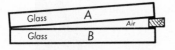

Fig. 34–7   A wedge-shaped air film.

monochromatic light is used, a series of parallel bright and dark lines will be observed if the two glass surfaces *A* and *B* are perfectly plane. If these surfaces are not perfectly plane, the shape of these bands will vary from place to place. If one surface is known to be perfectly plane from previous tests, it can be used to test the flatness of other surfaces by observing the interference pattern produced either when a wedge-shaped film of air is set up between them or when they are placed in contact.

A beautiful demonstration of interference produced by thin films, suitable for viewing by a large audience, is one, originally suggested by Pohl, in which light from a small, intense mercury arc is allowed to fall on a thin sheet of mica placed about 5 cm away. Light reflected from these two surfaces is then allowed to fall on a large screen a few feet away. A circular interference pattern, such as that shown in Figure 34–8, will be

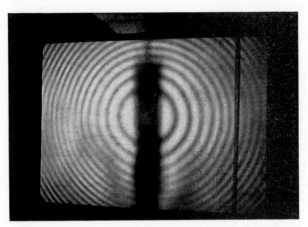

FIG. 34–8   Interference rings produced by mercury light reflected from a thin sheet of mica. Meter stick on right side of screen for comparison. Center shadow is that of the mercury arc. Light photographed through green filter. Thickness of mica is 0.05 mm. (Photographed by M. W. Zemansky, H. Semat, and I. Antman.)

clearly visible. In this experiment the sheet of mica had a thickness of about 0.05 mm. The size of the pattern can be judged from the meter stick placed near the right edge of the screen.

The interference produced by thin films has been used to reduce the loss of light which takes place at the glass surfaces of lenses used in optical instruments. Under the best conditions, about 5 per cent of the incident light is reflected at each surface, so that, if there are six such surfaces, only about 75 per cent of the light is transmitted through the instrument. By coating each surface with a thin film of a suitable material, this reflection loss can be diminished considerably. The film must satisfy two conditions for best results: (a) its thickness must be a quarter of a wavelength of light in the film, and (b) its index of refraction should be equal to the square root of the index of refraction of the glass to which it is applied.

Since the index of refraction varies with the wavelength, and white light contains many different wavelengths, it is not possible to reduce the reflection completely to zero, but good results can nevertheless be obtained. For example, the index of refraction of one common type of flint glass is 1.66. The square root of this is 1.29. It is difficult to find a substance of such low index of refraction. Lithium fluoride has an index of refraction of 1.39, and calcium fluoride has an index of 1.43. If the thickness of the film is made one quarter the wavelength of sodium light, the reflection will be reduced to about 1 per cent. One method of putting the thin film on the glass is to heat the calcium fluoride in a good vacuum and allow the calcium fluoride to vaporize and deposit on the glass in the vacuum. This or a similar process is used to produce the so-called "coated" lenses of modern cameras and other optical instruments.

34-3 DIFFRACTION OF LIGHT

We have already noted that in the case of sound, the waves bend around corners and also spread out in going through a narrow aperture; that is, sound waves are *diffracted*. Since the interference experiments show definitely that light is propagated as a wave motion, it should be possible to show diffraction phenomena with light. One very interesting diffraction effect, originally suggested by Fresnel, is outlined in Figure 34–9. *S* is a

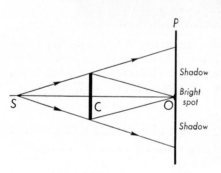

FIG. 34–9   Diffraction produced by the passage of light past a spherical obstacle.

point source of light, and *C* is the circular cross section of an obstacle such as a sphere. If it were not for diffraction effects, there would be simply a sharp circular shadow, the so-called *geometrical shadow* cast on the screen *P*. But, due to the fact that light is propagated as a wave motion, the light will bend around the rim of the sphere; according to Huygens' principle, each point on the rim can be considered as sending waves of light into the region of shadow. Now point *O* in the center of the shadow is equally distant from each point on the rim of the sphere; therefore the waves reaching point *O* will all be in the same phase, and *O* will be a bright spot. This spot can be seen in a photograph of the shadow, or it may be located with the aid of a magnifying glass or a small telescope (see Figure 34–10).

Another diffraction effect can be observed when light from a point source passes through a narrow aperture, such as a pinhole in a card. If the light strikes a screen several feet from the pinhole, the pattern on the

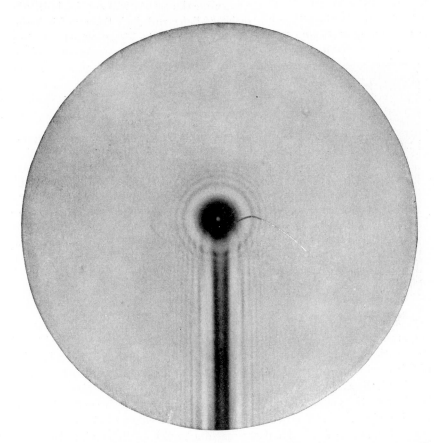

FIG. 34–10   Photograph of the shadow of a ball bearing supported on a rod. Note the diffraction pattern around the rod and ball bearing and the bright spot in the center of the shadow of the ball bearing. (Reproduced by permission from *College Physics*, 2nd ed., by Sears and Zemansky, 1952; Addison-Wesley, Cambridge, Mass.)

screen will consist not of a single spot of light but of a series of dark and bright rings surrounding the central bright spot. The light spreads out into the region of the geometrical shadow, thus producing this circular diffraction pattern. This diffraction pattern may be observed readily by looking through a single pinhole at a small source of light such as the bright filament of an automobile lamp bulb placed 10 or 15 ft from the observer.

34-4   DIFFRACTION THROUGH A NARROW SLIT

When a beam of light passes through a narrow slit and falls on a screen at some distance from it, the pattern on the screen will consist both of a bright image of the slit and a series of light and dark lines or fringes on either side of the central bright spot, as shown in Figure 34–11. Only a

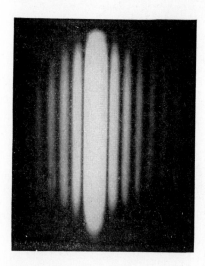

Fig. 34–11   Photograph of a diffraction pattern produced by the passage of light through a narrow slit. (Reproduced by permission from *College Physics*, 2nd ed., by Sears and Zemansky, 1952; Addison-Wesley, Cambridge, Mass.)

very small portion of the incident wave front passes through the narrow slit to produce this diffraction pattern. The appearance of the bright and dark regions on the screen can be explained by assuming that each point of this section of the wave front acts as a source of light sending out wavelets in all directions. The effect produced at any point on the screen depends upon the phase relationships of those wavelets which reach this point.

Imagine AB of Figure 34–12(a) to be the edges of the slit, greatly magnified, and the wave front approaching it to be a plane monochromatic wave; every point in this wave front sends out waves in the same phase. Point C is in the center of the slit, and CO is a perpendicular line from the slit to the screen. For every point in the wave front in AC which sends light to O, there is a symmetrically placed point in CB which sends light to O in the same phase; hence O will be a bright spot.

Let us now consider a point D on the screen above O such that the distance BD exceeds the distance AD by one wavelength λ. To a very good approximation, CD exceeds AD by $\lambda/2$; similarly BD exceeds CD by $\lambda/2$. Now consider a typical point e at a distance x below A sending waves to D; there is a corresponding point f an equal distance below C sending waves to D; the waves from these two points will be out of phase by $\lambda/2$ on reaching D. Similarly, for every point between A and C sending waves to

D, there is a corresponding point between *C* and *B* sending waves to *D,* such that the waves from these two points reach *D* out of phase by $\lambda/2$; hence *D* will be a dark region. There will be a symmetrical point *D'* below *O* which will also be dark.

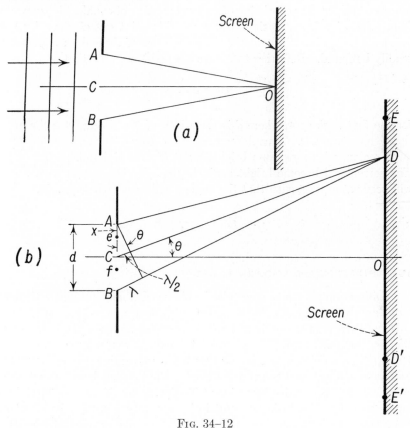

Fɪɢ. 34–12

As we proceed along the screen away from *D,* the above conditions will no longer hold, so that these points will increase in brightness until a point *E* is reached, such that the distance *BE* exceeds *AE* by $3\lambda/2$. If we divide the aperture *AB* into three equal parts, then, using the same type of argument as above, we find that waves from corresponding points in two adjacent sections will be out of phase by $\lambda/2$ upon reaching *E,* thus contributing nothing to the light at *E.* Only those points in the third remaining section will be sending waves to *E* which will not be out of phase by $\lambda/2$, even though not entirely in phase; hence point *E* will be bright, but not as bright as the central region. There will be a symmetrical point *E'* below *D'* which will be as bright as *E* and for the same reason.

The above type of argument can be used to explain the appearance of other bright and dark regions in the diffraction pattern. Wherever the distances from the edges of the slit to a point on the screen differ by a whole number of wavelengths, that point will be dark. In such cases the slit may be considered as consisting of an even number of equal regions; waves from pairs of adjacent regions will reach this point out of phase by $\lambda/2$, and thus this point will be dark. The positions of these dark regions can readily be found. Referring to Figure 34–12(b), we note that

$$\sin \theta = \frac{\lambda}{d} \qquad (2)$$

for the first dark spot, where d is the width of the slit and θ is the angle between CO and CD. Thus the central image extends over a comparatively large region, with maximum brightness at O and minimum at D and D'. The screen will become bright again beyond D; the second dark region will occur at a point such that the angle θ will satisfy the equation

$$\sin \theta = \frac{2\lambda}{d} \qquad (3)$$

34-5 DIFFRACTION AND RESOLVING POWER

Diffraction phenomena can also be observed when light passes through large apertures such as the lenses of telescopes and microscopes. The effect of such phenomena is to *limit the resolving power* of the instrument, that is, the ability of the instrument to show increasingly greater detail. If light from a point source is sent through a converging lens, for example, its image will not be a sharp point even if the lens has been corrected for spherical and chromatic aberrations. To determine the exact shape of the image and the distribution of light in it, one must consider the contributions made to it by the wavelets coming from every point of the wave front which comes through the lens. The detailed analysis of this problem is beyond the scope of this book; but, using arguments similar to those of the preceding section, it can be shown that the image will consist of a central bright spot surrounded by dark and bright rings, as shown in Figure 34–13.

The size of the central disk of the diffraction pattern can be shown to depend upon three factors: (a) the focal length of the lens, (b) the wavelength of the light used, and (c) inversely as the diameter of the lens.

If we consider two points sending light through an optical system, the image of each point will be a diffraction pattern. If the points are close together, these patterns may overlap, so that it will not be possible to distinguish them as two separate points. Two images are said to be resolved if the dark ring of one pattern passes through the center of the disk of the other pattern or if the two central disks are separated a distance equal to the radius of one of them. If two points cannot be resolved by an instrument, merely increasing its magnification without increasing the resolving power serves no useful purpose.

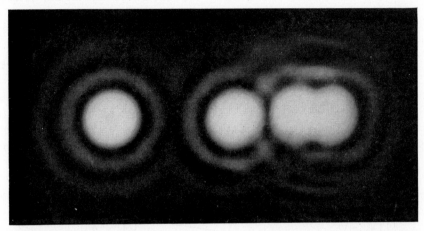

Fig. 34-13 Photograph of the diffraction patterns of light produced by a lens. Four point sources of light were used. The two patterns on the right can just be resolved as due to two sources. (Reproduced by permission from *College Physics*, 2nd ed., Sears and Zemansky, 1952; Addison-Wesley, Cambridge, Mass.)

In the case of a telescope, one method of getting higher resolving power is to increase the diameter of the objective. If the optical instrument is used for visual work, the resolution is limited by the wavelength of light. If a photographic plate is used to record the image, then light of shorter wavelength—ultraviolet light—may be used to increase the resolution. Microscopes have been built with quartz lenses so that ultraviolet light can be used for increasing their resolving power.

34-6 THE DIFFRACTION GRATING

The *diffraction grating* is widely used for the measurement of the wavelength of light and for spectrum analysis. Diffraction gratings are used in one of two ways, either as *reflection* gratings or as *transmission* gratings. A reflection grating consists of a series of parallel rulings or scratches made on a polished reflecting surface. The number of rulings varies from about 400 per centimeter in some gratings to about 6,000 per centimeter in other gratings. A transmission grating has a series of parallel rulings made on a flat glass surface. The light is transmitted through the spacings between the scratches. Good diffraction gratings are difficult to make. For many ordinary purposes, replicas are used. These replicas can be made by pouring a solution of collodion in ether over a ruled grating. After the ether has evaporated, the thin collodion layer is stripped off and placed between two flat glass plates. The collodion retains the impression and acts as a fairly good diffraction grating.

To understand the action of a grating, let us consider a set of plane parallel waves incident on a transmission grating, as shown in Figure 34–14. The spaces between rulings can be considered a series of equally spaced

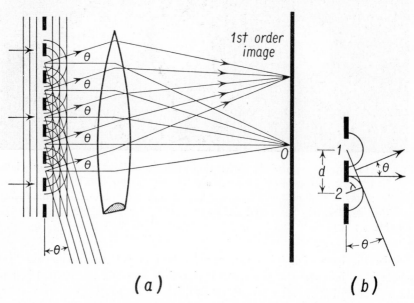

FIG. 34–14   (a) Action of a diffraction grating on a parallel beam of mono-chromatic light. The relative dimensions of the grating and the lens are drawn out of correct proportion in order to illustrate the effect of the lens on the diffracted beam. (b) The relationship between the grating space d, the wavelength λ, and the angle of diffraction θ.

narrow slits, a few of which are shown in the figure. The light which passes through the grating can be considered as coming from these slits, and, according to Huygens' principle, the slits can be considered sources of waves. These waves will be circular in a plane perpendicular to the rulings. For the sake of simplicity, let us assume that the incident light is mono-chromatic and of wavelength λ. Since the incident wave front is plane and parallel to the plane of the grating, the light emerging from each of the slits at any one time is all in the same phase and spreads out in con-centric circles from each slit as a center. The circular wave fronts from a few of these slits are shown in the figure; the distance between successive wave fronts is λ, the wavelength of the incident light. The resultant wave front produced by these individual waves from all the slits can be found by drawing a line tangent to the circles. All points on this line will be in the same phase; therefore this line is a wave front. Several such resultant wave fronts are shown in the figure. One set of wave fronts is parallel to the incident wave fronts and proceeds in the same direction. These parallel wave fronts can be brought to a point focus by a converging lens and will produce what is known as the *central image* at O.

Another set of wave fronts is shown traveling at an angle θ to the original direction of the beam. It will be observed that each such wave front is tangent to circular wave fronts from adjacent slits which differ in phase by *one whole period*. These parallel wave fronts can also be brought to a point focus by a converging lens. This point is called the *first-order image*. Let us consider waves emitted from adjacent slits 1 and 2 which differ in phase by one whole period and whose path difference is one wavelength λ. From Figure 34–14(b), it can be seen that the resultant wave front makes an angle θ with the plane of the grating such that

$$\sin \theta = \frac{\lambda}{d}, \tag{4}$$

where d is the distance between two slits,

from which $\qquad\qquad \lambda = d \sin \theta. \tag{5}$

The longer the wavelength, the greater is the angle θ. Thus, if violet light is used, its first-order image will be deviated through a smaller angle than that for the first-order image of red light. Equations (4) and (5) are valid only for light all of which is incident normally on the surface of the grating.

If a plane is drawn tangent to circles from adjacent slits such that these circles differ in path by two whole wavelengths, then, when focused at a point, these wave fronts will produce a *second-order image* for the particular wavelength used. The angle θ_2 that such a wave front makes with the plane of the grating will be given by

$$\sin \theta_2 = \frac{2\lambda}{d}. \tag{6}$$

In general, wave fronts formed by waves which differ in path by n whole wavelengths, when emitted by adjacent slits, will be inclined at an angle θ_n, given by

$$\sin \theta_n = \frac{n\lambda}{d}$$

or $\qquad\qquad\boxed{n\lambda = d \sin \theta_n.} \tag{7}$

There will be first-order, second-order, and so on, images on the other side of the central image. If white light is incident on the diffraction grating, a series of spectra will be obtained on each side of the central image. The central image itself will be white; θ is zero for the central image and so is n; that is, the waves of all wavelengths are in the same phase. For $n = 1$, we get the first-order spectrum with violet light deviated least— that is, closest to the central image—and red light deviated by the greatest amount. Then farther on there will be a second-order spectrum, again extending from violet to red, but fainter than the first-order spectrum. The highest order $n_{\max}$ in which a given wavelength can appear may be determined by setting $\sin \theta_n = 1$, its maximum value; Equation (7) then yields

$$n_{\max} = d/\lambda.$$

34-7   THE DIFFRACTION GRATING SPECTROMETER

A spectrometer, with a diffraction grating mounted on its table, forms one of the most convenient instruments for measuring the wavelength of light. Light from some source illuminates the slit S of the collimator C, as shown in Figure 34–15. The parallel light coming out of the collimator

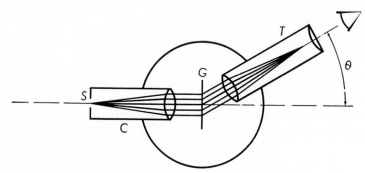

Fɪɢ. 34–15   The diffraction grating spectrometer.

goes through the grating G, which sends out waves in various directions; images of the slit will be formed in directions making angles θ_n with the direct beam, when the wavelengths satisfy the grating equation

$$n\lambda = d \sin \theta_n.$$

When the telescope T is in line with the collimator, θ is zero and the central image is observed in its field of view. As the telescope is rotated about the spectrometer axis, the shortest wavelength is observed in the first order, when the angle θ_1 is reached such that

$$\lambda = d \sin \theta_1.$$

If the source sends out white light, the shortest wavelength is in the violet region. The other wavelengths then appear at larger angles up to the longest visible wavelength, which appears red. It will be noted that the order in which the colors appear in the grating spectrum is the reverse of that in the spectrum produced by a prism; in the spectrum formed by a diffraction grating, the violet is deviated least, while in the prism spectrum, the red is deviated least.

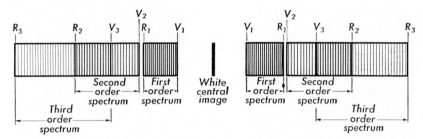

Fig. 34-16   Relative positions of the first three orders of spectra produced by a diffraction grating on either side of the central white image. Notice that the second and third orders overlap considerably.

There is a break after the red in the first-order spectrum, and then the violet appears once more (see Figure 34-16). This is the beginning of the second-order spectrum, and the angle of the telescope θ_2 satisfies the condition

$$2\lambda = d \sin \theta_2.$$

The third-order spectrum, however, overlaps the second-order spectrum. This can be seen from the values of $\sin \theta$ for violet light in the third order, which is approximately

$$d \sin \theta_3 = 3 \times 3{,}800 \text{ A} = 11{,}400 \text{ A},$$

and its value for red light in the second order, which is approximately

$$d \sin \theta_2 = 2 \times 7{,}500 \text{ A} = 15{,}000 \text{ A}.$$

Thus, irrespective of the number of lines per centimeter in the grating, the third order will always overlap the second order. This is illustrated in Figure 34-16.

The prism spectroscope has one advantage over the diffraction grating spectroscope in that all of the energy which goes through the prism is concentrated in a single spectrum. In a diffraction grating spectroscope, the energy from the source of light is spread over several orders, and a large fraction of this energy is concentrated in the zero order or central image.

On the other hand, the dispersion produced by a diffraction grating is given by the simple Equation (7), whereas the dispersion produced by a prism does not follow a simple law. For most optical glass, the dispersion is much greater in the violet region than in the red region. Diffraction gratings are used where great accuracy in wavelength measurements is desired.

A circular scale is provided with the spectrometer so that the angle θ can be measured for each position of the telescope; if d is known, the wavelength of light is then easily measured. The grating space d is usually supplied by the manufacturer of the diffraction grating. If it is desired to check this value, monochromatic light of known wavelength is sent through the collimator and the positions of the first- and second-order images are measured on both sides of the central image. The grating space d can then be calculated from these results.

Illustrative Example. Light from a mercury arc is observed through a diffraction grating spectrometer. The spectrum consists of a series of 7 lines: 2 yellow, 1 green, 1 blue-green, 1 blue, and 2 violet. The wavelength of the green line is 5,461 A, where 1 A is 10^{-8} cm. Determine the angular deviation of this green line in the first and second orders, if the grating has 6,000 lines per centimeter ruled on it.

The distance between rulings is

$$d = \frac{1}{6,000} \text{ cm.}$$

The angle θ_1 in the first order satisfies the equation

$$\sin \theta_1 = \frac{\lambda}{d} \, ;$$

hence

$$\sin \theta_1 = \frac{5,461 \times 10^{-8}}{1/6,000} \, ,$$

from which

$$\sin \theta_1 = 0.32766,$$

so that

$$\theta_1 = 19° \, 7'36''.$$

In the second order,

$$\sin \theta_2 = \frac{2\lambda}{d} \, ,$$

from which

$$\sin \theta_2 = 0.65532,$$

so that

$$\theta_2 = 40° \, 56'38''.$$

Notice that angle θ_2 is not twice the angle θ_1.

QUESTIONS

1. What happens to the spacings between bright lines in the interference pattern produced by light from two slits when the slits are placed closer together?

2. Why are the colors of thin oil films on pavements most frequently seen when the pavement is wet?

3. Suppose that in the experiment on Newton's rings, we used first red light and then blue light. Which set of rings would have the larger diameters and therefore the greater spacings between rings?

4. Could Newton's rings also be observed with transmitted light? If so, would the center spot be dark?

5. Which would give more orders of spectra, a diffraction grating with 500 lines per centimeter or one with 5,000 lines per centimeter?

6. In the spectrum formed by a grating, the violet light is deviated least, while the red light is deviated through the largest angle in any one order. The reverse is the case in the spectrum formed by a prism. Explain the reason for this difference.

PROBLEMS

1. Yellow sodium light whose wavelength is 5,893 A comes from a single source and passes through two narrow slits 1.0 mm apart. The interference pattern is observed on a screen 175 cm away. How far apart are two adjacent bright bands?

2. Light from a mercury arc, after passing through a green filter, is then incident on two narrow slits 0.06 cm apart. The interference pattern is formed on a screen 250 cm away. The distance between two adjacent green lines is found to be 2.27 mm. Determine the wavelength of the light.

3. Five per cent of the light which strikes a glass-air surface is reflected back. What percentage of the incident light is transmitted after passage through an optical system containing eight surfaces?

4. Calculate the thickness, in centimeters, of a nonreflecting film for coating a lens of index of refraction 1.65, assuming sodium light incident on it.
(Note: The wavelength of light in a medium of index of refraction n is λ/n.)

5. (a) Referring to Figure 34–7, show that if the thickness of the object placed between the two glass plates to produce the wedge-shaped air film is T, and if monochromatic light of wavelength λ is incident normally on the top surface, then the total number N of dark lines produced is given by $N = 2T/\lambda$.
(b) Calculate the number of dark lines that will be produced when green light of wavelength 5,461 A is incident normally on a wedge-shaped air film produced by inserting a piece of steel 0.02 cm thick between the two glass plates.

6. Two glass plates 10 cm long are in contact at one end and separated by a thin sheet of paper at the other end, forming a wedge-shaped air film. Red light of wavelength 6,600 A is incident normally on the glass. Experiment shows that there are 17 dark lines per centimeter. (a) Calculate the thickness of the paper. (b) How many lines per centimeter would be produced by green light of wavelength 5,400 A?

7. A diffraction grating has 6,000 lines per centimeter. White light is incident on the slit of a diffraction grating spectrometer so that the collimated beam falls normally on this diffraction grating. At what angle will the blue light of 4,400 A wavelength be found (a) in the first order and (b) in the second order?

8. In the experiment described in Problem 7, at what angle will the red light of 7,200 A wavelength be found (a) in the first order and (b) in the second order?

9. In the experiment described in Problem 7, determine (a) whether the violet light will appear in a third-order spectrum and (b) whether the red light will appear in the third-order spectrum.

10. Yellow light from a sodium arc is incident on the slit of a diffraction grating spectrometer which has a grating of 2,000 lines per centimeter mounted on its table. Determine the highest order spectrum that may be observed with this grating.

11. Blue light of 4,500 A is used to determine the number of lines on a grating. When this grating is used with a spectrometer, the second-order image is found at an angle of 30° from the central image. Determine the number of lines per centimeter on the grating.

12. A diffraction pattern is formed by sending green light of wavelength 5,500 A through a circular aperture 1.0 mm in diameter and allowing it to fall on a screen 60 cm away. Determine the diameter of the first dark ring of the diffraction pattern.

13. The yellow line in the spectrum of sodium, sometimes called the D line, consists of two lines very close together when viewed with a spectroscope of moderate resolving power. The wavelengths of these lines are $D_1 = 5,896$ A and $D_2 = 5,890$ A. Determine the angular separation of these lines when examined with a diffraction grating having 6,000 lines/cm and viewed (a) in the first order and (b) in the second order.

35

Polarized Light

35-1 POLARIZATION. TRANSVERSE WAVES

The phenomena of interference and diffraction show that light is propagated as a wave motion, but they do not show whether light is a *longitudinal* wave or a *transverse* wave. In a longitudinal wave, the direction of vibration is parallel to the direction of propagation, while in a transverse wave, the direction of vibration is perpendicular to the direction of propagation of the wave. This means that in a transverse wave all the vibrations are in a plane at right angles to the direction of motion of the wave (see Figure 35-1). But there are an infinite number of directions in this plane at

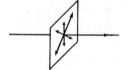

FIG. 35-1 The vibrations in a transverse wave are in a plane at right angles to the direction of propagation

right angles to the direction of motion of the wave. If light is a transverse wave motion, it should be possible to produce a beam of light in which all the vibrations are in one direction only. A beam of light in which all the vibrations are in one direction is called a *linearly polarized* beam. Such a beam of light should be distinguishable from one in which the vibrations are in a different direction, say at right angles to it. This can be done in several different ways. One way is to reflect the light from a glass surface at a special angle; another way is to send the light through certain crystals, such as tourmaline, which transmit vibrations in one direction but absorb the other vibrations; a third method is to scatter the light from small particles.

Besides being of theoretical interest in showing that light waves are transverse waves, polarized light has many practical applications to chemistry, engineering, and industrial processes.

35-2 POLARIZATION BY REFLECTION

Light can be polarized by reflection from a plate of glass by the proper choice of the angle of incidence. For example, if the index of refraction of the glass is 1.54, the angle of incidence should be 57°, as shown in Figure 35–2(a). At this angle of incidence, the angle between the refracted ray

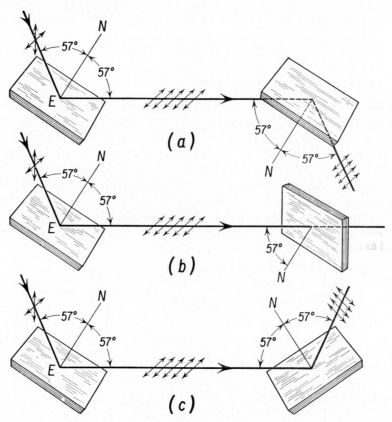

Fig. 35–2   Polarization of light by reflection from a glass plate.

and the reflected ray is 90°. Let the reflected ray strike another glass plate at the same angle of incidence; the incident beam will be reflected from the second glass plate in the usual manner. Now, if the second glass plate is rotated through 90° about the ray incident on it as an axis, it will be found that no light is reflected from it; instead, all the light is transmitted through it, as illustrated in Figure 35–2(b). When the second mirror is turned through another 90° about the ray incident on it as an axis, the light will again be reflected [see Figure 35–2(c)].

This peculiar behavior of the beam reflected from the first mirror can be explained by assuming that only those vibrations which are parallel to the surface of the mirror are reflected from it, when the angle of incidence is such that the reflected and refracted rays are at right angles to each other. Let us call this particular angle of incidence i_p, the *polarizing angle*. The vibrations in the light incident on the first glass plate probably have all possible directions in a plane at right angles to its direction of motion. We may imagine all of these vibrations resolved into two components: one vibrating parallel to the surface of the first glass plate, and the other component at right angles to this direction. When the angle of incidence is the polarizing angle, the reflected beam contains only vibrations which are parallel to the glass surface. When this reflected beam strikes the second glass plate at an angle of incidence equal to the polarizing angle, it will be reflected with maximum intensity when the surface of the glass plate is parallel to the direction of the vibrations. As the second glass plate is turned about the ray incident on it as an axis, the intensity of the light reflected from it decreases and becomes zero after a rotation of 90° and then starts increasing again as the glass plate is turned beyond this position and becomes of maximum intensity after a rotation of 180°. Thus, as the second glass plate rotates about the ray incident on it at the polarizing angle, there will be two positions of maximum intensity of the reflected beam and two positions of zero intensity.

This combination of two glass surfaces arranged so that the incident light strikes the first surface at the polarizing angle, and the second glass surface, mounted so that it can rotate about the reflected beam as an axis, is called a *polariscope*. The first glass plate, which reflects polarized light, is called the *polarizer*, and the second glass plate, which is used to analyze the light, is called the *analyzer*. The correct polarizing angle i_p for the particular glass used can be found by applying Snell's law to the beam which strikes the first piece of glass

$$\frac{\sin i_p}{\sin r'} = n, \tag{1}$$

where r' is the angle of refraction (see Figure 35–3). Since the angle of reflection is equal to the angle of incidence and the reflected ray is perpendicular to the refracted ray, $i_p + r' = 90°$; that is, the angles i_p and r' are complementary. In this case,

$$\sin r' = \cos i_p;$$

hence Snell's law becomes

$$\frac{\sin i_p}{\cos i_p} = n = \tan i_p. \tag{2}$$

Thus the tangent of the polarizing angle is equal to the index of refraction of the glass. If $n = 1.54$, the polarizing angle is 57°.

Only about 8 per cent of the incident light is reflected from the first glass surface. By using a bundle of thin glass plates, say seven or eight

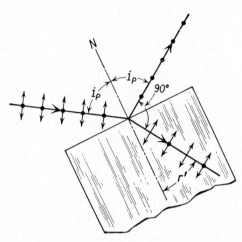

FIG. 35–3   The incident ray is unpolarized. The vibrations are shown resolved into two components; the component parallel to the glass surface is represented by dots. The reflected ray is completely polarized; the refracted ray is only partially polarized.

plates, the intensity of the reflected beam may be increased to about 40 per cent of the incident beam. This light is all linearly polarized with the direction of vibration parallel to the glass surfaces. A small percentage of the light will be absorbed by the glass plates, and the remainder will be transmitted. If the number of reflecting surfaces is sufficient to reflect all of the vibrations which are parallel to these surfaces, the transmitted beam will consist only of vibrations perpendicular to those which were reflected; that is, the transmitted beam should also be linearly polarized. Usually, however, some of the parallel vibrations are also transmitted, so that the transmitted beam is not completely polarized.

On the basis of the electromagnetic theory of light, a linearly polarized monochromatic beam consists of a varying electric field accompanied by a similarly varying magnetic field traveling forward with the velocity of light. If we take the direction of motion of the beam of light as the x-direction, the vectors representing the electric and magnetic fields, at any point along the beam, will be in a plane perpendicular to the x-axis, such as the y-z plane. Figure 35–4 is a graph representing the electric and magnetic fields of a linearly polarized monochromatic wave of wavelength λ at a given instant of time. *The direction of vibration of a linearly polarized beam of light is arbitrarily taken as the direction of the electric field intensity, in this case, the y-direction.*

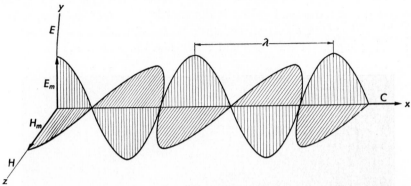

Fig. 35-4   The electric and magnetic field intensities of a linearly polarized beam of light moving in the x-direction. The direction of vibration of the beam is taken arbitrarily as the direction of the electric field, in the above case, the y-direction.

35-3   POLARIZATION BY CRYSTAL ABSORPTION

Some crystals, such as tourmaline, possess the property of absorbing those vibrations which are perpendicular to the axis of the crystal and of transmitting the vibrations which are parallel to this axis. If a beam of light, which is unpolarized, is sent through a thin plate of tourmaline, the transmitted beam will be linearly polarized parallel to the crystal axis.

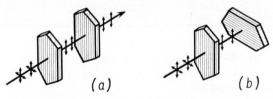

Fig. 35-5   Polarization by absorption in a crystal. (a) Linearly polarized light from the polarizing crystal is transmitted by the analyzer. (b) The linearly polarized light is absorbed by the analyzer when it is turned through 90°.

If this linearly polarized beam is now allowed to fall on a second tourmaline plate set so that its axis is at right angles to the axis of the first crystal, no light will be transmitted through the second crystal (see Figure 35-5). But, if the second tourmaline crystal is rotated through 90° about the incident beam as an axis, thus making the axes of the two crystals parallel, the linearly polarized beam will be transmitted through the second crystal. At intermediate positions, the intensity of the transmitted beam will be smaller than that transmitted when the axes were parallel.

These two crystals also form a polariscope; the first crystal is the polarizer, and the second crystal is the analyzer. One of the tourmalines can be used as an analyzer of the light reflected from the glass plate at the polarizing angle. It will be found that when the axis of the tourmaline

FIG. 35–6 Photograph showing the action of two Polaroid films on light. The axes of the crystals in one film are at right angles to those in the second film. No light can pass through the region where the two films overlap. (Courtesy of Polaroid Corporation.)

crystal is parallel to the surface of the glass plate, it will transmit the reflected beam; at right angles to this direction, it will absorb the reflected beam.

Within the past few years, a polarizing material, known commercially as Polaroid, has come into fairly common use. The Polaroid consists of a sheet of transparent material in which are embedded tiny crystals with their axes all parallel to one another. A polariscope can be made out of two sheets of Polaroid. Each sheet of Polaroid will transmit only those vibrations whose directions are parallel to the crystal axes. If two sheets of Polaroid are crossed so that their axes are at right angles to each other, linearly polarized light will be transmitted through the first sheet of Polaroid but completely absorbed by the second sheet (see Figure 35–6).

35-4 POLARIZATION BY DOUBLE REFRACTION

When a narrow beam of ordinary unpolarized light is sent through certain transparent crystals, such as calcite and quartz, the refracted beam is split into two parts which travel through the crystal and emerge as two

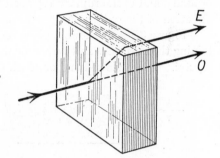

Fig. 35–7 Double refraction by a crystal.

separate beams, as shown in Figure 35–7. When an object is viewed through such a crystal, two separate images will be seen. If the emergent beams are analyzed with a Polaroid film, it will be found that each beam is polarized, but that the directions of their vibrations are at right angles to each other. One of these beams obeys the ordinary laws of refraction and is called the *ordinary ray;* it is designated as O in Figure 35–7. The other

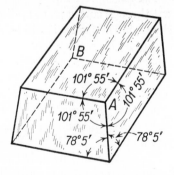

Fig. 35–8 Sketch of calcite crystal.

ray *E*, known as the *extraordinary ray*, does not always lie in the plane of incidence; its speed, and hence its index of refraction, depends upon its direction of propagation through the crystal.

In general, if a nonpolarized beam of light is sent through a crystal

at any arbitrary angle, two linearly polarized beams will emerge. However, it is possible to find one direction in the crystal such that both the
ordinary ray and the extraordinary ray will travel with the same speed;
for this particular direction, there will be no splitting of the unpolarized
beam into two beams. This particular direction in the crystal is known as
the *optic axis*. Figure 35–8 is a sketch of a calcite crystal, sometimes
called *Iceland spar*. At each of the corners *A* and *B*, the angles formed
by the three intersecting faces are the same; each angle is 101°55′. A line
at *A* or *B* drawn so that it makes equal angles with the three intersecting
edges is the direction of the optic axis. The directions of vibration of the
ordinary and extraordinary rays can now be specified with respect to the
direction of the optic axis.

Figure 35–9(a) shows a plane section through the calcite crystal containing the optic axis and perpendicular to two opposite faces of the natural
crystal. When viewed end on, each of these faces is a parallelogram with

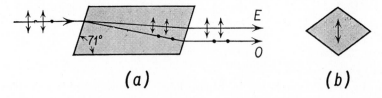

$$(a) \qquad\qquad (b)$$

FIG. 35–9   (a) Double refraction of light by a calcite crystal when the beam goes
through a principal section. The two beams *E* and *O* are linearly polarized
with their directions of vibration at right angles to each other. (b) Direction
of vibration of the extraordinary ray.

one diagonal shorter than the other. If a narrow beam of unpolarized light
is sent through such a plane section, also called a principal section of calcite,
as shown in the figure, it will be split into two beams which will emerge as
two parallel beams, each of which is linearly polarized. The direction of
vibration in the ordinary ray is perpendicular to the plane of the principal
section, while the direction of vibration in the extraordinary ray is parallel
to, or in the plane of, the principal section. Another way of specifying it
is to say that the direction of vibration of the extraordinary ray is parallel
to the shorter diagonal of the emergent face of the crystal, as shown in
Figure 35-9(b).

It may be noted here that tourmaline is also a doubly refracting crystal; the difference between it and a calcite crystal is that a small thickness
of tourmaline absorbs the ordinary ray, so that only the extraordinary ray
is transmitted. It can thus be used either as a polarizer or an analyzer.
The substance used in the production of Polaroid film behaves in an analogous manner.

35-5 THE NICOL PRISM

A calcite crystal may be modified so that it can be used as a polarizer or analyzer by removing one of the polarized rays from the transmitted beam. One method of doing this is shown in Figure 35–10. Using a fairly long, clear crystal, the end faces are cut so that the angle in the principal section is reduced from 71° to 68° (see Figure 35–10). The crystal is

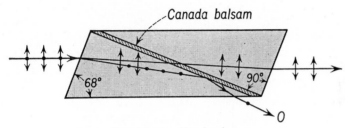

Fig. 35–10   Nicol prism.

then cut in half along a diagonal *AC* perpendicular to the plane of the principal section. The two halves are then cemented together with clear Canada balsam. This optical device is called a *Nicol prism*. The index of refraction of the ordinary ray in calcite is 1.66, and in Canada balsam it is 1.55. The angle of incidence of the ordinary ray when it strikes the Canada balsam surface is greater than the critical angle, so that this ray is totally reflected. The index of refraction of the extraordinary ray in calcite depends upon its direction of propagation in the calcite. For the possible directions in the Nicol prism, the index of refraction of the *E*-ray is about 1.49; hence it will be transmitted through the Canada balsam and emerge from the prism.

Nicol prisms are used in optical devices as analyzers, polarizers, or both. The light which is transmitted through this prism vibrates in a direction parallel to the short diagonal of its end face.

35-6 POLARIZATION BY SCATTERING

Light can be polarized by scattering from small particles or by molecules of a substance. For example, the blue light of the sky, which is produced by the scattering of sunlight by air molecules, is polarized. This can be verified by looking at a blue sky through a sheet of Polaroid. When the Polaroid is rotated, the intensity of the transmitted light will change and become a minimum when the axis of the Polaroid is at right angles to the direction of vibration of the light.

Polarization by scattering can be demonstrated by sending unpolarized light vertically down a tube of water containing some fine particles in suspension, as shown in Figure 35–11. The directions of vibration of the incident light are in a horizontal plane. The light that is scattered in a horizontal direction, when examined with a sheet of Polaroid or a Nicol prism, will be found to be polarized with the vibrations in a horizontal

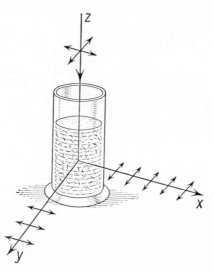

FIG. 35–11   Light traveling downward, z-direction, is scattered by small particles in the liquid. Light scattered in the x-direction has its vibrations in the y-direction. Light scattered in any horizontal direction is linearly polarized.

direction at right angles to the direction of observation. Since light is a transverse wave motion, the light scattered in the x-direction, for example, can have no vibrations in the x-direction; hence the only vibrations present, when it is examined along the x-axis, will be those in the y-direction.

35-7 INTERFERENCE WITH POLARIZED LIGHT

We have already considered the phenomenon of interference using ordinary or unpolarized light. Interference can also be produced with polarized light, providing the directions of vibration in the two beams are parallel to each other. Consider, for example, a polariscope arranged in the *crossed* position, as shown in Figure 35–12. Suppose that unpolarized monochromatic light—yellow light, for example—is incident on the polarizer P set so that linearly polarized light with its vibrations in the vertical direction passes through it. The analyzer A is set in the crossed position: that is, it will transmit light vibrating in the horizontal direction only; hence the polarized light from P will not pass through it.

Now let us put a thin piece of quartz crystal C between P and A so that its optic axis is at an angle of 45° with the direction of vibration. Quartz, being a doubly refracting crystal, will divide the beam into two parts, the extraordinary ray with its vibrations parallel to the optic axis and the ordinary ray vibrating perpendicular to it (see Figure 35–13).

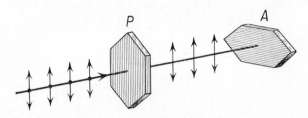

Fig. 35–12   A crossed polariscope.

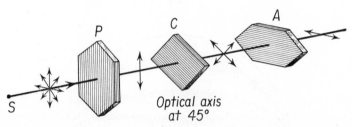

Fig. 35–13   A doubly refracting crystal C placed between the polarizer P and the analyzer A when P and A are in crossed positions.

Since they travel through the crystal with different velocities, there will be a difference in phase when they emerge. However, there can be no interference, because they vibrate at right angles to each other. But, when they pass through the analyzer A, only the horizontal components of these vibrations will be transmitted, and interference will occur between these two transmitted rays. If the path difference due to passage through the crystal is a half wavelength or an odd number of half wavelengths, these two rays will annul each other. If now white light is incident on the polarizer, all the wavelengths will be polarized and transmitted as shown above, but the yellow light will be missing, so that the light will appear colored, the color being the complement of yellow, that is, blue. Hence specimens of clear, colorless, doubly refracting crystals will appear colored when viewed through a crossed polariscope.

35-8   PHOTOELASTICITY

Many transparent materials such as glass, lucite, and bakelite, which are not ordinarily doubly refracting, become so when subjected to stresses.

When such a substance is placed between the polarizer and analyzer of a crossed polariscope, a colored pattern will be observed due to the interference effect of the polarized light.   The pattern of colors observed can be

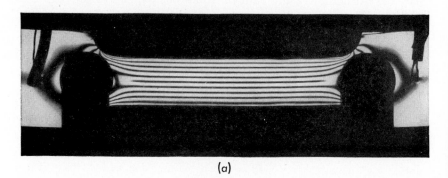

(a)

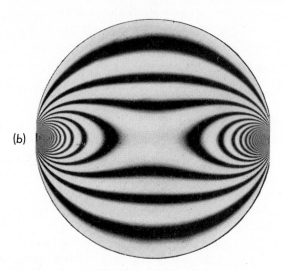

(b)

FIG. 35–14   Interference pattern produced by passing polarized light through a piece of transparent plastic in a crossed polariscope.   (a) Strain pattern when a bar is subjected to a bending moment.   (b) Strain pattern in a cylindrical disk subject to a diametral compression.   (Photographs by George Gerard, New York University.)

related to the strains in the substance produced by the stresses.   Figure 35–14 shows such a strain pattern.   In modern engineering practice, models of structures are built out of transparent plastic materials and the strains produced in them studied with the aid of polarized light.   This type of study of stresses and strains forms the subject *photoelasticity*.

35-9 FURTHER APPLICATIONS OF POLARIZED LIGHT

There are many different applications involving polarized light. For example, there are many solids and liquids which will *rotate* the direction of vibration of linearly polarized light. A sugar solution is one such substance. If a tube containing a sugar solution is placed between crossed Polaroids, it will be found that light is transmitted through the analyzer. It will be necessary to rotate the analyzer through some angle θ to reduce the light intensity to zero. The angle θ through which the analyzer is rotated depends upon the length of the solution, its concentration, and the kind of sugar used. For some types of sugar, it is necessary to rotate the analyzer clockwise to produce extinction of the light beam; in other cases, the rotation is counterclockwise. The angle is measured when looking toward the solution. The rotations are usually referred to as right-handed for clockwise and left-handed for counterclockwise. The former type is also called dextrorotatory; the latter, levorotatory. A polariscope used for measuring the rotation of the direction of vibration produced by sugar solutions is called a *saccharimeter*.

Another application of polarization is the reduction of *glare*. Light reflected from a rough surface is scattered diffusely in all directions. At small angles of incidence, only a small fraction of the light is scattered in any one direction. But, at large angles of incidence, most of the light is reflected at an angle of incidence equal to the angle of reflection, just as in the case of smooth surfaces. This results in *glare*. When this reflected light is analyzed with a Polaroid, it is found that the component with its vibrations parallel to the surface is much more intense than the component with its vibrations at right angles to the surface. Glare may be reduced considerably by using spectacles made of a polarizing material, such as Polaroid, set to absorb the horizontal vibrations.

QUESTIONS

1. What important facts concerning the propagation of light have been established by the experiments on (a) interference and diffraction and (b) polarization?

2. What is meant by the polarizing angle of a piece of glass?

3. Does the polarizing angle of a piece of glass depend upon the wavelength of the incident light? If so, how does the polarizing angle vary with increasing wavelength?

4. A beam of light strikes a glass plate at an angle of about 55°. Outline a method of testing the reflected beam for polarization.

5. Outline a method for measuring the index of refraction of coal, making use of its polarizing angle.

PROBLEMS

1. The index of refraction of one type of flint glass is 1.65. Determine the polarizing angle for this glass. Would you expect the reflected light to be completely polarized?

2. Diamond has an index of refraction of 2.4. Determine its polarizing angle.

3. Determine the polarizing angle of water, assuming its index of refraction to be 1.33.

4. Referring to Figure 35–10, assume that the incident light travels parallel to the base of the parallelogram forming the section of the Nicol prism. Determine (a) the angle of incidence of the beam of light on the face of the prism and (b) the angle of refraction of the ordinary ray in the calcite.

5. The index of refraction of the ordinary ray in calcite is 1.66 and is 1.55 in Canada balsam. Determine the critical angle for this ray in going from calcite to the Canada balsam medium.

6. Referring to Problems 4 and 5, show that the angle of incidence of the ordinary ray on the Canada balsam surface is greater than the critical angle; assume that the length of the principal section is four times its height.

7. The indices of refraction of yellow light of 6,000 A in a doubly refracting medium are 1.710 for the ordinary ray and 1.740 for the extraordinary ray. (a) Determine the velocity of each of these waves in this medium. (b) Determine the minimum thickness of this material to produce a path difference of half a wavelength for these two rays. (c) If white light is incident on a polariscope in the crossed position, what will be observed when the above thickness of this doubly refracting material is placed between the polarizer and analyzer?

Part Six

ATOMICS AND
NUCLEONICS

36

Foundations of Atomics and Nucleonics

36-1 ELEMENTS AND ATOMS

We have given our present views concerning the structure of matter and the structure of atoms in several sections throughout this book (see particularly Chapters 10, 14, and 24). In Part Six, we shall present some of the experimental evidence for our present view of the structure of the atom, of its behavior when interacting either with radiant energy or with particles, and of the changes in the structure of the atom which occur either spontaneously or under the action of external agents. Atomic physics is essentially a twentieth-century development, although it had its origin at the close of the nineteenth century. Its development has followed two practically parallel streams, as shown in Figure 36-1, one dealing with the electronic structure of the atom and the other dealing with its nuclear structure. These two streams were fed from practically all the other branches of physics, but only a few of the more important contributions are shown in the figure. These concern mainly the theories of the nature of radiation, matter, and energy.

Before proceeding with a discussion of atomic structure, it will be worth while to recapitulate some of the phenomena treated previously so that they will be available for this discussion. There are at present 101 known elements (see Table 6 in the Appendix). Each element is characterized by two numbers, (a) its *atomic number* and (b) its *atomic weight*. The atomic numbers run consecutively from 1 for the simplest and lightest element, hydrogen, to 101 for one of the heaviest elements, mendelevium. The atomic weights of the elements range from about 1 to more than 250, with the atomic weight of oxygen taken as the standard and assigned the value 16.0000. The Avogadro number, $N_0 = 6.0247 \times 10^{23}$, is the number of atoms in a gram-atomic weight of each element.

We shall take for granted at present, and show later, that each atom consists of a positively charged nucleus of very small diameter, surrounded by an appropriate number of electrons so that the atom is electrically neutral in its normal state. The electron carries a negative charge whose

Development of Atomic and Nuclear Physics

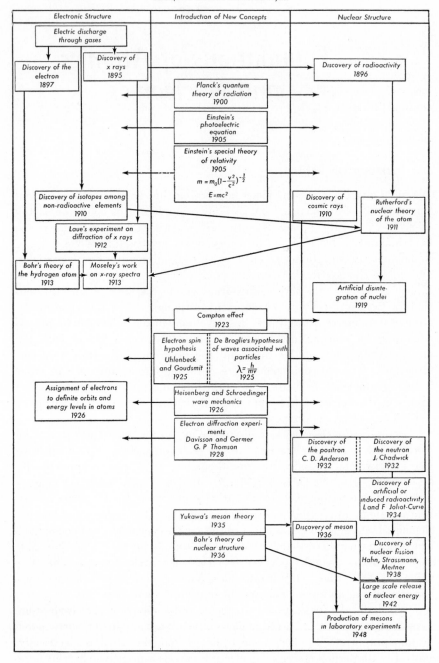

Fɪɢ. 36–1   Development of atomic and nuclear physics.

value is

$$e = 4.802 \times 10^{-10} \text{ stcoul}$$
$$= 1.602 \times 10^{-19} \text{ coul}$$
$$= 1.602 \times 10^{-20} \text{ abcoul.}$$

A proton has a positive charge of the same magnitude as that of the electron. We shall show that the atomic number Z of an element represents the number of protons in the nucleus of the atom and also represents the number of electrons outside the nucleus in the normal state of the atom of this element.

36-2 RESTRICTED THEORY OF RELATIVITY

One of the most important developments of twentieth-century physics was the formulation of the *special or restricted theory of relativity*. It was an outgrowth of the failure of all attempts to show that the motion of the source of light relative to the observer had any effect on the speed of light. One of the best of these was the experiment performed by Michelson and Morley in 1887 using an interferometer, shown in simplified form in Figure 36–2. Light from a source at S strikes a half-silvered mirror A at

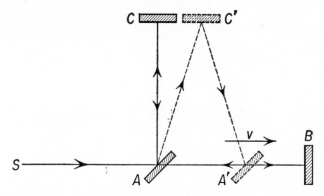

Fig. 36–2 Schematic diagram of the Michelson-Morley experiment. v is the velocity of the earth through the aether. The path of the ray of light ACA is actually that shown by the dotted lines $AC'A'$.

an angle of 45°; part of the light is transmitted to mirror B and reflected back to A; the other part is reflected to mirror C and then back to A. The two beams meet at A, where they produce a set of interference fringes which can be viewed through a telescope T. The entire apparatus is mounted on a rigid platform which can be rotated about an axis perpendicular to the plane of the figure.

Suppose that the interferometer is set so that the arm AB is parallel to the velocity v of the earth through space at any instant. Suppose that c is the velocity of light in space or in some hypothetical *aether*, which is assumed to fill all space. On the Newtonian or classical theory, the velocity of light relative to the instrument along AB is $c - v$ forward and $c + v$ when reflected. The velocity of light in the direction AC will be $\sqrt{c^2 - v^2}$. If the lengths of the arms AB and AC are equal, the time taken by the beam of light to travel from A to B and back to A will be different from that taken to travel from A to C and back to A.

In the experiment performed by Michelson and Morley, the positions of the interference fringes were noted in the telescope when the interferometer was placed so that the arm AB was parallel to the earth's velocity. The instrument was then rotated through 90° so that AC was parallel to the earth's velocity and AB thus perpendicular to it. Since the times of travel of the two light beams were now different, a shift in the positions of the fringes should have occurred. None was observed, within the limits of accuracy of the experiment.

It is impossible to account for the results, or lack of results, of this experiment on the basis of classical mechanics and electromagnetism. A. Einstein, in 1905, put forth the suggestion that these results could be explained if it was assumed that *the speed of light is a constant and is independent of the motion of the source and of the observer.* This statement forms the *first postulate* of the special or restricted theory of relativity. The *second postulate* of this theory is that *all systems which are in uniform motion relative to one another are equally valid frames of reference, and that the fundamental physical laws must have the same mathematical forms in each of these reference frames.*

Einstein undertook an examination of the fundamental concepts and ideas of physics in the light of the postulates of the theory of relativity. The results were very startling at that time, but have since become accepted and incorporated into the science of physics. We shall mention a few of them of interest to us. Suppose that the length of a rigid bar AB is measured by an observer who is at rest with respect to it and found to be L_0. Now suppose that the length of this rigid bar is measured by another observer who is moving in a direction parallel to the length of the bar with a velocity v. He calls the length L. When the two observers compare their results, they find that L is less than L_0; the relationship between the two lengths measured by the observers, according to the theory of relativity, is shown to be

$$L = L_0 \left(1 - \frac{v^2}{c^2} \right)^{1/2}, \tag{1}$$

where c is the speed of light.

Historically, a phenomenon of this kind was anticipated by G. F. Fitzgerald and H. A. Lorentz and was used by them to explain the results of the Michelson-Morley experiment. They suggested that the dimensions of the system in motion contracted along the direction of motion, sufficient to compensate for the change in velocity of light along the path.

The concept of time also undergoes a significant change. If there are two identical clocks, one at rest with respect to an observer and the other moving with uniform velocity v with respect to him, the moving clock will run slower.

The equation for the relative velocity of a particle must be modified from that given in Section 3–3 and becomes

$$\mathbf{v} = \frac{\mathbf{w} + \mathbf{u}}{1 + \dfrac{\mathbf{u}\mathbf{w}}{c^2}}, \tag{2}$$

where $\mathbf{w}$ is the velocity of the particle referred to a system which has a constant velocity $\mathbf{u}$ in a parallel direction with respect to the observer who is considered at rest. When $\mathbf{u}$ and $\mathbf{w}$ are small in comparison with the velocity of light c, the above equation reduces to the equation of Newtonian mechanics

$$\mathbf{v} = \mathbf{w} + \mathbf{u}. \tag{3}$$

An important result of the theory of relativity is that no material particle can have a speed greater than the speed of light and that no signal and no energy can be transmitted with a speed greater than the speed of light.

Before the advent of the theory of relativity, the concepts of mass and energy were independent ones. It was assumed that the mass of a body was a property of the body which remained constant and was independent of its motion. But, on the basis of the theory of relativity, if m_0 is the mass of a particle when it is at rest with respect to an observer, then its mass m when it is moving with a velocity v relative to the observer is given by

$$m = \frac{m_0}{\sqrt{1 - v^2/c^2}}, \tag{4}$$

where c is the speed of light.

In experiments with large-size objects, or even with small particles, the speed v is generally an extremely small fraction of the speed of light. Hence the ratio $(v/c)^2$ is negligible in comparison with unity, and $m = m_0$. But, when the speed v of a particle becomes an appreciable fraction of the speed of light, then the ratio $(v/c)^2$ is no longer negligible in comparison with unity, and mass m differs from the mass m_0 of the same particle when at rest. It is very common for the particles dealt with in atomic physics to have very large speeds; hence these can be used to verify the correctness of Equation (4). Such experiments have been performed with electrons moving at speeds comparable with the speed of light; the variation of the mass of the electron with its velocity has been demonstrated and measured in such experiments with a high degree of precision.

FIG. 36-3   Albert Einstein (1879–1955). He developed the theory of relativity and revolutionized the mode of thinking about fundamental physical problems. One consequence of this theory was the extension of the concept of energy to include mass as a form of energy. Another part of the theory gives us a new insight into gravitational phenomena. He also developed the fundamental equation of the photoelectric effect and the theory of Brownian motion. (Official U.S. Navy Photo from Acme.)

One interesting conclusion can be drawn from an examination of Equation (4), and that is, that if a particle has a rest mass m_0, then its speed v can never exceed the speed of light c. When $v = c$, $1 - v^2/c^2 = 0$, and m becomes infinite; hence, in order to accelerate a particle until its speed v becomes equal to c, an infinite force, something not available, would be required.

36-3   EQUIVALENCE OF MASS AND ENERGY

Until the advent of the special theory of relativity, one of the fundamental principles of physics and chemistry was the *principle of the conservation of mass*, which stated that the mass of an isolated system remained constant under all changes of physical states and chemical composition. But this principle is not in accord with the result deduced from the theory of relativity. Einstein resolved this difficulty by postulating that *mass is a form of energy and that a mass* m *is equivalent to an amount of energy* $\mathcal{E}$. He deduced the relationship between $\mathcal{E}$ and m in his theory of relativity. If m is measured in grams or kilograms and $\mathcal{E}$ is expressed in ergs or joules, then the relationship between $\mathcal{E}$ and m is

$$\mathcal{E} = mc^2,$$ (5)

where c is the speed of light.

The principle of the conservation of energy has thus been enlarged to include mass as a form of energy. It will be recalled that the principle of conservation of energy was first formulated about 1847, when it was shown definitely that heat is a form of energy. Previous to this period, there was a conservation theorem which concerned only the mechanical forms of energy, kinetic and potential energy, for transformations which occurred in frictionless systems. After the convincing work of Joule on the mechanical equivalent of heat, the concept of energy was extended to include heat. With the formulation of Maxwell's electromagnetic theory of light and the discovery of various forms of electromagnetic radiation, the principle of conservation of energy was readily extended to include electromagnetic radiations among the forms of energy. And now, mass is included as one aspect of energy along with all the other forms of energy.

Suppose that a process could be devised in which a system were to convert 1 gm of its mass into some other form of energy, say electrical energy. Then, from Equation (5), the amount of electrical energy obtained from this mass of 1 gm is

$$\mathcal{E} = 1 \text{ gm} \times (3 \times 10^{10} \text{ cm/sec})^2,$$

$$\mathcal{E} = 9 \times 10^{20} \text{ ergs},$$

or $$\mathcal{E} = 9 \times 10^{13} \text{ joules}.$$

This is a very large amount of energy; this may become more evident if we change the unit of energy from joules to kilowatt hours. It will be recalled that

$$1 \text{ joule} = 1 \text{ watt} \times 1 \text{ sec};$$

hence $$1 \text{ kw hr} = 1{,}000 \text{ watts} \times 3{,}600 \text{ sec},$$

or $$1 \text{ kw hr} = 36 \times 10^5 \text{ joules}.$$

Hence
$$\mathcal{E} = \frac{9 \times 10^{13}}{36 \times 10^5} \text{ kw hr,}$$

or
$$\mathcal{E} = 25 \times 10^6 \text{ kw hr;}$$

that is, 1 gm of mass is equivalent to 25 million kw hr of energy.

The conversion of mass into energy is believed to be going on continuously in the sun and the other stars. This process is the basis for the construction of nuclear reactors and nuclear weapons. The fundamental mode of conversion of mass into energy is through changes in the nuclear constitution of atoms. An important clue to this mode is the precise measurement of the masses of the atoms and a comparison of these values with the masses of constituent particles.

36-4 POSITIVE IONS. MASS SPECTROGRAPH

The methods used for determining the ratio of the charge to the mass of an electron can be used, with appropriate modifications, for determining the ratio of the charge to mass of the positive ions. From this ratio, it is usually a simple matter to determine the mass of an ion, since, in most cases, its charge is equivalent to one, and occasionally two or three, electrons. An instrument designed for this purpose is known either as a *mass spectrograph* or a *mass spectrometer*, depending upon whether a photographic plate or an electrical method is used to detect the ions. Modern mass spectrographs and spectrometers are instruments of very high precision. Not only have atomic masses been determined very accurately with them, but the number and relative abundance of the *isotopes* of which the elements are composed have been determined for most of the elements.

The term *isotopes* was introduced by Soddy as a result of the study of the radioactive elements. It was found that several groups of elements having identical chemical properties but different atomic weights were formed in the process of radioactive disintegration. This means that apparently several groups of elements occupy the same place in the periodic table. The term *isotopes* was used to designate the elements which occupy the same place in the periodic table. Because some elements had atomic weights which differed considerably from whole numbers, it was suggested that these elements consisted of two or more different isotopes having different atomic weights. The search for isotopes among the nonradioactive elements was begun by J. J. Thomson in 1910, and the first element successfully investigated was neon, whose atomic weight, 20.2, differs appreciably from a whole number. By sending the positive ions formed in a gas-discharge tube through electric and magnetic fields, Thomson determined the ratio of the charge to the mass of these ions and found that neon consists of at least two isotopes of atomic masses very close to 20 and 22. Many variations of the original method were made by later investigators to improve the accuracy of this method.

In order to avoid confusion, let us introduce two new terms: (a) the *atomic mass* refers to the mass of an isotope of an element, based on a scale in which the oxygen isotope of atomic mass 16.0000 is taken as the standard; this is the lightest of the three isotopes found in ordinary oxygen; (b) the *mass number* of an isotope of an element refers to the whole number which is nearest to the atomic mass of the isotope.

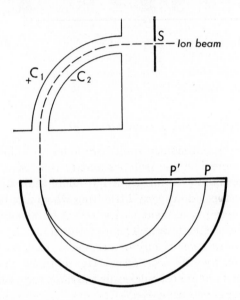

Fɪɢ. 36–4   Dempster's mass spectrograph which uses a capacitor with cylindrical plates.

There are many varieties of mass spectrographs and spectrometers in use in research and industrial laboratories. The essential parts of a mass spectrograph designed by A. J. Dempster are sketched in Figure 36–4. These parts are enclosed in a vacuum chamber. Positive ions from some convenient source pass through the narrow slit S into a radial electric field between two cylindrical plates C_1 and C_2 of a capacitor. The ions are deflected from C_1 toward C_2; those which have the appropriate kinetic energy travel in a circular arc between the plates, their path being deviated by 90° from the original direction. A short distance beyond the electric field, the ions enter a uniform magnetic field which is at right angles to the plane of the paper and, after traversing a semicircular path, strike the photographic plate PP' on which they are recorded. A typical spectrogram obtained with this apparatus is illustrated in Figure 36–5, which shows the isotopes of the rare-earth element ytterbium. The mass number of each isotope is shown above the line formed by its ions on the photographic plate.

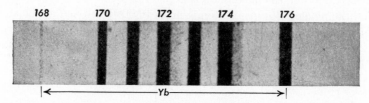

Fɪɢ. 36–5   A photograph of the isotopes of ytterbium obtained with Dempster's mass spectrograph. The mass numbers of the isotopes can be obtained from the number scale printed above the lines. (Reprinted from a photograph supplied to the author by Prof. A. J. Dempster.)

36-5   MASSES OF ISOTOPES AND ATOMIC STRUCTURE

Investigations with the mass spectrograph have established that there are about 300 different stable isotopes among the 101 known elements. The range of mass numbers runs from 1 to more than 250. The atomic masses of these isotopes differ very little from whole numbers. The number of stable isotopes per element varies from 1 for elements fluorine and gold to 10 for the element tin. There is one thing, however, which is common to all the isotopes of any one element: that is the *total positive charge carried by the nucleus of the atom.* Hence, in the neutral atom, the number of electrons around the nucleus is the same for each isotope of any one element.

Experiments on the scattering of alpha particles by matter (see Section 39–3) and experimental evidence from x-ray and optical spectra (Chapters 37 and 38) have established the fact that the nucleus of an atom has a net positive charge which can be represented by Ze, in which e is a positive charge equal in magnitude to that of an electron and Z is a whole number called the *atomic number* of the element. There are Z electrons surrounding the nucleus of a neutral atom. The atomic number Z ranges in value from 1 to 101. The isotopes of any one element have the same atomic number Z but have different mass numbers.

Since the isotopes of any one element have the same atomic number Z, every atom of the element has the same nuclear charge and the same number of electrons outside the nucleus. Differences among the atomic masses of the different isotopes of an element must therefore be due to differences in their nuclei; the fact that the atomic masses of all isotopes are nearly integers suggests that nuclei are made up of particles (called nucleons) of approximately unit atomic mass, with the unit of atomic mass equal to one sixteenth the mass of the nucleus of oxygen of atomic mass 16.00. At present two particles of nuclear size and of mass nearly equal to unity are known. These are the proton and the neutron. The proton is the positively charged nucleus of the hydrogen atom of mass number 1. This hydrogen atom consists of 1 proton as the nucleus and 1 electron outside the nucleus. Since the mass of the hydrogen atom is about 1,840 times the mass of the electron, practically the entire mass of the atom is due to the proton. On our scale of atomic units, the atomic mass of hydrogen is 1.00815, the mass of the electron is 0.00055, and hence the mass of the proton is 1.00760. The neutron, a nuclear particle discovered experimentally by Chadwick in 1932 as a result of experiments on nuclear disintegration, has no electric charge and has a mass of 1.00899.

Our present theory of the structure of the nucleus is that a nucleus consists of protons and neutrons; the total number of such particles is equal to the mass number A of the isotope of the element. The number of protons in the nucleus is equal to the atomic number Z of the element, and the number of neutrons in the nucleus is $N = A - Z$. Thus the isotopes of any one element differ only in the number of neutrons in the nuclei of

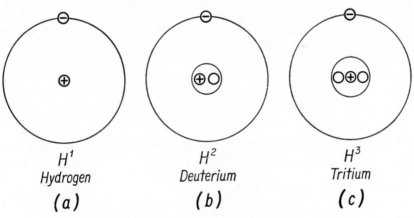

H^1
Hydrogen
(a)

H^2
Deuterium
(b)

H^3
Tritium
(c)

Fig. 36–6   Three isotopes of hydrogen.

the atoms. For example, hydrogen, $Z = 1$, has three isotopes with mass numbers $A = 1, 2,$ and 3, respectively. The nucleus of the isotope with $A = 1$ is simply a proton; the neutral atom has one electron outside the nucleus, as shown in Figure 36–6(a). The hydrogen isotope of mass number 2, sometimes called deuterium, has a nucleus consisting of two nucleons, one proton, and one neutron, as shown in Figure 36–6(b). The hydrogen isotope of mass number 3, sometimes called tritium, has a nucleus consisting of three nucleons, 1 proton, and 2 neutrons, as shown in Figure

36-6(c). The lightest isotope of hydrogen is the most abundant; deuterium constitutes about 0.015 per cent of the hydrogen in a common sample of a substance, such as water, which is made up of hydrogen and oxygen. Tritium is extremely rare; in a given sample of hydrogen, only about one atom in 10^{18} will be tritium. The two lighter isotopes of hydrogen are stable; tritium, on the other hand, is unstable. Tritium undergoes radioactive decay or disintegration with a half life of 12.5 years (see Section 39–14).

Helium, the second element in the order of atomic numbers, has $Z = 2$; its nucleus contains two protons. Its most abundant isotope has a mass number $A = 4$; its nucleus has two neutrons in addition to the two protons, as shown in Figure 36–7(a). The much rarer isotope of

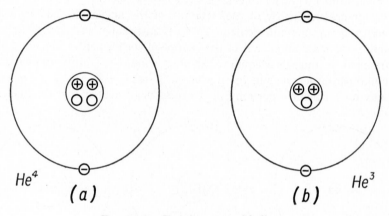

FIG. 36–7   Two isotopes of helium.

helium, $A = 3$, has only one neutron in its nucleus, as shown in Figure 36–7(b). The neutral atom in each case has two electrons outside the nucleus.

The particles which constitute an atom exert forces on each other; one type of force—that due to their electric charges—is well known. We have already discussed the law of force between charges, Coulomb's law, in great detail. Magnetic forces are also well understood. However, these forces are not sufficient to account for the fact that nuclei are essentially stable configurations. There must therefore be another type, or other types, of forces which exist between nucleons; these are termed *specifically nuclear forces*. The exact nature of these forces is not well known and is at present being investigated extensively. One thing is fairly certain, however; that is, that these specifically nuclear forces act through very short distances. Hence the nucleus of an atom occupies a very small fraction of the total space occupied by the atom. In general, the diameter of the nucleus is found to be about $1/10,000$ the diameter of the atom.   In the following chapters we shall present some of the experimental evidence on which our present knowledge of the structure of the atom is based.

36-6 BINDING ENERGY OF ATOMS

Atoms are comparatively stable structures. Suppose that a neutral atom of mass number A and atomic number Z is formed by bringing together A nucleons (Z protons plus N neutrons) in the nucleus and Z electrons outside the nucleus under the actions of both the specifically nuclear forces and the electrical forces. Since this atom is a stable structure, its total energy must be less than that of a system consisting of these same particles separated by such large distances that the effect of the above mentioned forces is negligible. The difference between the total energy of the separated particles and the total energy of the neutral atom composed of these particles is the *binding energy of the atom*. From the principle of equivalence of mass and energy, it can be concluded that the decrease in energy, produced in the formation of the atom by bringing together its constituent particles, should be evidenced by a decrease in mass of the system; that is, *the mass of the atom should be less than the sum of the masses of its constituent particles*. This was first brought to light as a result of the very precise determinations of the masses of the isotopes by means of the mass spectrometer.

As a simple example, let us consider the formation of deuterium, which consists of a proton and a neutron in the nucleus and one electron outside it. Its atomic mass is 2.01474 amu. The sum of the masses of its constituent particles, in atomic mass units, is

$$
\begin{aligned}
\text{mass of proton} &= 1.00760, \\
\text{mass of neutron} &= 1.00899, \\
\text{mass of electron} &= 0.00055, \\
\hline
\text{sum of masses} &= 2.01714 \text{ amu.}
\end{aligned}
$$

The mass of a deuterium atom is thus less than the sum of the masses of its constituent particles by 0.00240 amu.

To appreciate the meaning of these numbers, let us convert the atomic mass unit into more commonly used units. Now 1 amu is one sixteenth of the mass of an oxygen atom of mass number 16 and atomic mass 16. Since there are N_0 atoms in 16 gm of oxygen, one atom has a mass of $16 \text{ gm}/N_0$, so that 1 amu, which is one sixteenth of this, is simply

$$
1 \text{ amu} = \frac{1 \text{ gm}}{N_0} = \frac{1 \text{ gm}}{6.025 \times 10^{23}} ,
$$

from which $1 \text{ amu} = 1.66 \times 10^{-24} \text{ gm.}$

Using the relationship

$$\mathcal{E} = mc^2,$$

we find that   1 amu $= 1.49 \times 10^{-3}$ erg.

Another convenient energy unit is the *electron volt* (ev), which is equal to the kinetic energy acquired by a particle that has a charge e equivalent to that of an electron, when it is accelerated in an electric field produced by a difference of potential of one volt. Since the work done by a difference of potential V acting upon a charge e is Ve, then, since $e = 1.60 \times 10^{-19}$ coul,

we have   1 ev $= 1.60 \times 10^{-19}$ coul $\times$ 1 volt

$$= 1.60 \times 10^{-19} \text{ joule,}$$

or   1 ev $= 1.60 \times 10^{-12}$ erg.

An energy of one million electron volts, usually abbreviated 1 Mev, is

$$1 \text{ Mev} = 1.60 \times 10^{-6} \text{ erg.}$$

It is now possible to express the atomic mass unit in Mev. Since 1 amu $= 1.49 \times 10^{-3}$ erg and 1 Mev $= 1.60 \times 10^{-6}$ erg,

$$\boxed{1 \text{ amu} = 931.2 \text{ Mev.}} \qquad \text{(6)}$$

The binding energy $\mathcal{E}_B$ of the deuterium atom, which has been determined to be 0.00240 amu, can now be written as

$$\mathcal{E}_B = 0.00240 \times 931.2 \text{ Mev,}$$

or $\mathcal{E}_B = 2.23$ Mev.

Another way of viewing this is that in order to separate deuterium into its constituent particles, an amount of energy equal to 2.23 Mev will have to be supplied to it. It will be shown in the next chapter that the binding energy of the electron in this system is only about 14 ev and thus is negligible in comparison with 2.23 Mev. Hence practically this entire binding energy is that of the two nucleons in the nucleus of deuterium.

We shall devote the next two chapters to further considerations of the problem of the structure of the atom, of the formation of atomic systems, and of their modes of disintegration.

QUESTIONS

1. State the fundamental postulates of the restricted theory of relativity.
2. The mass of a particle in motion is twice as big as when it is at rest. Discuss the source of this additional mass.

3. In modern particle accelerators, the velocities of the particles differ very little from the velocity of light. Is it possible to increase the energies of these particles by a factor of 100?

4. Can you suggest a practical use for a mass spectrograph?

5. In what respects do the isotopes of any element differ from one another?

6. In what respects are the isotopes of any one element alike?

7. A molecule of water consists of 2 hydrogen atoms and 1 oxygen atom. The density of water at 4°C is 1 gm/cm^3. Suppose we had some "heavy" water, that is, water composed of deuterium and oxygen, would its density be greater than that of ordinary water?

8. What is the nature of the path of a charged particle moving in a uniform electric field?

PROBLEMS

1. A thin rod of length L_0, when measured by an observer at rest with respect to it, has a velocity $v = 3c/4$ with respect to a second observer. The direction of its velocity is parallel to its length. Determine the length L measured by the second observer.

2. A small particle is in the form of a sphere of radius R_0 when at rest. Determine its shape as seen by an observer if this particle is moving in the x-direction with a velocity $v = c/2$ with respect to this observer.

3. Two charged particles are emitted by a substance in opposite directions, each moving with a velocity $v = 0.9c$ with respect to the emitting substance. Determine the velocity of one particle relative to the other.

4. An electron has a rest mass of m_0. Determine its mass when it is moving with a velocity $v = 0.9c$ with respect to the observer.

5. What is the velocity of an electron if an observer determines its mass to be $2m_0$?

6. A gas-discharge tube contains both hydrogen and deuterium. What is the ratio of the velocities of their nuclei if they have the same kinetic energy?

7. A discharge tube containing helium gas has both singly charged helium ions and doubly charged helium ions. If these ions are accelerated from one point to another under a difference of potential of 1,500 volts, how much additional kinetic energy does each type of ion acquire?

8. Express the mass of an electron at rest in terms of its equivalent (a) in electron volts and (b) in atomic units of mass.

9. How much energy, expressed in million electron volts, is released when a neutron combines with the nucleus of a lithium atom of mass number 6 to form an isotope of lithium of mass number 7?

37

Optical Spectra
and Atomic Structure

37-1 TYPES OF OPTICAL SPECTRA

When light passes through a prism spectroscope or a diffraction grating spectroscope, an optical spectrum is obtained which is suitable for analysis. The two most important quantities to be measured are the wavelengths and the intensities of the lines comprising the spectrum. Visual examination of the spectrum is satisfactory for measuring the wavelength of that part of the spectrum which is in the visible region. For that part of the spectrum which lies beyond the visible region—that is, in the ultraviolet or infrared regions—a photographic plate is substituted for the eyepiece of the spectroscope. The wavelengths of the lines can be determined from their positions on the photographic plate, and the intensities of the lines can be determined from the amount of blackening of the plate.

Optical spectra can be grouped into two general types: one type is the *emission* spectrum which is obtained directly from a source of light; the other is the *absorption* spectrum which is obtained when light from some source is sent through a substance before entering the spectroscope. The type of emission spectrum obtained depends upon the manner in which it is produced. Solids at high temperatures emit *continuous* spectra; so do liquids and dense, opaque gases. Gases at low pressures emit *band* or *line* spectra. Analyses show that band spectra have their origin in the energy changes which take place in the molecules of the gas, while line spectra have their origin in the energy changes which take place in the atoms of the gas.

The absorption spectra of solids and liquids are usually obtained by sending white light from some high-temperature source through the solid or liquid. The spectra obtained in this way usually show regions of color separated by dark spaces. These dark regions are characteristic of the substance absorbing the light. When white light goes through a gas or vapor, the bright regions of the spectrum are separated by very narrow *dark lines;* these dark lines forming the absorption spectrum are characteristic of the gas or vapor.

The emission spectrum of sodium vapor is shown in Figure 37–1, and a portion of the absorption spectrum of sodium vapor is shown in Figure 37–2. One is a bright-line spectrum; the other is a dark-line spectrum.

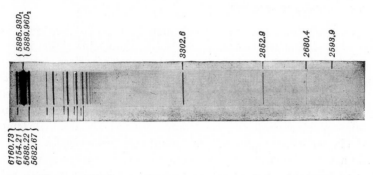

FIG. 37–1 Photograph of the emission spectrum of sodium. The lines are classified into different series. The numbers represent the wavelengths of the lines in A. (Reprinted by permission from *Atomic Spectra and Atomic Structure*, by G. Hertzberg, Dover Publications.)

FIG. 37–2 Photograph of the absorption spectrum of sodium showing some of the lines in the ultraviolet region. (Reproduced by permission from *Atomic Spectra and Atomic Structure*, by G. Hertzberg, Dover Publications.)

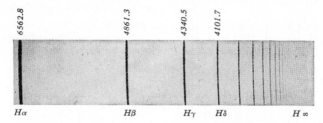

FIG. 37–3 Photograph of the emission spectrum of hydrogen showing the Balmer series lines in the visible and the near ultraviolet regions. The numbers represent the wavelengths of the corresponding lines in A. (Reprinted by permission from *Atomic Spectra and Atomic Structure*, by G. Hertzberg, Dover Publications.)

Figure 37–3 shows the emission spectrum of hydrogen in the visible region and some of the lines in the ultraviolet region.

Analyses of the various types of spectra have yielded valuable information about the states of the emitting and absorbing substances, about the

structure of the atom, and about the nature of radiation. These topics
will be considered in some detail in this and succeeding chapters.

37-2 THE CONTINUOUS SPECTRUM

The light from a hot tungsten filament produces a continuous spectrum. That part of the spectrum which is in the visible region has wavelengths which range from about 7,600 A for the longest red rays down to
about 3,800 A for the shortest visible violet rays. Wavelengths longer
than 7,600 A are said to be in the *infrared* region, while wavelengths
shorter than 3,800 A are said to be in the *ultraviolet* region. Although
there is a continuous range of wavelengths from a body at a high temperature, the intensities are different for the different wavelengths.

Of particular interest is the distribution of intensities among the wavelengths emitted by a *black body*. As stated in Chapter 16, such a body
can be constructed by placing a tungsten filament inside a hollow enclosure
which has a small aperture in it. The walls of the enclosure should be
well insulated. The tungsten filament can be heated to any desired temperature by passing a current through it; after temperature equilibrium
has been reached, the radiation coming out of the aperture is passed into a

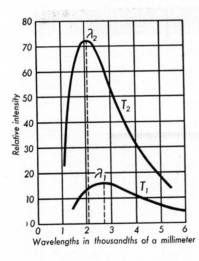

FIG. 37-4 Black-body radiation curves
showing the distribution of intensities among the different wavelengths at two different temperatures.

spectroscope, and the intensities, that is, the energies within very narrow
ranges of wavelengths, are then measured throughout the spectrum.
Figure 37-4 shows the intensity as a function of the wavelength at any one
absolute temperature T_1. The curve is characteristic of this temperature.
It will be observed that there is one particular wavelength λ_1 for which the
intensity is a maximum. If the black body is at a higher temperature T_2,

the curve has the same general features except that the intensities of all waves are increased and the wavelength λ_2, at which the intensity is a maximum, is shifted toward shorter wavelengths. A very simple relationship exists between the wavelength at which the intensity is a maximum and the temperature of the black body. This relationship is

$$\lambda_1 T_1 = \lambda_2 T_2 = b = \text{const.} \tag{1}$$

The constant b, as evaluated experimentally, is

$$b = 0.2897 \text{ cm } ^\circ\text{abs}$$

or $\quad\quad\quad b = 28.97 \times 10^6 \text{ A } ^\circ\text{abs} \quad\bigg\} \tag{2}$

This suggests a convenient method for determining the temperature of a black body or one which closely approximates a black body. The light from such a body is examined spectroscopically, and the wavelength which has the greatest intensity is determined. Its temperature can then be calculated from Equation (1). For example, the sun approximates a black body; its most intense radiation is at 5,000 A; this corresponds to a temperature of about 6,000° abs. Temperatures of some of the bright stars have been determined by this method.

Several attempts were made to explain the distribution of energy in black-body radiation on the basis of Maxwell's electromagnetic theory of light, but none of these was completely successful. The classical concept is that radiation, in its interaction with matter, is emitted or absorbed in a continuous manner. A very radical idea, introduced into physics by Max Planck in 1900, is aimed at deriving the correct equation for the distribution of energy among the different wavelengths of this radiation. Planck's idea is that radiation is emitted or absorbed by a body at temperature T in *discrete units or quanta;* each such unit is called a *quantum of radiation.* A quantum of radiation possesses a certain amount of energy $\mathcal{E}$ which is proportional to the frequency f of the radiation; that is,

$$\mathcal{E} \propto f$$

or $\quad\quad\quad\quad\quad \mathcal{E} = hf, \tag{3}$

where f is the frequency of the radiation and h is a constant known as *Planck's constant.* This quantum of energy is also called a *photon.* The measured value of Planck's constant is

$$h = 6.624 \times 10^{-27} \text{ erg sec.}$$

The hypothesis that radiant energy is emitted and absorbed in whole quanta, or bundles of energy of amount hf, first formulated by Planck, was later extended and developed by Einstein, Bohr, and others to help explain many of the phenomena observed when there is an interaction between radiation and matter.

37-3 SPECTRUM OF HYDROGEN

Hydrogen, the simplest of all the elements, has been investigated most extensively both experimentally and theoretically. The knowledge obtained from this study has acted as a guide to the study of the more complex elements. One of the greatest aids in determining the structure of the atoms of any one element has been the study of the radiation emitted and absorbed by the element. As shown in Figure 37–3, the radiation emitted by hydrogen yields a bright-line spectrum. The wavelengths of these lines have been accurately measured, and it has been found that a simple relationship exists among the wavelengths of the lines in the visible region. This relationship can be put in the form

$$\frac{1}{\lambda} = R\left(\frac{1}{2^2} - \frac{1}{n^2}\right) \qquad n = 3, 4, 5, \ldots, \tag{4}$$

where λ is the wavelength of any line in the visible region, R is a constant known as Rydberg's constant for hydrogen, and n is a whole number greater than 2. The empirical value of Rydberg's constant for hydrogen is

$$R = 109,677.76 \text{ cm}^{-1}.$$

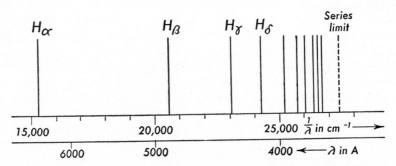

Fig. 37–5 Graph of the positions of the lines of the Balmer series. The upper scale is the reciprocal of the wavelength in centimeters, while the lower scale is the wavelength in A.

By substituting for n in Equation (4) the successive values 3, 4, 5, 6, . . . , we obtain the wavelengths of the lines in the visible region and also in the near ultraviolet region. These lines form a *series* known as the Balmer series of hydrogen. The relative positions of these lines are shown in Figure 37–5. It is obvious from Equation (4) that as n approaches infinity the wavelength difference gets smaller; the lines crowd together and approach a limit known as the *series limit*.

The first quantitatively correct derivation of the formula for the Balmer series on the basis of an atomic model was given by Bohr in 1913 in his theory of the hydrogen atom. This theory has played such an important role in the development of atomic physics that, even though it has been modified and extended by later developments, it will be worth while presenting the original simplified theory.

37-4 BOHR'S THEORY OF THE HYDROGEN ATOM

On the basis of Rutherford's nuclear theory of the structure of the atom, the hydrogen atom of mass number 1 and atomic number 1 consists of a singly charged positive nucleus and 1 electron revolving around the nucleus. In Bohr's theory of the hydrogen atom, the electron of charge $-e$ is assumed to move in a circular path around the nucleus of charge $+e$ under the force of attraction F due to these charges. This force is given by Coulomb's law

$$F = -\frac{e^2}{r^2}, \tag{5}$$

in which r is the radius of the circular orbit. The nucleus, because its mass is very large in comparison with that of the electron, is assumed to remain stationary at the center of the circle. The force on the electron owing to the attraction of the two charges is directed toward the center, and its value is given by

$$F = -\frac{mv^2}{r}, \tag{6}$$

in which m is the mass of the electron and v is its speed. The minus sign indicates that the force is directed toward the center.

The energy of this system is partly potential and the rest kinetic. The potential energy is that of the electron in the field of the nucleus. We have already shown (Section 21–11) that the potential at a distance r from a charge e is e/r; the potential energy of an electron with a charge $-e$ at this point is thus

$$-\frac{e^2}{r};$$

the negative sign is due to the negative charge on the electron. Its kinetic energy is due to the motion of the electron relative to the stationary nucleus and is simply $\frac{1}{2}mv^2$. From Equations (5) and (6), we get, for the kinetic energy,

$$\tfrac{1}{2}mv^2 = \frac{e^2}{2r}. \tag{7}$$

The total energy $\mathcal{E}$ is thus

$$\mathcal{E} = -\frac{e^2}{r} + \frac{e^2}{2r} = -\frac{e^2}{2r}. \tag{8}$$

The minus sign for the total energy indicates that it is assigned the value zero when the electron is far removed from the nucleus or when r is very great, theoretically when $r = \infty$; as the electron gets closer to the nucleus, the atom loses energy, presumably in the form of radiation.

There is nothing in this theory so far which indicates that the radiation should be emitted in the form of sharp spectral lines. It was at this point that Bohr deviated from the classical physics of the nineteenth century and introduced two hypotheses to account for the emission of sharp spectral lines by the atom. The first postulate limits the number of circular orbits of the electron to those only which satisfy a restrictive condition which may be put in the form of the equation

$$mvr = nh/2\pi, \tag{9}$$

where mv is the momentum of the electron at any point in its circular orbit of radius r. Since the direction of the momentum is at right angles to the radius, the quantity mvr is the *angular momentum* of the electron. n is an integer that can have any one of the values 1, 2, 3, . . . , and h is the Planck constant. Bohr's first postulate can then be stated as follows: *only those electron orbits are permissible for which the angular momentum of the electron is a whole multiple of $h/2\pi$.* The orbits which satisfy this restrictive condition are usually called *stationary* orbits. The integer n is called a *quantum number.*

The second postulate states that *whenever the energy of the atom is decreased from its initial value $\mathcal{E}_i$ to some final value $\mathcal{E}_f$, the atom emits radiation of frequency f in the form of whole quanta or photons of energy hf, given by the equation*

$$\mathcal{E}_i - \mathcal{E}_f = hf. \tag{10}$$

It is interesting and simple to calculate the radii and the energies of the permissible orbits and then to compare the frequencies of the radiations predicted by Bohr's second postulate with that actually observed experimentally.

The radii of the permissible orbits can be obtained by eliminating v from Equations (7) and (9) and solving for r, yielding

$$r = n^2 \frac{h^2}{4\pi^2 m e^2}. \tag{11}$$

The radii of the stationary orbits are thus given in terms of previously determined constants and the integers $n = 1, 2, 3, \ldots$, characterizing the particular orbits. By substituting the known values of h, m, and e, and setting $n = 1$, we find that the radius of the first orbit is

$$r_1 = 0.529 \times 10^{-8} \text{ cm} = 0.529 \text{ A.}$$

The energy of any orbit characterized by quantum number n can be determined by eliminating r from Equations (8) and (11), yielding

$$\mathcal{E} = -\frac{2\pi^2 m e^4}{n^2 h^2}. \tag{12}$$

FIG. 37–6 Niels Bohr. He made outstanding contributions to the modern theory of the nuclear structure of the atom and formulated the theory of nuclear processes. (Courtesy of American Institute of Physics.)

Applying Bohr's second postulate, we find that the frequency f of the radiation emitted when an electron goes from its initial orbit n_i to another orbit n_f is

$$f = \frac{\mathcal{E}_i - \mathcal{E}_f}{h},$$

so that

$$f = \frac{2\pi^2 m e^4}{h^3} \left(\frac{1}{n_f^2} - \frac{1}{n_i^2} \right). \tag{13}$$

Here is a result that can be tested by comparison with experiment. Actually it is more convenient to make the comparison with the wavelength λ of the radiation, since this is the quantity which is measured in spectroscopy.

The wavelength λ and the frequency f are related by the equation

$$\lambda f = c,$$

where c is the speed of light,

so that

$$\frac{1}{\lambda} = \frac{f}{c},$$

and, from Equation (13),

$$\frac{1}{\lambda} = \frac{2\pi^2 m e^4}{ch^3}\left(\frac{1}{n_f^2} - \frac{1}{n_i^2}\right). \tag{14}$$

This equation can be checked directly with the experimental results, since all the constants appearing in this equation are known from other experimental data. It was shown previously that the lines observed in the visible region of the hydrogen spectrum form a series known as the Balmer series, and that their wavelengths are given by the equation

$$\frac{1}{\lambda} = R\left(\frac{1}{2^2} - \frac{1}{n_i^2}\right) \tag{4}$$

with different lines appearing for the values $n_i = 3, 4, 5, \ldots$; and R is a constant, known as the Rydberg constant.

The forms of the Equations (14) and (4) are identical. If we put in the known values for the constants in Equation (14), we get

$$\frac{2\pi^2 m e^4}{ch^3} = 109,740 \text{ cm}^{-1}.$$

This quantity is in remarkably good agreement with the value of the constant R obtained empirically. The Bohr theory thus provided the first successful and satisfying explanation of the emission of sharp spectral lines by hydrogen, not only qualitatively but quantitatively as well.

The satisfaction that the scientists got from the Bohr theory was in large measure due to the fact that this theory explained the emission of radiation by means of a mechanical model of the atom. The hydrogen atom was pictured as a series of imaginary concentric rings surrounding the nucleus, as shown in Figure 37–7, with the electron at any instant in one of them. These rings represented the stationary orbits of the electron, and their radii were known from Equation (11). Each ring was characterized by a quantum number n and a definite energy $\mathcal{E}$ given by Equation (12). If the electron were initially in the orbit for which $n = 3$ and then "jumped" to the orbit for which $n = 2$, radiation would be emitted of such wavelength as to yield the red line of the visible spectrum. If it jumped from orbit $n = 4$ to orbit $n = 2$, the wavelength of the radiation corresponded to the blue line. In other words, an electron starting from any orbit for which n was greater than 2 and then jumping to the orbit for which $n = 2$ would emit radiation of a wavelength equal to that of one of the lines of the Balmer series. Since any small quantity of hydrogen con-

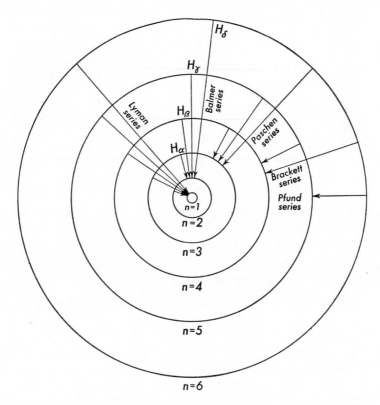

Fig. 37-7   Possible quantum jumps between stationary orbits, giving rise to the different spectral series of hydrogen.

tains an enormous number of atoms, when hydrogen is excited to emit radiation, all the lines of the Balmer series are emitted simultaneously.

In addition to the Balmer series lines, other spectral lines of hydrogen were known; some in the far ultraviolet region had been discovered by Lyman in 1906, others in the infrared region had been discovered by Paschen in 1908. The lines of the Lyman series are accounted for on the Bohr theory by jumps of electrons from outer orbits to the innermost orbit of atoms for which $n_f = 1$. In a similar manner, the lines of the Paschen series are accounted for by jumps of electrons from outer orbits to the orbit

for which $n_f = 3$.   Lines of two other series in the far infrared region for
for which $n_f = 4$ and for which $n_f = 5$ were later found by Brackett and
Pfund.   The relative positions of the lines of the known series of hydrogen
are shown in Figure 37–8.

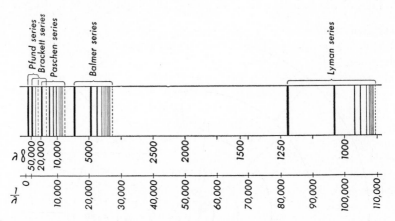

FIG. 37–8   Relative positions of the lines of the different spectral series of
hydrogen. The upper scale is in A, while the lower scale is the reciprocal
of the wavelength in centimeters.

37-5   ADDITIONAL SUCCESSES OF THE THEORY

One might stop here for a moment and inquire as to how the electrons
of the hydrogen atoms get into these various levels.   In Chapter 30, we
studied the operation of gas-discharge tubes containing such gases as hydrogen, neon, and argon.   Before the voltage is applied to such a tube, say
one containing hydrogen, most of the atoms are in the normal state; that
is, in the most stable state, or state of lowest energy.   On the basis of the
Bohr model, this would correspond to the state for which $n = 1$, with the
electron in its smallest orbit and the atom in its lowest energy level.   The
picture is complicated by the fact that under ordinary conditions hydrogen
gas consists mostly of diatomic molecules.   Because of the thermal motion
of the molecules and atoms, many collisions take place, and in some cases
these collisions produce a transfer of energy resulting in the raising of a few
atoms to higher energy levels and perhaps even in the ionizing of a few of
them.   When a high voltage is applied to the electrodes, the ions in the gas
acquire greater kinetic energy, so that more of their collisions with other
atoms and molecules result in the production of new ions.   When a steady
state is reached, there are ionized atoms and molecules and free electrons
moving under the influence of the electric field, other atoms and molecules
raised to higher energy levels but not ionized, and radiation emitted by the

atoms and molecules. Radiation is emitted by the atoms when electrons in these atoms jump to lower energy levels, giving rise to the various sharp-line spectral series observed. Also, some of the free electrons may recombine with ionized atoms, landing in one of the upper levels, and may then jump to lower levels, causing the emission of this radiation. Changes in the energy configurations of the molecules also take place; these give rise to a different type of spectrum known as a *band* spectrum. This spectrum consists of a series of bands, each of which, under very high resolving power, shows up as a series of lines very close together.

Another method of raising the hydrogen atom from its normal state to an excited state is by the absorption of light from some external source. For example, if light of wavelength equal to one of the lines of the Lyman series, say 1,025.8 A, is absorbed by the hydrogen atom, then it will raise the electron from the level for which $n = 1$ to that for which $n = 3$. Once in this higher state, the atom can return to the normal state either by the emission of the same wavelength, or in two steps, first going from orbit $n = 3$ to orbit $n = 2$ and then to orbit $n = 1$, emitting the red line of the Balmer series of wavelength 6,562.8 A and the first line of the Lyman series of wavelength 1,215.7 A. Radiation emitted as a result of the absorption of other radiation is called *fluorescent radiation*. These results have been frequently checked experimentally.

Hydrogen atoms may also be ionized by the absorption of light, providing the frequency of the incident light is greater than that of the limit of the Lyman series. The electron will then leave the atom with additional kinetic energy $\frac{1}{2}mv^2$, given by

$$\frac{1}{2}mv^2 = hf - hf_L, \tag{15}$$

in which f is the frequency of the incident radiation and f_L is the frequency corresponding to the limit of the Lyman series.

The possibilities of Bohr's theory for predicting new results have by no means been exhausted. Suppose, for example, an electron has a large amount of kinetic energy, $\frac{1}{2}mv^2$, and falls into the orbit $n = 1$ of a previously ionized atom. Then this atom should emit energy of a frequency greater than that of the Lyman series. Since there are no restrictions on the amount of energy that an electron may have outside the atom, the radiation emitted when such an electron falls into the first orbit of an ionized atom can have any frequency greater than the series limits. In other words, these should be a *continuous* spectrum beyond the Lyman series. Similarly, there should be a continuous spectrum beyond the limit of the Balmer series. These continuous spectra were looked for and actually found there.

37-6 THE HYDROGEN ENERGY-LEVEL DIAGRAM

The results discussed above can be represented in a simple and elegant manner by means of an energy-level diagram, shown in Figure 37–9. In this diagram, the energies of the various orbits corresponding to the different quantum numbers n are plotted on a vertical scale. Two different sets of numbers are shown in the diagram. The numbers on the right are the reciprocals of wavelengths in centimeters and, when multiplied by the constants ch, will yield the energy $\mathcal{E}$ in ergs. Differences between these numbers for any two energy levels give the reciprocal of the wavelength of the radiation emitted when an electron goes from the upper level to the lower one. The numbers on the left, when multiplied by the electronic charge, express the energies of the levels in electron volts, but, with the zero level as the lowest energy level and the ionization energy as the energy of the outermost level, $n = \infty$. Beyond this region the electron is outside the atom and can have any value of kinetic energy; this is the shaded region in the diagram. The numbers on the vertical lines between any two levels represent the wavelengths in Angstrom units of the radiation emitted when the energy of the atom changes from one level to the other. All lines ending at the same energy level represent spectral lines of the same series; an attempt has been made to represent the relative intensities of the spectral lines by the thickness of the lines in the diagram.

The advantage of an energy-level diagram is that it is independent of any particular model of the atom; only experimental data are used in its construction. Its construction is based upon the fact that in radiating light of frequency f, the energy of the atom is changed from a higher level $\mathcal{E}_i$ to a lower level $\mathcal{E}_f$ according to Bohr's postulate, which may be written as

$$f = \frac{\mathcal{E}_i - \mathcal{E}_f}{h}. \tag{16}$$

This condition can be, and has been, extended to account for the spectra of other atoms; and energy-level diagrams, somewhat more complicated than that for hydrogen, have been constructed from the data obtained experimentally.

37-7 THE DISCOVERY OF DEUTERIUM

Deuterium has played such an important role in the progress of nuclear physics that it is worth while presenting the history of its discovery; this discovery was another triumph of Bohr's theory of the hydrogen atom. It must be remembered that, until the discovery of deuterium in 1932, hydrogen was considered to consist of only a single isotope of mass number unity; the neutron had not yet been discovered. From the very precise

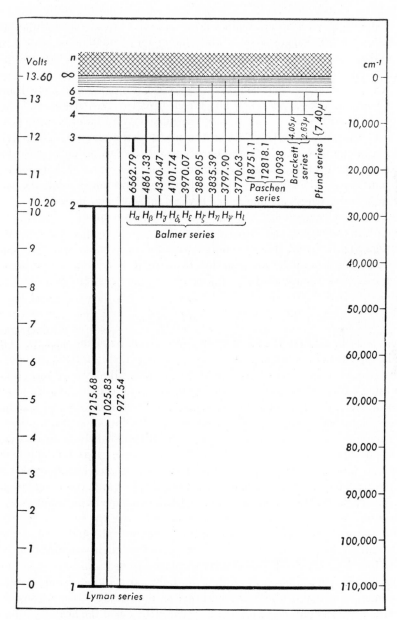

FIG. 37–9   The energy-level diagram for hydrogen.

measurements of atomic masses with the mass spectrograph, Aston computed the atomic weight of hydrogen and found that his result differed from the chemical atomic weight by about 2 parts in 10,000. Birge and Menzel, in 1931, suggested that this discrepancy could be explained by assuming that, under normal conditions, hydrogen consists of two isotopes of mass numbers 1 and 2 in the ratio of 4,500:1.

In our simplified treatment of the hydrogen atom, it was assumed that the nucleus remained stationary and the electron revolved around it. This would be correct only if the mass of the nucleus were infinite. Since the mass of the proton is 1,840 times the mass of the electron, the actual motion is one in which both the electron and the proton move with the same angular velocity about a common center, the center of mass of the two particles. Their center of mass lies along the line joining the two particles and divides this line in the inverse ratio of their masses.

If the motion of the nucleus of the hydrogen atom is taken into account, the energy of the hydrogen atom for any given quantum number n differs slightly from that calculated with the nucleus stationary. This difference consists in the introduction of a small correction factor in the denominator of Equation (14); this correction factor is simply

$$1 + \frac{m}{M},$$

where m is the mass of the electron and M is the mass of the nucleus. For the isotope of mass number 1, the ratio m/M is $1/1,840$; for the isotope of mass number 2, this ratio should be about $1/3,680$. If there are two different kinds of atoms in ordinary hydrogen, each one should give the same type of spectral series, but the corresponding lines from the two isotopes should be displaced slightly. For example, in the Balmer series, there is a blue line due to the lighter isotope, and, displaced slightly from it, there should be another blue line due to the heavier isotope. It is very simple to calculate this displacement; the two lines differ in wavelength by 1.3 A, a quantity which is measurable with a spectrograph of high resolving power.

Urey, Brickwedde, and Murphy, in 1932, performed a series of experiments on the spectrum of hydrogen in order to find the heavier isotope. They first used ordinary hydrogen in the discharge tube and, with a concave diffraction grating spectrograph, analyzed the light coming from it. They found a very faint line slightly displaced from the intense blue line of hydrogen. On the assumption that this faint line was due to the presence of a small quantity of the heavier isotope in ordinary hydrogen, they decided to prepare hydrogen with a larger concentration of the heavier isotope for use in the discharge tube. They took liquid hydrogen and allowed it to evaporate; since the lighter constituent evaporates at a greater rate, the residue should contain a greater concentration of the heavier constituent.

They put a small quantity of the residual hydrogen into the discharge tube and again examined its spectrum. This time, they found that the displaced line due to the heavier isotope was much more intense, and that its measured value of the displacement was in very good agreement with that calculated from Bohr's theory. They called the heavier isotope *deuterium.*

The existence of deuterium once having been shown, it was a comparatively simple matter to produce hydrogen and compounds containing hydrogen enriched with large concentrations of deuterium and even to prepare some with deuterium only.

37-8 CHANGES IN OUR FUNDAMENTAL CONCEPTS

Attempts to extend the Bohr theory quantitatively to the more complex atoms met with failure. The best that could be accomplished was to use the Bohr theory and model of hydrogen as a guide in a qualitative, or at best in a semiquantitative, way. For example, the Z electrons of a neutral atom of an element of atomic number Z were assumed to be moving in circular orbits about the nucleus. Since most chemical processes involve comparatively small energy changes, usually much less than 100 ev when expressed on this scale of energy, it may be assumed that the chemical properties are related to the interaction of the outer electrons of the atoms of an element. Therefore the atoms of all elements in the same column in the periodic table should have the same outer electronic structure. See Tables 5 and 6 in the Appendix. Thus the elements lithium, sodium, and potassium, which have similar chemical properties and a valence of $+1$, should each have a single electron in the outermost orbit of each of its atoms. This electron, being farthest from the nucleus, can be easily detached from the rest of the atom, leaving a singly charged positive ion. Furthermore, all of these elements present the same types of optical spectra. Analyses of these spectra into several series of lines, each one of which can be represented by an equation similar to Equation (4), together with the second Bohr postulate

$$\mathcal{E}_i - \mathcal{E}_f = hf, \tag{10}$$

can be used to determine the energy levels of the atom which give rise to the spectral lines.

What has been said above for the elements in the first column of the periodic table can be repeated for the elements in each of the other columns. For example, the elements in the second column of the periodic table, beryllium, magnesium, calcium, and so on, have valences of 2 and have similar types of optical spectra. Two electrons are assigned to the outermost orbits of each of the atoms in this column. If one electron is removed from an atom of one of these elements, the atom will be singly ionized and have the same electronic structure as an atom of the preceding group of elements. The spectra produced by these singly ionized atoms are found to be similar to those produced by the elements in the first column of the periodic table.

To determine the arrangement of the electrons which are close to the nucleus, it is necessary to consider larger energy changes than those involved in optical spectra. As we shall show later (Section 38–2), the study of x-ray spectra forms a convenient method of determining the energy levels of the electrons close to the nucleus. The present accepted assignment of electrons to the various levels of the atoms, based upon the best available chemical and physical data, is given in Table 5 of the Appendix.

Some of the difficulties of the Bohr theory were removed by the introduction of the concept of the *spin* of the electron. This concept was introduced by Uhlenbeck and Goudsmit in 1925. The spin of an electron helps to explain the *fine structure of the energy levels of an atom* which, in turn, gives rise to the fine structure of the spectral lines emitted by the atom. For example the yellow line of sodium and all the other lines of the principal series, when viewed with a good spectroscope, can be seen to consist of two lines very close together; that is, each line forms a doublet. The spin of the electron also helps to explain many of the magnetic properties of the atom, since a spinning electron behaves as a very small magnet.

At this time (1925) a new concept was introduced by Louis de Broglie to the effect that every particle of mass m moving with speed v, has associated with it a wave of wavelength λ, given by

$$\lambda = \frac{h}{mv},$$
(17)

where h is Planck's constant. Thus an electron, as well as any other particle in motion, should have a wave associated with it. The existence of the waves associated with electrons was verified in a series of remarkable experiments in 1927 and 1928 by Davisson and Germer, and by G. P. Thomson (see Section 38–6) and has led to the development of an entirely new field of physics known as *electron optics*.

These new ideas concerning the spin of the electron and the waves associated with electrons in motion were incorporated into a new theory known as *wave mechanics* or *quantum mechanics*, mainly through the work of Heisenberg, Schroedinger, Dirac, and Pauli, beginning about 1926. As a result of these developments, remarkably rapid progress was made in the next few years in putting the finishing touches to our ideas concerning the arrangement of the electrons outside the nucleus. The mathematical theory is beyond the scope of this book, but the results obtained from them will be given and discussed.

QUESTIONS

1. What is meant by (a) an optical spectral series and (b) the limit of a spectral series?

2. Name the different types of spectra and outline the origin of each type.

3. What fundamental hypotheses were introduced by Bohr to account for the hydrogen spectral lines?

4. How does the spectrum of deuterium differ from that of hydrogen?

5. What is meant by the normal state of an atom?

6. Describe the normal state of the hydrogen atom.

7. Describe two experiments with light whose results can be explained only on the basis that light is propagated as a wave motion.

8. Describe two phenomena which show that light behaves as though it consists of a stream of particles.

9. (a) What factor determines the energy of a photon? (b) Can the energy of a photon be changed? If so, describe how this can be done.

PROBLEMS

1. A tungsten filament is enclosed in a light-tight box with insulating walls; there is a small aperture in one of the walls. The filament is heated by means of an electric current, and its temperature is maintained at 3000° abs. The light coming through the aperture is analyzed with a spectrograph. (a) What kind of spectrum will be obtained? (b) Determine the wavelength which will have maximum intensity.

2. A spectroscopic analysis of the light emitted by a well-enclosed carbon arc shows a maximum intensity at the wavelength 7,213 A. Assuming that the light from the arc may be considered black-body radiation, determine the temperature of the arc.

3. Light from tungsten which is being melted in a crucible is examined with an infrared spectrometer. The maximum intensity of its spectrum is found to be at a wavelength of 7,880 A. Determine the melting point of tungsten, assuming the radiation to be that of a black body.

4. The red line of the Balmer series of hydrogen has a wavelength of 6,563 A. Determine the energy of a quantum or a photon of this radiation (a) in ergs and (b) in electron volts.

5. Calculate the energy, in electron volts, of a photon of the yellow light from a sodium lamp; the wavelength of this light is 5,890 A.

6. The first line of the Lyman series of hydrogen has a wavelength of 1,216 A and is emitted in a jump from the second Bohr orbit to the first one. Calculate the energy, in electron volts, of a photon of this radiation.

7. Using Equation (4), calculate the wavelength of the blue line of the Balmer series for which $n_i = 4$. Compare this result with the value given in Table 33–1.

8. Ultraviolet light of wavelength 2,000 A is incident on a tube containing hydrogen. Determine the minimum kinetic energy with which an electron will be ejected from hydrogen.

38

X-Rays

The study of the electric discharge through gases led directly to the discovery of x-rays by W. C. Roentgen in 1895. While operating such a tube at very low pressure, he observed that a platinum-barium cyanide screen at some distance from the tube fluoresced. He shielded the tube so that no visible radiation could reach the screen, but the fluorescence could still be observed. He also interposed various absorbing materials between the tube and the screen and found that, although the intensity of the fluorescence was reduced, it was not completely obliterated. He interpreted the phenomena as being due to radiations which, coming from the walls of the tube, penetrated these otherwise opaque materials and, upon reaching the screen, caused it to fluoresce. He called these radiations *x-rays*. The x-rays were produced when the cathode rays struck the glass walls of the electric discharge tube.

Ever since their discovery, x-rays have played an important part in the investigations of atomic physics and have added immeasurably to our knowledge of the structure of the atom. The uses of x-rays were not confined merely to the physics laboratory. Almost immediately after their discovery, they were used by physicians as aids in diagnosis and later in therapeutics. Industry turned to the use of x-rays for the study of the properties and internal structure of materials, and for the examination of castings to determine the presence of flaws so that they could be eliminated before the castings were incorporated into the final product.

X-rays are produced whenever a stream of electrons strikes some substance. There are three types of tubes in general use for the production of x-rays. An early type, shown in Figure 38–1, utilizes the electrons liberated in a low-pressure gas-discharge tube by the bombardment of the cathode by the positive ions moving under the influence of the difference of potential between the target and cathode. Since the electrons come from the cathode, they are sometimes referred to as cathode rays. These cathode rays move perpendicular to the surface of the cathode when they leave it. The cathode rays can be focused on any desired region by properly curving the cathode. If the difference of potential between the target and

792

cathode is V, the electrons reach the target with an amount of energy Ve, where e is the charge of an electron.   The target then becomes the source of x-rays.   These gas x-ray tubes are usually operated at about 30,000 to 50,000 volts.

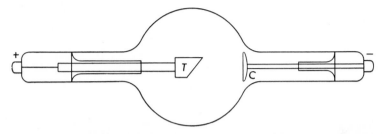

FIG. 38-1   A gas-discharge x-ray tube; C is the cathode and T is the target.

The second type of tube differs from the first one in that the source of electrons is a heated filament and the vacuum in the tube is made as high as possible (see Figure 38-2).   The filament may be heated by a battery or a step-down transformer.   The filament is usually surrounded by a

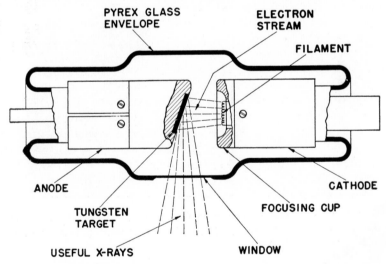

PYREX GLASS
ENVELOPE

ELECTRON
STREAM

FILAMENT

ANODE

CATHODE

TUNGSTEN
TARGET

FOCUSING CUP

USEFUL X-RAYS

WINDOW

FIG. 38-2   A modern Coolidge type x-ray tube.   (Courtesy of General Electric X-ray Department.)

metallic cup shaped to produce the desired focusing of the electron beam. One of the chief advantages of the heated-filament type of x-ray tube is the greater ease in controlling the current and voltage of the tube.   A high voltage applied to the terminals of the tube accelerates the electrons to the target; the target then becomes the source of x-rays. This type of tube is sometimes referred to as a Coolidge type of x-ray tube. Tubes of this type have been operated at voltages from a few hundred volts to about a million volts. The higher the voltage across the tube, the greater the penetrating power of the x-rays produced.

A device called a *betatron*, developed by D. W. Kerst in 1941, is the third type of x-ray tube now coming into general use wherever x-rays of very great penetrating power are desired. A betatron consists of a doughnut-shaped vacuum tube placed between the poles of a large electromagnet (see Figure 38–3). The mode of operation of a betatron can be

Fig. 38–3   The 100,000,000 electron-volt betatron. The betatron tube is in the center between the poles of the electromagnet. (Courtesy of General Electric Company.)

seen from the diagram of Figure 38–4 which shows the doughnut-shaped tube in cross-section. Electrons from a heated filament F are accelerated by a small difference of potential through a grid G. An alternating magnetic field is applied perpendicular to the path of the electrons. This produces two effects: the electron is made to travel in a circular path of radius R perpendicular to the magnetic field, and, since the field is changing, an induced emf is produced which is tangent to the circular path and thus accelerates the electron, increasing its speed and giving it additional kinetic energy as it circulates in this path. The pole pieces of the electromagnet have to be carefully shaped so that the magnetic field at every instant will be of the right form in order to keep the electrons moving in

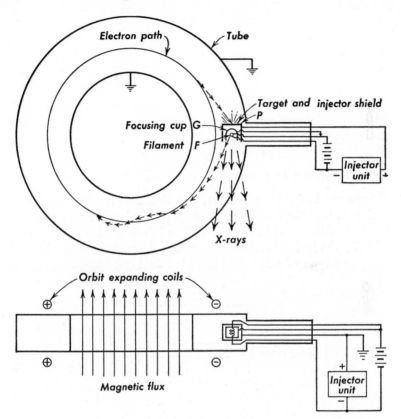

Fig. 38–4   Path of an electron in a betatron tube.

the same circular orbit. The alternating magnetic field is produced by supplying 60-cycle alternating current to the field coils of the electromagnet. The electrons are injected into the tube for a very short time at the beginning of a cycle of the alternating current, and then continue traveling around the circular orbit until the magnetic field reaches its maximum value in 1/240 sec. Each electron makes several hundred thousand revolutions in this quarter of a cycle. During each revolution the electron gains additional energy. When the electron has acquired its maximum energy, current is sent through an auxiliary set of coils; this changes the magnetic field so that the electron now moves in a larger orbit and strikes the back of the plate *P*, which acts as the target and is the source of the x-rays.

Betatrons are now being operated at energies up to 300 Mev, and modified forms of the betatron are being designed to operate at still higher energies. An unusual feature of the betatron as an x-ray tube is the fact that the x-rays, instead of coming out in all directions from the target *P*, come out in the forward direction. The x-rays are practically confined within a very small angle, from 2° to 15°, with respect to the forward direction. The efficiency of a betatron as an x-ray tube is much higher than that of a conventional x-ray tube. In one betatron, operated at 20 Mev, about 65 per cent of the electron energy was converted into x-rays. By suitable modification of the betatron, the high-energy electrons may be conducted out of the tube; these electrons may then be used for the study of atomic and nuclear phenomena.

38-2   SOME PROPERTIES OF X-RAYS

X-rays are invisible to the eye, but they can be detected by their blackening of a photographic plate or by the ionization they produce in their passage through a gas or vapor. The intensity of the x-rays can be measured by the ionization they produce in a specially designed ionization chamber, one type of which is illustrated in Figure 38–5. The x-rays

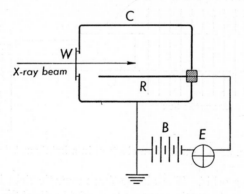

Fig. 38–5   Ionization chamber and electrometer for measuring the intensity of x-rays.

enter the chamber through a thin window made of mica or aluminum and ionize the gas in the chamber. A difference of potential between the rod *R* and cylinder *C* causes these ions to move; the motion of these ions constitutes the current in the ionization chamber. This current, though very small, can be measured with an electrometer *E*, or it may first be amplified

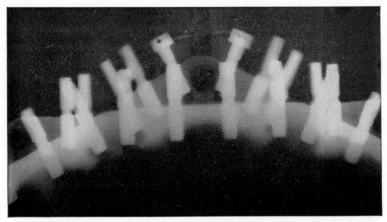

FIG. 38–6   Radiograph of an airplane motor's crankcase showing the exact position and depth of studs.   (Courtesy of General Electric X-ray Department.)

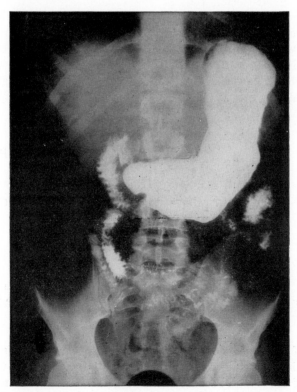

FIG. 38–7   Radiograph showing opaque barium in a stomach.   (Courtesy of General Electric X-ray Department.)

with the aid of an amplifying circuit using radio tubes, and this amplified current can then be measured with a galvanometer.

Besides being able to blacken a photographic plate and to ionize gases, x-rays can penetrate various thicknesses of substances, including those which are opaque to visible radiation. In their passage through matter, some of the x-rays are absorbed, their energy being converted into other forms, while some of the x-rays pass through and can be detected and measured. The fraction of the energy absorbed depends upon the atomic number of the substance, upon its density and thickness, and upon the wavelength of the incident x-rays.

If a beam of x-rays is sent through a composite substance made of different types of materials, the photograph can be used to reveal the nature of the materials and their locations inside the substance (see Figures 38–6 and 38–7).

38-3 DIFFRACTION AND INTERFERENCE OF X-RAYS

As a result of the fundamental work of Laue and his collaborators in 1912, it was definitely shown that x-rays are of the same nature as light and radio waves; that is, they are electromagnetic waves but of very short wavelength. If a narrow pencil of x-rays is sent through a small thin crystal, such as a piece of rock salt, and received on a photographic plate a short distance away, as shown in Figure 38–8, the photograph will show

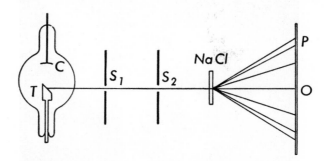

FIG. 38–8   Arrangement of apparatus for producing a Laue diffraction pattern using a rock-salt crystal. S_1 and S_2 are pinholes, and P is the photographic plate.

a series of small spots arranged in a definite pattern. This pattern, as indicated in Figure 38–9, is a diffraction pattern formed by the action of the ions of the crystal because of their regular arrangement in the crystal. The crystal in this case acts as a three-dimensional diffraction grating, and the pattern obtained on the photographic plate is called a Laue pattern.

From the distribution and intensities of the points on the photographic plate, the arrangement of the ions in the crystal can be deduced.

FIG. 38–9   Photograph of Laue diffraction pattern of rock salt. (From photograph by J. G. Dash.)

A slightly different arrangement of the x-ray beam and crystal used by Bragg gives a simpler pattern that is more easily interpreted. This is shown in Figure 38–10, in which x-rays coming from the target T of the x-ray tube pass through two narrow slits and then are incident upon the

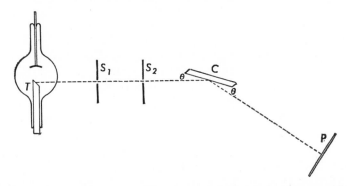

FIG. 38–10   The single crystal x-ray spectrometer with photographic plate. S_1 and S_2 are narrow slits, C is the crystal, and P is the photographic plate.

face of a crystal which is mounted on a spectrometer table. The crystal scatters the x-rays in all directions, but the photographic plate is set so as to receive only that part which comes from the face of the crystal. The angle θ between the incident beam and the face of the crystal is changed slowly by rotating the crystal. In general, the photograph will show a series of sharp lines against a continuous background. An ionization chamber can be used instead of a photographic plate. In this case, the ionization chamber measures the intensity of the x-ray beam entering it. With a very narrow slit in front of the window of the ionization chamber, it is found that the intensity of the x-ray beam coming from the crystal face is a maximum when this beam makes an angle θ with the crystal. It is for this reason that the beam is sometimes said to be "reflected" from the crystal.

A simple explanation of the action of the crystal in this case can be given with the aid of Figure 38–11, in which the ions of the crystal are

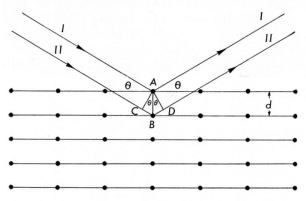

FIG. 38–11   Reflection of x-rays from atomic planes.

arranged in layers parallel to the surface of the crystal. The distance d between atomic layers is shown greatly enlarged. The x-ray beam incident upon the crystal at an angle θ to its face penetrates the crystal and is scattered by the ions in all directions. Consider two rays I and II very close together, and consider only that part of the scattered beam which makes an angle θ with the surface of the crystal. Ray I strikes the upper surface at A and is reflected; ray II strikes the next layer at B and is reflected. These two rays, which are so close together that they give a single impression on the photographic plate, have traveled different distances. From the figure, it is evident that ray II has traveled a longer distance than ray I. If originally they started out in phase, they will now differ in phase because of the difference in their paths. This difference in path is $CB + BD$, which is related to the distance d between atomic planes and the angle θ by the relationships

$$CB = d \sin \theta,$$

$$BD = d \sin \theta,$$

or $$CB + BD = 2d \sin \theta.$$

If this difference in path is a whole wavelength λ or a whole number n of wavelengths, then the two rays will reinforce each other after scattering and will produce an intense spot on the photographic plate or be registered as an intense beam by the ionization chamber. Thus, whenever

$$n\lambda = 2d \sin \theta, \qquad (1)$$

there will be reinforcement of the waves "reflected" by the crystal.

Equation (1) is called the *Bragg equation;* it is of fundamental importance in determining x-ray wavelengths and in the analysis of the structure of crystals. If the distance d between atomic or ionic planes is known, then the wavelength can readily be determined. n is an integer called the order of the spectrum; when n is 1, the path difference $CB + BD$ is 1 wavelength and is in the first-order spectrum; when n is 2, the path difference is 2 wavelengths, and the wavelength is said to appear in the second order. It will be noted that a crystal acts as a three-dimensional diffraction grating for x-rays; the distance d is frequently referred to as the *crystal grating space.*

Illustrative Example. An x-ray line of wavelength 1.541 A is reflected from a quartz crystal in which the distance d between atomic planes is 4.255 A. Determine the angle between the x-ray beam and the atomic planes (a) in the first order and (b) in the second order.

Solving the Bragg equation for $\sin \theta$, we get

$$\sin \theta = \frac{n\lambda}{2d}.$$

(a) Now $\lambda = 1.541 \times 10^{-8}$ cm, $d = 4.255 \times 10^{-8}$ cm, and, in the first order, $n = 1$; calling θ_1 the angle between the x-ray beam and the atomic planes for the first-order reflection, we have

$$\sin \theta_1 = \frac{1.541}{2 \times 4.255},$$

from which $\qquad\qquad\qquad \sin \theta_1 = 0.1811$

and $\qquad\qquad\qquad\qquad \theta_1 = 10°26'.$

(b) In the second order, $n = 2$; calling the angle between the x-ray beam and the atomic planes θ_2 for the second-order reflection, we have

$$\sin \theta_2 = \frac{2 \times 1.541}{2 \times 4.255},$$

from which $\qquad\qquad\qquad \sin \theta_2 = 0.3622$

and $\qquad\qquad\qquad\qquad \theta_2 = 21°14'.$

38-4 X-RAYS AND CRYSTAL STRUCTURE

In using the Bragg equation, it is essential that we know independently either the x-ray wavelength λ, or the spacing d between atomic or ionic planes. At the time of the discovery of x-ray diffraction and interference, the crystal grating space of rock salt was determined from other data, and the value d so obtained was used to measure x-ray wavelengths. Figure 38–12 shows the arrangement of the ions in a rock-salt crystal. The

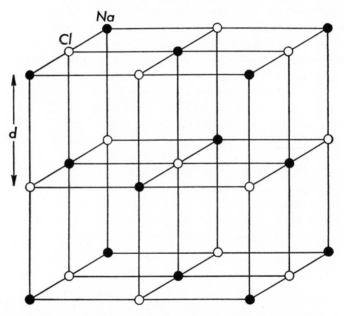

Fig. 38–12 The arrangement of sodium (Na) ions and chlorine (Cl) ions in a crystal of salt.

crystal is known to be a cube from crystallographic studies; the centers of the ions are at the corners of the cubes. It will be observed that each sodium ion (Na^+) is surrounded by 6 chlorine ions (Cl^-), and that each chlorine ion is surrounded by 6 sodium ions. If d is the length of the cube, then the volume of each cube is $V = d^3$. This is the volume associated with each ion. If M is the gram-molecular weight of sodium chloride and if ρ (rho) is its density, then the volume v of 1 mole of sodium chloride is

$$v = \frac{M}{\rho}.$$

Now, there are $2N_0$ ions in each mole of sodium chloride, where N_0 is the

Avogadro number; hence the volume associated with each ion is

$$V = \frac{v}{2N_0} = \frac{M}{2\rho N_0} .$$

The distance d between ions is therefore

$$d = \sqrt[3]{\frac{M}{2\rho N_0}} . \tag{2}$$

All the quantities on the right-hand side of Equation (2) are known; hence d can be calculated as follows:

The gram-molecular weight M is the sum of the gram-atomic weights of sodium and chlorine and is

$$M = 22.997 + 35.457 = 58.454 \text{ gm};$$

the density is $\rho = 2.164 \text{ gm/cm}^3$ at 18°C,

and $N_0 = 6.0248 \times 10^{23}$;

hence $d = \sqrt[3]{\dfrac{58.454}{2 \times 2.164 \times 6.0248 \times 10^{23}}} \text{ cm},$

from which $d = 2.820 \times 10^{-8} \text{ cm}$

or $d = 2.820 \text{ A}$ at 18°C.

With the value of the grating space of rock salt known, it is now possible to measure x-ray wavelengths with a single-crystal spectrometer and study x-ray spectra and, using known wavelengths, to determine the grating spaces of other crystals. However, in order to use a crystal with an x-ray spectrometer, the crystal must be of a reasonable size, say 1 or 2 cm in length and width. Such large crystals, sometimes called single crystals, may be found in nature, or may sometimes be grown from saturated solutions in the case of various types of salt crystals or by the slow cooling of molten material in the case of metals.

The ordinary solid is not a large single crystal but is made up of many very small crystals called *microcrystals*. Even when the solids are in powder form, they consist of many microcrystals. A very powerful method of x-ray analysis of these microcrystals was developed by A. W. Hull, and independently by P. Debye and P. Scherrer. This method consists in sending a very narrow pencil of x-rays of a single wavelength or of a few known wavelengths through a very small sample of the powder or solid, as shown in Figure 38–13. Since the powder or solid consists of a great many microcrystals oriented at random, there is some probability that one of these microcrystals will be oriented so that its atomic planes make an angle θ with the incident radiation, which will satisfy the Bragg equation for the particular wavelength λ of the incident x-rays. Because of the random orientation of these microcrystals, there undoubtedly will be other microcrystals whose atomic planes make the same angle θ with the incident

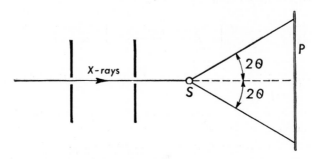

FIG. 38–13 Method of obtaining x-ray diffraction patterns using a powder.

x-rays but in different planes of incidence. In each plane of incidence, the angle between the original beam and the reflected beam will be 2θ. A photographic plate, placed at right angles to the incident beam at a convenient distance from the sample, will record the diffraction pattern. It

FIG. 38–14 X-ray powder diffraction pattern of aluminum. (Reproduced with the permission of A. W. Hull.)

will be found that this pattern consists of a series of circles, as shown in Figure 38–14. Each circle is the intersection of a cone of central angle 4θ and the plane of the photographic plate. The radius of such a circle depends upon the distance of the plate from the sample, upon the wavelength of the incident x-rays, upon the order n of the diffraction, and upon the grating space d of the crystal.

In a variation of the above method, the photographic plate is replaced by a photographic film bent in the form of a cylinder with the sample at its center. Holes are cut in the film so that the direct pencil of x-rays can

W Powder

FIG. 38–15 X-ray powder diffraction pattern of tungsten obtained with a photographic film bent in the form of a circular cylinder. X-rays from a copper target were used in making this photograph. (From a photograph made by L. L. Wyman and supplied by A. W. Hull.)

enter and leave this camera without blackening the film. When this film is unrolled and developed, we obtain the type of pattern shown in Figure 38–15.

The x-ray powder diffraction method is capable of very high precision and is being used extensively for the analyses of crystal structures.

38-5 X-RAY SPECTRA AND ATOMIC STRUCTURE

When x-rays from any target are analyzed with a crystal spectrometer, the spectrum is found to consist of a series of sharp lines superposed on a continuous background of radiation (see Figure 38–16). The energy in the continuous radiation, sometimes referred to as the *continuous spectrum*, is found to depend upon the voltage across the tube, the current in it, and the atomic number of the element which constitutes the target; the higher the atomic number, the greater is the energy, the other quantities remaining constant. The sharp lines which are superposed on the continuous radiation are found to be characteristic of the element of the target.

The first systematic study of the characteristic x-ray spectra of the elements was made by Moseley in 1913. He used a modification of the Bragg method; the crystal spectrometer and the photographic plate were placed in an evacuated chamber to avoid absorption in air of the x-rays of long wavelength. Each element investigated was used as the target of an x-ray tube. He found that all the elements gave similar types of spectra; the lines emitted by each element were classified into two groups or series: a group of short wavelength called the K series, and a group of comparatively long wavelength called the L series. These two series are widely separated from one another in wavelength, as illustrated in Figure 38–17 for the case of silver. Other investigators have found two other series of still longer wavelengths in the heavier elements, classified as M series and N series.

The high frequencies and short wavelengths of the x-ray lines, as well as the high voltages needed to produce them, indicate that the atom undergoes large energy changes when emitting x-rays. It may therefore be assumed that these energy changes involve those electrons which are close

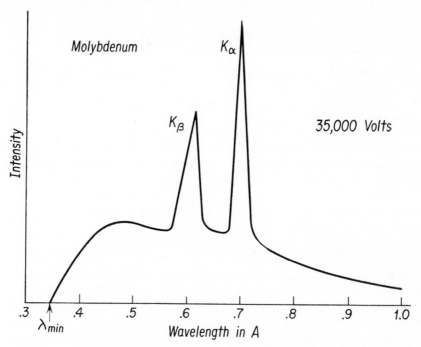

FIG. 38-16 Characteristic K_α and K_β lines superposed on the continuous x-ray spectrum of molybdenum. Note the sharp cutoff at the wavelength $\lambda_{\min}$.

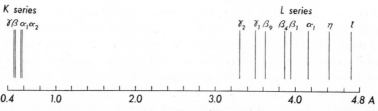

FIG. 38-17 Relative positions of the K and L x-ray series lines of silver.

to the nucleus. The results of many different types of experiments lead to the conclusion that the electrons of an atom are grouped in certain *shells* or *levels*, and the present accepted assignment of electrons to the various levels in the normal atom is given in Table 5 of the Appendix. These levels are designated by either a letter or a number. Both designations are given in the table. The letters start with K for the innermost level and continue with L, M, and so on, for the outer levels. The numbers used to designate these levels are called the *principal quantum numbers* and are obtained as a result of the extension of Bohr's theory of the hydrogen spectrum to the x-ray spectra of the elements. The K level thus is assigned the principal quantum number 1, the L level is assigned the principal quantum number 2, and so on. All of the heavier elements have a K level of principal quantum number 1, containing 2 electrons. These elements also have an L level, of principal quantum number 2, containing 8 electrons in the normal state. Some atoms also have M, N, ... levels of principal quantum numbers 3, 4, ... , respectively.

The fact that all heavier elements emit lines of the K series indicates that these series have common origins. The same thing holds true for those elements which emit L series lines and M series lines. For example, the frequency of the most intense line of the K series can be written in the form

$$f = cR(Z-1)^2 \left(\frac{1}{1^2} - \frac{1}{2^2} \right), \tag{3}$$

in which R is the Rydberg constant, c is the velocity of light, and Z is the atomic number of the element emitting this line of frequency f. The interpretation of this equation is that this line is emitted when an electron goes from the orbit of principal quantum number 2 to the orbit of principal quantum number 1.

To understand the appearance of the factor $(Z-1)$ in the equation rather than Z, let us consider how the x-rays are produced. In the atoms of the elements investigated, the orbits of principal quantum numbers 1 and 2 are completely filled. An electron coming from the cathode of the x-ray tube approaches the target with an amount of energy Ve, where V is the voltage across the tube. When such an electron approaches an atom in the target, this electron may, if it has sufficient energy, knock an electron out of the orbit for which $n = 1$. Since the other electrons in this atom are in their normal states, the electron which has been knocked out of the innermost orbit must go outside the atom; that is, the atom has been ionized by the removal of an electron from the innermost orbit. The atom is thus left in an excited state. It is highly probable that an electron from the next orbit for which $n = 2$ may jump into the innermost orbit for which $n = 1$, thereby emitting radiation of the frequency f given by the above equation. As for the factor $(Z-1)$, since normally the orbit $n = 1$ has 2 electrons, when one is removed, the other electron still remaining in this orbit has the effect of "screening" the Z positive charges of the nucleus. Hence, when an electron goes from orbit $n = 2$ to orbit $n = 1$, it moves in an electric field due to Z positive charges and 1 negative charge or effectively $(Z - 1)$ positive charges.

It is also possible for an electron from orbit $n = 3$ to go into the orbit $n = 1$; if this happens it will give rise to another line of the K series. Considering all the atoms in the target which have electrons knocked out of the innermost orbit $n = 1$, we find that it is more probable that an electron from orbit $n = 2$ will go into orbit $n = 1$ than that an electron from orbit $n = 3$ will go into orbit $n = 1$. This will manifest itself in the greater intensity of the line due to the transition 2 to 1 than that due to the transition 3 to 1; this is in agreement with observed results. Of course, the transition of an electron from $n = 4$ to $n = 1$ is also possible, but the probability will be very small; hence the line of the K series due to this transition will be very weak.

The interpretation of the x-ray spectra is simplified by the use of an energy-level diagram, such as that shown in Figure 38–18. Let us take the

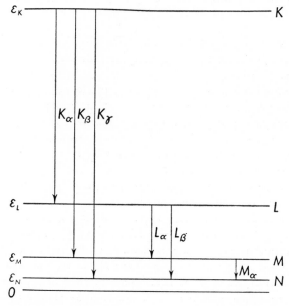

Fɪɢ. 38–18   Simplified x-ray energy-level diagram.

normal atom with all its electrons in their normal states as our zero level of energy. When an electron is removed from the innermost orbit, a certain amount of energy has to be supplied to do this; let us call this amount of energy $\mathcal{E}_K$, and we shall say that the atom is in the K state. If, however, an electron from orbit $n = 2$ is removed from the neutral atom, then a smaller amount of energy will be needed; let us call this amount of energy

$\mathcal{E}_L$ and say that the atom is now in the L state. If an electron from orbit $n = 3$ is removed from the neutral atom, a still smaller amount of energy $\mathcal{E}_M$ will be needed, and the atom will be in the M state. An atom in the N state would correspond to one which had an electron removed from the orbit $n = 4$. These energy states are plotted in the diagram.

Suppose that an atom has been raised to the K state by the removal of an electron from orbit $n = 1$. If an electron goes from orbit $n = 2$ to orbit $n = 1$, the atom will be left in the L state, and radiation of frequency

$$f = \frac{\mathcal{E}_K - \mathcal{E}_L}{h} \tag{4}$$

will be emitted; we shall call this radiation the K_α line. If, however, an electron from orbit $n = 3$ should go to orbit $n = 1$, the atom will go from the K state to the M state with the emission of radiation of frequency

$$f = \frac{\mathcal{E}_K - \mathcal{E}_M}{h} \, . \tag{5}$$

In the diagram, this is called the K_β line. The K_γ line will be emitted when an electron goes from orbit $n = 4$ to orbit $n = 1$, the atom going from the K state to the N state.

If an atom is in the L state, either because of the ejection of an electron from orbit $n = 2$ or because an electron from this orbit went to orbit $n = 1$, an electron from another orbit will go to orbit $n = 2$ with the emission of a line of the L series. The frequency of each of these lines will be given by the same type of formula given above, a formula first introduced by Bohr in his theory of the hydrogen atom.

Advances in the study of x-ray spectra, due in great part to the increase in the precision and the resolving power of the instruments used, and also to the amount of energy available from improved types of x-ray tubes, have shown that many of the lines have two or more components. The simple energy-level diagram used above must obviously be modified, principally by the introduction of more energy levels very close to some of the existing ones. There is another method of studying the electronic structure of the atom which is more instructive. This makes use of x-rays from an external source incident upon the element to be investigated. Here we may expect that x-rays will behave just like other forms of radiation incident upon matter; that is, that they will knock electrons out of the atom. This is the *photoelectric effect* with x-rays. There are two general methods for investigating this phenomenon: one is to study the x-rays after they have traversed a known thickness of an element; the other is to study the electrons which are ejected from the element by the incident x-rays.

A simple type of experiment for determining the energy of the ejected electron is outlined in Figure 38–19. X-rays of known wavelength and frequency enter an evacuated chamber through a thin window W and are incident upon the substance under investigation mounted on a holder C.

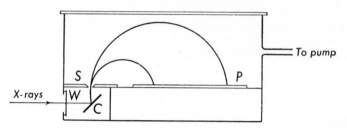

FIG. 38–19   Magnetic spectrograph for determining the atomic energy levels.

Electrons which are ejected from this substance come out in all directions; some of them pass through the narrow slit S into the upper region of the chamber. The entire chamber is placed in a magnetic field whose direction is perpendicular to the plane of the figure. This magnetic field causes the electrons to move in circular paths and strike the photographic plate P. The distance from the slit S to the point at which the electrons strike the photographic plate is the diameter of the circle.

The force exerted by the magnetic field is Bev, where B is the magnetic flux density, e the charge on the electron, and v its velocity. This is the centripetal force and is therefore equal to mv^2/R or

$$Bev = \frac{mv^2}{R},$$

from which
$$v = BR\,\frac{e}{m}. \tag{6}$$

In these equations B and e are in electromagnetic units. The velocity of the electron is thus readily determined, since all the other quantities are known or measurable. The energy required to remove the electron from its particular orbit can be easily calculated. If f is the frequency of the incident x-rays, each photon possesses an amount of energy hf. Suppose that an electron is knocked out from the innermost orbit of the atom; the energy required to do this is $\mathcal{E}_K$. The difference between these two energies is the kinetic energy with which the electron leaves the atom; that is,

$$hf - \mathcal{E}_K = \tfrac{1}{2}mv^2. \tag{7}$$

Since the frequency f is known and v is measured, $\mathcal{E}_K$ can be calculated. Many of the atomic energy levels have been determined in this manner.

The information obtained by the study of optical and x-ray spectra has played an important part in establishing our present view of atomic structure, particularly the arrangement and distribution of electrons outside the nucleus. In addition, other chemical and physical evidence has been used to supply much-needed information. It is beyond the scope of this book to go into greater detail in this matter. For information concerning the nucleus of the atom, we must delve into the subject of radioactivity; this is done in the next chapter.

38-6 PARTICLES AND WAVES

We have shown the different stages in the development of our present concept concerning the nature of radiation; that is, radiation has a dual character, that of a wave motion and that of a corpuscular or particle nature. We look upon these as two complementary modes of describing the interaction between radiation and matter. The wave character of radiation has been amply verified by all the phenomena which are classified as interference or diffraction phenomena. These waves are now known to be electromagnetic waves.

The corpuscular character of radiation was first introduced by Planck to explain the distribution of energy in the continuous spectrum of a black body at a high temperature. In order to account for this energy distribution, he had to assume that whenever radiation is emitted or absorbed by matter, it is emitted or absorbed in whole quanta, each quantum or photon having energy

$$\mathcal{E} = hf, \tag{8}$$

where f is the frequency of the radiation. Bohr made use of this idea in his theory of the hydrogen atom; his second postulate states that whenever the energy of an atom changes from $\mathcal{E}_i$ to $\mathcal{E}_f$ by the emission of radiation, the energy is radiated as a whole quantum of frequency f, given by

$$\mathcal{E}_i - \mathcal{E}_f = hf, \tag{9}$$

where h is the Planck constant.

Einstein used the corpuscular nature of radiation in explaining the photoelectric effect. Einstein's photoelectric equation is

$$hf = \tfrac{1}{2}mv^2 + \mathcal{E}, \tag{10}$$

where hf is the energy of the photon, $\tfrac{1}{2}mv^2$ is the kinetic energy of the electron ejected from a substance, and $\mathcal{E}$ is the energy required to remove the electron from the substance.

Furthermore, from the principle of equivalence of mass and energy,

$$\mathcal{E} = mc^2; \quad [\text{Equation (5) in Chapter 36}]$$

a photon of frequency f can be considered a particle of mass m, given by

$$m = \frac{hf}{c^2}.$$

It may also be assigned a momentum, which, it will be recalled, is the product of the mass of the particle by its velocity. Since the velocity of a photon is c, its momentum p is

$$p = mc \tag{11}$$

$$= \frac{hf}{c^2} \cdot c,$$

or

$$p = \frac{hf}{c}. \tag{12}$$

Another very convincing type of evidence concerning the corpuscular nature of radiation is provided by the *Compton effect*. Suppose a beam of x-rays of frequency f and wavelength λ is incident upon a substance which then scatters it in various directions. If we examine the scattered beam with an x-ray crystal spectrometer, we find that the beam consists of x-rays not only of frequency f and wavelength λ but also of lower frequency f' and thus of higher wavelength λ'. The explanation of this effect, given by A. H. Compton, is that the x-ray photon collides with an electron and is scattered by it, and, if the electron is free to move, the photon gives up some of its energy to the electron. Using the principle of conservation of energy, we can write

$$hf = hf' + \tfrac{1}{2}mv^2, \tag{13}$$

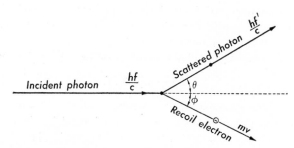

Fɪɢ. 38–20   The Compton effect: scattering of a photon and recoil of an electron as a result of a collision.

where hf is the energy of the incident photon, hf' the energy of the scattered photon, and $\tfrac{1}{2}mv^2$ the kinetic energy of the scattered electron. Since this is a collision between two particles, we can apply the principle of conservation of momentum to this process. Figure 38–20 shows the incident photon with momentum hf/c, the photon scattered through an angle θ with momentum hf'/c, and the electron recoiling as a result of the collision with momentum mv in a direction making an angle ϕ (phi) with the original direction of the incident radiation. From the principle of conservation of momentum, we get the equations

$$\frac{hf}{c} = \frac{hf'}{c} \cos\theta + mv \cos\phi \qquad (14)$$

and

$$0 = \frac{hf'}{c} \sin\theta - mv \sin\phi. \qquad (15)$$

Equation (14) states that the initial momentum along the original direction of the x-ray beam is equal to the components in this direction of the final momenta of the scattered photon and the recoil electron. Equation (15) is a similar expression for the components of the momenta at right angles to the original direction of motion.

If the above three equations are solved for the frequency of the scattered photon, and the result is then converted to their corresponding wavelengths, the result obtained is

$$\boxed{\lambda' - \lambda = \frac{h}{mc}(1 - \cos\theta),} \qquad (16)$$

where λ' is the wavelength of the ray scattered at an angle θ and λ is the original wavelength. The change in wavelength depends only upon the angle of scattering and not upon the substance. The results predicted by Equation (16) have been amply verified by many careful experiments. The energy and momentum of the recoil electron have also been measured, and the results were found to be in agreement with the predictions obtained from solutions of the above equation.

As has previously been stated, Louis de Broglie, using the dual character of radiation as a guide, put forth the hypothesis that there should be a wave motion associated with every material particle. If m is the mass of a particle and v its speed, then the wavelength λ associated with this particle is, from de Broglie's hypothesis,

$$\lambda = \frac{h}{mv}. \qquad (17)$$

Equation (17) can be shown to be identical in form with Equation (12) For a photon,

$$\lambda f = c,$$

or

$$f/c = \frac{1}{\lambda};$$

hence Equation (12) becomes

$$p = \frac{h}{\lambda},$$

or
$$\lambda = \frac{h}{p}.$$
(18)

If we call the momentum of a material particle $mv = p$, then Equation (17) also becomes

$$\lambda = \frac{h}{p}.$$
(18)

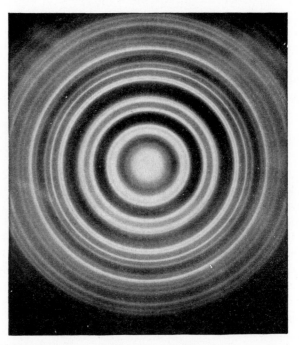

FIG. 38–21   Electron diffraction pattern of gold; thickness of the gold film was about 250 A.   (Reproduced from photograph by Oliver Row and N. R. Mukherjee.)

De Broglie's hypothesis was verified by two classic experiments—one performed by Davisson and Germer in 1927, and the other performed by G. P. Thomson in 1928.   In the Davisson-Germer experiment, a stream of electrons was reflected from a nickel crystal.   Intense maxima were observed at certain angles of reflection which could be explained only in terms of the reinforcement of the electron waves from different atomic layers of the nickel crystal. The Bragg equation holds for electron waves just as it does for x-ray waves. The wavelength computed in this manner agrees completely with the wavelength predicted by the de Broglie equation.

In the Thomson experiment, a stream of electrons of known velocity was sent through a very thin metal foil. Since a metal foil consists of many microcrystals oriented at random, the pattern obtained is similar to that obtained with the powdered crystal x-ray diffraction experiments. From the results of these experiments, G. P. Thomson was able to compute the grating space of the metallic crystals in the thin foil, and the results agreed very well with those obtained by x-ray diffraction and interference experiments. Figure 38–21 shows the diffraction pattern obtained when a narrow beam of electrons has gone through a very thin gold foil.

The wave character of material particles is not limited to electrons but is characteristic of all matter. Diffraction patterns have been obtained by reflecting hydrogen and helium molecules from crystal surfaces. The wavelengths computed from the results of these experiments agreed with those calculated from Equation (18), where the velocity v of the molecules was determined from a knowledge of the temperature of the gas.

38-7 THE ELECTRON MICROSCOPE

One of the practical results which followed from de Broglie's hypothesis was the development of a new field of physics known as *electron optics*. For example, surface phenomena are studied by reflecting electrons of known velocity and hence of known wavelength from surfaces, and the resulting diffraction patterns are interpreted in terms of the atomic, molecular, and crystal structure in and near the surface. If some chemical reaction takes place, corrosion of the surface, for example, the electron diffraction pattern will change; from the change in this pattern, we can infer what took place during the corrosive process.

It will be recalled that the optical microscope has certain limitations; one of these is that its resolving power is limited by the wavelength of light used. With shorter wavelengths, greater resolving power may be obtained. It is possible to get shorter wavelengths using electron waves rather than light waves. For example, if we use electrons which have been accelerated through a difference of potential V, then the velocity of such electrons is given by the equation

$$Ve = \tfrac{1}{2}mv^2,$$

from which

$$v = \sqrt{2V\frac{e}{m}},$$

and the wavelength associated with such electrons is. from de Broglie's equation,

$$\lambda = \frac{h}{mv} \; ; \tag{17}$$

hence

$$\lambda = \frac{h}{\sqrt{2Vme}} \cdot \tag{19}$$

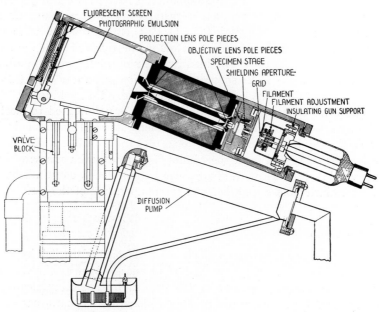

FLUORESCENT SCREEN
PHOTOGRAPHIC EMULSION
PROJECTION LENS POLE PIECES
OBJECTIVE LENS POLE PIECES
SPECIMEN STAGE
SHIELDING APERTURE
GRID
FILAMENT
FILAMENT ADJUSTMENT
INSULATING GUN SUPPORT
VALVE BLOCK
DIFFUSION PUMP

FIG. 38–22 A simplified cross section of a small electron-microscope unit. (Courtesy of RCA Laboratories.)

Suppose that $V = 100$ volts. Since the electronic charge

$e = 1.60 \times 10^{-19}$ coul,

$Ve = 1.60 \times 10^{-17}$ joule,

or $Ve = 1.60 \times 10^{-10}$ erg.

Now $h = 6.62 \times 10^{-27}$ erg sec   and $m = 9.1 \times 10^{-28}$ gm.

Substituting these values in Equation (19) will yield the wavelength in cm; thus

$$\lambda = \frac{6.62 \times 10^{-27}}{\sqrt{2 \times 1.60 \times 10^{-10} \times 9.1 \times 10^{-28}}} \text{ cm,}$$

from which $\lambda = 1.23 \times 10^{-8}$ cm,

or $\lambda = 1.23$ A.

This wavelength is of the order of atomic dimensions.

Figure 38–22 is a simplified diagram of an electron microscope. Instead of glass lenses, permanent magnets are used to focus the electron

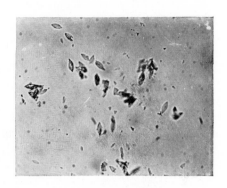

Fig. 38–23 Photograph with an optical microscope of crystals of monohydrated aluminum oxide. Magnification 500×. (Courtesy of J. Hillier, RCA Laboratories.)

Fig. 38–24 Electron-microscope photograph of the tip of one of the crystals of Figure 38–23. Magnification 90,000×. (Courtesy of J. Hillier, RCA Laboratories.)

stream which passes through the object under investigation. The final image can be viewed on a fluorescent screen or photographed on a photographic plate or film. Just as with the optical microscope, the image formation can be determined by tracing rays, that is, tracing the paths of the electrons as particles, through the magnetic lens system. But the limit of the resolving power can be determined only from a knowledge of the waves associated with the electrons. Electron microscopes are being operated at voltages ranging from 20 kv to about 100 kv. The highest resolving power so far attained is about 20 A.

The meaning of resolving power and a comparison of the resolving powers of a very good optical microscope and a very good electron microscope are shown in the photographs of Figures 38–23 and 38–24. In each case the actual resolving power is about a factor of three from the theoretical limit of resolution of the microscopes used.

QUESTIONS

1. Compare an optical spectrum such as that emitted by hydrogen and an x-ray spectrum such as that emitted by silver with respect to (a) method of production, (b) energy changes of the atom, and (c) the origin of each one.

2. What is the essential difference between the optical energy-level diagram and the x-ray energy-level diagram?

3. Suppose that silver, $Z = 47$, is used as the target of an x-ray tube and that some of its atoms have been put into the K energy state by the action of the electrons which struck the target. (a) How many electrons are there in each atom in the K state? (b) Discuss the possible energy changes which may occur as a result of this. (c) Which lines of the x-ray spectrum will be emitted as a result of these atoms being in the K energy state?

4. When the square root of the frequency of a characteristic x-ray line such as the K_α line is plotted as ordinate and the atomic number of the element emitting it is plotted as abscissa, the resulting graph is called a Moseley diagram. What kind of curve should one obtain on this diagram?

5. State the fundamental law of electromagnetism which is involved in the method used to accelerate the electrons in a betatron.

6. What factor determines the change in wavelength produced in the Compton effect?

PROBLEMS

1. A single-crystal x-ray spectrometer with a quartz crystal is used to analyze the x-rays from an x-ray tube with a molybdenum target. The wavelength of the K_α line of molybdenum is 0.7078 A. Determine the angle between the incident beam and the face of the crystal so that this line may be reflected from the crystal.

2. A single-crystal x-ray spectrometer with a calcite crystal is used to analyze the x-rays from an x-ray tube with a silver target. A very intense line is obtained when the beam makes an angle of 5°17′ with the crystal. Determine the wavelength of this line. The grating space of calcite is 3.0294 A.

3. The K energy level of silver is 25,500 ev. X-rays of wavelength 0.40 A incident upon a silver foil eject electrons from the K levels of some of the silver atoms. (a) Determine the energy of the incident photons. (b) Determine the kinetic energy of the ejected electrons.

4. Determine the change in wavelength produced when an x-ray photon is scattered by a substance (a) through an angle of 90° and (b) through an angle of 180°.

5. X-rays of wavelength 0.500 A are incident upon a block of carbon. (a) Determine the energy of the photons of the incident beam. (b) Determine the change in energy of the photons which are scattered through an angle of 90°. (c) Assuming that this scattering is due to free electrons which originally had negligible energy and momenta, determine the energy of the recoil electrons.

6. Referring to Problem 5, determine (a) the momenta of the incident photons, (b) the momenta of the photons scattered through 90° and (c) the momenta of the recoil electrons.

7. (a) Determine the wavelength associated with an electron whose energy is 1,600 ev. (b) Assuming Bragg's law to hold for the waves associated with electrons, determine the angle at which a stream of electrons should be directed toward the surface of a rock-salt crystal to obtain maximum reflection, if the energy of these electrons is 1,600 ev.

8. An electron is moving with a velocity of 2×10^8 cm/sec. Determine (a) its momentum and (b) the wavelength associated with this electron.

9. A proton is moving with a velocity of 2×10^8 cm/sec. Determine (a) its momentum and (b) the wavelength associated with this proton.

10. A stream of gas consists of helium atoms moving with an average speed of 3×10^5 cm/sec. Determine (a) the average momentum of these atoms and (b) the wavelength associated with these atoms.

39

Natural Radioactivity

39-1 THE DISCOVERY OF RADIOACTIVITY: EVIDENCE FROM THE NUCLEUS

The discovery of an important phenomenon usually leads to other important discoveries. The discovery of x-rays by Roentgen in 1895 led to the discovery of radioactivity by Becquerel in 1896. In the gas type of x-ray tube used by Roentgen, the glass walls of the tube were observed to fluoresce. Becquerel was interested in determining whether there was any relationship between the fluorescence of the glass of an x-ray tube and the phosphorescence of certain salts which were irradiated by ordinary light. One of the salts used by Becquerel was the double sulphate of uranium and potassium. He wrapped a photographic plate in very thick black paper, placed a crystal of the uranium salt on it, and exposed the whole thing to sunlight. Later, on developing the plate, he found the silhouette of the crystals on the negative; he interpreted this as produced by radiations coming from the crystal. He also performed other experiments in which he placed various absorbing materials between the uranium salt and the photographic plate; in each case, upon developing the plate, he found the shadow of the absorbing material imaged on the plate; he interpreted this as being due to the absorption of the radiation by the substance which had been placed between the uranium salt and the photographic plate. The crowning experiment was the one in which he decided not to irradiate the salt with light from an external source but to determine whether the salt was itself the source of these radiations. For these experiments he built a light-tight box that would hold a photographic plate at the bottom. In one experiment, some uranium salt crystals were placed on the photographic plate; later, on developing this plate, Becquerel obtained the silhouettes of the individual crystals. In another experiment, he put a piece of aluminum between the uranium crystals and the photographic plate, and, on developing the plate, he again found the silhouettes of the crystals, but they were of decreased intensity due to the absorption of some of the radiations by the aluminum. From these experiments, Becquerel concluded that the radiations came from the uranium salt, and that the external light had no influence on these radiations.

Becquerel then proceeded with a series of experiments to determine the origin of these radiations. He used a variety of compounds of uranium in these experiments and came to the conclusion that the radiations were emitted by the uranium in the compounds. Some of the compounds used were phosphorescent; others were not. Becquerel also discovered a most important property of these radiations; namely, they could cause the discharge of electrically charged bodies. This made it possible to investigate the phenomenon quantitatively with the aid of ionization chambers and electroscopes or electrometers. Shortly thereafter, Rutherford studied the penetrating power of the radiation from uranium salt by measuring the ionization produced by the radiation in an ionization chamber. He found that the radiation consisted of two components: a very soft radiation, easily absorbed in matter, which he called *alpha rays*, and a more penetrating type which he called *beta rays*. It is known now that the radiation which affected the photographic plate in Becquerel's experiment consisted of beta rays.

Using an ionization method, Mme. Curie made quantitative measurements on the activity of uranium salt and showed that this activity was directly proportional to the mass of uranium in the salt, demonstrating that radioactivity is an atomic phenomenon. M. and Mme. Curie then subjected uranium pitchblende to a systematic chemical analysis and, again using an electrical method, measured the activity of the different elements obtained from the pitchblende. In 1898, they succeeded in discovering two new radioactive elements, polonium and radium. Radium was precipitated as a salt in the form of radium chloride. Its activity was found to be more than a million times that of an equal mass of uranium. It was not until 1910 that pure radium metal was first obtained by electrolysis from the fused salt. Its atomic weight was found to be 226.05. Radium fits in at the end of the second group in the periodic table; it is chemically similar to calcium, strontium, and barium. Many more radioactive substances have been discovered since then, thus filling many gaps which existed in the periodic table prior to the discovery of radioactivity.

In addition to the alpha and beta rays, naturally radioactive substances emit a third type of radiation called *gamma rays*. The existence of these three types of radiations can be demonstrated very simply. A small amount of some radioactive salt is placed at the bottom of a long, narrow groove in a lead block, as shown in Figure 39–1. A fairly parallel beam will come from the radioactive substance R through the slit S; rays going in all other directions will be absorbed by the lead block. The latter is placed in an air-tight chamber containing a photographic plate P situated above the slit S. The air is pumped out of the chamber to avoid absorption of the rays. A strong magnetic field is applied at right angles to the plane of the paper and directed away from the reader. After a reasonable exposure, three distinct lines will be found on the photographic plate. The line which is deflected to the left in the figure is produced by the alpha rays; this shows that the alpha rays must consist of a stream of positively charged particles; these are called *alpha particles*. The line deflected to the right is produced by the beta rays; this shows that the beta rays consist of a stream

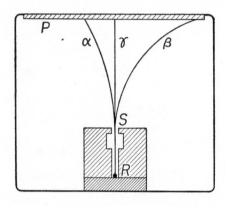

Fig. 39–1   Paths of the rays from a radioactive substance *R* in a magnetic field. The magnetic field is perpendicular to the plane of the paper and directed into the paper.

of negatively charged particles; these are called *beta particles*. The undeviated line is produced by the gamma radiation, which is unaffected by a magnetic field and hence must be due either to a stream of neutral particles or to a beam of electromagnetic radiation. Experiments on interference and diffraction of the gamma rays, similar to those performed with x-rays, show that the gamma rays are electromagnetic radiations of very short wavelengths of the order of 0.1 A or less.

Studies of the naturally radioactive elements show that some elements emit alpha particles, and other elements emit beta particles, while gamma rays sometimes accompany the emission of alpha particles and sometimes accompany the emission of beta particles.

It was early surmised that these rays come from the nucleus as a result of some spontaneous change taking place in it. On this basis, if a nucleus emits a charged particle, its atomic number changes and it must become the nucleus of a new type of atom. Here chemistry played a very important role in deciding the question. By starting with a known radioactive element, say radium, and allowing these disintegrations to continue for some time and then analyzing the substance again, it was found that many new elements had been formed as a result of these disintegrations. A careful study of the nature and properties of the rays emitted during radioactive disintegrations, supplemented by chemical analyses of the substances, should yield valuable evidence concerning nuclear structure and nuclear processes. It may also shed some light on how the physicist is to proceed to induce nuclear changes in order to make available many new types of atoms and atomic processes not only for the physicist but for the chemist, biologist, physician, and engineer as well. This has actually been the history of radioactivity.

39-2 PROPERTIES AND NATURE OF ALPHA PARTICLES

It has already been shown that alpha rays consist of a stream of positively charged particles. The ratio of the charge E to the mass M of these particles can be determined by measuring the deflections of the alpha rays in their passage through known electric and magnetic fields. The results of such measurements show this value to be $E/M = 48{,}200$ coul/gm.

If the charge on the alpha particle could be determined independently, then its mass would be known. One method of determining the charge is to count the number of alpha particles emitted by some radioactive element in a given time interval and then to determine the total charge carried by these alpha particles. There are two methods that are frequently used to count alpha particles. One is known as the scintillation method, the other the Geiger-counter method.

In the scintillation method, alpha particles strike a screen made of very small crystals such as zinc sulphide; these crystals convert the kinetic energy of the alpha particles into visible radiation. In the early experiments, the fluorescent screen was viewed through a low-power microscope; a small crystal that was struck by an alpha particle emitted a brilliant flash of light which lasted a very short time, hence the name *scintillation*. The field of view of the microscope was made small so that not more than from 2 to 4 scintillations per second were seen and hence could readily be counted by the viewer using a mechanical counter. From a knowledge of the area of the field of view and the distance of the radioactive material from it, the number of alpha particles emitted by the radioactive material in a given time can be calculated. With the development of modern types of photoelectric tubes, known as *photomultiplier tubes*, and appropriate electronic circuits, it has become possible to count the scintillations by utilizing the photoelectric effect produced by the radiation from the fluorescent material. Such devices are called *scintillation counters* and are now being widely used to count alpha particles and other radiations which can produce fluorescence in various types of transparent substances. The fluorescent material may be either in the liquid or the solid phase.

In the Geiger-counter method, use is made of the fact that the alpha particle produces intense ionization along its path in its passage through a gas. There are now many different types of counters. Essentially a Geiger counter consists of a cylinder C having a fine wire W mounted parallel to its axis and insulated from it, as shown in Figure 39–2. The cylinder contains a gas such as air or argon at a pressure between 5 cm and

12 cm of mercury. A difference of potential slightly less than that necessary to produce a discharge through the gas is maintained between the wire and the cylinder. Alpha particles can enter the counter through the aperture A, which is usually covered with a thin sheet of mica, glass, or aluminum. An alpha particle which enters the counter ionizes the gas along its path; the

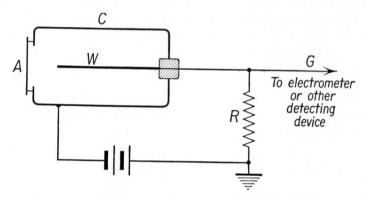

Fɪɢ. 39–2   Essentials of a Geiger counter.

ions so formed are accelerated by the electric field between the wire and the cylinder and, in turn, produce more ions by collisions with the gas molecules, so that the ionization current builds up very rapidly. A very high resistance R is connected between the wire and the ground to dissipate rapidly the energy of the ionization current. The effect of this is to produce a momentary current which may be registered on an electrometer connected at G, or it may be amplified by means of specially designed amplifiers so that this surge operates a loud-speaker or a mechanical counter. By proper design of the tube and choice of resistance, the time required for the momentary current to be dissipated may be made very short, so that each alpha particle which enters the counter is registered.

Using this method, Rutherford and Geiger found, for example, that 3.57×10^{10} alpha particles are emitted by 1 gm of radium in 1 sec. The charge carried by a known number of alpha particles can be determined by allowing them to fall on a plate connected to an electrometer and measuring the total charge received by the plate. Dividing this charge by the total number of alpha particles incident on the plate yields the charge on an alpha particle. This charge was found to be 3.19×10^{-19} coulomb or practically twice the charge on an electron, but opposite in sign.

From this value of the charge on the alpha particle and the previously determined ratio of the charge to its mass, the mass of the alpha particle can be calculated and is found to be 6.62×10^{-24} gm. The mass of the hydrogen atom is 1.67×10^{-24} gm. The mass of the alpha particle is thus four times the mass of the hydrogen atom. This result strongly suggests that the alpha particle is the nucleus of a helium atom, since helium has an atomic weight of 4 and an atomic number 2. To make this identification certain, Rutherford and Royds, in 1909, carried out a spectroscopic analysis by collecting the alpha particles emitted by the radioactive element radon into a spectroscopic tube which had previously been thoroughly evacuated. They collected alpha particles through a thin window in this tube and, after about six days, had accumulated enough particles in it to produce an electrical discharge through it by the application of a high voltage. With a spectroscope they examined the light emitted by this discharge and observed the spectrum of helium. This spectroscopic evidence proves conclusively that alpha particles are helium nuclei. The alpha particles become helium atoms by the capture of electrons in their passage through the walls of the glass tube.

Table 39-1   Velocities of Alpha Particles from Some Isotopes

Z	Element	A	Radioactive Isotope	Velocity in 10^9 cm/sec
83	Bismuth	214	Radium C	1.628
				1.619
		212	Thorium C	1.711
				1.705
				1.665
				1.645
				1.642
84	Polonium	210	Polonium	1.597
		215	Actinium A	1.882
		218	Radium A	1.699
86	Emanation	222	Radon	1.625
88	Radium	226	Radium	1.517
				1.488

A very important property of an alpha particle is the speed with which it travels when emitted by a radioactive element. Its speed can be measured by making it travel at right angles to a very intense magnetic field and measuring the radius of its circular path. The results of such experiments show that alpha particles move with speeds of the order of 1.6×10^9 cm/sec or about 10,000 miles per second. This is a very high speed for such massive particles. But much more interesting is the fact that the speed of the alpha particle is characteristic of the isotope which ejects it, as seen by a glance at Table 39–1. In some cases, such as radon, an isotope of the element emanation, with $A = 222$, all the alpha particles emitted by it

have exactly the same speed. In other cases, such as radium, $A = 226$, the
alpha particles are emitted with one of two definite speeds. In a few cases,
such as thorium C, a radioactive isotope of the element bismuth with
$A = 212$, there is a group of speeds characteristic of the alpha particles
emitted by the element. As a matter of history, the characteristic speed
of an alpha particle had been used to ascertain the nature of the isotope
emitting it. We shall return to a discussion of these characteristic speeds
of alpha particles in our study of the structure of the nucleus.

39-3 SCATTERING OF ALPHA PARTICLES BY NUCLEI

An alpha particle is a comparatively massive particle possessing a considerable amount of kinetic energy. Its mass is about 7,500 times that of an
electron, and its kinetic energy is of the order of several million electron
volts. It thus forms an ideal projectile for investigating some of the
properties of other atoms. Beginning about 1910, Rutherford and his co-
workers Geiger and Marsden undertook a series of experiments in which
alpha particles of known energy were fired at thin metallic foils (see
Figure 39-3). Most of the alpha particles went straight through the foil

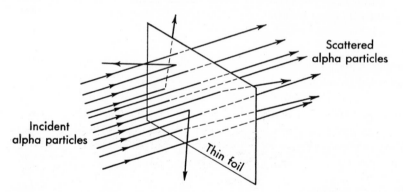

Fig. 39-3   Alpha particles directed against a thin foil. Most of them go through
the foil either without any deviation or with very slight deviations from the
original direction. A few alpha particles, however, are deviated through
very large angles.

without deviation, many others were deviated or scattered through small
angles, but a few were deviated through angles greater than 90°; that is,
they were scattered backward toward the side facing the incident beam.

Alpha particles, it will be recalled, carry a positive charge equivalent
to twice that of an electron. Because of their large energy and great mass,
the only way to account for the backward scattering of the alpha particles
was to assume that they came very close to another massive, charged

particle. Furthermore, since most alpha particles incident on the foil went through it with little or no deviation, the massive, charged particles must be very small in size in comparison with the distance between them (see Figure 39–4). On the basis of these experiments, Rutherford, in 1911,

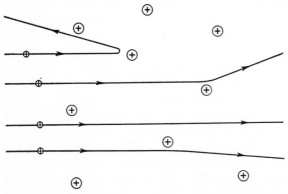

FIG. 39–4   Schematic diagram showing the paths of some alpha particles through a thin foil. The distances between nuclei (larger circles) are much greater than those shown here. A close approach of an alpha particle to a nucleus will therefore be a very rare event.

proposed his nuclear theory of the atom. These experiments were then extended to determine the nuclear charge and the nuclear radius and to produce nuclear disintegrations artificially by bombarding the nuclei with alpha particles.

The results of many different types of experiments show that the radius R of a nucleus of an atom of mass number A is given approximately by the equation

$$R = 1.4 \times 10^{-13} A^{1/3} \text{ cm.} \tag{1}$$

Since A probably does not exceed 250 for any atom, the values of R range from 1 to less than 7 times 1.4×10^{-13} cm. It will be recalled that x-ray data show that the distance between atomic centers in crystals is of the order of 10^{-8} cm, that is, about 10,000 to 100,000 times the sizes of the nuclei; it soon becomes apparent that, even in a solid, the nuclei are comparatively far apart.

39-4   RADIOACTIVE DISINTEGRATION BY ALPHA-PARTICLE EMISSION

The nucleons inside the nucleus of an isotope have comparatively large amounts of energy, due to the actions of the electrical forces and the specifically nuclear forces. To account for the emission of an alpha particle from a nucleus consisting of A nucleons, that is, N neutrons and Z protons, one must imagine a situation in which 2 protons and 2 neutrons combine to form a single unit, an alpha particle, and then to acquire a sufficiently large amount of kinetic energy to be able to escape from the nucleus. This is essentially a rare event. Given a specific nucleus, say a radium nucleus, it is impossible, in our present state of knowledge, to be able to predict when such an event will occur. A given nucleus may disintegrate immediately, or within the next second, or may remain a radium nucleus for billions of years. However, if we start with a large number of such nuclei, the rate of disintegration is constant. This rate of disintegration is expressed in terms of the *half life* of the isotope; the *half life* is defined as *the time required for a given mass of an isotope to disintegrate to half its original value.* In the case of radium, $A = 226$, the half life is 1,620 years.

The energy released in a radioactive disintegration comes from the masses of the particles involved. For example, when radium, $Z = 88$, $A = 226$, emits an alpha particle, the product is an atom of the element emanation; this particular isotope is called radium emanation or radon, $Z = 86$, $A = 226$.

This disintegration may be written as a nuclear reaction equation as follows:

$$_{88}RA^{226} \rightarrow {}_{86}Rn^{222} + {}_2He^4 + Q, \qquad (2)$$

where $_2He^4$ represents the alpha particle and Q represents the energy liberated in this disintegration process. The lower left-hand number is the atomic number and the upper right-hand number is the mass number of the isotope. The value of Q can be calculated from the known atomic masses of the particles involved as follows:

mass of Ra	= 226.10309 amu,
mass of Rn	= 222.09397 amu,
mass of He	= 4.00388 amu,
mass of final products	= 226.09785 amu,
mass difference = Q	= 0.00524 amu.

Since 1 amu = 931 Mev, the disintegration energy Q may be expressed as

$$Q = 4.88 \text{ Mev.}$$

The kinetic energy of the alpha particle emitted by radium, as determined from its velocity, is 4.80 Mev. The difference between the two values can be accounted for by the fact that when an alpha particle is emitted, the product nucleus recoils. Although the momentum of the alpha particle is equal and opposite to the momentum of the recoil nucleus, the velocity of the latter is much smaller, and its kinetic energy is also much smaller.

39-5 RADIOACTIVE DISINTEGRATION BY BETA-PARTICLE EMISSION

When a radioactive isotope of atomic number Z, neutron number N, and mass number A disintegrates by the emission of a beta particle, that is, an electron, the atomic number of the product nucleus becomes $Z + 1$, but the mass number A remains unchanged. Hence the neutron number must decrease to $N - 1$. For example, the radioactive isotope of bismuth, $Z = 83$, $A = 210$, also sometimes known as radium E, emits a beta particle; the product nucleus is polonium, $Z = 84$, $A = 210$. The half life of this disintegration is 5 days. We can write this radioactive disintegration as a nuclear reaction equation as follows:

$$_{83}\mathrm{Bi}^{210} \rightarrow {_{84}}\mathrm{Po}^{210} + \beta + Q, \tag{3}$$

where Q is the disintegration energy or the energy released in this reaction and comes from the difference in masses of initial and final particles. On the basis of the above reasoning one would expect to find that the beta

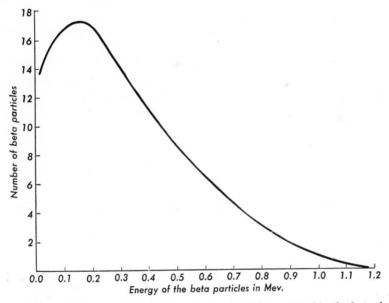

FIG. 39-5   Distribution of energy among beta particles emitted in the beta decay of bismuth, $A = 210$, or radium E.

particles emitted by Bi^{210} all have the same velocity. However, when these velocities are measured by a magnetic spectrograph, it is found that there is a continuous distribution of velocities up to a maximum velocity; that is, there is a continuous distribution of energies among them. Such a distribution of energies is called an *energy spectrum*. Figure 39–5 shows the distribution of energies among the beta particles emitted by Bi^{210}. The ordinate is the number of beta particles within a given energy range, and the abscissa is the energy of these particles expressed in Mev. It will be observed that there is a continuous distribution of energy up to the maximum value or *end-point energy*.

To account for the above facts concerning radioactive disintegration by beta-particle emission, sometimes called *beta decay*, we can imagine a neutron in the nucleus to break up into a proton and an electron, with the proton remaining in the nucleus and the electron ejected from it. However, this would not account for the continuous distribution of energy among the beta particles. It was suggested by W. Pauli, in 1931, that this difficulty could be overcome if it were assumed that two particles were emitted in beta decay, one an electron, and the other a new type of particle called a *neutrino*. The neutrino is a neutral particle with negligible mass in comparison with that of an electron. The total energy is shared by the electron and neutrino; if an electron is emitted with a large amount of energy, the neutrino is emitted with a small amount of energy and vice versa. There are other good reasons for introducing the neutrino hypothesis, one involving the conservation of angular momentum in this process. The discussion of these reasons is left to more advanced texts.

The neutrino, by its nature, that is, with no charge and negligible mass, is a very elusive particle. Most of the evidence for its existence is of an indirect nature, as that described above. Within recent years, however, several experiments have been performed which seem to confirm the existence of the neutrino.

Our present theory of beta decay can be represented by the equation

$$n \text{ (in nucleus)} \rightarrow p \text{ (in nucleus)} + \beta + \nu, \tag{4}$$

where n represents the neutron, p the proton, β the ejected electron, and ν (nu) the neutrino.

39-6 GAMMA RAYS

In many cases, gamma rays are found to accompany the emission of alpha particles and beta particles by radioactive elements. By means of interference and diffraction experiments, similar to those used with x-rays, it can be shown that gamma rays are of the same nature as x-rays. The gamma-ray spectrum of any one element is a sharp-line spectrum. Some of the longer gamma-ray wavelengths have been measured with a single-crystal spectrometer, while shorter wavelengths have been measured with a modified type, known as a curved crystal spectrometer. Indirect methods, such as the measurements of the energies of the electrons ejected in either a photoelectric effect with gamma rays or a Compton effect, have been widely used for determining the energies of gamma rays.

Just as x-rays were shown to be emitted as a result of changes in atomic-energy states, so the emission of gamma rays can be ascribed to nuclear-energy changes. When a nucleus emits an alpha particle or a beta particle, the new nucleus formed, called the *product nucleus*, may be left in a state of higher energy. It could then go to the normal state by the emission of gamma rays of suitable energy. One example will be given to illustrate this point.

Radium emits an alpha particle, and the product nucleus is the nucleus of the isotope radon. A gamma ray of wavelength $\lambda = 0.0652$ A has been found to accompany this emission. The energy of this gamma-ray photon is 0.19 Mev. It has previously been shown that the alpha particles of radium have two slightly different velocities. The energies of these two alpha particles are 4.80 Mev and 4.61 Mev, respectively. The difference between these two energies is 0.19 Mev, which is the energy of the gamma-ray photon. This fact can be explained by assuming that when a normal radium nucleus emits an alpha particle of higher energy, the product nucleus, radon, is in its normal state; but, when a lower-energy alpha particle is emitted, the product nucleus is left in a state of higher energy and then goes to the normal state by the emission of a gamma-ray photon of appropriate energy.

By correlating alpha-ray energies and gamma-ray energies, it has been possible in some cases to construct energy-level diagrams for the nuclei of several atoms similar to x-ray energy-level diagrams.

39-7 RADIOACTIVE SERIES

In the years following the discovery of the radioactivity of uranium by Becquerel, many radioactive elements and isotopes of elements were discovered. Most of the naturally radioactive isotopes were found to be genetically related and fitted into one of three *radioactive series*. These are known as the *uranium series*, the *thorium series*, and the *actinium series*. Radium, for example, is a member of the uranium series. This series starts with the isotope of uranium, $Z = 92$ and $A = 238$, which has a very long half life of 4.50×10^9 years; the other members of the series are formed through a succession of alpha-particle and/or beta-particle emissions, as shown in Figure 39–6. Originally these radioactive isotopes were given special names, but the modern method is simply to identify them by the appropriate values of A for a given value of Z.

As we have already seen, the emission of an alpha particle by an isotope having given values of Z and A results in the production of a new isotope of atomic number $Z - 2$ and mass number $A - 4$. On the other hand, the emission of a beta particle leaves the mass number unchanged but increases the atomic number of the product nucleus to $Z + 1$, where Z is the atomic number of the parent nucleus.

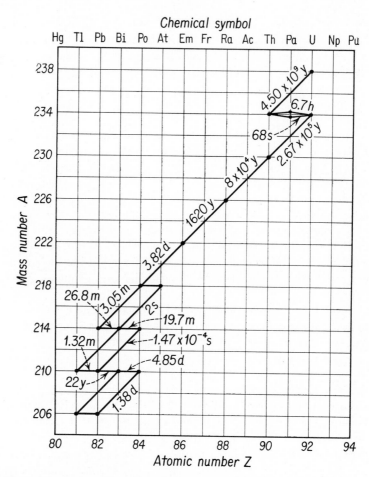

FIG. 39-6   The naturally radioactive uranium series.   The half lives of the disintegrations are expressed either in years (y), days (d), hours (h), minutes (m), or seconds (s).

Each of the three naturally radioactive series terminates with a non-radioactive isotope of lead.   In the uranium series this isotope has a mass number of 206, in the actinium series its mass number is 207, and in the thorium series its mass number is 208.

The half lives of the radioactive isotopes are indicated in Figure 39–6. If a sample of ore containing uranium is analyzed chemically and the percentage of uranium and lead measured, it is possible to calculate, from the ratio of uranium to lead, how long a time must have elapsed for the production of this amount of lead. This value can thus be used as an indication of the age of the earth.

In our discussion of radioactive decay, it was tacitly assumed that a given isotope will have only one mode of disintegration, that is, either by alpha-particle emission or by beta-particle emission. However, a glance at Figure 39-6 will show many interesting cases of *branching*. For example, the isotope of polonium with $Z = 84$ and $A = 218$, also known as radium A, will decay most often (in 99.96 per cent of the cases) with the emission of an alpha particle forming the product nucleus $Z = 82$, $A = 214$, a radioactive isotope of lead. However, in a few cases (0.04 per cent) the nuclei will emit beta particles forming the product nucleus $Z = 85$ and $A = 218$, an isotope of a comparatively new element called astatine.

QUESTIONS

1. Describe some of the properties of alpha particles.
2. What important information about the structure of the atom can be obtained by scattering alpha particles from thin films of matter?
3. What is meant by the alpha-particle spectrum of an isotope? What is the nature of this spectrum?
4. What is meant by the half life of a radioactive isotope?
5. What is the source of the kinetic energy of the alpha particles emitted in radioactive decay?
6. What is meant by the Q-value of a reaction?
7. What are beta rays? What is the origin of these rays?
8. What are the characteristics of the energy spectrum of the beta particles from a radioactive isotope? How does this differ from an alpha-particle spectrum?
9. Describe some of the properties of a neutrino.
10. Discuss the origin of gamma rays.
11. What is the nature of a gamma-ray spectrum of a radioactive isotope?
12. What is the essential distinction between gamma rays and x-rays?
13. Are there any isotopes of lead that are radioactive?
14. Discuss the phenomenon of branching in a radioactive series.

PROBLEMS

1. Using the data of Table 39-1, determine (a) the kinetic energy of the alpha particle emitted by radon, (b) the energy of recoil of the product nucleus, and (c) the Q-value of this disintegration.
2. Using the data of Table 39-1, calculate (a) the momentum of the alpha particle emitted by radon and (b) the De Broglie wavelength associated

with this alpha particle. (c) Compare this wavelength with the radius of the radon nucleus.

3. Using Coulomb's law, calculate the force of repulsion between a nucleus of radon and an alpha particle when the distance between centers is 2×10^{-12} cm.

4. Determine the potential at a distance of 2×10^{-12} cm from the center of a nucleus of radon.

5. Using the result of Problem 4, calculate the potential energy of an alpha particle at a point a distance 2×10^{-12} cm from a nucleus of radon. Express this in Mev.

6. If we start with 16 milligrams of radon, how much will be left at the end of 15.28 days?

7. Calculate the difference in mass between the neutron and the proton. Express the result in amu and in Mev.

8. Referring to Problem 7, determine the maximum kinetic energy of the beta rays emitted in the radioactive decay of the neutron.

40

Nuclear Disintegration

40-1 NUCLEAR DISINTEGRATION BY ALPHA-PARTICLE BOMBARDMENT

The artificial transmutation of one element into another was first definitely accomplished by Rutherford, in 1919, in a very simple type of experiment. A diagram of the apparatus used by Rutherford is shown in Figure 40–2. The chamber C was filled with a gas such as nitrogen, and alpha particles

FIG. 40–1 Ernest Rutherford (1871–1937). He discovered properties of alpha and beta rays. Originated the nuclear theory of the structure of the atom. Performed the first successful experiments on the artificial disintegration of nuclei. (Courtesy of Ramsey & Muspratt, Cambridge, England.)

from a radioactive source at A were absorbed in the gas. A sheet of silver foil F, thick enough to absorb the alpha particles, was placed over an opening in the side of the chamber. A zinc sulphide screen S was placed outside this opening, and a microscope M was used for observing any scintillations produced on the screen S. Scintillations were observed when the chamber was filled with nitrogen, but, when the nitrogen was replaced by oxygen or carbon dioxide, no scintillations were observed. Rutherford concluded that the scintillations were produced by high-energy particles which were

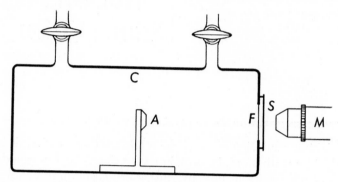

FIG. 40–2   Diagram of the apparatus used by Rutherford in the first successful experiments on artificial disintegration of atomic nuclei.

ejected from nitrogen nuclei as a result of the bombardment of these nuclei by the alpha particles. Magnetic deflection experiments showed that these high-energy particles were protons or hydrogen nuclei. Other light elements in the range from boron to potassium were also disintegrated by bombardment with alpha particles.

The bombardment of nuclei with alpha particles was also studied with the aid of a Wilson cloud chamber, which is essentially a device for making the paths of the particles visible. The Wilson cloud chamber consists essentially of a cylinder C and a tightly fitting piston P (see Figure 40–3).

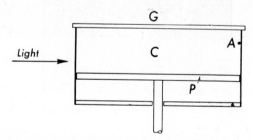

FIG. 40–3   Schematic diagram of a Wilson cloud chamber.

A quantity of liquid, say water, rests on the piston; the air above it is thus normally saturated with water vapor. A glass cover G closes the cylinder, and light entering through a side window illuminates the volume of air. If the piston is suddenly lowered, the air expands practically adiabatically;

its temperature therefore drops, and it becomes supersaturated. If there are any ions in the air, the water vapor will condense on these ions, forming small drops.

Suppose there is a source of alpha particles at A; in their passage through the air, the alpha particles will produce many pairs of ions ($+$ and $-$) along their paths. Upon the expansion of the volume of the cloud chamber, drops of liquid will condense on these ions, thus making the paths of the alpha particles visible. Gases other than air may be used in a Wilson cloud chamber; also, the tracks of any other ionizing particles can be observed and studied in such a chamber.

Figure 40–4 shows a series of alpha-particle tracks in nitrogen. It will be observed that one of these tracks branches into two parts—one is a short, heavy track, and the other is a longer, light track. The lighter track is due to the proton.

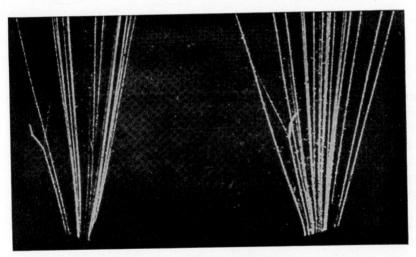

Fɪɢ. 40–4   A pair of stereoscopic photographs of alpha-particle tracks showing a collision with a nitrogen nucleus which results in the ejection of a proton. (Reproduced by permission from *Radiations from Radioactive Substances*, J. Rutherford, J. Chadwick, and C. D. Ellis, The Macmillan Company.)

On the basis of a theory of the nucleus advanced by Bohr in 1936, the disintegration of nitrogen by bombardment with alpha particles may be thought of as consisting of two parts. The first is the *capture* of the alpha particle by the nitrogen nucleus, resulting in the formation of a new *compound nucleus;* the second is the immediate breaking up of the compound nucleus into two particles, one of which is a proton (see Figure 40–5). These two processes can be represented by means of a *nuclear reaction* equation analogous to one representing a chemical reaction   Thus

$$_2\text{He}^4 + {_7}\text{N}^{14} \rightarrow (_9\text{F}^{18}) \rightarrow {_8}\text{O}^{17} + {_1}\text{H}^1 + Q. \qquad (1)$$

Since the total charge must be conserved, the atomic number of the compound nucleus must be the sum of the atomic numbers of helium and nitrogen. The compound nucleus in this case is fluorine, $Z = 9$. Since this isotope of fluorine disintegrates with the emission of a proton, the remaining part, the product nucleus, must be oxygen, $Z = 8$.

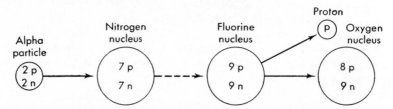

FIG. 40–5   An alpha particle, directed toward a nitrogen nucleus, may penetrate it, forming a compound nucleus of fluorine, which then disintegrates into a fast-moving proton and a nucleus of oxygen.

The guiding principle in determining which isotope of an element is formed during a nuclear reaction is that the mass number of the compound nucleus must equal the sum of the mass numbers of the initial particles, and also the sum of the mass numbers of the final particles. This is not the same as the principle of conservation of mass. As previously stated, mass may be converted into energy and energy into mass. As a matter of fact, the initial and final masses of the atoms are not equal; the difference in the masses of the initial and final particles is called the *nuclear reaction energy*, Q. If the sum of the masses of the final particles exceeds that of the initial particles, energy is absorbed in the reaction; this energy must come from the initial kinetic energies of the particles. In this case, Q is negative. If the sum of the masses of the final particles is less than that of the initial particles, the difference in mass is released in the form of kinetic energy of the final particles. In this case, Q is positive.

For example, in the nuclear reaction represented by Equation (1), the masses of the initial and final particles are, from Table 3 in the Appendix,

$$\begin{array}{ll} _2\text{He}^4 = 4.00388 & \qquad _8\text{O}^{17} = 17.00453 \\ _7\text{N}^{14} = 14.00755 & \qquad _1\text{H}^1 = 1.00815 \\ \hline \phantom{_7\text{N}^{14} = }18.01143 & \qquad \phantom{_1\text{H}^1 = }18.01268 \end{array}$$

The masses of the final particles exceed those of the initial particles; hence the value of Q is negative and equal to -0.00125 amu, which is equivalent to -1.16 Mev. This energy must be supplied by the initial kinetic energy of the alpha particle for the above reaction to occur. It is obvious, from the tracks shown in Figure 40–4, that the final particles are in motion. The measured values of the kinetic energies were found to be less than the kinetic energy of the alpha particle by about 1.26 Mev, in good agreement with the predicted value. Thus energy is absorbed in this particular reaction.

Two typical reactions involving alpha-particle capture and emission of protons, sometimes called α-p reactions, are

$$_{13}Al^{27} + {_2}He^4 \rightarrow ({_{15}}P^{31}) \rightarrow {_{14}}Si^{30} + {_1}H^1 \tag{2}$$

$$_{19}K^{39} + {_2}He^4 \rightarrow ({_{21}}Sc^{43}) \rightarrow {_{20}}Ca^{42} + {_1}H^1. \tag{3}$$

The protons which are emitted in these reactions have definite energy ranges. This is interpreted as showing definite energy levels in the nucleus. The normal state of the product nucleus is formed when the protons are ejected with maximum energy. When protons are ejected with smaller energy, the product nucleus is left in an excited state or a state of higher energy and may return to the normal state by the emission of a gamma-ray photon. Gamma rays of appropriate energy have been observed in such reactions.

40-2   THE NEUTRON

The capture of an alpha particle by a nucleus does not always result in the emission of a proton by the compound nucleus formed as a result of this capture. In one particular reaction studied, that resulting from the bombardment of beryllium by alpha particles, a very penetrating type of radiation was found to be emitted by the newly formed compound nucleus. Various attempts to explain this in terms of gamma rays led to many discrepancies. Finally Chadwick, in 1932, as a result of many experiments, suggested that the radiation consisted of neutral particles, called *neutrons*, of mass nearly equal to that of protons. The nuclear reaction which takes place is

$$_4Be^9 + {_2}He^4 \rightarrow ({_6}C^{13}) \rightarrow {_6}C^{12} + {_0}n^1, \tag{4}$$

where $_0n^1$ is the symbol representing the neutron, showing that it has zero charge and mass number 1. This type of reaction is called an α-n reaction.

One arrangement used by Chadwick for demonstrating the existence and properties of neutrons is shown in Figure 40–6. The source of alpha particles is a disk D on which polonium has been deposited. This disk and the beryllium target are placed in an evacuated chamber C. The neutrons coming from the beryllium pass through the thin wall of the chamber and enter the ionization chamber I through the thin window W. The ionization chamber is connected to an amplifier and then to a recording device such as an electrical counter or a loud-speaker.

Since the neutrons possess no charge, they produce no ionization directly in their passage through the chamber. But some neutrons which strike the walls of the ionization chamber cause the ejection of nuclei which then produce ions in the chamber and are thus recorded in the electrical counter; or if a loud-speaker is used, a "click" is heard for every nucleus

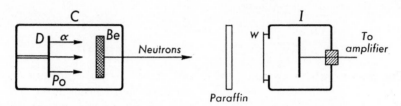

Fɪɢ. 40–6   Arrangement of apparatus for the detection of neutrons.

which produces intense ionization. Now when neutrons from the beryllium go directly into the chamber, only a few counts per minute are recorded. If thin sheets of lead are placed in front of the ionization chamber, the number of counts is not reduced appreciably. If, however, a thin slab of paraffin is placed in front of the ionization chamber, the number of counts per minute increases markedly. This increase is due to the fact that neutrons, in collisions with the nuclei of the hydrogen atoms contained in the paraffin, give up a considerable fraction of their energy to these protons and eject them from the paraffin. These protons enter the ionization chamber and are recorded by the ionization produced by them. If the paraffin is removed and the neutrons enter the chamber directly, the number of counts per minute falls immediately to its former low value. This is just the opposite of what would happen if the radiation consisted of gamma rays; that is, the introduction of any absorbing material in the path of the gamma rays would produce a decrease in the intensity of the transmitted radiation.

Since the discovery of the neutron, many different types of nuclear reactions have been used for obtaining neutrons. The mass of a neutron has been accurately determined as a result of these studies: its mass is 1.00899. Since neutrons have no charge, they should be able to penetrate atomic nuclei very easily, and a study of these reactions should yield valuable information concerning nuclear properties and nuclear reactions.

Neutrons coming from a nucleus generally have very high energies. If it is desired to slow down these neutrons, they are allowed to pass through some hydrogen-containing substance such as paraffin or water. A neutron gives up a large fraction of its energy in a collision with a hydrogen nucleus, and after many collisions it will come to thermal equilibrium with the material; that is, its average energy will be equal to the energy of thermal agitation, which at room temperature is equivalent to 1/40 ev. An interesting reaction involving slow neutrons is

$$_5B^{10} + {_0}n^1 \rightarrow (_5B^{11}) \rightarrow {_3}Li^7 + {_2}He^4 + Q. \tag{5}$$

In this reaction, the capture of a slow neutron by boron of mass number 10 yields a compound nucleus which is itself, of course, an isotope of boron, and this disintegrates with the emission of an alpha particle. The energy released in this nuclear reaction is $Q = 2.79$ Mev. This reaction is widely used as a sensitive detector of neutrons; the ionization chamber is lined with some boron compound, and the capture of a neutron by the boron causes the liberation of an alpha particle which is easily detected by the ionization it produces in the chamber.

40-3 THE POSITRON

The year 1932 also saw the discovery of another new particle, called a *positron*. C. D. Anderson discovered the positron while investigating *cosmic-ray* phenomena with a Wilson cloud chamber. Cosmic rays consist

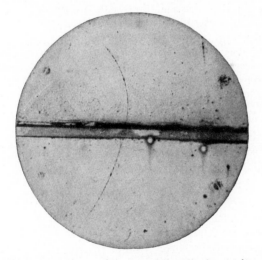

Fig. 40-7   Cloud-chamber photograph of the path of a positron in a magnetic field. The positron originated at the bottom of the chamber and passed through a sheet of lead 6 mm thick. The magnetic field is directed into the paper. (Photograph by Carl D. Anderson.)

of a wide variety of radiations which are continually traversing the atmosphere of the earth. The exact nature and origin of the *primary* cosmic rays which reach the earth's atmosphere are not known, but, from the studies of the cosmic rays at various depths below the top of the atmosphere, several new particles and new types of nuclear reactions have been observed. We shall discuss a few of them in this chapter.

In the particular experiment in which we are now interested, the Wilson cloud chamber was placed in a magnetic field, expansions of the chamber took place at definite intervals, and photographs were taken of the tracks formed during these expansions. In one of these photographs, a track was observed which had the same appearance as that of an electron track but had a curvature opposite to that of an electron with a negative charge. To make identification certain, C. D. Anderson placed a lead plate 6 mm thick in the center of the chamber and obtained the photograph shown in Figure 40–7. The particle, in passing through the lead plate, lost some of its energy; since the curvature of its path above the plate is greater than that below it, the particle must have originated at the bottom of the chamber. From the known direction of the magnetic field and from the direction of the curvature of the path, it was concluded that the particle must be positively charged. This particle is called a *positron;* measurements show that it has the same mass as that of an electron and the same charge but of opposite sign. The symbol frequently used to represent it is $_{+1}e^0$; it is also sometimes called a β^+ particle.

Shortly after this discovery, sources of positrons were found among many of the artificially produced radioactive substances.

40-4 ARTIFICIAL OR INDUCED RADIOACTIVITY

In the course of experiments in which nuclei of some of the lighter elements were bombarded with alpha particles, M. and Mme. Curie-Joliot, 1934, observed that the bombarded substances continued to emit radiations even after the source of alpha particles had been removed. Ionization measurements and magnetic deflection experiments showed that the radiations consisted of *positrons.* Furthermore, the intensity of the radiation was found to decrease with the time, in the same way as radiations from a naturally radioactive substance. The half life of the positron radiation was measured in each case studied. This was the first time that radioactivity was ever induced in a substance. One of the reactions, for example, was the bombardment of boron by alpha particles accompanied by the emission of neutrons according to the reaction equation

$$_5B^{10} + {}_2He^4 \rightarrow ({}_7N^{14}) \rightarrow {}_7N^{13} + {}_0n^1. \tag{6}$$

Now, nitrogen of mass number 13 is not a stable isotope. It disintegrates with the emission of a positron according to the reaction equation

$$_7N^{13} \rightarrow {}_6C^{13} + {}_{+1}e^0 \tag{7}$$

with a half life $T = 10$ min. The symbol $_{+1}e^0$ is used to represent the positron, since its charge is equal to that of a proton and its mass number is zero. The carbon atom of mass number 13 is a stable isotope of carbon.

The identification of the radioactive atom as nitrogen was made certain by chemical analysis. Since the amount available for analysis is very minute, special methods have to be developed for each case. For example, in the boron reaction, the target was made of boron nitride. After bombarding it with alpha particles for several minutes, it was heated with caustic soda. One of the products of this chemical reaction was gaseous ammonia, NH_3. This was found to be radioactive with a half life of 10 min, showing that the nitrogen of the ammonia was the radioactive element.

Since the discovery of artificially induced radioactivity, it has become possible to induce radioactivity in all elements, that is, to produce one or more radioactive isotopes of every known element. It has also been possible to produce new elements, both to fill in gaps which had existed in the periodic table of elements and to extend the number of elements to more than 100. These developments were made possible by two essentially different types of devices: one known as *particle accelerators* (see Section 40–6), the other known as *nuclear reactors* (see Section 40–9).

40-5 RADIOACTIVE DISINTEGRATION BY POSITRON EMISSION

In our study of the naturally radioactive isotopes, we found no cases of positron emission. However, positron emission is fairly common among the artificially produced radioactive isotopes. There are some similarities between radioactive decay by electron β^- emission and by positron β^+ emission. In each case, the mass numbers of the parent atom and product atom are the same. The energy spectrum of the positrons from any one isotope has a continuous distribution up to a maximum, the end-point energy, similar to that of the β^- energy spectrum. It is thus reasonable to postulate an analogous process for β^+ decay, that is, that a proton in the nucleus disintegrates into a neutron, which remains in the nucleus, and a positron and a neutrino, which are ejected from the nucleus; thus

$$p \text{ (in nucleus)} \rightarrow n \text{ (in nucleus)} + \beta^+ + \nu. \tag{8}$$

There is one important difference, however, between β^+ emission and β^- emission; this difference is that the mass of the proton is less than the mass of the neutron. Hence, for the above process to occur, the proton must get sufficient energy from the other nuclear particles in order to disintegrate into a neutron, positron, and neutrino. This minimum amount of energy is $2m_0c^2$ where m_0 is the rest mass of the electron (or positron). This can be inferred from the fact that when a positron is emitted by a nucleus of atomic number Z, the atomic number of the product nucleus is $Z - 1$;

hence one of the outer electrons is in excess for this neutral atom. Essentially two electrons, β^+ and β^-, are emitted in positron decay.

The energy for beta decay comes from the difference in mass between the parent atom and the product or daughter atom. For β^+ decay, this difference in mass must be at least $2m_0$. In general, the mass difference is greater than this value, the remaining value appearing as kinetic energy of the positron and neutrino.

The radioactive decay of an atom of atomic number Z into one of atomic number $Z - 1$ can occur in a manner other than positron emission; that is, the nucleus may capture an electron from one of the rings of electrons around it, say the K-shell. This process, known as *electron capture*, actually competes with positron emission. For example, the cadmium isotope, $A = 107$ and $Z = 48$, decays to silver, $A = 107$ and $Z = 47$, mostly by electron capture (99.7%) and only rarely by positron emission (0.3%). The nuclear reaction equations for these cases are

$$_{48}\text{Cd}^{107} + {_{-1}e^0} \rightarrow {_{47}\text{Ag}^{107}}$$
$$_{48}\text{Cd}^{107} \rightarrow {_{47}\text{Ag}^{107}} + \beta^+. \tag{9}$$

No charged particle is emitted in the process of electron capture; a neutrino is emitted, but is very difficult to detect. Electron capture is detected by the fact that x-rays are emitted from the product atom, since the remaining electrons will go to lower energy levels once the K-electron (or L-electron) has been captured by the nucleus.

There are interesting cases in which the only way that an atom of atomic number Z can decay into an atom of atomic number $Z - 1$ is by electron capture. Such cases are those in which the mass difference between parent and daughter atoms is less than $2m_0$. For example, beryllium, $Z = 4$ and $A = 7$, decays to lithium, $Z = 3$ and $A = 7$, only by electron capture. The difference in mass between these two atoms is 0.00094 amu equivalent to 0.875 Mev, while $2m_0 = 0.0011$ amu equivalent to 1.02 Mev.

40-6 PARTICLE ACCELERATORS

There are many different types of devices designed and built to accelerate charged particles to high energies. We have already described some of these such as the step-up transformer, usually used with a rectifier, and the betatron. It is beyond the scope of this book to discuss the different types of particle accelerators now in use; we merely note that at present (1956) electrons can be accelerated up to energies of about two billion electron volts (usually written 2 Bev), and that protons can be accelerated to about 6 Bev. Designs and experiments are now in progress for a device which will accelerate protons to 100 Bev.

The forerunner of this development of particle accelerators is the *cyclotron*, which was originally designed and built by E. O. Lawrence and M. S. Livingston in 1931. It consists essentially of a short, hollow metal cylinder divided into two sections *A* and *B*, as shown in Figures 40–8 and 40–9. This cylinder is placed between the poles of a very large electro-

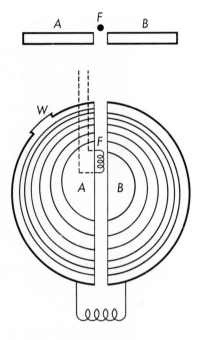

Fig. 40–8   The paths of particles in a cyclotron.

magnet. Some of the magnets built have pole pieces from 30 to 60 in. in diameter, and a modified form of the cyclotron now in use in California has a diameter of 184 in. The magnetic field is perpendicular to the plane of the figure, that is, along the axis of the cylinder. The two half-cylinders are connected to the terminals of a high-frequency a-c circuit, so that the charge on each half changes a few million times per second. These two half-cylinders are placed in another metal box, and a gas, such as hydrogen, is introduced in this system at a low pressure. One method of producing positive ions is to ionize this gas by bombarding it with electrons from a heated filament *F* maintained at a difference of potential with respect to the metal box. When the half-cylinder *A* is positive, the protons between the half-cylinders are accelerated toward *B*. When the proton gets inside *B*, the magnetic field causes it to move in a circular path. After completing a semicircle, the proton reaches the edge of *B*. If the timing is just right, *B* should now be positive with respect to *A* so that the proton will now be accelerated toward *A* and travel in a circular path of larger radius inside *A*.

After traversing a semicircle in A, the proton, upon reaching the edge of A, will receive an additional acceleration toward B, because in the meantime the potential difference between A and B will have changed sign. The proton will travel in semicircles of increasing radii, since its energy is increased at each passage between A and B.

FIG. 40–9   Shop assembly photograph of the M.I.T. cyclotron chamber showing the construction of the chamber and dees. (Reproduced from *Journal of Applied Physics*, January, 1944. Courtesy of the Radioactivity Center at Massachusetts Institute of Technology.)

After the protons have traversed many semicircular paths and approach the circumference of the cylinder A, an auxiliary electric field is used to deflect them from the circular path and make them come out through the thin window W. The substance to be bombarded by the protons is placed near W, and the investigations of the results of this bombardment can then be made.

To obtain high-energy deuterons, hydrogen of mass number 2 is used in the chamber; or, if helium is used in this chamber, we have an artificial source of alpha particles.

The voltage between the sections A and B is usually of the order of 50,000 to 200,000 volts; the energies of the particles coming out of the

Fig. 40–10 The 184-in. Berkeley cyclotron in operation at the Radiation Laboratory of the University of California at Berkeley. The vacuum chamber is in place between the pole pieces of the electromagnet. The tube extending into the chamber at the left carries the target, which is bombarded by the high-energy ions in the cyclotron chamber. (Photograph supplied by Prof. R. I. Thornton, Radiation Laboratory, University of California, Berkeley, Calif.)

conventional cyclotron may be several million electron volts. The modified type of cyclotron, called a synchro-cyclotron, in use at Berkeley, Calif., can produce protons and alpha particles with energies of 400 Mev (see Figure 40–10).

40-7 NUCLEAR DISINTEGRATIONS BY PROTONS, DEUTERONS, AND NEUTRONS

With the high-energy particles now available, many different types of nuclear reactions have been produced. Only a few of these can be mentioned here. For example, when lithium of mass number 7 is bombarded with protons, the compound nucleus thus formed breaks up into two alpha particles of very high energy, about 8.63 Mev each. The nuclear reaction is

$$_3\text{Li}^7 + {}_1\text{H}^1 \rightarrow ({}_4\text{Be}^8) \rightarrow {}_2\text{He}^4 + {}_2\text{He}^4. \tag{10}$$

Sometimes, however, the proton which is captured by the lithium nucleus remains with the compound nucleus, beryllium, and the excess energy is given off in the form of a gamma ray of 17 Mev energy; the equation is

$$_3\text{Li}^7 + {}_1\text{H}^1 \rightarrow ({}_4\text{Be}^8) \rightarrow {}_4\text{Be}^8 + \text{gamma rays}. \tag{11}$$

Thus several different reactions may occur in any one experiment, and one of the important problems of nuclear physics is to be able to predict which process is more likely to occur in any given experiment.

Another interesting reaction occurs when high-energy deuterons bombard deuterium, that is, hydrogen of mass number 2. Two different reactions have been observed:

$$_1\text{H}^2 + {}_1\text{H}^2 \rightarrow ({}_2\text{He}^4) \rightarrow {}_1\text{H}^3 + {}_1\text{H}^1. \tag{12}$$

$$_1\text{H}^2 + {}_1\text{H}^2 \rightarrow ({}_2\text{He}^4) \rightarrow {}_2\text{He}^3 + {}_0n^1. \tag{13}$$

The first of these reactions results in the production of a new isotope of hydrogen of mass number 3. This isotope is unstable; it is radioactive and emits a beta ray with a half life of about 12 years. The second reaction results in the production of a neutron. This is one of the simplest methods for obtaining neutrons.

Elements can be made radioactive and then allowed to take part in some chemical or physiological process; the progress of such a process can be traced by observing the radiations emitted by the elements. Elements used in this way are called "tracers." For example, ordinary salt NaCl, when bombarded with deuterons, becomes radioactive because the sodium in it is made radioactive according to the following reactions:

$$_{11}\text{Na}^{23} + {}_1\text{H}^2 \rightarrow ({}_{12}\text{Mg}^{25}) \rightarrow {}_{11}\text{Na}^{24} + {}_1\text{H}^1, \tag{14}$$

followed by

$$_{11}\text{Na}^{24} \rightarrow {}_{12}\text{Mg}^{24} + \beta^-. \tag{15}$$

The radioactive sodium emits beta rays β^- of half life $T = 14.8$ hr. When the salt takes part in some reaction, the sodium can be traced by the beta rays which it emits.

Another important radioactive isotope is carbon $A = 14$, produced by bombarding nitrogen with neutrons, according to the following reactions:

$$_7\text{N}^{14} + {}_0n^1 \rightarrow ({}_7\text{N}^{15}) \rightarrow {}_6\text{C}^{14} + {}_1\text{H}^1, \tag{16}$$

followed by

$$_6\text{C}^{14} \rightarrow {}_7\text{N}^{14} + \beta^-. \tag{17}$$

Carbon 14 has a half life of 5,580 years. It is found in nature in carbon compounds in small concentrations. In terms of the age of the earth, the half life of carbon 14 is very small; hence the supply of carbon 14 must be replenished continually. It is believed that this occurs in the atmosphere where neutrons from cosmic rays bombard atmospheric nitrogen to form carbon 14.

Fɪɢ. 40–11   Cloud-chamber photograph of beta-ray tracks in a magnetic field of 1,000 gausses. The beta rays come from the disintegration of boron of mass number 12; their energies range from about 6 to 12 Mev. The heavy track across the diameter of the chamber is that of a proton of about 9 Mev energy. (Photograph by H. R. Crane.)

Carbon is a constituent of all living matter; when a living organism dies, its intake of carbon ceases. The percentage of carbon 14 then begins to decrease. It is thus possible to determine the age of archaeological and geological samples containing carbon, by determining the percentage of carbon 14 in it and assuming that the rate of production of this isotope has remained reasonably constant. Wherever possible, age determinations by carbon dating are compared with other reliable methods as a check; these results have been very satisfactory. It is now possible to use carbon dating for age determinations up to about 15,000 years.

The nature of the particles which are emitted by the nucleus of an element which has been made artificially radioactive, as well as the energies of these particles, can be determined by investigating the paths of these particles in a magnetic field with the aid of a Wilson cloud chamber. Figure 40–11 is a Wilson cloud-chamber photograph of beta-ray tracks in a magnetic field. These beta rays are emitted by a radioactive isotope of boron, B^{12}. The energies of these beta rays can be determined by measuring the radii of their circular paths.

40-8 NUCLEAR FISSION

All the nuclear disintegrations described thus far have concerned the emission of comparatively light particles, such as electrons, positrons, protons, and alpha particles. A new type of nuclear process, known as

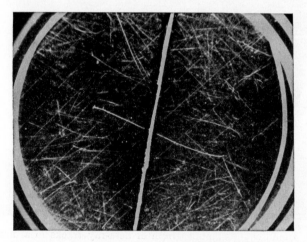

FIG. 40–12 Cloud-chamber photograph showing the fission of uranium. The foil in the center of the cloud chamber is coated with uranium and bombarded by neutrons. The tracks of the two heavy fission particles can be seen coming from the foil where a uranium atom has undergone fission as the result of the capture of a neutron. (From a photograph by J. K. Boggild, K. K. Brostom, and T. Lauritsen.)

nuclear fission, was discovered by Hahn and Strassmann in 1939 in a series of experiments in which uranium was bombarded by neutrons. Chemical analysis of the products of disintegration showed the presence of barium, $Z = 56$, lanthanum, $Z = 57$, and other elements of medium atomic weights. The interpretation of these results is that when a neutron is captured by a uranium nucleus, the latter becomes unstable and disintegrates into two particles of intermediate masses; for example, if one of the particles is barium, $Z = 56$, the other particle is krypton, $Z = 36$. Cloud-chamber photographs (see Figure 40–12) have amply verified this hypothesis.

The particles which are produced in the fission of uranium have energies of the order of 200 Mev. The source of this energy is the difference in mass between the initial products, that is, the neutron and the uranium nucleus, and the final or fission products. There is a decrease in mass of about 0.1 per cent in this process; thus, in the nuclear fission of 1 kg of uranium, there is a decrease in mass of 1 gm, and, as we have seen, this corresponds to about 25×10^6 kw hr of energy.

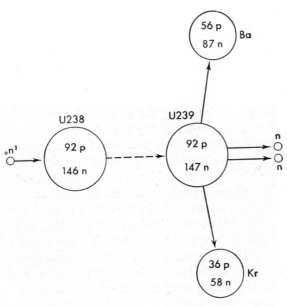

F<small>IG</small>. 40–13   Nuclear fission of uranium. A fast neutron is captured by a nucleus of uranium of mass number 238 forming uranium 239; the latter splits into two comparatively massive particles, in the above case, krypton and barium, with the simultaneous emission of two fast neutrons.

The masses of the fission products are found to be those of unstable isotopes; that is, they have many more neutrons than the stable isotopes of the corresponding elements. One of the first questions investigated was the manner in which these unstable fission products disintegrated, particularly whether any of the excess neutrons were emitted in this process. Early experiments showed that between 2 and 3 neutrons were emitted per nuclear fission. The process can now be represented schematically, as shown in Figure 40–13: when a neutron is captured by a uranium nucleus of mass number 238, a new isotope of uranium of mass number 239 is formed; in the process of nuclear fission, the latter splits into two isotopes of intermediate masses, say barium and krypton, with the prompt emission of 2 neutrons. A variety of other pairs of nuclei may be produced in the fission process, all of them radioactive, most of them decaying to a stable form by the emission of beta rays; gamma rays are also emitted by many of these isotopes.

In addition to uranium, thorium, $Z = 90$, and protoactinium, $Z = 91$, have been found to be fissionable by the capture of neutrons, and a new element, plutonium, $Z = 94$, is also fissionable by the capture of neutrons. Fission may also occur spontaneously, by excitation of a nucleus with high-energy gamma rays and by bombardment of heavy nuclei with protons, deuterons, or alpha particles. In the following sections, we shall discuss only neutron-induced nuclear fission.

40-9 A NUCLEAR CHAIN REACTION

The concept of a nuclear chain reaction is very simple: if a single nuclear-fission process involving the capture of one neutron results in the release of energy and simultaneously the release of more than one neutron, it should be possible to so arrange the mass of fissionable material to ensure the capture of the newly released neutrons. Or, stated another way, the mass of fissionable material should be so arranged that at any one place the number of new neutrons produced should be equal to the number of free neutrons originally present at that place. The ratio of these two numbers of neutrons is called the *multiplication factor K*. If $K = 1$, the chain reaction will be self-sustaining; if K is less than 1, the process will ultimately come to a halt; if K is greater than 1, the neutron density will increase and may lead to an explosive reaction. A mass of fissionable material so arranged that the multiplication factor is equal to or greater than 1 constitutes a *nuclear reactor*.

In order to be able to design a nuclear reactor, it is essential to know the conditions under which neutrons are captured by nuclei and the conditions under which such capture of neutrons results in the fission of the product nuclei. We shall restrict this discussion to the fission of uranium. Ordinary uranium consists of 3 isotopes: one of mass number 238, another of mass number 235, and a third of mass number 234. The most abundant of these is U238—about 99.3 per cent abundance. The amount of U234 in ordinary uranium is negligible. U235 constitutes about 0.7 per cent of ordinary uranium. Experiments show that U238 is fissionable only if it captures *fast* neutrons, that is, neutrons having energies of 1 Mev or greater. On the other hand, U235 is fissionable with neutrons of any speed and particularly with *slow* neutrons, that is, neutrons having energies corresponding to the thermal energies at ordinary temperatures. These energies are much less than 1 ev.

The neutrons released in nuclear fission have a wide range of energies. In the case of the fission of U235, these energies extend up to about 17 Mev, with a maximum number having energies of about 0.75 Mev. If such neutrons are captured by other uranium nuclei, they produce nuclear fission. However, not every collision between a fast neutron and a uranium nucleus results in capture of the neutron; the collision may simply produce a decrease in the energy of the neutron. Thereafter the probability of its capture will be very small; additional collisions will produce further reductions in the energy of the neutrons. At some particular values of energy, the neutron will be readily captured by U238, but such a capture does not result in nuclear fission. Instead, the newly formed isotope of uranium, U239, emits a gamma-ray photon and then becomes radioactive, emitting a beta ray with a half life of 23 min. The nuclear reaction equations are

$$_{92}U^{238} + {}_0n^1 \rightarrow ({}_{92}U^{239}) \rightarrow {}_{92}U^{239} + \text{gamma ray},$$

then $$_{92}U^{239} \rightarrow {}_{93}Np^{239} + \beta^-. \qquad T = 23 \text{ min.} \qquad \textbf{(18)}$$

The new element thus formed, called neptunium, Np, is itself radioactive, emitting a beta particle with a half life of 2.3 days. The product nucleus formed in this reaction is plutonium, Pu, of atomic number 94. The reaction in which this is formed is

$$_{93}Np^{239} \rightarrow {}_{94}Pu^{239} + \beta^-. \qquad T = 2.3 \text{ days.}$$

It is followed by $$_{94}Pu^{239} \rightarrow {}_{92}U^{235} + {}_2He^4. \qquad T = 24,000 \text{ years.} \qquad \textbf{(19)}$$

The isotope of plutonium is radioactive, emitting an alpha particle, but it has a very long half life—24,000 years. In this sense, it is a comparatively stable element. It will be noted that neptunium and plutonium are *transuranic* elements, that is, elements with atomic numbers greater than that of uranium. When plutonium disintegrates with the emission of an alpha particle, the resulting nucleus is U235. The plutonium isotope formed in the above process is fissionable by the capture of neutrons of any energy and is thus similar to U235 as far as the fission process is concerned. Since it is chemically different from uranium, it can be separated more readily from the uranium metal than the uranium isotope of mass number 235.

If ordinary uranium is to be used in a nuclear reactor, it is essential to avoid loss of neutrons by nonfission capture. Since slow neutrons can produce fission in U235 and since the probability of capture varies inversely with the speed of the neutron, one method of ensuring its fissionable capture is to slow down the neutrons very rapidly to thermal energies. This is done with the aid of a *moderator,* that is, a light element in which the probability of nuclear capture of a neutron is negligible, but in which collisions between neutrons and nuclei will cause a rapid decrease of the energy of the neutron. Deuterium and carbon are two elements suitable for use as moderators.

The first nuclear reactor, or *uranium pile* as it is sometimes called, was operated successfully in Chicago on December 2, 1942; it was built under the direction of E. Fermi and operated by groups headed by W. H. Zinn and H. L. Anderson. A schematic diagram of the construction of a graphite (carbon) moderated uranium pile is shown in Figure 40–14. Rods of

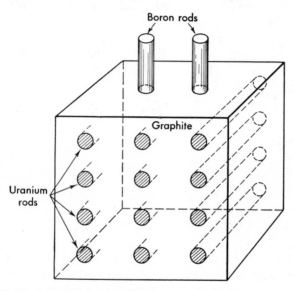

Fig. 40–14   Schematic diagram of a uranium pile. Cylindrical rods of uranium are embedded in a large mass of graphite which acts as a moderator to slow down neutrons. Boron rods, which are inserted into the pile, control its rate of activity.

uranium metal are embedded in blocks of graphite; rods of boron metal are inserted at various places in the pile to control the flux of neutrons; boron nuclei capture neutrons very readily. No special source of neutrons is needed to start this pile; there are always neutrons present from cosmic rays, or from spontaneous fission, to start the nuclear reactor. The mode of its operation can be understood by referring to Figure 40–15. Suppose that a neutron is captured by a uranium nucleus, so that fission results and that two new neutrons are released with energies of about 1 Mev each. These neutrons then make several collisions with nuclei of the moderator, graphite, until their energies are reduced to thermal energies. Whenever one of these slow neutrons is captured by U235, fission will again occur with the release of, say, 2 neutrons. Some neutrons may be lost through the surface of the reactor; one way to reduce this loss is to make the reactor very large; the increase in the surface area is proportional to the square of its linear dimension, while the volume is proportional to the cube of the

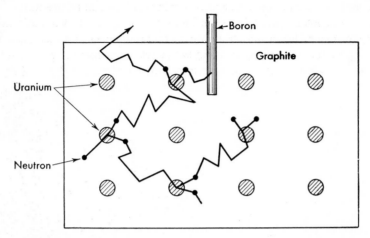

FIG. 40–15   Schematic diagram of the action of a neutron in a uranium pile based on the assumption that each fission process yields two neutrons.   The shaded circles represent rods of uranium; the small circular dots represent neutrons.   Sudden changes in direction of the neutron path are due to collisions with nuclei of the moderator graphite.

linear dimension. Other neutrons may be lost through capture by impurities or through nonfissionable capture by U238. But if $K = 1$, the reaction will be self-sustaining. To prevent the multiplication factor from becoming excessive, boron rods are inserted to various depths in the pile to absorb the excess neutrons. One other control factor may be mentioned here; that is, not all of the neutrons are emitted promptly in nuclear fission; a small percentage of the neutrons are delayed, some by 0.01 sec, others by as much as 1 min.

A whole new field of nuclear science and engineering has been opened as the result of the discovery of nuclear fission and following the successful construction of the first nuclear reactor. Nuclear reactors designed for many different purposes are now in operation throughout the world. Some are used as sources of energy for power plants; others are used for experimental purposes. A nuclear reactor is one of the best sources of neutrons for use in physical, chemical, and biological experiments. It is also a source of radioactive isotopes for medical and industrial uses. A nuclear reactor may also be designed as a military weapon known as an *atomic bomb* or *A-bomb*. The latter is a type of nuclear reactor in which the multiplication factor K is greater than 1. It may consist of uranium containing a large percentage of U235 or of plutonium 239. If the mass of fissionable material is less than a certain *critical* amount, K will be less than 1, and there will be no chain reaction. If the mass is built up rapidly so that the total exceeds the critical mass, a very fast chain reaction will be produced. One of the problems in exploding an atomic bomb is to hold the material together for a sufficient time, probably several millionths of a second, so that a large quantity of the material will take part in the fission process. It has been estimated that the energy released in an atomic bomb is sufficient to raise the temperature of this material to several million degrees and produce pressures upon explosion of perhaps a few million atmospheres. In addition, great quantities of radioactive materials and gamma rays are produced.

40-10   THE NEW PARTICLES OF PHYSICS

There were only two fundamental particles known in physics before 1932, the proton and the electron. It was then believed that all matter in the universe was composed of these two particles. The picture changed when the neutron was discovered in 1932, followed shortly by the discovery of the positron in 1934. Among the theories proposed to explain nuclear forces and nuclear phenomena was one put forward by H. Yukawa in 1935 in which it was assumed that a nuclear field of force, called a *meson field*, exists between nucleons. Furthermore, this field has particles, called *mesons*, associated with it in a manner analogous to the association of photons with an electromagnetic field. The Yukawa theory predicted that the mass of the mesons should be intermediate between the mass of an electron and that of a proton. This Yukawa particle or meson could have a positive charge, a negative charge, or zero charge, the charge being equivalent to that of one electron.

Many such particles have since been discovered; the first one, known as a *mu meson* (μ meson) or *muon*, was discovered in 1937 by S. H. Neddermyer and C. D. Anderson and independently by J. C. Street and E. C. Stevenson. All the others were discovered after 1947. Most of these new particles were discovered in the study of *cosmic rays*, a type of very energetic radiation which reaches the earth's atmosphere from outside, penetrates the atmosphere, and, in so doing, reacts with atmospheric particles giving rise to many nuclear disintegrations. The cosmic rays as observed at various places in the atmosphere will usually consist of a combination of *primary cosmic rays*, which consist almost entirely of protons and other nuclei, plus the secondary radiations or particles produced by the interactions of the primaries with matter. With the development of high-energy particle accelerators, many of the new particles can be produced and studied under controlled conditions.

The particle which reacts most strongly with nuclei and is assumed to be the Yukawa particle is the *pi meson* (π meson) or *pion*. This was first discovered by Lattes, Occhialini, Powell, and D. H. Perkins in 1947 in high-altitude cosmic-ray investigations using special photographic plates.

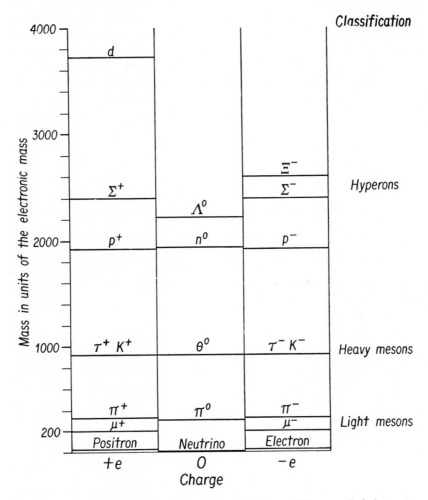

Fɪɢ. 40–16   Diagram showing the masses and charges of the so-called elementary particles; the mass of the electron is taken as unity.

In 1948, E. Gardner and M. Lattes, using the 184-in. Berkeley cyclotron, bombarded a carbon target with 380-Mev alpha particles and showed that pi mesons are emitted by the carbon nuclei as a result of this bombardment. The mesons were bent in circular paths by the magnetic field of the cyclotron, the positively charged pions traveling in one direction, say clockwise, the negative ones counterclockwise. They were detected by special photographic plates placed at suitable positions along these paths. The existence of a *neutral pi meson* (π^0 meson) was verified in other experiments.

The pi and mu mesons are only two of the types of particles discovered. Figure 40–16 shows the other new particles known at present (1956). The mass of each particle is shown on the vertical scale for charge $+e$, 0, and $-e$. The unit of mass is the mass of one electron. The particle most recently discovered (1955) is the *negative proton*, that is, a particle with a negative charge and a mass equal to that of the proton. All of these particles, with the exception of the electron, proton, and deuteron, are unstable; that is, they either disintegrate when in the free state or combine with other particles. For example, the neutron is radioactive with a half life of about 12 minutes, decaying into a proton, electron, and neutrino. The positron combines with an electron and the energy of the two, which is essentially the rest mass energy $2m_0c^2$, is converted into the energy of one or more, usually two, gamma-ray photons. The charged pi meson disintegrates into a charged mu meson and a neutrino in about 10^{-8} sec, while the mu meson disintegrates into an electron and two neutrinos with an average lifetime of about 2 microseconds.

The discovery of these new particles, sometimes called elementary particles, has opened up a whole new field of physics, coming to be known as particle physics. It is hoped that a study of particle physics will shed new light on nuclear forces and nuclear process.

QUESTIONS

1. (a) List the different types of energy that are now known; (b) list the energy units commonly associated with each of these types of energy; (c) list the conversion factors between some of these units.

2. Discuss the meaning of the Q-value of a nuclear reaction, distinguishing between those reactions which have positive Q-values and those having negative Q-values.

3. Compare radioactive disintegration by β^+ emission with that by β^- emission for similarities and for differences. Describe the origin of the particle in each case.

4. Why is it possible for slow neutrons to penetrate a nucleus, while alpha particles need a large amount of energy to penetrate the same nucleus?

5. How do the particles in the cyclotron obtain their high energies?

6. Suppose you ate some salt (NaCl) which had previously been bombarded with deuterons. How could you trace the progress of this salt through your body?

7. Examine recent scientific literature for information on modern high-energy particle accelerators. Compare the linear dimensions of the accelerators with the energies of the particles obtained from them. Use these data to make

ꭤ rough estimate of the size of an accelerator which will produce singly charged particles of about 1,000 Bev.

8. What is the source of the energy released in nuclear fission?

9. What type of "fuel" is used in a nuclear reactor? What are the sources of this fuel?

10. What are the "ashes" from a nuclear reactor? What are some of the problems involved in the disposal of these ashes? Suggest some solution to this problem.

PROBLEMS

(Note: Use the data on Atomic Masses from Table 3 of the Appendix.)

1. Determine nuclear reaction energy, or Q-value, of the nuclear reaction given in Equation (2).

2. Determine the nuclear reaction energy, or Q-value, of the nuclear reaction given in Equation (3).

3. Referring to Equation (6), calculate the mass of the compound nucleus $_7N^{14}$ and compare it with the atomic mass of stable $_7N^{14}$. Discuss the reaction given by Equation (6).

4. (a) Calculate the binding energy of the nucleus of lithium, $A = 7$, by comparing the sum of the masses of its constituent particles with the atomic mass of stable lithium. (b) What is the binding energy per nucleon?

5. (a) Write the nuclear reaction equation for the fission process illustrated in Figure 40–13. (b) Determine the difference in mass between the initial products and the final products of this reaction. (c) Express the result of (b) in Mev. (d) How much energy is released in this reaction?

APPENDICES

Table 1. Four-Place Logarithms of Ordinary Numbers

N	0	1	2	3	4	5	6	7	8	9
10	0000	0043	0086	0128	0170	0212	0253	0294	0334	0374
11	0414	0453	0492	0531	0569	0607	0645	0682	0719	0755
12	0792	0828	0864	0899	0934	0969	1004	1038	1072	1106
13	1139	1173	1206	1239	1271	1303	1335	1367	1399	1430
14	1461	1492	1523	1553	1584	1614	1644	1673	1703	1732
15	1761	1790	1818	1847	1875	1903	1931	1959	1987	2014
16	2041	2068	2095	2122	2148	2175	2201	2227	2253	2279
17	2304	2330	2355	2380	2405	2430	2455	2480	2504	2529
18	2553	2577	2601	2625	2648	2672	2695	2718	2742	2765
19	2788	2810	2833	2856	2878	2900	2923	2945	2967	2989
20	3010	3032	3054	3075	3096	3118	3139	3160	3181	3201
21	3222	3243	3263	3284	3304	3324	3345	3365	3385	3404
22	3424	3444	3464	3483	3502	3522	3541	3560	3579	3598
23	3617	3636	3655	3674	3692	3711	3729	3747	3766	3784
24	3802	3820	3838	3856	3874	3892	3909	3927	3945	3962
25	3979	3997	4014	4031	4048	4065	4082	4099	4116	4133
26	4150	4166	4183	4200	4216	4232	4249	4265	4281	4298
27	4314	4330	4346	4362	4378	4393	4409	4425	4440	4456
28	4472	4487	4502	4518	4533	4548	4564	4579	4594	4609
29	4624	4639	4654	4669	4683	4698	4713	4728	4742	4757
30	4771	4786	4800	4814	4829	4843	4857	4871	4886	4900
31	4914	4928	4942	4955	4969	4983	4997	5011	5024	5038
32	5051	5065	5079	5092	5105	5119	5132	5145	5159	5172
33	5185	5198	5211	5224	5237	5250	5263	5276	5289	5302
34	5315	5328	5340	5353	5366	5378	5391	5403	5416	5428
35	5441	5453	5465	5478	5490	5502	5514	5527	5539	5551
36	5563	5575	5587	5599	5611	5623	5635	5647	5658	5670
37	5682	5694	5705	5717	5729	5740	5752	5763	5775	5786
38	5798	5809	5821	5832	5843	5855	5866	5877	5888	5899
39	5911	5922	5933	5944	5955	5966	5977	5988	5999	6010
40	6021	6031	6042	6053	6064	6075	6085	6096	6107	6117
41	6128	6138	6149	6160	6170	6180	6191	6201	6212	6222
42	6232	6243	6253	6263	6274	6284	6294	6304	6314	6325
43	6335	6345	6355	6365	6375	6385	6395	6405	6415	6425
44	6435	6444	6454	6464	6474	6484	6493	6503	6513	6522
45	6532	6542	6551	6561	6571	6580	6590	6599	6609	6618
46	6628	6637	6646	6656	6665	6675	6684	6693	6702	6712
47	6721	6730	6739	6749	6758	6767	6776	6785	6794	6803
48	6812	6821	6830	6839	6848	6857	6866	6875	6884	6893
49	6902	6911	6920	6928	6937	6946	6955	6964	6972	6981
50	6990	6998	7007	7016	7024	7033	7042	7050	7059	7067
51	7076	7084	7093	7101	7110	7118	7126	7135	7143	7152
52	7160	7168	7177	7185	7193	7202	7210	7218	7226	7235
53	7243	7251	7259	7267	7275	7284	7292	7300	7308	7316
54	7324	7332	7340	7348	7356	7364	7372	7380	7388	7396
N	0	1	2	3	4	5	6	7	8	9

Table 1. Four-Place Logarithms of Ordinary Numbers (Cont.)

N	0	1	2	3	4	5	6	7	8	9
55	7404	7412	7419	7427	7435	7443	7451	7459	7466	7474
56	7482	7490	7497	7505	7513	7520	7528	7536	7543	7551
57	7559	7566	7574	7582	7589	7597	7604	7612	7619	7627
58	7634	7642	7649	7657	7664	7672	7679	7686	7694	7701
59	7709	7716	7723	7731	7738	7745	7752	7760	7767	7774
60	7782	7789	7796	7803	7810	7818	7825	7832	7839	7846
61	7853	7860	7868	7875	7882	7889	7896	7903	7910	7917
62	7924	7931	7938	7945	7952	7959	7966	7973	7980	7987
63	7993	8000	8007	8014	8021	8028	8035	8041	8048	8055
64	8062	8069	8075	8082	8089	8096	8102	8109	8116	8122
65	8129	8136	8142	8149	8156	8162	8169	8176	8182	8189
66	8195	8202	8209	8215	8222	8228	8235	8241	8248	8254
67	8261	8267	8274	8280	8287	8293	8299	8306	8312	8319
68	8325	8331	8338	8344	8351	8357	8363	8370	8376	8382
69	8388	8395	8401	8407	8414	8420	8426	8432	8439	8445
70	8451	8457	8463	8470	8476	8482	8488	8494	8500	8506
71	8513	8519	8525	8531	8537	8543	8549	8555	8561	8567
72	8573	8579	8585	8591	8597	8603	8609	8615	8621	8627
73	8633	8639	8645	8651	8657	8663	8669	8675	8681	8686
74	8692	8698	8704	8710	8716	8722	8727	8733	8739	8745
75	8751	8756	8762	8768	8774	8779	8785	8791	8797	8802
76	8808	8814	8820	8825	8831	8837	8842	8848	8854	8859
77	8865	8871	8876	8882	8887	8893	8899	8904	8910	8915
78	8921	8927	8932	8938	8943	8949	8954	8960	8965	8971
79	8976	8982	8987	8993	8998	9004	9009	9015	9020	9025
80	9031	9036	9042	9047	9053	9058	9063	9069	9074	9079
81	9085	9090	9096	9101	9106	9112	9117	9122	9128	9133
82	9138	9143	9149	9154	9159	9165	9170	9175	9180	9186
83	9191	9196	9201	9206	9212	9217	9222	9227	9232	9238
84	9243	9248	9253	9258	9263	9269	9274	9279	9284	9289
85	9294	9299	9304	9309	9315	9320	9325	9330	9335	9340
86	9345	9350	9355	9360	9365	9370	9375	9380	9385	9390
87	9395	9400	9405	9410	9415	9420	9425	9430	9435	9440
88	9445	9450	9455	9460	9465	9469	9474	9479	9484	9489
89	9494	9499	9504	9509	9513	9518	9523	9528	9533	9538
90	9542	9547	9552	9557	9562	9566	9571	9576	9581	9586
91	9590	9595	9600	9605	9609	9614	9619	9624	9628	9633
92	9638	9643	9647	9652	9657	9661	9666	9671	9675	9680
93	9685	9689	9694	9699	9703	9708	9713	9717	9722	9727
94	9731	9736	9741	9745	9750	9754	9759	9763	9768	9773
95	9777	9782	9786	9791	9795	9800	9805	9809	9814	9818
96	9823	9827	9832	9836	9841	9845	9850	9854	9859	9863
97	9868	9872	9877	9881	9886	9890	9894	9899	9903	9908
98	9912	9917	9921	9926	9930	9934	9939	9943	9948	9952
99	9956	9961	9965	9969	9974	9978	9983	9987	9991	9996
N	0	1	2	3	4	5	6	7	8	9

Table 2.   Four-Place Values of Functions and Radians

Degrees	Radians	Sin	Cos	Tan	Cot	Sec	Csc		
0° 00′	.0000	.0000	1.0000	.0000	——	1.000	——	1.5708	90° 00′
10	029	029	000	029	343.8	000	343.8	679	50
20	058	058	000	058	171.9	000	171.9	650	40
30	.0087	.0087	1.0000	.0087	114.6	1.000	114.6	1.5621	30
40	116	116	.9999	116	85.94	000	85.95	592	20
50	145	145	999	145	68.75	000	68.76	563	10
1° 00′	.0175	.0175	.9998	.0175	57.29	1.000	57.30	1.5533	89° 00′
10	204	204	998	204	49.10	000	49.11	504	50
20	233	233	997	233	42.96	000	42.98	475	40
30	.0262	.0262	.9997	.0262	38.19	1.000	38.20	1.5446	30
40	291	291	996	291	34.37	000	34.38	417	20
50	320	320	995	320	31.24	001	31.26	388	10
2° 00′	.0349	.0349	.9994	.0349	28.64	1.001	28.65	1.5359	88° 00′
10	378	378	993	378	26.43	001	26.45	330	50
20	407	407	992	407	24.54	001	24.56	301	40
30	.0436	.0436	.9990	.0437	22.90	1.001	22.93	1.5272	30
40	465	465	989	466	21.47	001	21.49	243	20
50	495	494	988	495	20.21	001	20.23	213	10
3° 00′	.0524	.0523	.9986	.0524	19.08	1.001	19.11	1.5184	87° 00′
10	553	552	985	553	18.07	002	18.10	155	50
20	582	581	983	582	17.17	002	17.20	126	40
30	.0611	.0610	.9981	.0612	16.35	1.002	16.38	1.5097	30
40	640	640	980	641	15.60	002	15.64	068	20
50	669	669	978	670	14.92	002	14.96	039	10
4° 00′	.0698	.0698	.9976	.0699	14.30	1.002	14.34	1.5010	86° 00′
10	727	727	974	729	13.73	003	13.76	981	50
20	756	756	971	758	13.20	003	13.23	952	40
30	.0785	.0785	.9969	.0787	12.71	1.003	12.75	1.4923	30
40	814	814	967	816	12.25	003	12.29	893	20
50	844	843	964	846	11.83	004	11.87	864	10
5° 00′	.0873	.0872	.9962	.0875	11.43	1.004	11.47	1.4835	85° 00′
10	902	901	959	904	11.06	004	11.10	806	50
20	931	929	957	934	10.71	004	10.76	777	40
30	.0960	.0958	.9954	.0963	10.39	1.005	10.43	1.4748	30
40	989	987	951	992	10.08	005	10.13	719	20
50	.1018	.1016	948	.1022	9.788	005	9.839	690	10
6° 00′	.1047	.1045	.9945	.1051	9.514	1.006	9.567	1.4661	84° 00′
10	076	074	942	080	9.255	006	9.309	632	50
20	105	103	939	110	9.010	006	9.065	603	40
30	.1134	.1132	.9936	.1139	8.777	1.006	8.834	1.4573	30
40	164	161	932	169	8.556	007	8.614	544	20
50	193	190	929	198	8.345	007	8.405	515	10
7° 00′	.1222	.1219	.9925	.1228	8.144	1.008	8.206	1.4486	83° 00′
10	251	248	922	257	7.953	008	8.016	457	50
20	280	276	918	287	7.770	008	7.834	428	40
30	.1309	.1305	.9914	.1317	7.596	1.009	7.661	1.4399	30
40	338	334	911	346	7.429	009	7.496	370	20
50	367	363	907	376	7.269	009	7.337	341	10
8° 00′	.1396	.1392	.9903	.1405	7.115	1.010	7.185	1.4312	82° 00′
10	425	421	899	435	6.968	010	7.040	283	50
20	454	449	894	465	6.827	011	6.900	254	40
30	.1484	.1478	.9890	.1495	6.691	1.011	6.765	1.4224	30
40	513	507	886	524	6.561	012	6.636	195	20
50	542	536	881	554	6.435	012	6.512	166	10
9° 00′	.1571	.1564	.9877	.1584	6.314	1.012	6.392	1.4137	81° 00′
		Cos	Sin	Cot	Tan	Csc	Sec	Radians	Degrees

Table 2. Four-Place Values of Functions and Radians (Cont.)

DEGREES	RADIANS	Sin	Cos	Tan	Cot	Sec	Csc		
9° 00'	.1571	.1564	.9877	.1584	6.314	1.012	6.392	1.4137	81° 00'
10	600	593	872	614	197	013	277	108	50
20	629	622	868	644	084	013	166	079	40
30	.1658	.1650	.9863	.1673	5.976	1.014	6.059	1.4050	30
40	687	679	858	703	871	014	5.955	1.4021	20
50	716	708	853	733	769	015	855	992	10
10° 00'	.1745	.1736	.9848	.1763	5.671	1.015	5.759	1.3963	80° 00'
10	774	765	843	793	576	016	665	934	50
20	804	794	838	823	485	016	575	904	40
30	.1833	.1822	.9833	.1853	5.396	1.017	5.487	1.3875	30
40	862	851	827	883	309	018	403	846	20
50	891	880	822	914	226	018	320	817	10
11° 00'	.1920	.1908	.9816	.1944	5.145	1.019	5.241	1.3788	79° 00'
10	949	937	811	974	066	019	164	759	50
20	978	965	805	.2004	4.989	020	089	730	40
30	.2007	.1994	.9799	.2035	4.915	1.020	5.016	1.3701	30
40	036	.2022	793	065	843	021	4.945	672	20
50	065	051	787	095	773	022	876	643	10
12° 00'	.2094	.2079	.9781	.2126	4.705	1.022	4.810	1.3614	78° 00'
10	123	108	775	156	638	023	745	584	50
20	153	136	769	186	574	024	682	555	40
30	.2182	.2164	.9763	.2217	4.511	1.024	4.620	1.3526	30
40	211	193	757	247	449	025	560	497	20
50	240	221	750	278	390	026	502	468	10
13° 00'	.2269	.2250	.9744	.2309	4.331	1.026	4.445	1.3439	77° 00'
10	298	278	737	339	275	027	390	410	50
20	327	306	730	370	219	028	336	381	40
30	.2356	.2334	.9724	.2401	4.165	1.028	4.284	1.3352	30
40	385	363	717	432	113	029	232	323	20
50	414	391	710	462	061	030	182	294	10
14° 00'	.2443	.2419	.9703	.2493	4.011	1.031	4.134	1.3265	76° 00'
10	473	447	696	524	3.962	031	086	235	50
20	502	476	689	555	914	032	039	206	40
30	.2531	.2504	.9681	.2586	3.867	1.033	3.994	1.3177	30
40	560	532	674	617	821	034	950	148	20
50	589	560	667	648	776	034	906	119	10
15° 00'	.2618	.2588	.9659	.2679	3.732	1.035	3.864	1.3090	75° 00'
10	647	616	652	711	689	036	822	061	50
20	676	644	644	742	647	037	782	032	40
30	.2705	.2672	.9636	.2773	3.606	1.038	3.742	1.3003	30
40	734	700	628	805	566	039	703	974	20
50	763	728	621	836	526	039	665	945	10
16° 00'	.2793	.2756	.9613	.2867	3.487	1.040	3.628	1.2915	74° 00'
10	822	784	605	899	450	041	592	886	50
20	851	812	596	931	412	042	556	857	40
30	.2880	.2840	.9588	.2962	3.376	1.043	3.521	1.2828	30
40	909	868	580	994	340	044	487	799	20
50	938	896	572	.3026	305	045	453	770	10
17° 00'	.2967	.2924	.9563	.3057	3.271	1.046	3.420	1.2741	73° 00'
10	996	952	555	089	237	047	388	712	50
20	.3025	979	546	121	204	048	356	683	40
30	.3054	.3007	.9537	.3153	3.172	1.049	3.326	1.2654	30
40	083	035	528	185	140	049	295	625	20
50	113	062	520	217	108	050	265	595	10
18° 00'	.3142	.3090	.9511	.3249	3.078	1.051	3.236	1.2566	72° 00'
		Cos	Sin	Cot	Tan	Csc	Sec	RADIANS	DEGREES

Table 2. Four-Place Values of Functions and Radians (Cont.)

Degrees	Radians	Sin	Cos	Tan	Cot	Sec	Csc		
18° 00'	.3142	.3090	.9511	.3249	3.078	1.051	3.236	1.2566	**72° 00'**
10	171	118	502	281	047	052	207	537	50
20	200	145	492	314	018	053	179	508	40
30	.3229	.3173	.9483	.3346	2.989	1.054	3.152	1.2479	30
40	258	201	474	378	960	056	124	450	20
50	287	228	465	411	932	057	098	421	10
19° 00'	.3316	.3256	.9455	.3443	2.904	1.058	3.072	1.2392	**71° 00'**
10	345	283	446	476	877	059	046	363	50
20	374	311	436	508	850	060	021	334	40
30	.3403	.3338	.9426	.3541	2.824	1.061	2.996	1.2305	30
40	432	365	417	574	798	062	971	275	20
50	462	393	407	607	773	063	947	246	10
20° 00'	.3491	.3420	.9397	.3640	2.747	1.064	2.924	1.2217	**70° 00'**
10	520	448	387	673	723	065	901	188	50
20	549	475	377	706	699	066	878	159	40
30	.3578	.3502	.9367	.3739	2.675	1.068	2.855	1.2130	30
40	607	529	356	772	651	069	833	101	20
50	636	557	346	805	628	070	812	072	10
21° 00'	.3665	.3584	.9336	.3839	2.605	1.071	2.790	1.2043	**69° 00'**
10	694	611	325	872	583	072	769	1.2014	50
20	723	638	315	906	560	074	749	985	40
30	.3752	.3665	.9304	.3939	2.539	1.075	2.729	1.1956	30
40	782	692	293	973	517	076	709	926	20
50	811	719	283	.4006	496	077	689	897	10
22° 00'	.3840	.3746	.9272	.4040	2.475	1.079	2.669	1.1868	**68° 00'**
10	869	773	261	074	455	080	650	839	50
20	898	800	250	108	434	081	632	810	40
30	.3927	.3827	.9239	.4142	2.414	1.082	2.613	1.1781	30
40	956	854	228	176	394	084	595	752	20
50	985	881	216	210	375	085	577	723	10
23° 00'	.4014	.3907	.9205	.4245	2.356	1.086	2.559	1.1694	**67° 00'**
10	043	934	194	279	337	088	542	665	50
20	072	961	182	314	318	089	525	636	40
30	.4102	.3987	.9171	.4348	2.300	1.090	2.508	1.1606	30
40	131	.4014	159	383	282	092	491	577	20
50	160	041	147	417	264	093	475	548	10
24° 00'	.4189	.4067	.9135	.4452	2.246	1.095	2.459	1.1519	**66° 00'**
10	218	094	124	487	229	096	443	490	50
20	247	120	112	522	211	097	427	461	40
30	.4276	.4147	.9100	.4557	2.194	1.099	2.411	1.1432	30
40	305	173	088	592	177	100	396	403	20
50	334	200	075	628	161	102	381	374	10
25° 00'	.4363	.4226	.9063	.4663	2.145	1.103	2.366	1.1345	**65° 00'**
10	392	253	051	699	128	105	352	316	50
20	422	279	038	734	112	106	337	286	40
30	.4451	.4305	.9026	.4770	2.097	1.108	2.323	1.1257	30
40	480	331	013	806	081	109	309	228	20
50	509	358	001	841	066	111	295	199	10
26° 00'	.4538	.4384	.8988	.4877	2.050	1.113	2.281	1.1170	**64° 00'**
10	567	410	975	913	035	114	268	141	50
20	596	436	962	950	020	116	254	112	40
30	.4625	.4462	.8949	.4986	2.006	1.117	2.241	1.1083	30
40	654	488	936	.5022	1.991	119	228	054	20
50	683	514	923	059	977	121	215	1.1025	10
27° 00'	.4712	.4540	.8910	.5095	1.963	1.122	2.203	1.0996	**63° 00'**
		Cos	Sin	Cot	Tan	Csc	Sec	Radians	Degrees

Table 2. Four-Place Values of Functions and Radians (Cont.)

DEGREES	RADIANS	Sin	Cos	Tan	Cot	Sec	Csc		
27° 00'	.4712	.4540	.8910	.5095	1.963	1.122	2.203	1.0996	63° 00'
10	741	566	897	132	949	124	190	966	50
20	771	592	884	169	935	126	178	937	40
30	.4800	.4617	.8870	.5206	1.921	1.127	2.166	1.0908	30
40	829	643	857	243	907	129	154	879	20
50	858	669	843	280	894	131	142	850	10
28° 00'	.4887	.4695	.8829	.5317	1.881	1.133	2.130	1.0821	62° 00'
10	916	720	816	354	868	-134	118	792	50
20	945	746	802	392	855	136	107	763	40
30	.4974	.4772	.8788	.5430	1.842	1.138	2.096	1.0734	30
40	.5003	797	774	467	829	140	085	705	20
50	032	823	760	505	816	142	074	676	10
29° 00'	.5061	.4848	.8746	.5543	1.804	1.143	2.063	1.0647	61° 00'
10	091	874	732	581	792	145	052	617	50
20	120	899	718	619	780	147	041	588	40
30	.5149	.4924	.8704	.5658	1.767	1.149	2.031	1.0559	30
40	178	950	689	696	756	151	020	530	20
50	207	975	675	735	744	153	010	501	10
30° 00'	.5236	.5000	.8660	.5774	1.732	1.155	2.000	1.0472	60° 00'
10	265	025	646	812	720	157	1.990	443	50
20	294	050	631	851	709	159	980	414	40
30	.5323	.5075	.8616	.5890	1.698	1.161	1.970	1.0385	30
40	352	100	601	930	686	163	961	356	20
50	381	125	587	969	.675	165	951	327	10
31° 00'	.5411	.5150	.8572	.6009	1.664	1.167	1.942	1.0297	59° 00'
10	440	175	557	048	653	-169	932	268	50
20	469	200	542	088	643	171	923	239	40
30	.5498	.5225	.8526	.6128	1.632	1.173	1.914	1.0210	30
40	527	250	511	168	621	175	905	181	20
50	556	275	496	208	611	177	896	152	10
32° 00'	.5585	.5299	.8480	.6249	1.600	1.179	1.887	1.0123	58° 00'
10	614	324	465	289	590	181	878	094	50
20	643	348	450	330	580	184	870	065	40
30	.5672	.5373	.8434	.6371	1.570	1.186	1.861	1.0036	30
40	701	398	418	412	560	188	853	1.0007	20
50	730	422	403	453	550	190	844	977	10
33° 00'	.5760	.5446	.8387	.6494	1.540	1.192	1.836	.9948	57° 00'
10	789	471	371	536	530	195	828	919	50
20	818	495	355	577	520	197	820	890	40
30	.5847	.5519	.8339	.6619	1.511	1.199	1.812	.9861	30
40	876	544	323	661	501	202	804	832	20
50	905	568	307	703	1.492	204	796	803	10
34° 00'	.5934	.5592	.8290	.6745	1.483	1.206	1.788	.9774	56° 00'
10	963	616	274	787	473	209	781	745	50
20	992	640	258	830	464	211	773	716	40
30	.6021	.5664	.8241	.6873	1.455	1.213	1.766	.9687	30
40	050	688	225	916	446	216	758	657	20
50	080	712	208	959	437	218	751	628	10
35° 00'	.6109	.5736	.8192	.7002	1.428	1.221	1.743	.9599	55° 00'
10	138	760	175	046	419	223	736	570	50
20	167	783	158	089	411	226	729	541	40
30	.6196	.5807	.8141	.7133	1.402	1.228	1.722	.9512	30
40	225	831	124	177	.393	231	715	483	20
50	254	854	107	221	385	233	708	454	10
36° 00'	.6283	.5878	.8090	.7265	1.376	1.236	1.701	.9425	54° 00'
		Cos	Sin	Cot	Tan	Csc	Sec	RADIANS	DEGREES

Table 2. Four-Place Values of Functions and Radians (Cont.)

Degrees	Radians	Sin	Cos	Tan	Cot	Sec	Csc		
36° 00'	.6283	.5878	.8090	.7265	1.376	1.236	1.701	.9425	**54° 00'**
10	312	901	073	310	368	239	695	396	50
20	341	925	056	355	360	241	688	367	40
30	.6370	.5948	.8039	.7400	1.351	1.244	1.681	.9338	30
40	400	972	021	445	343	247	675	308	20
50	429	995	004	490	335	249	668	279	10
37° 00'	.6458	.6018	.7986	.7536	1.327	1.252	1.662	.9250	**53° 00'**
10	487	041	969	581	319	255	655	221	50
20	516	065	951	627	311	258	649	192	40
30	.6545	.6088	.7934	.7673	1.303	1.260	1.643	.9163	30
40	574	111	916	720	295	263	636	134	20
50	603	134	898	766	288	266	630	105	10
38° 00'	.6632	.6157	.7880	.7813	1.280	1.269	1.624	.9076	**52° 00'**
10	661	180	862	860	272	272	618	047	50
20	690	202	844	907	265	275	612	.9018	40
30	.6720	.6225	.7826	.7954	1.257	1.278	1.606	.8988	30
40	749	248	808	.8002	250	281	601	959	20
50	778	271	790	050	242	284	595	930	10
39° 00'	.6807	.6293	.7771	.8098	1.235	1.287	1.589	.8901	**51° 00'**
10	836	316	753	146	228	290	583	872	50
20	865	338	735	195	220	293	578	843	40
30	.6894	.6361	.7716	.8243	1.213	1.296	1.572	.8814	30
40	923	383	698	292	206	299	567	785	20
50	952	406	679	342	199	302	561	756	10
40° 00'	.6981	.6428	.7660	.8391	1.192	1.305	1.556	.8727	**50° 00'**
10	.7010	450	642	441	185	309	550	698	50
20	039	472	623	491	178	312	545	668	40
30	.7069	.6494	.7604	.8541	1.171	1.315	1.540	.8639	30
40	098	517	585	591	164	318	535	610	20
50	127	539	566	642	157	322	529	581	10
41° 00'	.7156	.6561	.7547	.8693	1.150	1.325	1.524	.8552	**49° 00'**
10	185	583	528	744	144	328	519	523	50
20	214	604	509	796	137	332	514	494	40
30	.7243	.6626	.7490	.8847	1.130	1.335	1.509	.8465	30
40	272	648	470	899	124	339	504	436	20
50	301	670	451	952	117	342	499	407	10
42° 00'	.7330	.6691	.7431	.9004	1.111	1.346	1.494	.8378	**48° 00'**
10	359	713	412	057	104	349	490	348	50
20	389	734	392	110	098	353	485	319	40
30	.7418	.6756	.7373	.9163	1.091	1.356	1.480	.8290	30
40	447	777	353	217	085	360	476	261	20
50	476	799	333	271	079	364	471	232	10
43° 00'	.7505	.6820	.7314	.9325	1.072	1.367	1.466	.8203	**47° 00'**
10	534	841	294	380	066	371	462	174	50
20	563	862	274	435	060	375	457	145	40
30	.7592	.6884	.7254	.9490	1.054	1.379	1.453	.8116	30
40	621	905	234	545	048	382	448	087	20
50	650	926	214	601	042	386	444	058	10
44° 00'	.7679	.6947	.7193	.9657	1.036	1.390	1.440	.8029	**46° 00'**
10	709	967	173	713	030	394	435	999	50
20	738	988	153	770	024	398	431	970	40
30	.7767	.7009	.7133	.9827	1.018	1.402	1.427	.7941	30
40	796	030	112	884	012	406	423	912	20
50	825	050	092	942	006	410	418	883	10
45° 00'	.7854	.7071	.7071	1.000	1.000	1.414	1.414	.7854	**45° 00'**
		Cos	Sin	Cot	Tan	Csc	Sec	Radians	Degrees

Table 3. Isotopic Masses

Mass No.	Atomic No.	Element	Atomic Mass
1	0	n	1.008987
1	1	H	1.008145
2	1	H	2.014741
3	1	H	3.016997
3	2	He	3.016977
4	2	He	4.003879
5	2	He	5.0137
5	3	Li	5.0136
6	2	He	6.020833
6	3	Li	6.01697
7	3	Li	7.01822
7	4	Be	7.01916
8	3	Li	8.02502
8	4	Be	8.00785
8	5	B	8.0264
9	4	Be	9.01503
9	5	B	9.01620
10	4	Be	10.01677
10	5	B	10.016110
10	6	C	10.0206
11	5	B	11.012811
11	6	C	11.01495
12	6	C	12.003844
12	7	N	12.0227
13	6	C	13.007505
13	7	N	13.00988
14	6	C	14.00767
14	7	N	14.007550
15	6	C	15.0143
15	7	N	15.004902
15	8	O	15.0078
16	7	N	16.0109
16	8	O	16.000000
17	7	N	17.0139
17	8	O	17.004533
17	9	F	17.007505
18	8	O	18.004883
18	9	F	18.006651
19	8	O	19.0091
19	9	F	19.004444
19	10	Ne	19.007952

Table 3.   Isotopic Masses (Cont.)

Mass No.	Atomic No.	Element	Atomic Mass
20	9	F	20.006350
20	10	Ne	19.998772
21	10	Ne	21.000504
21	11	Na	21.004286
22	10	Ne	21.998382
22	11	Na	22.001409
23	10	Ne	23.001768
23	11	Na	22.997055
23	12	Mg	23.001453
24	11	Na	23.998568
24	12	Mg	23.992628
25	12	Mg	24.993745
26	12	Mg	25.990802
27	12	Mg	26.992876
27	13	Al	26.990109
28	13	Al	27.990760
28	14	Si	27.985825
29	14	Si	28.985705
30	14	Si	29.983307
31	14	Si	30.985140
31	15	P	30.983619
32	15	P	31.984016
32	16	S	31.982274
33	15	P	32.982166
33	16	S	32.981941
34	16	S	33.978709
35	17	Cl	34.980064
36	18	A	35.97926
37	17	Cl	36.977675
38	18	A	37.97491
39	19	K	38.97606
40	18	A	39.975148
40	20	Ca	39.97545
41	19	K	40.97490
42	20	Ca	41.97216
43	20	Ca	42.97251
44	20	Ca	43.96924
45	21	Sc	44.97010
46	22	Ti	45.96697
47	22	Ti	46.96668
48	20	Ca	47.96778

Table 3. *Isotopic Masses* (Cont.)

Mass No.	Atomic No.	Element	Atomic Mass
48	22	Ti	47.96317
49	22	Ti	48.96358
50	22	Ti	49.96077
50	24	Cr	49.96210
51	23	V	50.96052
52	24	Cr	51.95707
53	24	Cr	52.95772
54	24	Cr	53.9563
54	26	Fe	53.95704
55	25	Mn	54.95581
56	26	Fe	55.95272
57	26	Fe	56.95359
58	26	Fe	57.9520
58	28	Ni	57.95345
59	27	Co	58.95182
60	27	Co	59.95250
60	28	Ni	59.94901
61	28	Ni	60.94907
62	28	Ni	61.94681
63	29	Cu	62.94926
64	28	Ni	63.94755
64	30	Zn	63.94955
65	29	Cu	64.94835
66	30	Zn	65.94722
67	30	Zn	66.94815
68	30	Zn	67.94686
70	30	Zn	69.94779
70	32	Ge	69.9447
74	32	Ge	73.9426
74	34	Se	73.9439
75	33	As	74.9432
76	32	Ge	75.9433
79	35	Br	78.944
81	35	Br	80.943
82	36	Kr	81.938
84	36	Kr	83.938
85	37	Rb	84.931
86	38	Sr	85.93533
87	37	Rb	86.9295
88	38	Sr	87.93374
94	42	Mo	93.9343

Table 3. *Isotopic Masses* (Cont.)

Mass No.	Atomic No.	Element	Atomic Mass
98	42	Mo	97.93610
102	46	Pd	101.9375
104	46	Pd	103.93655
105	46	Pd	104.9384
106	46	Pd	105.9368
106	48	Cd	105.93984
108	46	Pd	107.93801
108	48	Cd	107.93860
110	46	Pd	109.93965
110	48	Cd	109.93857
111	48	Cd	110.93978
112	48	Cd	111.93885
113	48	Cd	112.94061
113	49	In	112.94045
114	48	Cd	113.93997
115	49	In	114.94040
115	50	Sn	114.94014
116	48	Cd	115.94202
116	50	Sn	115.93927
117	50	Sn	116.94052
118	50	Sn	117.93978
119	50	Sn	118.94122
120	50	Sn	119.94059
120	52	Te	119.94288
122	50	Sn	121.94249
122	52	Te	121.94193
123	52	Te	122.94368
124	50	Sn	123.94490
124	52	Te	123.94278
124	54	Xe	123.94578
125	52	Te	124.94460
126	52	Te	125.94420
126	54	Xe	125.94476
127	53	I	126.94528
128	52	Te	127.94649
128	54	Xe	127.94446
129	54	Xe	153.94601
130	52	Te	129.94853
130	54	Xe	129.94501
131	54	Xe	130.94673
132	54	Xe	131.94615

Table 3. Isotopic Masses (Cont.)

Mass No.	Atomic No.	Element	Atomic Mass
134	54	Xe	133.94803
136	54	Xe	135.95046
136	56	Ba	135.9488
137	56	Ba	136.9502
138	56	Ba	137.9498
140	58	Ce	139.9489
141	59	Pr	140.9514
142	58	Ce	141.9537
144	60	Nd	143.9560
150	60	Nd	149.9687
176	72	Hf	175.9923
178	72	Hf	177.9936
180	72	Hf	180.0029
181	73	Ta	181.0031
182	74	W	182.0033
183	74	W	183.0059
184	74	W	184.0052
194	78	Pt	194.0256
196	78	Pt	196.02744
205	82	Pb	205.04559
206	81	Tl	206.04702
206	82	Pb	206.04519
207	81	Tl	207.04934
207	82	Pb	207.04725
208	81	Tl	208.05290
208	82	Pb	208.04754
208	83	Bi	208.04968
209	81	Tl	209.05778
209	82	Pb	209.05398
209	83	Bi	209.05325
209	84	Po	209.05496
210	81	Tl	210.06264
210	82	Pb	210.05622
210	83	Bi	210.05614
210	84	Po	210.05488
211	82	Pb	211.06196
211	83	Bi	211.06047
211	84	Po	211.05927
212	82	Pb	212.06487
212	83	Bi	212.06345
212	84	Po	212.06094

Table 3.   Isotopic Masses (Cont.)

Mass No.	Atomic No.	Element	Atomic Mass
212	85	At	212.06079
213	83	Bi	213.06824
213	83	Po	213.06696
214	82	Pb	214.07362
214	83	Bi	214.07225
214	84	Po	214.06852
214	85	At	214.06955
215	84	Po	215.07392
215	85	At	215.07313
216	84	Po	216.07617
216	85	At	216.07586
216	86	Em	216.07358
217	85	At	217.07979
217	86	Em	217.07939
218	84	Po	218.08407
218	85	At	218.08369
218	86	Em	218.08017
218	87	Fr	218.08108
219	86	Em	219.08527
219	87	Fr	219.08501
220	86	Em	220.08693
220	87	Fr	220.08706
220	88	Ra	220.08567
221	87	Fr	221 09057
221	88	Ra	221 09060
222	86	Em	222.09397
222	88	Ra	222.09116
222	89	Ac	222.09342
223	87	Fr	223.09697
223	88	Ra	223.09559
223	89	Ac	223.09615
224	88	Ra	224.09703
224	89	Ac	224.09769
224	90	Th	224.09743
225	88	Ra	225.10102
225	89	Ac	225.10081
225	90	Th	225.10170
226	88	Ra	226.10309
226	90	Th	226.10193
226	91	Pa	226.10494
227	88	Ra	227.10723

Table 3. Isotopic Masses (Cont.)

Mass No.	Atomic No.	Element	Atomic Mass
227	89	Ac	227.10666
227	90	Th	227.10642
227	91	Pa	227.10710
228	88	Ra	228.11005
228	89	Ac	228.11005
228	90	Th	228.10685
228	91	Pa	228.10823
228	92	U	228.10863
229	90	Th	229.11021
229	91	Pa	229.11088
229	92	U	229.11258
230	90	Th	230.11206
230	91	Pa	230.11441
230	92	U	230.11222
231	90	Th	231.11628
231	91	Pa	231.11607
231	93	Np	231.11776
232	90	Th	232.11852
232	91	Pa	232.11768
232	92	U	232.11650
232	94	Pu	232.11973
233	90	Th	233.12198
233	91	Pa	233.12027
233	92	U	233.11937
234	90	Th	234.12394
234	91	Pa	234.12281
234	92	U	234.12115
234	94	Pu	234.12269
235	92	U	235.12517
236	94	Pu	236.12667
237	92	U	237.13010
237	93	Np	237.12932
238	92	U	238.13232
238	93	Np	238.13255
238	94	Pu	238.13106
239	92	U	239.13704
239	93	Np	239.13620
239	94	Pu	239.13494
239	95	Am	239.13568
240	96	Cm	240.13744
241	94	Pu	241.13909

Table 3.   Isotopic Masses (Cont.)

Mass No.	Atomic No.	Element	Atomic Mass
241	95	Am	241.13919
242	95	Am	242.14215
242	96	Cm	242.14160

Collins, T. L., A. O. Nier, and W. H. Johnson, Jr., *Phys. Rev.*, 86, 408, 1952.

Duckworth, H. E., C. L. Kegley, J. M. Olson, and G. S. Stanford, *Phys. Rev.*, 83, 1114, 1951.

Halsted, R. E., *Phys. Rev.*, 88, 660, 1952.

Hays, E. E., P. I. Richards, and S. A. Goudsmit, *Phys. Rev.*, 84, 824, 1951.

Hornyak, W. F., T. Lauritsen, P. Morrison, and W. A. Fowler, *Rev. Modern Phys.*, 22, 291, 1950.

Ogata, K., and H. Matsuda, *Phys. Rev.*, 89, p. 27, 1953.

Stern, N. O., *Revs. Modern Phys.*, 21, 316, 1949.

Table 4.   Atomic Weights of the Elements

Element	Symbol	Atomic Number	Atomic Weight[a]
Actinium	Ac	89	227
Aluminum	Al	13	26.98
Americium	Am	95	[243]
Antimony	Sb	51	121.76
Argon	A	18	39.944
Arsenic	As	33	74.91
Astatine	At	85	[210]
Barium	Ba	56	137.36
Berkelium	Bk	97	[249]
Beryllium	Be	4	9.013
Bismuth	Bi	83	209.00
Boron	B	5	10.82
Bromine	Br	35	79.916
Cadmium	Cd	48	112.41
Calcium	Ca	20	40.08
Californium	Cf	98	[249]
Carbon	C	6	12.011
Cerium	Ce	58	140.13
Cesium	Cs	55	132.91
Chlorine	Cl	17	35.457
Chromium	Cr	24	52.01
Cobalt	Co	27	58.94
Copper	Cu	29	63.54
Curium	Cm	96	[245]
Dysprosium	Dy	66	162.51
Erbium	Er	68	167.27
Europium	Eu	63	152.0
Fluorine	F	9	19.00
Francium	Fr	87	[223]
Gadolinium	Gd	64	157.26
Gallium	Ga	31	69.72
Germanium	Ge	32	72.60
Gold	Au	79	197.0
Hafnium	Hf	72	178.50
Helium	He	2	4.003
Holmium	Ho	67	164.94
Hydrogen	H	1	1.0080
Indium	In	49	114.82
Iodine	I	53	126.91
Iridium	Ir	77	192.2
Iron	Fe	26	55.85
Krypton	Kr	36	83.80
Lanthanum	La	57	138.92
Lead	Pb	82	207.21
Lithium	Li	3	6.940
Lutetium	Lu	71	174.99
Magnesium	Mg	12	24.32
Manganese	Mn	25	54.94
Mendelevium	Mv	101	[256]
Mercury	Hg	80	200.61

[a] A value given in brackets denotes the mass number of the most stable known isotope. From *Journal of the American Chemical Society,* Vol. 78, p. 3235, 1956.

Table 4. Atomic Weights of the Elements (Cont.)

Element	Symbol	Atomic Number	Atomic Weight[a]
Molybdenum	Mo	42	95.95
Neodymium	Nd	60	144.27
Neon	Ne	10	20.183
Neptunium	Np	93	[237]
Nickel	Ni	28	58.71
Niobium (Columbium)	Nb	41	92.91
Nitrogen	N	7	14.008
Osmium	Os	76	190.2
Oxygen	O	8	**16**
Palladium	Pd	46	106.4
Phosphorus	P	15	30.975
Platinum	Pt	78	195.09
Plutonium	Pu	94	[242]
Polonium	Po	84	210
Potassium	K	19	39.100
Praseodymium	Pr	59	140.92
Promethium	Pm	61	[145]
Protactinium	Pa	91	231
Radium	Ra	88	226.05
Radon	Rn	86	222
Rhenium	Re	75	186.22
Rhodium	Rh	45	102.91
Rubidium	Rb	37	85.48
Ruthenium	Ru	44	101.1
Samarium	Sm	62	150.35
Scandium	Sc	21	44.96
Selenium	Se	34	78.96
Silicon	Si	14	28.09
Silver	Ag	47	107.880
Sodium	Na	11	22.991
Strontium	Sr	38	87.63
Sulfur	S	16	32.066
Tantalum	Ta	73	180.95
Technetium	Tc	43	[99]
Tellurium	Te	52	127.61
Terbium	Tb	65	158.93
Thallium	Tl	81	204.39
Thorium	Th	90	232.05
Thulium	Tm	69	168.94
Tin	Sn	50	118.70
Titanium	Ti	22	47.90
Tungsten	W	74	183.86
Uranium	U	92	238.07
Vanadium	V	23	50.95
Xenon	Xe	54	131.30
Ytterbium	Yb	70	173.04
Yttrium	Y	39	88.92
Zinc	Zn	30	65.38
Zirconium	Zr	40	91.22

[a] A value given in brackets denotes the mass number of the most stable known isotope. From *Journal of the American Chemical Society*, Vol. 78, p. 3235, 1956.

Table 5. *Distribution of Electrons in the Atoms*

X-Ray Notation	K	L		M			N			
Quantum Numbers n, l	1,0	2,0	2,1	3,0	3,1	3,2	4,0	4,1	4,2	4,3
Element / Atomic Number Z										
H 1	1									
He 2	2									
Li 3	2	1								
Be 4	2	2								
B 5	2	2	1							
C 6	2	2	2							
N 7	2	2	3							
O 8	2	2	4							
F 9	2	2	5							
Ne 10	2	2	6							
Na 11				1						
Mg 12				2						
Al 13		Neon		2	1					
Si 14		Configuration		2	2					
P 15		10 electron		2	3					
S 16		core		2	4					
Cl 17				2	5					
A 18				2	6					
K 19							1			
Ca 20							2			
Sc 21						1	2			
Ti 22						2	2			
V 23						3	2			
Cr 24						5	1			
Mn 25						5	2			
Fe 26		Argon				6	2			
Co 27		Configuration				7	2			
Ni 28		18 electron				8	2			
Cu 29		core				10	1			
Zn 30						10	2			
Ga 31						10	2	1		
Ge 32						10	2	2		
As 33						10	2	3		
Se 34						10	2	4		
Br 35						10	2	5		
Kr 36						10	2	6		

Table 5. Distribution of Electrons in the Atoms (Cont.)

X-Ray Notation		K	L	M	N				O			P			Q	
Quantum Numbers n, l		1	2	3	4,0	4,1	4,2	4,3	5,0	5,1	5,2	6,0	6,1	6,2	7,0	7,1
Element	Atomic Number Z															
Rb	37								1							
Sr	38								2							
Y	39	Krypton					1		2							
Zr	40	Configuration					2		2							
Nb	41	36 electron					4		1							
Mo	42	core					5		1							
Ma	43						6		1							
Ru	44						7		1							
Rh	45						8		1							
Pd	46						10									
Ag	47								1							
Cd	48								2							
In	49	Palladium							2	1						
Sn	50	Configuration							2	2						
Sb	51	46 electron							2	3						
Te	52	core							2	4						
I	53								2	5						
Xe	54								2	6						
Cs	55	Xenon Configuration										1				
Ba	56	54 electron core										2				
La	57								2	6	1	2				
Ce	58							1	2	6	1	2				
Pr	59							2	2	6	1	2				
Nd	60							3	2	6	1	2				
Pm	61							4	2	6	1	2				
Sm	62	Shells						5	2	6	1	2				
Eu	63	1,0 to 4,2						6	2	6	1	2				
Gd	64	contain						7	2	6	1	2				
Tb	65	46 electrons						8	2	6	1	2				
Dy	66							9	2	6	1	2				
Ho	67							10	2	6	1	2				
Er	68							11	2	6	1	2				
Tm	69							13	2	6	0	2				
Yb	70							14	2	6	0	2				
Lu	71							14	2	6	1	2				

Table 5.   *Distribution of Electrons in the Atoms* (Cont.)

X-Ray Notation		K L M N	O			P			Q	
Quantum Numbers n, l		1 2 3 4	5,0 5,1	5,2	5,3	6,0	6,1	6,2	7,0	7,1
Element	Atomic Number Z									
Hf	72	Shells 1,0 to 5,1 contain 68 electrons		2		2				
Ta	73			3		2				
W	74			4		2				
Re	75			5		2				
Os	76			6		2				
Ir	77			7		2				
Pt	78			9		1				
Au	79			10		1				
Hg	80			10		2				
Tl	81			10		2	1			
Pb	82			10		2	2			
Bi	83			10		2	3			
Po	84			10		2	4			
At	85			10		2	5			
Rn	86			10		2	6			
Fr	87	Radon Configuration 86 electron core							1	
Ra	88								2	
Ac	89					2	6	1	2	
Th	90				1	2	6	1	2	
Pa	91				2	2	6	1	2	
U	92				3	2	6	1	2	
Np	93				4	2	6	1	2	
Pu	94				5	2	6	1	2	
Am	95				6	2	6	1	2	
Cm	96				7	2	6	1	2	
Bk	97				8	2	6	1	2	
Cf	98				9	2	6	1	2	
E	99				10	2	6	1	2	
Fm	100				11	2	6	1	2	
Mv	101				12	2	6	1	2	

Table 6. Periodic Table of the Elements

	I	II	III	IV	V	VI	VII	VIII		
1	1 H 1.0080							2 He 4.003		
2	3 Li 6.940	4 Be 9.013	5 B 10.82	6 C 12.011	7 N 14.008	8 O **16**	9 F 19.00	10 Ne 20.183		
3	11 Na 22.991	12 Mg 24.32	13 Al 26.98	14 Si 28.09	15 P 30.975	16 S 32.066	17 Cl 35.457	18 A 39.944		
4	19 K 39.100	20 Ca 40.08	21 Sc 44.96	22 Ti 47.90	23 V 50.95	24 Cr 52.01	25 Mn 54.94	26 Fe 55.85	27 Co 58.94	28 Ni 58.71
	29 Cu 63.54	30 Zn 65.38	31 Ga 69.72	32 Ge 72.60	33 As 74.91	34 Se 78.96	35 Br 79.916	36 Kr 83.80		
5	37 Rb 85.48	38 Sr 87.63	39 Y 88.92	40 Zr 91.22	41 Nb 92.91	42 Mo 95.95	43 Tc [99]	44 Ru 101.1	45 Rh 102.91	46 Pd 106.4
	47 Ag 107.880	48 Cd 112.41	49 In 114.82	50 Sn 118.70	51 Sb 121.76	52 Te 127.61	53 I 126.91	54 Xe 131.30		
6	55 Cs 132.91	56 Ba 137.36	57–71 Rare Earths*	72 Hf 178.50	73 Ta 180.95	74 W 183.86	75 Re 186.22	76 Os 190.2	77 Ir 192.2	78 Pt 195.09
	79 Au 197.0	80 Hg 200.61	81 Tl 204.39	82 Pb 207.21	83 Bi 209.00	84 Po 210	85 At [210]	86 Rn 222		
7	87 Fr [223]	88 Ra 226.05	89–101 Actinide† Series							

*Rare Earth or Lanthanide Series.

57 La 138.92	58 Ce 140.13	59 Pr 140.92	60 Nd 144.27	61 Pm [145]
62 Sm 150.35	63 Eu 152.0	64 Gd 157.26	65 Tb 158.93	66 Dy 162 51
67 Ho 164.94	68 Er 167.27	69 Tm 168.94	70 Yb 173.04	71 Lu 174.99

† Actinide Series.

89 Ac 227	90 Th 232.05	91 Pa 231	92 U 238.07
93 Np [237]	94 Pu [242]	95 Am [243]	96 Cm [245]
97 Bk [249]	98 Cf [249]	99 E (Einsteinium)	100 Fm (Fermium)
101 Mv [256]			

Appendix B

THE GREEK ALPHABET

Lower-case Letter	Capital Letter	Name of Letter
α	A	alpha
β	B	beta
γ	Γ	gamma
δ	Δ	delta
ϵ	E	epsilon
ζ	Z	zeta
η	H	eta
θ	Θ	theta
ι	I	iota
κ	K	kappa
λ	Λ	lambda
μ	M	mu
ν	N	nu
ξ	Ξ	xi
o	O	omicron
π	Π	pi
ρ	P	rho
σ, s	Σ	sigma
τ	T	tau
υ	Υ	upsilon
ϕ	Φ	phi
χ	X	chi
ψ	Ψ	psi
ω	Ω	omega

Appendix C

ANSWERS TO ODD-NUMBERED PROBLEMS

CHAPTER 1. Page 11

1. No answer.
3. 346 mi.
5. 146 ft.
7. 191 ft; 178 ft.

CHAPTER 2. Page 39

1. 3 lb/in.
3. 2,450 dynes/cm.
5. 327 dynes/cm.
7. No answer.
9. 238 lb; 66°30′.
11. 38.8 lb; 280.3 lb.
13. 200 lb.
15. (a) 75 lb, 130 lb; (b) 75 lb; (c) 75lb.
17. 230 lb; 227 lb.
19. 10,400 lb; 9,600 lb.
21. 10 lb.
23. 1,225 lb; 980 lb; 285 lb.
25. 2.4 ft from 60-lb weight.
27. 72 lb; 108 lb.
29. (a) 1,200 lb; (b) 2,000 lb.
31. (a) 115.5 lb; (b) 693 lb.

CHAPTER 3. Page 67

1. (a) 50 mi/hr; (b) 73.3 ft/sec.
3. (a) 3 hr and 20 min; (b) 5 hr.
5. 31.6 ft/sec; 30.0 ft/sec; 28.6 ft/sec.
7. 306 mi/hr, 11°20′ east of north.
9. 86.6 mi/hr.
11. 6.3 sec.
13. -30.3 ft/sec^2
15. (a) -18.8 ft/sec^2; (b) 2.34 sec.
17. (a) 4 ft; (b) 16 ft/sec.
19. (a) 9.6 cm/sec^2; (b) 48 cm/sec.
21. 1,500 ft/sec.
23. 13.25 mi.
25. (a) 0.98 ft/sec^2; (b) 2,970 ft.
27. (a) 667 cm/sec; (b) 520 cm/sec; (c) 138 cm.
29. 3,960 mi/hr.

CHAPTER 4. Page 101

1. 9,000 dynes.
3. 458 lb.
5. 37,500 dynes.
7. 55 tons.
9. (a) 375 lb; (b) 2,775 lb.
11. (a) 45,000 dynes; (b) 290,000 dynes.
13. (a) 12.8 ft/sec^2; (b) 28.8 lb.
15. (a) 89.1 cm/sec^2; (b) 2,673,000 dynes.
17. (a) 180 lb; (b) 31.5 mi/hr.
19. 84 lb.
21. 0.4.

23. (a) 115 cm/sec^2; (b) 865,000 dynes; (c) 517.5 cm.

25. 281 ft.

27. (a) 60,000 gm cm/sec; (b) 50 cm/sec.

29. (a) 25 lb; (b) 4.55 ft/sec^2, 6.4 ft/sec^2.

31. (a) 150,000 dyne sec; (b) 37,500,000 dynes.

CHAPTER 5. Page 124

1. 900 ft lb.

3. 1,260 ft lb.

5. 168 × 10^6 ft lb.

7. No answer.

9. (a) 1,440 ft lb; (b) 810 ft lb; (c) 7.38 lb.

11. (a) 5.25 × 10^6 ergs; (b) 162 cm/sec.

13. (a) 0.08; (b) 13.26 lb; (c) 575 ft lb.

15. 0.52 hp.

17. (a) $W/4$; (b) 0.67; (c) 2.7.

19. 36.8 in.

21. No answer.

23. 0; 80 cm/sec.

25. (a) 9,000 ft lb; (b) 19,500 lb.

27. No answer.

29. (a) 50 cm/sec; (b) 3.75 × 10^9 ergs; (c) 3.75 × 10^6 ergs.

CHAPTER 6. Page 149

1. 8,000 dynes.

3. 4.33 tons.

5. 0.0088 ft/sec^2.

7. 8.5°.

9. (a) 3,460 ft; (b) 1,440 lb.

11. (a) 18.5 mi/sec; (b) 0.0195 ft/sec^2; (c) 8.0 × 10^{21} lb.

CHAPTER 7. Page 164

1. (a) 0.40 sec; (b) 1.2 × 10^6 dynes; (c) 1,500 cm/sec^2.

3. (a) 17,640 dynes/cm; (b) 0.45 sec.

5. (a) 96 lb/ft; (b) 0.39 sec.

7. 2.22 sec.

9. (a) 51,000 dynes; (b) 170 cm/sec^2; (c) 54.6 cm/sec.

11. (a) 0.71 vib/sec; (b) 12.5 cm.

13. 977.2 cm/sec^2.

CHAPTER 8. Page 186

1. (a) 499.2 lb/ft^3; (b) 49.9 lb/ft^3.

3. Body will sink.

5. (a) 170 gm; (b) 1.7 gm/cm^3; (c) 68,600 dynes.

7. 90 lb.

9. 7.5 in.

11. 34 ft.

13. 1.026 × 10^6 dynes/cm^2.

15. (a) 9.5 lb/in.^{2}; (b) 750 lb.

17. (a) 45,300 lb/ft^2; (b) 9.73 × 10^6 tons.

19. 0.072 lb/in.^{2} above atmosphere.

21. 15% increase.

CHAPTER 9. Page 207

1. (a) 5.43 ft/sec; (b) 3.06 ft/sec.
5. 1.80×10^5 ft lb.
9. 9,720 lb.
13. 18.2 hp.

3. (a) 27 ft/sec; (b) 141 ft³/min.
7. (a) 18.2 ft/sec; (b) 1.63 ft³/sec.
11. (a) 22.6 ft/sec; (b) 0.39 ft³/sec.
15. 109 hp.

CHAPTER 10. Page 235

1. (a) 12×10^7 dynes/cm²; (b) 9.6×10^{-5}.
3. (a) 4,780 lb/in.²; (b) 3.64×10^{-4}; (c) 0.0132 in.
5. 11×10^{11} dynes/cm².
7. 1.8%.
9. (a) 36×10^5 dynes/cm²; (b) 8.5×10^{-6}; (c) 1.7 sec.
11. -8.7 mm; -5.8 mm; -4.4 mm.
13. (a) 104 dynes; (b) 416 ergs.
15. 6,300 dynes/cm².
17. 1.5 cm.
19. 0.03 mm.

CHAPTER 11. Page 264

1. $\pi/2$; π; $3\pi/2$.
3. 24,300 ft lb.
5. -15.7 rad/sec².
7. No answer.
9. (a) 22.3 rad/sec²; (b) 178 cm/sec²; (c) 120,000 dynes.
11. (a) 960 ft lb; (b) 960 ft lb; (c) 22.6 rad/sec.
13. (a) 115,200 gm cm²; (b) 30.6 rad/sec²; (c) 220,500 dynes.
15. No answer.

CHAPTER 12. Page 283

1. 37.0°C.
5. -450°F.
9. 0.174 ft.
13. 548 mm.
17. (a) 0.00366 per °C; (b) 66.9°C.
21. 9.9×10^8 dynes/cm².

3. -37.97°F.
7. $-40°$.
11. 270°C.
15. 388 cm³.
19. 7.1 sec/day loss.

CHAPTER 13. Page 300

1. 9.1°C.
5. 9.6°F.
9. 0.2°F.
13. 64 atm.
17. 754 Btu.

3. 0.091 cal/gm°C.
7. 5.7°C.
11. 125 ft lb.
15. (a) 3,900 cal; (b) 3,900 cal.

CHAPTER 14. Page 319

1. 98.4 cm.
3. 13.86 atm.
5. 61.6 cm.
7. 4.0 atm.
9. 1.86×10^5 cm/sec.
11. 1,420 joules.
13. 0.6 atm; 0.9 atm; 1.5 atm.
15. (a) 419 cal; (b) 299 cal; (c) 499 joules, zero.

CHAPTER 15. Page 340

1. 27,000 cal.
3. 27.6 gm.
5. 5,600 cal.
7. 5,100 cal.
9. 7.3°C.
11. 17.5 gm.
13. 12.8°C.
15. (a) 40.4 cal; (b) 500 cal.
17. 0.51.
19. 10 mm.
21. 0.66.

CHAPTER 16. Page 351

1. 0.31 cal/cm sec°C.
3. 9,620 cal/sec.
5. 15,100 Btu/hr.
7. 30 watts.

CHAPTER 17. Page 372

1. (a) 26.8%; (b) 536 cal; (c) 1,464 cal.
3. 46.9%.
5. (a) 600 cal; (b) 3,600 cal.

CHAPTER 18. Page 399

1. 2.12 ft.
3. 145 cm.
5. 373 m.
7. (a) 27.0 cm; (b) 270 m/sec.
9. (a) 80 ft/sec; (b) 1.88 in.
11. (a) 0.26; (b) 0.060; (c) 57°10′; (d) 21°40′.
13. 230 ft.
15. (b) 349.3 m/sec.

CHAPTER 19. Page 421

1. (a) 880 vib/sec; (b) 1.25 ft.
3. 34.4 vib/sec.
5. (a) 1,064 vib/sec; (b) 943.4 vib/sec.
7. (a) 996.4 vib/sec; (b) 1,003.6 vib/sec; (c) 7.2 beats/sec.
9. 4 beats/sec.
11. (a) 1.25 ft; (b) 880 vib/sec; (c) 1,320 vib/sec.
13. (a) 1.04×10^8 dynes; (b) 1,040 vib/sec; (c) 1,560 vib/sec.
15. (a) 2.46; (b) 24°.
17. (a) 55 ft; (b) 0.66 in.

CHAPTER 20.   Page 443

1. 1,667 dynes.

3. 3.36 oersteds.

5. 1.39 oersteds; 69°50′ with axis of magnet.

7. 2,880 dyne cm.

9. 758 pole cm.

11. 900 oersteds.

13. 57,600 dyne cm.

CHAPTER 21.   Page 467

1. 2,810 dynes.

3. 6 dynes/stcoul.

5. 3.52 dynes/stcoul.

7. 22.2 dynes/stcoul.

9. 6 cm from P, 10 cm from charge.

11. 7,200 dynes.

13. 3.24×10^7 dynes.

15. 384 dynes/stcoul.

CHAPTER 22.   Page 480

1. (a) 1,910 stfd; (b) 212×10^{-11} fd.

3. (a) 28,600 stfd; (b) 3.58×10^6 stcoul; (c) 2.24×10^8 ergs.

5. (a) 350 stfd; (b) 8,750 stcoul, 17,500 stcoul; (c) 218,750 ergs, 437,500 ergs.

7. (a) $2V$; (b) $\frac{1}{2}QV$; (c) $\frac{1}{2}QV$.

9. (a) 2.4 μfd; (b) 288×10^{-6} coul; (c) 72 volts, 48 volts; (d) 1.728×10^{-2} joule.

CHAPTER 23.   Page 497

1. 4 amp.

3. 660 joules.

5. 150,000 ergs.

7. (a) 0.50 amp; (b) 240 ohms.

9. 5.91 ohms.

11. (a) 36 ohms; (b) 2 amp; 1.33 amp.

13. (a) 1.50 amp; (b) 22.5 volts, 37.5 volts, 60 volts.

15. 1.15 watts; 1.84 watts; 2.76 watts.

17. (a) 112 volts; (b) 70 ohms.

19. (a) 720 ohms; (b) 20 watts.

21. 10°C.

CHAPTER 24.   Page 522

1. 2.0248 gm.

3. 224 sec.

5. 96,500 coul.

7. 5.40 volts.

9. (a) 0.075 ohm; (b) 1.56×10^6 joules; (c) 1.94×10^5 joules.

11. (a) 4.0 amp; (b) 10.8 volts; (c) 0.87.

13. (a) 2.73 volts; (b) 1.82 ohms.

CHAPTER 25.   Page 553

1. 1.18 oersteds.

3. 32°7′.

5. 0.192 oersted.

7. 87.1 oersteds.

9. (a) 0; (b) 1.33 oersteds.
11. 210 dyne cm.
13. 6,000 dynes southward.
15. 0.43 amp.
17. 2.4×10^{-9} erg.
19. 600 gausses.
21. 1.75×10^{-8} coul/gm.
23. 9.60×10^{-13} dyne cm.
25. 249,940 ohms.

CHAPTER 26. Page 577

1. 0.006 volt.
3. 0.043 volt.
5. 90×10^{-8} volt.
7. (a) 3 volts; (b) 6×10^5 dynes.
9. (a) 12.7 volts.
11. 0.031 henry.
13. (a) 0.80 amp; (b) 3.7 amp; (c) 112.6 amp; (d) 417 watts.
15. 0.96.

CHAPTER 27. Page 588

1. (a) 156×10^{-6} coul; (b) 55.8×10^{-6} coul/cm; (c) 14,280 gausses.
3. (a) 10 oersteds; (b) 8,000 gausses.

CHAPTER 28. Page 615

1. (a) 53.7 ohms; (b) 805 ohms.
3. (a) 87.8 volts; (b) 512 watts.
5. (a) 530 ohms; (b) 15.7 ohms.
7. (a) 1,385 ohms; (b) 0.174 amp; (c) 12.2 watts
9. 0.917.
11. (a) 483 ohms; (b) 0.456 amp
13. (a) 79 cycles/sec; (b) 5.0 amp; (c) 1.115 volts.
15. (a) 55; (b) 0.455 amp.

CHAPTER 29. Page 638

1. 349 m.
3. 4,595 cycles/sec.
5. 1.027×10^6 cycles/sec.
7. 10^{10} cycles/sec.
9. 116 volts.

CHAPTER 30. Page 660

1. 1.29 lumens/ft^2.
3. 27,400 lumens/ft^2.
5. 2,450 lumens.
7. (a) 2.94 ft; (b) 9.8 ft.
9. (a) 143.4 cm; (b) 63 lumens/m^2.
11. 500 sec.
13. 2.99711×10^{10} cm/sec.

CHAPTER 31. Page 676

1. (a) 2.254×10^{10} cm/sec; (b) 2.245×10^{10} cm/sec.
3. 28°52'.
5. (a) 32°7'; (b) 1.145

7. (a) $44°24'$; (b) $56°7'$.

11. (a) $51°10'$; (b) $55°35'$.

9. 1.414.

13. 1.50.

CHAPTER 32. Page 700

1. (a) 53.3 cm; (b) 3.33 cm.

5. (a) -6.7 cm; (b) 1.67 cm.

9. (a) -6.0 cm; (b) 4.5 cm.

13. 12.5 cm.

17. -48 cm.

21. (a) $s_2^1 = 4$ cm; (b) $-\dfrac{1}{3}$.

3. (a) -60 cm; (b) 12 cm.

7. 30 cm.

11. (a) -16.7 cm; (b) 25 cm^2.

15. 18.35 cm.

19. 3.33 cm.

CHAPTER 33. Page 720

1. 1 ft.

5. 8.3.

9. (a) 6; (b) 21 cm.

13. 73.85 cm, 6.15.

17. 6.75 cm.

3. 9.67 in.

7. -0.67 m.

11. 375.

15. 0.23 in.

CHAPTER 34. Page 741

1. 1.03 mm.

5. (a) No answer; (b) 732 lines.

9. No answer.

13. (a) $1.32'$; (b) $3.5'$.

3. 66.3%.

7. (a) $15°20'$; (b) $31°52'$.

11. 5,556 lines/cm.

CHAPTER 35. Page 756

1. $58°47'$.

5. $69°$.

7. (a) 1.753×10^{10} cm/sec, 1.723×10^{10} cm/sec; (b) 0.01 mm.

3. $53°4'$.

CHAPTER 36. Page 773

1. $0.65\ L_0$.

5. 0.866 c.

9. 7.21 Mev.

3. 0.9945 c.

7. 1,500 ev; 3,000 ev.

CHAPTER 37. Page 791

1. (a) No answer; (b) 9,657 A.

5. 2.1 ev.

3. 3,400°C.

7. 4862.7 A.

CHAPTER 38. Page 818

1. $4°46'$.   3. (a) 31,000 ev; (b) 5,500 ev.
5. (a) 24,820 ev; (b) 1,190 ev; (c) 1,190 ev.
7. (a) 0.307 A; (b) $3°8'$, $6°16'$, $9°25'$ ....
9. (a) 3.30×10^{-16} gm cm/sec; (b) 0.002 A.

CHAPTER 39. Page 833

1. (a) 5.43 Mev; (b) 0.096 Mev; (c) 5.53 Mev.
3. 9.90×10^6 dynes.   5. 12.72 Mev.
7. 0.000842 amu; 0.784 Mev.

CHAPTER 40. Page 859

1. 2.36 Mev.   3. 0.01244 amu greater.
5. (a) No answer; (b) 0.23 amu; (c) 190 Mev; (d) 190 Mev.

INDEX

Index

Force (*continued*)
  between two parallel wires carrying current, 538
  short-range, 209
  in simple harmonic motion, 151
Force pump, 202
Forced vibrations, 418
Forces, addition of, 15
    analytic method, 24
    polygon method, 17
  concurrent, 18
  coplanar, 24
  pairs of, 95
Foucault, J. B. L., 658
fps system of units, 10, 78
Frame of reference, 42
Franklin, B., 445
Free electrons, 450, 484, 519
Freely falling bodies, 56, 58
Frequency, 157
  of alternating current, 567
  of electromagnetic waves, 619
  of a musical tone, 401
  and period, 157
  and pitch, 402
  of resonant circuit, 619
  of a wave, 382
Fresnel, A., 730
Friction, 86
  coefficient of, 87
    table of, 89
  force of, 86
  kinetic, 88
  rolling, 86
  sliding, 86
  starting, 88
  work against, 119
Fulcrum, 30
Fundamental, of a musical tone, 414
Fundamental concepts, 5
Fusion, 321, 331
Fusion curve, 333

G

g, 56, 146
  determination of, 163
  at the moon, 148
  values of, 57
  variation with latitude, 57
Galilean telescope, 714
Galileo, G., 3, 16, 42, 56, 73, 140
Galileo, method of, 3
Galvani, L., 509
Galvanometer, 494, 530
  ballistic, 579
  D'Arsonval type, 547
  moving coil type, 545

Gamma rays, 821
  spectrum of, 830
Gas, 326
  adiabatic process with a, 298
  diffusion of, 310
    through porous cup, 311
  electric discharge through a, 647
  electron, 621
  ideal, 287, 302
    equation of, 303
    general law of, 302
  kinetic theory, 305
  specific heats of a, 296
  thermal expansion of, 278
  universal constant of, 304, 316
  work done by a, 294
Gas thermometer, 278
Gaseous phase, 211
Gasoline engine, 356
Gauss, the, 536
Gay-Lussac, J. L., 280
Gay-Lussac's law, 281
Geiger, H., 824, 826
Geiger counter, 823
General gas law, 302
Generator, electric, 564
  a-c, 566
  d-c, 566, 568
  emf induced in a, 566
Geocentric theory, 140
Geometrical optics, 663
Germer, L. H., 790, 814
Gilbert, William, 426
Glare, 755
Goudsmit, S. A., 790
Graham's law of diffusion, 312
Gram, the, 9
Gram molecular weight, 304
Grating space, 740
  of rock salt, 803
Gravitation, constant of, 143
  law of, 143
  Newton's law of, 143
Gravitational field, 135, 145
  of the earth, 146
Gravitational potential energy, 108
Gravity, center of, 32
Grid, 624
Grid bias, 625
Guericke, O. von, 445
Gyroscope, 261

H

h, 643, 777
Hahn, O., 850
Half-life, 828
Harmonics, of a musical tone, 414